COURSE OF THEORETICAL PHYSICS

Volume 5

STATISTICAL PHYSICS

COURSE OF THEORETICAL PHYSICS

STATISTICAL PHYSICS

by

L. D. LANDAU AND E. M. LIFSHITZ

INSTITUTE OF PHYSICAL PROBLEMS, USSR ACADEMY
OF SCIENCES

Volume 5 of *Course of Theoretical Physics*

Translated from the Russian by

E. PEIERLS AND R. F. PEIERLS

1958

PERGAMON PRESS LTD.

London - Paris

ADDISON-WESLEY PUBLISHING COMPANY, INC.

Reading, Massachusetts, U.S.A.

PERGAMON PRESS LTD.
4 and 5 Fitzroy Square, London W.1

PERGAMON PRESS S.A.R.L.
24 Rue des Écoles, Paris V^e

Copyright
©
1958
Pergamon Press Ltd.

First published in English 1958

U.S.A. edition distributed by Addison-Wesley Publishing Company, Inc.
Reading, Massachusetts, U.S.A.

Library of Congress Card Number 58–9181

CONTENTS

I. THE BASIC PRINCIPLES OF STATISTICAL PHYSICS

II. THERMODYNAMIC QUANTITIES

III. THE GIBBS DISTRIBUTION

IV. THE PERFECT GAS

IX. SOLUTIONS

X. CHEMICAL REACTIONS

XI. THE PROPERTIES OF MATTER AT VERY HIGH TEMPERATURES AND DENSITIES

XII. FLUCTUATIONS

XIII. THE SYMMETRY OF MACROSCOPIC BODIES

XIV. SECOND-ORDER PHASE TRANSITIONS

XV. SURFACES

PREFACE TO THE ENGLISH EDITION

THE PRESENT volume of the *Theoretical Physics* series is devoted to an exposition of statistical physics and thermodynamics. These two subjects are firmly interconnected, and in our opinion it is rational to present them together as one whole.

As in the other volumes, we have endeavoured, on the one hand, to state the general principles as clearly as possible, and on the other hand to present their many specific applications as fully as possible. However, the present book does not contain the theory of electric and magnetic properties of matter, which are treated in another volume which is dealing with the electrodynamics of material media. Similarly, problems of non-equilibrium phenomena are not treated; we propose to consider these in a separate volume.

We have not included in this book the various theories of ordinary liquids and of strong solutions, which to us appear neither convincing nor useful.

We do not share the view, which one encounters sometimes, that statistical physics is the least well-founded branch of theoretical physics (as regards its basic principles). We believe that the difficulties are created artificially, because the problems are often not stated sufficiently rationally. If one talks from the very beginning about the statistical distribution for small parts of a system (subsystems) and not for a closed system as a whole, then one avoids the whole question of the ergodic or similar hypotheses, which are not really essential for physical statistics.

The first edition of *Statistical Physics*, translated by Dr. SHOENBERG, was published by the Oxford University Press, in 1938. It contained only an exposition of classical statistics. However, a separate presentation of classical and quantum statistics is unsuitable both for the exposition of the general foundations, and for the treatment of many applications. For this reason the whole book has been re-written. This includes a complete revision also of the treatment of those problems which were included in the previous book. Thus the present book is quite new, and not a new edition of the old one.

In the present English edition we have made a number of changes and additions, intended to eliminate some of the weaknesses in the presentation, and to incorporate some essentially new results in this field of theoretical physics, which have been obtained during the five years which have passed since the appearance of the Russian edition.

We would like to express our sincere thanks to the Peierls family, who have undertaken the heavy task of translating this book.

Moscow.

L. D. LANDAU
E. M. LIFSHITZ

SOME ABBREVIATIONS

h Planck constant, divided by 2π
k Boltzmann constant
$\wedge$ over a letter denotes the operator

Phase amplitude

p, q generalized impulses and co-ordinates

$dpdq = dp_1 dp_2 \ldots dp_s dq_1 dq_2 \ldots dq_s$
volume element of phase amplitude (s is the number of degrees of freedom)

$$d\Gamma = \frac{dpdq}{(2\pi h)}\,s$$

$\int' \ldots d\Gamma$ integral for all physically different phase conditions

$d^3 p = dp_x dp_y dp_z$

Thermodynamic magnitudes

Temperature T
Volume V
Pressure P
Energy E
Entropy S
Thermal function $W = E + PV$
Free energy $F = E - TS$
Thermodynamic potential
$\Phi = E - TS + PV$
Thermodynamic potential $\Omega = -PV$
Thermal capacity $C_p,\ C_v$
    (molecular thermal capacity $c_p,\ c_v$)
Number of particles N
Chemical potential μ
Coefficient of surface tension α
Area of surface of separation s

CHAPTER I

THE BASIC PRINCIPLES OF STATISTICAL PHYSICS

§1. Statistical distribution

THE subject of statistical physics or, more simply, statistics, is the study of the particular laws which govern the behaviour and properties of macroscopic bodies, that is to say bodies made up of a very large number of separate particles (atoms and molecules). The general character of these laws depends very little on whether one describes the motion of separate particles of the body by classical mechanics or by quantum mechanics, but their basic justification needs a different approach in the two cases. For convenience of presentation we shall initially assume that classical mechanics is applicable.

If we write down the equations of motion of a mechanical system (of which there are as many as there are degrees of freedom of the system) and integrate them we can, in principle, completely determine the motion of the system. If, however, we are dealing with a classical system with a very large number of degrees of freedom, then the actual application of classical methods requires the statement and solution of an equally large number of differential equations which is usually impracticable. It should be emphasized that even if we could find the general solution of these equations, it would be quite impossible to substitute in this the initial values of the velocities and positions of the particles, if only because of the time and paper it would consume.

At first sight it would thus seem that, as the number of particles increases, the complexity and obscurity of the properties of a mechanical system should increase tremendously, and that we should be unable to find any trace of regularity in the behaviour of a macroscopic body. But this is not so, and we shall see later that in the case of a very great number of particles there appear new and distinctive regularities.

These so-called "statistical" laws which arise as a result of there being a large number of particles in the body, can never be explained in purely mechanical terms. Their special nature is shown by their becoming quite meaningless when applied to mechanical systems with few degrees of freedom. Thus, although the motion of a system with very many degrees of freedom obeys the same mechanical laws as that of a system consisting of a small number of particles, the presence of this large number of degrees of freedom gives rise to qualitatively new regularities.

The importance of statistics as a branch of theoretical physics lies in the fact that in nature we are dealing all the time with macroscopic bodies whose behaviour cannot be described by purely mechanical methods and which do, in fact, obey statistical laws.

To formulate the basic problem of classical statistics we must first of all introduce the concept of "phase space" which we shall be continually using later on.

Assume that our macroscopic system has s degrees of freedom. In other words the positions in space of the points of the system are described by s co-ordinates, which we denote by symbols q_i; where the index i runs through 1, 2, 3 .... Then the state of this system at a given time will be specified by the values of the s co-ordinates q_i at this time, and the corresponding velocities $\dot{q}_i$. In statistics it is usual to specify the system by its co-ordinates and by the momenta p_i rather than by the velocities, as this has considerable advantages. Different states of the system can be mathematically described by points in phase space (which is a purely mathematical concept); on the co-ordinate axes of this space we mark the co-ordinates and momenta of the given system. Every system has its own phase space with twice as many dimensions as the system has degrees of freedom. Every point in the phase space, corresponding to given values of the co-ordinates q_i and momenta p_i of our system, represents a definite state of the system. The state of the system will change with time and the corresponding point in phase space (which we shall call in future the phase point of the system) will describe a line in phase space which is called a phase trajectory.

Consider a macroscopic body or system of bodies. We assume that the system is closed, i.e. that it does not interact with any other bodies. Now consider a small part of this system, very small in comparison with the whole system but nevertheless macroscopic; clearly, if the whole system contains a sufficiently large number of particles, the number contained even in a small part of it may still be very large. Such comparatively small, yet macroscopic, systems we shall call "*subsystems*". A subsystem is a mechanical system, but certainly not a closed one. On the contrary, it undergoes all kinds of inter-actions with other parts of the system. These interactions will be extremely complicated owing to the extremely large number of degrees of freedom possessed by these other parts, and the state of the subsystem will change with time in a very complicated and involved way.

An exact solution of the problem of the behaviour of a subsystem can only be obtained by solving the mechanical problem for the whole closed system, i.e. by obtaining and solving all the differential equations of motion with the given initial conditions. This is impracticable, as we have seen above. Luckily the very complexity of this change in the state of a subsystem, which precludes its treatment by mechanical methods, makes possible another approach to the problem.

The basis for this approach is the fact that, owing to the complexity of its interactions with the other parts of the system, our subsystem will pass sufficiently often through all its possible states.

We may put this more exactly in the following way. Let us denote by

$\Delta p \Delta q$ a small region of phase space corresponding to the momenta p_i and co-ordinates q_i of our subsystem lying in the small intervals Δp_i and Δq_i. In a sufficiently large time interval T the extremely complicated phase trajectory will pass many times through such a region. Let Δt be the part of the time T during which the particle "was in" the given cell $\Delta p \Delta q$ of phase space.† As T becomes infinitely large, the fraction $\Delta t / T$ will tend to a limit

$$w = \lim_{T \to \infty} \frac{\Delta t}{T}. \tag{1.1}$$

This value may obviously be interpreted as the probability that the subsystem will be found in the given cell $\Delta p \Delta q$ if observed at an arbitrary time.

In the case of an infinitesimal element of phase space‡

$$dq dp = dq_1 dq_2 \dots dq_s dp_1 dp_2 \dots dp_s, \tag{1.2}$$

we may introduce the probability dw of the states described by points in this element, i.e. the probability that the co-ordinates q_i and momenta p_i have values lying in the infinitesimal intervals between q_i, p_i and $q_i + dq_i$, $p_i + dp_i$. This probability dw can be expressed in the form

$$dw = \rho(p_1, \dots p_n, q_1, \dots q_n) \, dp dq, \tag{1.3}$$

where $\rho(p_i, \dots p_n, q_i, \dots q_n)$ is a function of all the co-ordinates and momenta (we shall usually abbreviate it to $\rho(p, q)$ or even simply ρ). A function ρ acting as the "density" of a probability distribution in phase space is called a *statistical distribution function* (or simply a "distribution function") for the given body. A distribution function must obviously satisfy the so-called normalisation condition

$$\int \rho \, dp dq = 1 \tag{1.4}$$

where the integration extends over the whole of phase space. This simply expresses the fact that the sum of the probabilities of all possible states must equal unity.

The following fact is extremely important in statistics. The statistical distribution of a given subsystem is independent of the initial state of any other small part of the same system, because, after a sufficiently long time interval, the influence of this initial state will be completely outweighed by the influence of other, much larger, parts of the system. Nor does it depend on the initial state of our small part itself, since this passes through all possible states, and therefore any one of them could be chosen as the initial one. Thus one can find a statistical distribution for small parts of a system without solving the mechanical problem for this system, taking into account the initial conditions.

---

† It is usual to say that the system "is in" the element $\Delta p \Delta q$ of phase space, meaning that the system is in a state represented by a phase point in this element.

‡ In future we shall denote by dp and dq the products of the differentials of all the momenta and all the co-ordinates of the system respectively.

The determination of statistical distributions for any subsystem is the basic problem of statistics. When one talks of "small parts" of a closed system it must be remembered that the macroscopic bodies with which we are dealing are themselves "small parts" of a larger system which consists of these bodies and the external medium in which they are embedded.

Once this problem is solved and the statistical distribution of a given subsystem is known, we can calculate the probabilities of the occurrence of different values of any physical quantity which depends on the state of this subsystem (i.e. on its co-ordinates q and momenta p). We can also calculate the mean value of any such quantity $f(p, q)$ by multiplying all its possible values by their respective probabilities and integrating over all states. Denoting this process by a line over the symbol we have the relation

$$\bar{f} = \int f(p, q)\rho(p, q)\, \mathrm{d}p\mathrm{d}q, \tag{1.5}$$

by means of which we can calculate the average values of different quantities with the aid of the statistical distribution function.

Averaging by means of a distribution function (or, as it is called, statistical averaging) makes it possible to obtain the mean value of a quantity $f(p, q)$ without following its variation with time. At the same time it is evident from the definition of the probability in (1.1) that statistical averaging is completely equivalent to time averaging. The latter would mean that if we followed the time variation of the value of a quantity f we should have to construct a function $f = f(t)$ and then define its average value as

$$\bar{f} = \lim_{T \to \infty} \frac{1}{T} \int_0^T f(t)\, \mathrm{d}t. \tag{1.6}$$

From the above it is clear that the deductions and predictions about the behaviour of macroscopic bodies, which can be obtained from statistics, relate to probabilities. It is in this respect that they differ from those of ordinary (classical) mechanics, in which such deductions are of a deterministic nature. It should be stressed, nevertheless, that the probability character of classical statistics is not due to the intrinsic nature of its objects; it arises from the fact that these results depend on a much smaller number of data than a complete mechanical description would require (they do not involve the initial values of all the co-ordinates and momenta).

However, the probability nature of statistical mechanics does not appear when we apply it in practice to macroscopic bodies. The reason for this is that if one observes a macroscopic body (in external conditions which are stationary, independent of time) during a sufficiently large time interval, it will be found that physical quantities† remain practically constant (equal

---

† We are clearly referring to "macroscopic" properties of the body as a whole or of its macroscopic parts and not of separate particles.

to their average values) and only very rarely show any detectable deviations.†
This basic principle in statistical physics follows from very general considerations (which will be developed in the next section) and it holds more closely the larger and the more complex is the body with which we are dealing. We may express this by saying that if, by means of the function $\rho(p, q)$, we construct the probability distribution for the values of some quantity $f(p, q)$ then this will have a very sharp peak at $f == \bar{f}$ and it will differ appreciably from zero only in the immediate neighbourhood of this maximum.

Thus by permitting us to calculate the mean values of quantities describing macroscopic bodies, statistical physics allows us to make predictions which are valid with great accuracy for the overwhelming part of any time interval large enough to eliminate completely the effects of the initial conditions of the body. In this sense, the predictions of statistical physics acquire an almost deterministic rather than a probability character. (Bearing this in mind we shall in future nearly always omit the bar over a symbol indicating a mean value of a macroscopic quantity.)

If a closed macroscopic system is in such a state that for any macroscopic subsystems all "macroscopic" physical quantities approximate very closely to their mean values, then the closed system is said to be in a state of *statistical equilibrium*.‡ It is clear from the preceding, that if a closed macroscopic system is observed for a sufficiently long interval of time, then for the greater part of this interval it will be in a state of statistical equilibrium. If at some initial instant, the closed macroscopic system was not in a state of statistical equilibrium (if for example it was temporarily disturbed from this state by some external influence, afterwards again becoming a closed system) then eventually it must return to a state of equilibrium. The period of time in which the transition to statistical equilibrium occurs is called the relaxation time. When we talk, as above, about a "sufficiently large" interval of time we mean, in effect, intervals of time large relative to the relaxation time.

The theory of processes connected with the transition to an equilibrium state is called kinetics; it is not studied in statistics proper which deals with systems in statistical equilibrium (in this book we shall only be concerned with the latter).‖

§2. Statistical independence

Subsystems, which were discussed in §1, are not in themselves closed systems. On the contrary, they undergo continuous interaction with other parts of the system. However, while small in comparison with the whole

---

† Let us give an example to show how very accurate this rule is. If one isolates a small volume in a gas containing, say, only 1/100 of a gram-molecule, then the average relative deviation of the energy of this quantity of matter from its mean value is only $\sim 10^{-11}$. The probability of finding (in a single measurement) a relative deviation, say, of the order of 10^{-6} is given by the fantastically small number $\sim 10^{-3 \cdot 10^{15}}$.

‡ Statistical equilibrium is also called thermodynamic or thermal equilibrium.

‖ §§ 118 and 119 only, are devoted to kinetic questions.

system, they are themselves also macroscopic bodies, and therefore we can assume that they behave approximately like closed systems over not too great periods of time. In fact, the particles which take part in the interaction of a subsystem with neighbouring parts of the system, are mainly those near its surface. Their number in comparison with the total number of particles in the subsystem quickly falls with an increase in size of the latter. It follows that for a sufficiently large subsystem its interaction energy with neighbouring parts of the system will be small in comparison with its internal energy. We may describe such systems as "quasi-closed". It must be stressed again that this description can apply only for not too long periods of time. Over a sufficiently long period of time, the effect of the interaction of the subsystems, however weak it may be, will nevertheless become appreciable. Furthermore, it is just this comparatively weak interaction which is ultimately responsible for establishing statistical equilibrium.

This fact, that separate subsystems can be considered as only weakly interacting with each other, implies that we can also consider them as in-dependent in a statistical sense. "Statistical independence" means that the state of one of the subsystems has no effect on the probabilities of different states of the other subsystems.

Consider two subsystems, and let $dp^{(1)}dq^{(1)}$ and $dp^{(2)}dq^{(2)}$ be elements of their phase spaces. If we consider the combination of the two subsystems as one combined subsystem, then, from the mathematical point of view, statistical independence means that the probability that the combined subsystem lies in the element of its phase space $dp^{(12)}dq^{(12)} \equiv dp^{(1)}dq^{(1)} \cdot dp^{(2)}dq^{(2)}$ is the direct product of the probabilities that each subsystem lies in the corresponding element of its own phase space. Each one of these probabilities depends only on the co-ordinates and momenta of one of the given subsystems and we can therefore write:

$$\rho_{12}\, dp^{(12)}dq^{(12)} = \rho_1\, dp^{(1)}dq^{(1)} \cdot \rho_2\, dp^{(2)}dq^{(2)},$$

or

$$\rho_{12} = \rho_1\rho_2, \tag{2.1}$$

where ρ_{12} is the statistical distribution function of the combined system, and ρ_1, ρ_2 are those of the separate subsystems. An analogous relation can be written for the combination of several subsystems.† Evidently the converse can also be stated: if the probability distribution for a certain complex system splits up into the product of factors each one of which depends solely on the variables describing one of the parts of the system, then it follows that these parts are statistically independent, and that each factor is proportional to the probability of the corresponding state of its respective part.

If f_1 and f_2 are two variables referring to two different subsystems, then from (2.1) and from the definition of mean values (1.5) it follows that the mean value of the product f_1f_2 is equal to the product of the mean values of

---

† Subject, of course, to the condition that the combination of these subsystems must still be a small part of the whole system.

the separate variables f_1 and f_2; i.e.

$$\overline{f_1 f_2} = \overline{f_1} \cdot \overline{f_2}. \tag{2.2}$$

Consider a variable f referring to some macroscopic body and its separate parts. In the course of time, the value of this variable will change, fluctuating about its mean value. We now introduce a quantity which measures the width of the interval over which it fluctuates on the average. The mean value of the difference $\Delta f = f - \bar{f}$ will not serve as such a measure, since the variable deviates from its mean value in both directions, and $f - \bar{f}$ is equally liable to be positive and negative. Thus its mean value will always be zero independently of how often the variable f deviates considerably from its mean value. It is convenient to take instead the mean value of the square of this difference as a measure. Since the quantity $(\Delta f)^2$ is always positive, its mean value will tend to zero only when it tends to zero itself, i.e. it will be small only when the probabilities of large deviations of f from $\bar{f}$ are small. The quantity

$$\sqrt{\{\overline{(\Delta f)^2}\}} = \sqrt{\{\overline{(f-\bar{f})^2}\}}$$

is called the root mean square fluctuation of the variable f. Note that

$$\overline{(\Delta f)^2} = \overline{f^2 - 2f\bar{f} + \bar{f}^2} = \overline{f^2} - 2\bar{f}\bar{f} + \bar{f}^2,$$

whence

$$\overline{(\Delta f)^2} = \overline{f^2} - (\bar{f})^2, \tag{2.3}$$

i.e. the mean square fluctuation is defined as the difference between the mean value of the square, and the square of the mean value, of the quantity.

The expression

$$\frac{\sqrt{\{\overline{(\Delta f)^2}\}}}{\bar{f}}$$

is called the relative fluctuation of the quantity f. The smaller the value of this expression, the more insignificant is the fraction of time during which the body is in a state where the deviation of f from its mean value is an appreciable part of the latter.

We may now show that the relative fluctuations of physical quantities diminish rapidly with an increase in the physical dimensions (and hence the number of particles) of the bodies to which they refer. To do this notice, first of all, that most quantities of physical interest are additive. This means that the value of such a quantity for the whole body is the sum of its values for its separate (macroscopic) parts, and it is a consequence of the fact that the separate parts of the body are quasi-closed. For example since, as we have seen above, the internal energies of these parts are large compared with the energies of their interactions, the energy of the whole body can, with sufficient accuracy, be taken as the sum of the internal energies of its parts.

Let f be such an additive quantity. If we mentally divide the body under consideration into a large number, N, of approximately equal small parts, then $f = \sum_{i=1}^{N} f_i$, where the quantities f_i relate to the separate parts; the same is true of a mean value

$$\bar{f} = \sum_{i=1}^{N} \bar{f}_i.$$

It is clear that as the number of parts increases, $\bar{f}$ increases roughly in proportion with N. Next we write down the mean square fluctuation of the quantity f. We have

$$\overline{(\Delta f)^2} = \overline{\left(\sum_i \Delta f_i\right)^2}.$$

But owing to the statistical independence of different parts of the body, the mean value of the products

$$\overline{\Delta f_i . \Delta f_k} = \overline{\Delta f_i} . \overline{\Delta f_k} = 0 \qquad (i \neq k)$$

(as long as each $\overline{\Delta f_i} \equiv 0$). It follows that

$$\overline{(\Delta f)^2} = \sum_{i=1}^{N} \overline{(\Delta f_i)^2}. \tag{2.4}$$

From this we see that the mean square fluctuation $\overline{(\Delta f)^2}$ increases proportionally to N. The relative fluctuation will be thus inversely proportional to $\sqrt{N}$, i.e.

$$\frac{\sqrt{\{\overline{(\Delta f)^2}\}}}{\bar{f}} \propto \frac{1}{\sqrt{N}}. \tag{2.5}$$

On the other hand, if we divide the uniform body into parts of a given small size, it is clear that the number of such parts will be proportional to the total number of particles (molecules) in the body. The result we have obtained can therefore be equally well expressed by saying that the relative fluctuation of any additive quantity f decreases inversely as the square root of the number of particles in the macroscopic body. Thus with a sufficiently large number of particles the quantity f itself can be regarded as almost constant in time and equal to its mean value. This result was already used in the preceding section.

§3. Liouville's theorem

We now return to a further study of the statistical distribution function.

Assume that we are observing a certain subsystem over a very long interval of time. Let us divide this interval into a very large number (in the limit, into an infinite number) of small, equal, subintervals separated by instants of time t_1, t_2, ... At each one of these instants the subsystem under consideration will be represented in its phase space by a point. (We shall denote these points by A_1, A_2, A_3, ...) This set of points will be distributed in phase space with a density which at each point is proportional to the value of the distribution function $\rho(p, q)$ there. This follows from the meaning of the latter as defining the probabilities of different states of the subsystem.

Instead of examining the points representing the state of the subsystem at different times t_1, t_2, ... one can introduce, purely formally, a very large number (in the limiting case an infinite number) of completely identically constructed subsystems† which are, at one given instant (say, $t = 0$) in the states represented by A_1, A_2, ...

We can now follow the subsequent motion of the phase points representing the states of these subsystems over not too long a period of time (a period of time short enough for us to consider quasi-closed subsystems as closed). The motion of the phase points in this case will follow the equations of motion containing the co-ordinates and momenta only of particles of the subsystem.

Evidently, for the same reasons as for $t = 0$, at any time t these points will be distributed in phase space in accordance with the same distribution function $\rho(p, q)$. In other words as they move with time the phase points remain distributed so that their density at every point is constant and proportional to the corresponding value of ρ.

This motion of the phase points may be considered, purely formally, as the steady flow of a "gas" in $2s$-dimensional phase space and we may apply to it the well-known equation of continuity, which expresses the conservation of the total number of "particles" (in this case phase-points) of the gas. The usual equation of continuity is of the form

$$\frac{\partial \rho}{\partial t} + \mathrm{div}(\rho\mathbf{v}) = 0$$

(where ρ is the density, and $\mathbf{v}$ the velocity of the gas) and so for a steady flow ($\partial \rho/\partial t = 0$)

$$\mathrm{div}(\rho\mathbf{v}) = 0.$$

The generalisation of this for a many-dimensional space will clearly be

$$\sum_{i=1}^{2s} \frac{\partial}{\partial x_i}(\rho v_i) = 0.$$

---

† Such hypothetical set of identical subsystems is usually called a "statistical ensemble".

In this case the "co-ordinates" x_i are the co-ordinates q and momenta p, and the "velocities" $v_i = \dot{x}_i$ are the time derivatives $\dot{q}$ and $\dot{p}$ defined by the equations of motion. Thus we have

$$\sum_{i=1}^{s} \left[\frac{\partial}{\partial q_i}(\rho \dot{q}_i) + \frac{\partial}{\partial p_i}(\rho \dot{p}_i) \right] = 0.$$

On expanding the derivatives we obtain

$$\sum_{i=1}^{s} \left[\dot{q}_i \frac{\partial \rho}{\partial q_i} + \dot{p}_i \frac{\partial \rho}{\partial p_i} \right] + \rho \sum_{i=1}^{s} \left[\frac{\partial \dot{q}_i}{\partial q_i} + \frac{\partial \dot{p}_i}{\partial p_i} \right] = 0. \tag{3.1}$$

Expressing the equations of motion in Hamiltonian form

$$\dot{q}_i = \frac{\partial H}{\partial p_i}; \qquad \dot{p}_i = -\frac{\partial H}{\partial q_i},$$

where $H = H(p, q)$ is the Hamiltonian function of the subsystem in question, we see that

$$\frac{\partial \dot{q}_i}{\partial q_i} = \frac{\partial^2 H}{\partial q_i \partial p_i} = -\frac{\partial \dot{p}_i}{\partial p_i}.$$

Thus the second term in (3.1) is identically zero. The first term is simply the total derivative of the distribution function with respect to time. Thus we have

$$\frac{d\rho}{dt} = \sum_{i=1}^{s} \left(\frac{\partial \rho}{\partial q_i} \dot{q}_i + \frac{\partial \rho}{\partial p_i} \dot{p}_i \right) = 0. \tag{3.2}$$

We have arrived at the important result that the distribution function is constant along a phase trajectory of a subsystem. (LIOUVILLE's theorem); we must remember that as long as we are dealing with quasi-closed systems this result is valid only for not too long intervals of time, during which the subsystem behaves with sufficient accuracy like a closed one.

§4. The role of energy

It follows directly from Liouville's theorem that the distribution function can depend only on those combinations of the variables which remain constant while the subsystem moves like a closed system. These are the so-called integrals of motion which are, as we know, the first integrals of the equations of motion. Hence we may say that the distribution function, being itself a function of the integrals of motion is itself an integral of motion. Furthermore it appears that one can greatly reduce the number of such integrals on which the distribution function may depend. To do this we must use the fact that the distribution function ρ_{12} for a combination of two sub-systems is equal to the product of the distribution functions of these two subsystems separately: $\rho_{12} = \rho_1\rho_2$. (see 2.1). Hence

$$\log\rho_{12} = \log\rho_1 + \log\rho_2, \tag{4.1}$$

i.e. the logarithm of the distribution function is an additive quantity. We therefore arrive at the conclusion that the logarithm of the distribution function must be not merely an integral of motion, but an additive integral of motion.

As we know from mechanics, there exist only seven independent additive integrals of motion: the energy, the three components of the momentum vector, and the three components of the angular momentum vector. We shall denote these quantities for the subsystem a (as functions of the co-ordinates and momenta of its particles) respectively by $E_a(p, q)$, $\mathbf{P}_a(p, q)$, and $\mathbf{M}_a(p, q)$. The only additive function of these quantities is a linear combination of the type

$$\log \rho_a = \alpha_a + \beta E_a(p, q) + \boldsymbol{\gamma}\, \mathbf{P}_a(p, q) + \boldsymbol{\delta}\mathbf{M}_a(p, q) \tag{4.2}$$

with constant coefficients α_a, β, $\boldsymbol{\gamma}$, $\boldsymbol{\delta}$ where β, $\boldsymbol{\gamma}$, $\boldsymbol{\delta}$ are the same for all sub-systems of the given closed system.

We shall return later to a detailed study of (4.2) (in Chapter III). The following fact, however, is important for us at this stage. The coefficient α_a is simply a normalising constant defined by the condition $\int \rho_a\, \mathrm{d}p^{(a)}\mathrm{d}q^{(a)} = 1$. The coefficients β, $\boldsymbol{\gamma}$, $\boldsymbol{\delta}$ (only seven independent quantities) can clearly be expressed in terms of the seven constant values of the additive integrals of motion for the whole closed system.

Thus we reach the following most important conclusion. The values of the additive integrals of motion (energy, momentum, and angular momentum) completely determine the statistical properties of a closed system, i.e. the statistical distributions of any of its subsystems and together with them the mean values of any of their physical quantities. These seven additive integrals of motion replace the staggeringly large number of data (the initial conditions) required for a direct mechanical approach.

As a direct result of the above considerations, we may construct for a closed system a simple distribution function which can serve to describe its statistical properties. Since, as we now know, the values of the non-additive integrals of motion have no effect on these properties, we may use for their description any function ρ which depends only on the additive integrals of motion for the system and which satisfies Liouville's theorem. The simplest such function is the function $\rho = $ constant for all points of the phase space corresponding to given constant values of the energy (E_0), momentum $(\mathbf{P}_0)$, and angular momentum $(\mathbf{M}_0)$ of the system (independently of the values of the non-additive integrals), and $\rho = 0$ for all other points.

It is clear that the function defined in this way automatically remains constant along any phase trajectory, i.e. satisfies Liouville's theorem.

This formulation is not quite rigorous. In fact the points defined by the equations

$$E(p, q) = E_0, \quad \mathbf{P}(p, q) = \mathbf{P}_0, \quad \mathbf{M}(p, q) = \mathbf{M}_0, \tag{4.3}$$

form a subspace which has only $2s$—7 dimensions (and not the $2s$ dimensions of phase space). Thus in order for the integral $\int \rho \, dp dq$ to be non-zero, the function $\rho(p, q)$ must be infinite at these points. The correct expression for the distribution function of a closed system is

$$\rho = \text{const } \delta(E - E_0)\delta(\mathbf{P} - \mathbf{P}_0)\delta(\mathbf{M} - \mathbf{M}_0). \tag{4.4}$$

The presence of the δ function† ensures that ρ will vanish at all points of the phase space for which any of the quantities E, $\mathbf{P}$ or $\mathbf{M}$ differs from its given value E_0, $\mathbf{P}_0$ or $\mathbf{M}_0$. The integral of ρ over any phase volume containing any part of the above-mentioned subspace is finite. The distribution (4.4) is called *microcanonical*.‡

The momentum and angular momentum of a closed system are connected with its motion as a whole—with uniform translations and rotations. Hence we can say that the statistical state of a body performing a given motion depends only upon its energy. As a result the energy acquires a completely unique role in statistics.

The following device enables us to exclude momentum and angular momentum from any future considerations: imagine a system enclosed by a rigid "box" and consider a system of co-ordinates in which this "box" is at rest. Under these circumstances the momentum and angular momentum will cease to be integrals of motion and the only remaining additive integral of motion is the energy; at the same time the presence of the "box" will have no effect on the statistical properties of small parts of the system (subsystems). Hence for the logarithm of the distribution function we have, instead of (4.2), the simpler expression

$$\log \rho_a = \alpha_a + \beta E_a(p, q) \tag{4.5}$$

and a microcanonical distribution may be written in the form

$$\rho = \text{const } \delta(E - E_0). \tag{4.6}$$

So far we have assumed that the whole of the closed system is in statistical equilibrium, or in other words, that we have observed it for a time large in comparison with its relaxation time.

---

† For the definition and properties of the δ-function see for instance *Quantum Mechanics*, §5, Pergamon Press, London (1958).

‡ We must emphasise once more that this distribution is certainly not the real statistical distribution of a closed system. To suggest that this is so is equivalent to asserting that the phase trajectories of a closed system after a sufficiently long time will pass arbitrarily close to any arbitrary point of the subspace defined by (4.3). But such an assertion (known as the ergodic hypothesis) is certainly not true in general.

In practice, however, it is usually necessary to consider the system during periods comparable with or even small compared to the relaxation time. For large systems this is possible because there exist besides the complete equilibrium, states of so-called incomplete (or partial) equilibrium.

The point is that the relaxation time increases with an increase in size of the system. Due to this, separate small parts of the system themselves reach a state of equilibrium long before different small parts are brought into equilibrium with each other. This means that each small part of a system is described by a distribution function of the type (4.2) but the values of the parameters β, γ, δ vary from one part to another. In this case one says that the system is in a state of *partial equilibrium*. As time goes on, the partial equilibrium gradually becomes total, while the parameters β, γ, δ for each small part, varying slowly with time, eventually become the same for the whole system.

It is often necessary to consider also partial equilibria of a different kind. The origin of these is connected, not with the big difference in the relaxation times of the whole system and those of its small parts, but with the varying speeds with which different kinds of processes take place in the whole system. A good example is the partial equilibrium of a mixture of several substances which interact chemically. Owing to the relative slowness of chemical processes, the equilibrium connected with the motion of molecules occurs, in general, considerably sooner than the equilibrium connected with the interchange of atoms between the molecules, i.e. connected with the composition of the mixture. This fact allows us to consider the partial equilibria of a mixture as equilibria for given (non-equilibrium) chemical composition.

The existence of partial equilibria allows us to introduce the concept of "macroscopic states" of a system. A description which, unlike a mechanical, microscopic, description (i.e. specified co-ordinates and momenta for all particles in the system) describes the system by specifying the mean values of physical properties which define some particular partial equilibrium, is called a macroscopic description. For example, we may specify the mean values for sufficiently small, yet still macroscopic, parts of the system which can each be assumed to be in one of its own states of equilibrium.

§5. The statistical matrix

We turn now to the new features of quantum statistics. First of all, we note that a purely mechanical approach to the problem of explaining the behaviour of macroscopic bodies on the basis of quantum mechanics is just as hopeless as in the classical case. For such an approach we would need to solve Schrödinger's equation for the system consisting of all the particles of a body. This task is even more hopeless, we might say, than the integration of the classical equations of motion. Even if we could find a general solution of Schrödinger's equation in some cases, it would be quite impossible to select and write down the particular solution satisfying all the physical conditions of our problem, which are specified by particular values of an immense number of different quantum numbers. Furthermore we shall see later that for a macroscopic body the concept of stationary states becomes in a certain sense unrealistic. This is of great fundamental significance.

As a preliminary we may explain certain peculiarities which distinguish, in quantum mechanics, macroscopic bodies from those containing a comparatively small number of particles.

The main peculiarity is the extraordinarily high density of levels in the energy spectrum of a macroscopic body. The reason for this high density is easily understood if one notices that owing to the immense number of particles in the body, any energy can, roughly speaking, be "distributed" amongst different particles in an innumerable number of ways. The connection between this fact and the high density of the energy levels becomes particularly clear if one considers, for example, a macroscopic body which is a "gas" of N completely non-interacting particles confined in a certain volume. The energy levels of such a system represent simply the sums of the energies of the separate particles, each ranging over an infinite series of discrete values.† By choosing the values of the N terms of this sum in all possible ways it is clear that in any appreciable energy interval there will be an enormous number of possible values for the energy of the system, which must consequently lie very near to one another.

It can be shown generally (see 7.18) that the number of levels in a given finite interval of the energy spectrum of a macroscopic body, increases exponentially with the number of particles in the body, and the level spacing becomes something like a^{-N} (where $a > 1$ and N is a number of the order of magnitude of the number of particles in the body) whatever units are used, since the difference between different units is completely unimportant in dealing with such a fantastically small number.‡

Due to this extraordinary density of levels, a macroscopic body can never, in fact, be in a strictly stationary state. To start with, it is evident that the value of the energy of a system will in any case be "spread out" by an amount equal to the interaction energy of the system with its surroundings. But this interaction is extremely large in comparison with the separation of the levels not only for a "quasi-closed" subsystem, but also for systems which could be considered as rigorously closed from every other point of view. There exist, in nature, no rigorously closed systems whose interaction with any other body is zero; in fact all remaining interactions, even those which are so small

---

† The separation of adjacent energy levels of a single particle is inversely proportional to the square of the linear dimensions of the volume in which it is confined ($\sim \hbar^2/mL^2$ where m is the mass of the particle, $\hbar$ the quantum constant, equal to PLANCK's constant divided by 2π).

‡ Note that the above reasoning does not apply to the lowest interval of the energy spectrum; the separation of the first energy levels of a macroscopic body may even be independent of the size of the body, as for example in the electronic spectrum of a dielectric (see §69). This does not affect our further deductions, for, expressed as energy per particle, the distance between the first levels of a macroscopic body is negligibly small and the density of levels quoted in the text is already reached at quite insignificant energies per particle.

that they have no effect on any other properties of the system, will still appear very large in comparison with the vanishingly small spacing between energy levels.

Apart from this, however, there exists another deep reason why a macroscopic body cannot really be in a stationary state. As is known from quantum mechanics, the state of a quantum mechanical system, which is described by a wave function, results from some process of interaction between the system and another which obeys classical mechanics with sufficient accuracy. In obtaining a stationary state we meet very special features. We must here distinguish between the value E of the energy of a system before the interaction and E' the energy of the state resulting from the interaction. As is well known,† the indeterminacies ΔE and $\Delta E'$ of the quantities E and E' are connected with the duration Δt of the interaction process by the relation

$$|\Delta E' - \Delta E| \sim \hbar/\Delta t.$$

Both the indeterminacies ΔE, $\Delta E'$ are in general of the same order of magnitude, and further analysis shows that we cannot have $\Delta E' \ll \Delta E$. Hence we may assert that $\Delta E' \sim \hbar/\Delta t$. However, to enable us to consider the state as stationary one indeterminacy $\Delta E'$ must in any case be small in comparison with the separation of adjacent levels. Owing to the extreme smallness of the latter, we see that in order to bring the macroscopic body into a definite state, we would require an incredibly long time $\Delta t \sim \hbar/\Delta E'$. In other words, we once again conclude that it is impossible to realize an exactly stationary state of a macroscopic body.

Altogether the description of a macroscopic body by means of a wave function is impossible because the actual amount of data which it is possible to collect about the state of such a body falls far short of what is needed to construct a wave function for its state. This position is somewhat analogous to that encountered in classical statistics where a rigorous mechanical description of the behaviour of a body is rendered impossible by the impossibility of considering the initial conditions for all the particles in the body. The analogy is not really complete, as the impossibility of a complete quantum mechanical description and the absence of a wave function describing a macroscopic body might have, as we have seen, much deeper foundations.

A quantum mechanical description based on incomplete information about the system is carried out by means of the well-known method of the so-called "density matrix".‡ The knowledge of the density matrix permits us to calculate the mean value of any variable of the system, and also the probabilities of the different values of these variables. The incompleteness of the description lies here in the fact that the results of various measurements, which can be predicted to some degree of accuracy on the basis of a knowledge of the density matrix, could be predicted with greater or even complete

---

† See for instance *Quantum Mechanics*, §44.
‡ See *Quantum Mechanics*, §12.

accuracy on the basis of a complete knowledge of the data for the system, which would be sufficient for the construction of a wave function.

We are not going to quote here all the well-known quantum mechanical formulae concerning the density matrix in the co-ordinate representation, as this representation is in practice never used in statistics. We shall show, however, how the density matrix can be introduced directly in the energy representation required for statistical applications.

Consider some subsystem, and define its "stationary states" as the states resulting if its interaction with neighbouring parts of the closed system is neglected. Let $\psi_n(q)$ be the normalised wave functions (without the time factor) of these states, where q stands for the co-ordinates of the subsystem and the index n for the set of all quantum numbers labelling the stationary states; the energy of these states being denoted by E_n. Assume that at a given instant of time the subsystem is in some state completely described by a wave function Ψ. We can then expand this in terms of the complete set of functions $\psi_n(q)$. We write the expansion in the form

$$\Psi = \sum_n c_n \psi_n. \tag{5.1}$$

Then we know that the mean value of an arbitrary quantity f in this state can be calculated in terms of the coefficients c_n by the formula

$$\bar{f} = \sum_n \sum_m c_n{}^* c_m f_{nm} \tag{5.2}$$

where

$$f_{nm} = \int \psi_n{}^* \hat{f} \psi_m \, dq \tag{5.3}$$

are the matrix elements of the quantity f ($\hat{f}$ being the corresponding operator).

The transition from a complete to an incomplete quantum mechanical description of the subsystem can, in a certain sense, be regarded as averaging over its different Ψ states. As a result of such an averaging process the products $c_n{}^* c_m$ will give rise to quantities which we shall denote by w_{mn} which form a double sequence (as both indices vary) and which cannot be expressed as the products of quantities forming a single sequence. The mean value of a quantity will be given by an expression of the type

$$\bar{f} = \sum_m \sum_n w_{mn} f_{nm}. \tag{5.4}$$

The set of quantities w_{mn} (in general functions of time) forms the density matrix in the energy representation. In statistics it is called the *statistical matrix*.†

If we consider w_{mn} as matrix elements of some "statistical operator" $\hat{w}$ then the sum $\sum w_{mn} f_{nm}$ will be a diagonal element of the matrix of the operator

---

† We talk about the energy representation, as this is what we usually use in statistics. Nevertheless we have not yet used directly the fact that the Ψ_n are the wave functions of stationary states. Hence it is clear that we could in the same way define the density matrix in terms of an arbitrary complete set of wave functions.

product, $\hat{w}\hat{f}$, and the mean value $\bar{f}$ will be given by the trace (sum of the diagonal elements) of this operator.

$$\bar{f} = \sum_n (\hat{w}\hat{f})_{nn} = \mathrm{Tr}(\hat{w}\hat{f}). \tag{5.5}$$

This form of representation has the advantage that it allows us to calculate with the help of an arbitrary complete, orthogonal, normalised set of wave functions: the trace of an operator is known to be independent of the choice of the system of functions in terms of which the matrix elements are defined.†

Other quantum mechanical expressions involving the coefficients c_n may be transformed similarly, products $c_n^* c_m$ being replaced each time by the "average values" w_{mn}

$$c_n^* c_m \to w_{mn}.$$

Thus the probability that a subsystem is in the nth state is given by the corresponding diagonal element w_{mn} of the density matrix (instead of the square of the modulus $c_n^* c_n$). It is obvious that these elements, which we will denote subsequently by w_n, are always positive

$$w_n = w_{nn} > 0 \tag{5.6}$$

and satisfy the normalisation condition

$$\mathrm{Tr}\hat{w} = \sum_n w_n = 1$$

(corresponding to the condition $\sum_n |c_n|^2 = 1$).

We must emphasise that it is only in a very restricted sense that we can talk about this averaging over different Ψ-states, which we have introduced in order to make clear the transition from a complete to an incomplete quantum mechanical description. In particular it would be quite wrong to assume that the description in terms of a density matrix corresponds to the fact that the subsystem has a certain probability of being in each of the different Ψ-states, and that the averaging process is averaging over these probabilities. Such an assumption would contradict the basic principles of quantum mechanics.

States of a quantum-mechanical system described by wave functions are sometimes called "pure states" to distinguish them from the "mixed states" described by the density matrix. One must nevertheless guard against wrongly interpreting the latter in the sense indicated above.‡ The averaging

---

† See *Quantum Mechanics*, §91.

‡ We may state a criterion for distinguishing the "pure" and mixed states in terms of the nature of the density matrix. In the pure case the elements w_{mn} must be expressible in the form of a product $c_n^* c_m$. Hence we obtain

$$(w^2)_{mn} = \sum_k w_{mk} w_{kn} = \sum_k c_k^* c_m c_n^* c_k = c_m c_n^* \sum_k |c_k|^2 = c_m c_n^*$$

or

$$(w^2)_{mn} = w_{mn}.$$

i.e. the square of the density matrix must be equal to itself.

by means of the statistical matrix, as defined in (5.4) has a double nature. It includes both the averaging connected with the probability nature of even a quite complete quantum description, and also the statistical averaging made necessary by our incomplete knowledge of the observed object. In the "pure state" only the first type of averaging process is involved, but in statistical cases both types are always present. Nevertheless it is necessary to take into account the fact that these two elements cannot be separated from one another; the whole averaging process is performed at once and it cannot be represented as the result of applying consecutively a purely quantum mechanical and a purely statistical averaging.

The statistical matrix plays, in quantum statistics, the part which the distribution function plays in classical statistics. Everything which was said in previous sections about the almost deterministic character of the predictions of classical statistics is quite applicable to quantum statistics. The proof derived in §2 of the fact that the relative fluctuations of additive physical quantities tend to zero (as the number of particles increases) made no use of any properties particular to classical mechanics, and is hence equally applicable to the quantum case. Hence we can assert, as before, that macroscopic quantities remain nearly equal to their mean values.

In classical statistics the distribution function $\rho(p, q)$ gives directly the distribution of probabilities for different values of the co-ordinates and momenta of the particles in the body, but in quantum statistics this is not so. The quantities w_n give only the probabilities of finding the body in one quantum state or another, with no direct indication of the co-ordinates and momenta of the particles.

Owing to the very nature of quantum mechanics, in dealing with the statistics based on it we can talk only of finding the distribution of probabilities for the co-ordinates and momenta separately, and not for both together, insofar as the co-ordinates and momenta of a particle cannot have simultaneously definite values. The required probability distributions must involve both the statistical uncertainty and also the uncertainty due to the quantum mechanical description itself. To find these distributions let us use once more the method applied above. Assume, to start with, that the body is in a pure quantum mechanical state, with wave function (5.1). The resulting probability distribution for the co-ordinates will be the square of the modulus

$$|\Psi|^2 = \sum_n \sum_m c_n{}^* c_m \psi_n{}^* \psi_m$$

and the probability that the co-ordinates have values in the interval $dq = dq_1\, dq_2 \ldots dq_s$ is equal to $dw_q = |\Psi|^2\, dq$. The transition to a mixed state is achieved by replacing the products $c_n{}^* c_m$ by the elements w_{mn} of the statistical matrix, as a result of which $|\Psi|^2$ is transformed into the sum

$$\sum_n \sum_m w_{mn} \psi_n{}^* \psi_m.$$

But from the definition of the matrix elements it follows that we may write

$$\sum_m w_{mn}\psi_m = \hat{w}\psi_n.$$

Hence

$$\sum_n \sum_m w_{mn}\psi_n{}^*\psi_m = \sum_n \psi_n{}^*\hat{w}\psi_n.$$

Thus we find the following formula for the distribution of probabilities for the co-ordinates:

$$dw_q = \sum \psi_n{}^*\hat{w}\psi_n \,.dq. \tag{5.8}$$

In the expression written in this form, one can use for the functions ψ_n any complete set of normalised wave functions.

We may also define the probability distribution for the momenta. Quantum states in which all the momenta have definite values correspond to the free motion of all the particles. Denote the wave functions of these states by $\psi_p(q)$ where the index p stands for the set of values of all the momenta. As we know, the diagonal elements of the density matrix are the probabilities of finding the system in the corresponding states. Hence by defining the density matrix in terms of the set of functions ψ_p we will obtain the required distribution of probabilities for the momenta according to the formula†

$$dw_p = w_{pp}\,dp = dp \int \psi_p{}^*\hat{w}\psi_p \,dq, \tag{5.9}$$

where $dp = dp_1\,dp_2\,...\,dp_s$.

It is interesting to note that both the distribution for co-ordinates and that for momenta can be obtained by the integration of the same function

$$I = \psi_p{}^*(q)\hat{w}\psi_p(q). \tag{5.10}$$

By integrating it over dq we obtain the distribution for the momenta, and by integrating over dp we obtain the distribution for the co-ordinates (the expression (5.8) with the functions ψ_p as the complete set of wave functions). It must be stressed, however, that this does not mean that the function (5.10) can be taken as the distribution of probabilities for the co-ordinates and momenta simultaneously; quite apart from the fact that this would contradict the basic principles of quantum mechanics, the expression (5.10) is complex.

§6. The statistical distribution in quantum statistics

In quantum mechanics it is possible to prove a theorem quite analogous to Liouville's theorem deduced in §3 on the basis of classical mechanics.

To do this we first deduce the quantum mechanical equation defining the time-derivative of the statistical matrix of any closed system.‡

---

† The functions Ψ_p are assumed to be normalised to a δ-function of all the momenta.

‡ In the previous paragraph we were discussing the density matrix of a subsystem, bearing in mind its basic statistical applications. It is obvious that a density matrix can also be used to describe a closed system in a "mixed" state.

Using the method of the previous section we assume again, to begin with, that the system is in a "pure" state with a wave function represented by the series (5.1). Since the system is closed its wave function will be of the same form at all subsequent instants except that the coefficients c_n will now be functions of time proportional to the factors $e^{-iE_n t/\hbar}$. Hence we have

$$\frac{\partial}{\partial t} c_n{}^* c_m = \frac{i}{\hbar}(E_n - E_m) c_n{}^* c_m.$$

The transition to the statistical matrix in the general case of mixed states is now achieved by replacing the products $c_n{}^* c_m$ by w_{mn}. Thus we have the required equation

$$\dot{w}_{mn} = \frac{i}{\hbar}(E_n - E_m) w_{mn}. \tag{6.1}$$

These equations may be rewritten in general operator form by noticing that

$$(E_n - E_m) w_{mn} = \sum_l (w_{ml} H_{ln} - H_{ml} w_{ln}),$$

where H_{mn} are the matrix elements of the Hamiltonian $\hat{H}$ of the system, which is diagonal in the energy representation we have adopted. Hence

$$\dot{w} = \frac{i}{\hbar}(\hat{w}\hat{H} - \hat{H}\hat{w}). \tag{6.2}$$

(Note that this expression differs in sign from the usual quantum mechanical expression for the operator representing the time derivative of a quantity.)

We see that for the derivative to vanish, the operator $\hat{w}$ must commute with the Hamiltonian of the system. This result represents the quantum mechanical analogue of Liouville's theorem. In classical mechanics the condition that the distribution function must be stationary implies that w is an integral of motion; in quantum mechanics, the fact that the operator of any quantity commutes with the Hamiltonian just expresses its conservation.

In the energy representation which we are using, stationary quantities can be recognised very simply; as can be seen from (6.1) the matrix w_{mn} must be diagonal, which again corresponds to the usual matrix formulation of the quantum mechanical conservation of a quantity. (The matrix of a conserved quantity reduces to diagonal form simultaneously with the Hamiltonian.)

As in §3, we may now apply the results we have obtained to quasi-closed subsystems, considering only intervals of time for which they behave like closed ones. As the statistical distributions (in this case statistical matrices) of the subsystems must be stationary, from the very definition of statistical equilibrium, we immediately deduce that the matrices w_{mn} of all the sub-systems must be diagonal.† The problem of defining the statistical distribution is hence reduced to that of calculating the probabilities $w_n = w_{nn}$ which represent the "distribution function" in quantum statistics. The formula (5·4) for the mean value of any quantity becomes simply

$$\bar{f} = \sum_n w_n f_{nn};$$

(6.3)

it now involves only the diagonal elements f_{nn} of the matrix.

Furthermore, considering that w must be a quantum mechanical "integral of motion" and by using the fact that the subsystems are quasi-closed in a similar way to that in the derivation of (4.5) we find that the logarithms of the distribution functions of the subsystems must be

$$\log w_n^{(a)} = \alpha^{(a)} + \beta E_n^{(a)}$$

(6.4)

(the index a distinguishing the different subsystems). Thus the probability w_n can be expressed in terms of the value of the energy level alone: $w_n = w(E_n)$.

Finally, all the deductions of §4 about the role of the additive integrals of motion (in particular energy) in determining the statistical properties of a closed system still hold.

This again enables us to construct for the closed system a simple distribution function, suitable for the description of its statistical properties, though by no means the real distribution function (just as in the classical case).

For the mathematical formulation of this "quantum microcanonical distribution" we use the following device. Bearing in mind the "almost continuous character" of the energy spectra of macroscopic bodies, we introduce the concept of the number of quantum states of a closed system "belonging to" a certain infinitesimal energy interval.‡ We shall denote this number by $d\Gamma$; it plays here a role analogous to that of the phase volume element $dp dq$ in the classical case.

Regarding the closed system as made up of subsystems whose interactions we neglect, we see that each state of the system as a whole can be specified by giving the state of each subsystem and the number $d\Gamma$ will be represented by the product

$$d\Gamma = \prod_a d\Gamma_a$$

(6.5)

of the numbers $d\Gamma_a$ of quantum states of the subsystems (such that the sum of the energies of the subsystems lies in the given interval of the energy of the whole system). We may now express the microcanonical distribution in

---

† We must remember that we have agreed (§4) to ignore completely the momenta and angular momenta of the system as a whole, for which it was sufficient to imagine the system to be enclosed in a rigid box using a co-ordinate system in which the box is at rest.

‡ Since this assertion depends to a certain extent on neglecting the mutual interactions of the subsystems, it would be more accurate to say that the non-diagonal elements w_{mn} tend to zero as these interactions become relatively less important, and hence as the number of particles in the subsystems increases.

a form analogous to the classical expression (4.6) by writing, for the probability dw that the system is in one of the states $d\Gamma$,

$$dw = \text{const } \delta(E - E_0) \prod_a d\Gamma_a. \tag{6.6}$$

§7. Entropy

Consider a closed system which we observe for a time large in comparison with its relaxation time; this implies that the system is in total statistical equilibrium.

We make the following deduction for quantum statistics to begin with. Dividing the system into a large number of macroscopic parts (subsystems), we consider a particular one. Let w_n be the distribution function of this subsystem; for simplicity we shall omit for the time being from w_n (and other quantities) the index distinguishing the subsystem. With the help of w_n one can, in particular, calculate the probabilities of different values of the energy E of the subsystem. We have seen that w_n can be expressed as a function of the energy only

$$w_n = w(E_n) \quad \text{(see eq. 6.4)}.$$

To obtain the probability $W(E) \, dE$ that the energy of the subsystem lies between E and $E + dE$ we must multiply $W(E)$ by the number of quantum states with energies lying in this interval; we are using here the same concept of the "smeared out" energy spectrum which was introduced at the end of the previous section. Denote by $\Gamma(E)$ the number of quantum states with energies less than or equal to E; then the required number of states with energies between E and $E + dE$ may be written in the form

$$\frac{d\Gamma(E)}{dE} dE$$

and the distribution of probabilities over the energies will be

$$W(E) = \frac{d\Gamma(E)}{dE} w(E). \tag{7.1}$$

The normalisation condition

$$\int W(E) \, dE = 1$$

means geometrically that the area under the curve $W = W(E)$ is equal to unity.

According to the general conclusions of §1 the function $W(E)$ has an extremely sharp maximum at $E = \bar{E}$, differing appreciably from zero only in the immediate neighbourhood of this point. We may introduce the "width" ΔE of the curve $W = W(E)$, defining it as the width of a rectangle whose height is equal to the value of the function $W(E)$ at its maximum and whose area is equal to unity.

$$W(\bar{E})\Delta E = 1. \tag{7.2}$$

By using the relation (7.1) we may rewrite this condition in the form

$$w(\bar{E})\Delta\Gamma = 1. \tag{7.3}$$

where

$$\Delta\Gamma = \frac{d\Gamma(\bar{E})}{dE}\Delta E \tag{7.4}$$

is the number of quantum states corresponding to the range ΔE of energy values. The quantity $\Delta\Gamma$ defined in this way may be said to act as a measure of the "spread" of the macroscopic state of the subsystem over its microscopic states. The interval ΔE is of the same order of magnitude as the mean fluctuation of the energy of the subsystem.

The definitions we have made can be taken over directly into classical statistics, but instead of the function $w(E)$ we must talk about the distribution function ρ, and instead of $\Delta\Gamma$, about the volume of phase space defined by the formula

$$\rho(\bar{E})\,\Delta p\Delta q = 1. \tag{7.5}$$

The phase volume $\Delta\Gamma$, like $\Delta p\Delta q$, characterises the dimensions of the region of phase space in which the given subsystem remains nearly all the time.

It is not difficult to establish a connection between $\Delta\Gamma$ and $\Delta p\Delta q$ by regarding classical theory as a limiting case of quantum theory. As is known from quantum mechanics† one can establish, in the quasi-classical case, a definite relationship between the volume of some region of phase space and the number of quantum states "ascribed" to it; one can then say that to each quantum state there "corresponds" in phase space a "cell" of volume $(2\pi\hbar)^s$ (where s is the number of degrees of freedom of the system). Hence it is clear that in the quasi-classical case the number of states $\Delta\Gamma$ may be written in the form.

$$\Delta\Gamma = \frac{\Delta p\Delta q}{(2\pi\hbar)^s}, \tag{7.6}$$

where s is the number of degrees of freedom of the given subsystem. This formula establishes the required relationship between $\Delta\Gamma$ and $\Delta p\Delta q$.

The quantity $\Delta\Gamma$ is called the *statistical weight* of the subsystem and its logarithm

$$\sigma = \log\Delta\Gamma \tag{7.7}$$

† See for example, *Quantum Mechanics*, §§48, 52.

is called the entropy of the subsystem. In the classical case the entropy is similarly defined by the expression

$$\sigma = \log \frac{\Delta p \Delta q}{(2\pi\hbar)^s}. \tag{7.8}$$

Defined in this way, entropy, like the statistical weight itself, is a dimensionless quantity. Insofar as the number of states is never less than unity, the entropy cannot be negative. The concept of entropy is one of the most important in statistics.

It is as well to note that if one works from a completely classical standpoint one cannot introduce such a concept as the "number of microscopic states" and we would be obliged to define the statistical weight simply as the quantity $\Delta p \Delta q$. But the dimensions of this quantity, like those of any phase volume, are s of momenta and the same number of co-ordinates, i.e. its dimensions are action to the sth power [(erg . sec)^s]. Entropy, defined as $\log \Delta p \Delta q$, would in this case have the unusual dimension of a logarithm of action. This means that a change in the units of action would mean a change of the entropy by an additive constant; if the unit of action is changed by a factor a then $\Delta p \Delta q$ will become $a^s \Delta p \Delta q$ and $\log \Delta p \Delta q$ becomes $\log \Delta p \Delta q + s \log a$. Hence in purely classical statistics entropy is a quantity uncertain to the extent of an additive constant depending on the choice of units. The only uniquely determined quantities, not depending on the choice of units, are differences in entropy, i.e. the changes in entropy induced by some process or other.

This fact is bound up with the appearance of the quantum constant in the definition (7.8) of entropy for classical statistics. It is only the concept of the number of discrete quantum states, which inevitably depends upon the quantum constant being non-zero, which allows us to introduce a dimensionless statistical weight, and thus to define entropy as an unambiguously determined quantity.

Let us write the definition of entropy in a different form, expressing it directly in terms of the distribution function. In accordance with (6.4) the logarithm of the distribution function of a subsystem has the form

$$\log w(E_n) = \alpha + \beta E_n.$$

Owing to the linearity of this expression in E_n, the quantity

$$\log w(\bar{E}) = \alpha + \beta \bar{E}$$

may also be written as the mean value $\overline{\log w(E_n)}$ and hence the entropy $\sigma = \log \Delta\Gamma = -\log w(\bar{E})$ (from 7.3) can be written in the form

$$\sigma = -\overline{\log w(E_n)} \tag{7.9}$$

i.e. one can define the entropy as (minus) the mean value of the logarithm of the distribution function of the subsystem. From the meaning of mean value we have

$$\sigma = -\sum_n w_n \log w_n. \tag{7.10}$$

This expression can be written in general operator form independent of the choice of the set of wave functions in terms of which the elements of the statistical matrix are defined:†

$$\sigma = -\text{Tr}(\hat{w} \log \hat{w}). \tag{7.11}$$

Similarly, in classical statistics the definition of entropy can be written in the form

$$\sigma = -\overline{\log[(2\pi\hbar)^s\rho]} = -\int \rho \log[(2\pi\hbar)^s\rho] \, dp dq. \tag{7.12}$$

Returning to the closed system as a whole, let $\Delta\Gamma_1$, $\Delta\Gamma_2$, ... be the statistical weights of its different subsystems. If each subsystem can be in one of $\Delta\Gamma_a$ quantum states, then clearly,

$$\Delta\Gamma = \prod_a \Delta\Gamma_a \tag{7.13}$$

is the number of states for the system as a whole. This quantity is called the statistical weight, and its logarithm the entropy σ of the closed system. Clearly

$$\sigma = \sum_a \sigma_a, \tag{7.14}$$

i.e. the entropy defined in this way is an additive quantity. The entropy of the compound system is equal to the sum of the entropies of its parts.

In order to understand clearly this method of defining entropy it is important to take the following fact into account. The entropy of a closed system (whose total energy we denote by E_0) which is in a state of total statistical equilibrium can also be defined directly without splitting the system up into subsystems. To do this imagine that the system under consideration is in reality only a small part of some very large imaginary system (which in this connection is called a "thermostat" or "heat bath"). The thermostat is assumed to be in a state of total equilibrium such that the mean energy of our system (which is now a subsystem of the thermostat, and not closed) just coincides with the real value of the energy, E_0. Then we can, formally, postulate for our system a distribution function of the same form as for each of its subsystems, and by means of this distribution define its statistical weight $\Delta\Gamma$ and with it the entropy directly from formulae (7.3)–(7.12) which we have used for subsystems. It is clear that the presence of the thermostat in no way affects the statistical qualities of separate small parts

---

† The operator $\log \hat{w}$ must be understood, in accordance with the general rules, as the operator whose eigenvalues are equal to the logarithms of the eigenvalues of the operator $\hat{w}$ and whose eigenfunctions coincide with those of the latter.

(subsystems) of our system, as they are in any case not closed and are in equilibrium with the other parts of the system. Hence the presence of the thermostat will not change the statistical weights $\Delta\Gamma a$ of these parts and the statistical weight just defined will coincide with that defined previously as a product (7.13).

So far we have assumed that the closed system is in a state of total equilibrium. We must now generalise the definitions we have made for systems which are in arbitrary macroscopic states (partial equilibria).

We assume that the system is in some state of partial equilibrium and consider it for time intervals Δt small in comparison with the relaxation time of the total equilibrium. Then to define entropy we must proceed as follows. Divide the system mentally into parts so small that their own relaxation times would be small compared with Δt (remember that relaxation times in general grow smaller as the system decreases in size). Such subsystems can be considered as being, during the time Δt, in individual equilibria, described by specific distribution functions. Hence our previous definitions of statistical weights $\Delta\Gamma_a$ can be applied and so we can calculate their entropies σ_a. The statistical weight $\Delta\Gamma$ of the whole system is then defined as the product (7.13), and similarly the entropy σ as the sum of the entropies σ_a.

It must be emphasised, nevertheless, that the entropy of a system in a non-equilibrium state, defined as the sum of the entropies of its parts (subject to the above conditions) cannot now be calculated by means of the concept of a thermostat without splitting the system into parts. At the same time this definition is quite unambiguous in the sense that the further subdivision of the subsystems into even smaller parts will not change the value of the entropy, provided that each subsystem is itself in its own "total" equilibrium.

In particular the role of time in the definition of entropy must be noted. The entropy is a quantity which determines the average properties of the body over some non-zero time interval Δt. In order to define σ, once Δt is given, we must mentally divide the body into parts sufficiently small for their own relaxation times to be small compared with Δt. As these parts must themselves be macroscopic, it is clear that the concept of entropy loses all meaning for too small intervals Δt; in particular one cannot talk about its instantaneous value.

Having given a complete definition of entropy, let us now turn to studying its most important properties and basic physical significance. To do this we make use of the microcanonical distribution, which uses, for the description of the statistical properties of a closed system, a distribution function of the form (6.6)

$$dw = \text{const } \delta(E-E_0) \cdot \prod_a d\Gamma_a.$$

Here $d\Gamma_a$ can be interpreted as the differential of the function $\Gamma_a(E_a)$ which gives the number of quantum states of the subsystem in which its energy is less than or equal to E_a, we may rewrite dw in the form

$$dw = \text{const } \delta(E-E_0) \prod_a \frac{d\Gamma_a}{dE_a} dE_a. \tag{7.15}$$

The statistical weight $\Delta\Gamma_a$ is by definition a function of the mean energy $\bar{E}_a$ of the subsystem, and so is the entropy $\sigma_a = \sigma_a(\bar{E}_a)$. We may formally regard $\Delta\Gamma_a$ and σ_a as functions of the actual value of the energy E_a (the same functions which they actually are of $\bar{E}_a$). Then in (7.15) we may replace the derivatives $d\Gamma_a(E_a)/dE_a$ by the ratios $\Delta\Gamma_a/\Delta E_a$, where $\Delta\Gamma_a$ is understood in the above sense as a function of E_a and ΔE_a is the energy interval corresponding to $\Delta\Gamma_a$ (also a function of E_a). Lastly, by substituting $e^{\sigma_a(E_a)}$ for $\Delta\Gamma_a$ we have

$$dw = \text{const } \delta(E-E_0)e^{\sigma} \prod_a \frac{dE_a}{\Delta E_a}, \tag{7.16}$$

where

$$\sigma = \sum_a \sigma_a(E_a)$$

is the entropy of the whole closed system, interpreted as a function of the exact values of the energies of its own parts. The factor e^{σ}, whose exponent is an additive quantity, is a very quickly varying function of the energies E_a. In comparison with this the dependence of the quantity $\prod_a \Delta E_a$ on the energies is quite negligible, and hence we can replace (7.16) with great accuracy by the expression

$$dw = \text{const } \delta(E-E_0)e^{\sigma} \prod_a dE_a. \tag{7.17}$$

But dw expressed in a form proportional to the product of all the differentials is simply the probability that all the subsystems have energies in the given intervals between E_a and E_a+dE_a. Thus we see that this probability is defined by the entropy of the system as a function of the energies of the subsystems; the factor $\delta(E-E_0)$ ensures that the sum $E = \sum E_a$ is equal to the given value E_0 of the energy of the system. This property of the entropy is the basis of its statistical applications.

We know that the most probable values of the energies E_a are their mean values $\bar{E}_a$. This means that the function $\sigma(E_1, E_2, \ldots)$ will have its maximum possible value (subject to $\sum E_a = E_0$) at $E_a = \bar{E}_a$. But the $\bar{E}_a$ are just those values of the energies of the subsystems which correspond to the state of total statistical equilibrium of the system. Thus we arrive at the following most important deduction. The entropy of a closed system has its greatest value (for a given value of the energy of the system) in a state of total equilibrium.

Lastly we may point out another interesting interpretation of the function $\sigma = \sigma(E)$, the entropy of some subsystem or of a closed system. (In the latter case it is assumed that the system is in a state of total equilibrium and hence that its entropy can be expressed as a function of its total energy alone.) The statistical weight $\Delta\Gamma = e^{\sigma(E)}$ is by definition the number of energy levels belonging to the interval ΔE, which in a certain way characterises the width of the probability distribution in energy. Dividing ΔE by $\Delta\Gamma$ we obviously obtain the mean distance between adjacent levels in the given interval (the neighbourhood of the value E) of the energy spectrum of the system under consideration. Denoting this distance by $D(E)$ we may write:

$$D(E) = \Delta E e^{-\sigma(E)}. \tag{7.18}$$

Thus the function $\sigma(E)$ determines the density of the energy levels in the spectrum of the macroscopic system. Since entropy is additive, we may say that the mean spacing between levels of a macroscopic body decreases exponentially as its size (i.e. the number of particles in it) is increased.

§8. The law of increase of entropy

If a closed system is not in a state of statistical equilibrium, then its macroscopic state will vary with time until the system eventually reaches total equilibrium. We may specify every macroscopic state of the system by the distribution of its energy between its various subsystems; we can then say that successive states through which the system passes correspond to energy distributions of successively greater probabilities. This increase in probability is, in general, extremely important owing to its exponential nature which was demonstrated in the last section. As we have seen, the probability is given by the expression e^{σ}, whose exponent is an additive quantity (the entropy of the system). We can hence say that processes taking place in a closed system which is not in equilibrium occur in such a manner that the system steadily passes from states of lower entropy to those of higher entropy, until finally the entropy attains its maximum possible value, corresponding to total statistical equilibrium.

Thus if a closed system is at some instant of time in a macroscopic state not in equilibrium, then the most probable consequence will be that the entropy of the system will increase monotonically in successive instants of time. This is the so-called law of increase of entropy or the "second law of thermodynamics". It was discovered by R. CLAUSIUS and its statistical foundation was given by L. BOLTZMANN.

When we talk about the "most probable consequence" we must bear in mind the fact that in reality the probability of a change to a state of higher entropy is so overwhelmingly large compared with the probability of any appreciable decrease that the latter cannot in fact be observed in nature. Neglecting decreases of entropy due to negligible fluctuations, we can thus formulate the law of increase of entropy in the following form. If at any given moment of time the entropy of a closed system differs from its maximum value then in succeeding moments the entropy does not decrease; it increases or, in the extreme, remains constant.

There can be no doubt that the simple formulations which we have given correspond to reality; they are confirmed by all our everyday observations. Nevertheless, a deeper consideration of the question of the physical nature and the origin of these laws leads to considerable difficulties, which to some extent still remain unsolved at the present time.

First of all, if we try to apply these formulations to the universe as a whole, considered as a single closed system, then we immediately arrive at a striking disagreement between theory and experiment. In accordance with these formulations the universe ought to be in a state of total statistical equilibrium. More exactly any arbitrarily large but nevertheless finite part of it, whose relaxation time is at any rate finite, should be in equilibrium.

But everyday experience convinces us that the properties of nature have nothing in common with the properties of a system in equilibrium, and astronomical data show that the same is true of the whole of the colossal part of the universe which we can observe.

We could try to remove this contradiction by assuming that the part of the universe which we can observe is nothing but a gigantic fluctuation in a system in equilibrium as a whole (the so-called "Fluctuation Hypothesis"). The fact that we are enabled to observe such a fluctuation could be explained by suggesting that the occurrence of such a fluctuation is a necessary condition for the existence of an observer (the condition making biological development of organisms possible). However this argument does not hold water, as there would be a much greater probability of a fluctuation in, say, the volume of the solar system which would be quite sufficient to ensure the possibility of the existence of an observer.

The answer is to be sought in the general theory of relativity. The point is that when we consider large regions of the system, the gravitational fields which they contain begin to become important. According to the general theory of relativity, the latter represent simply changes in the space time metric which is described by the metric tensor g_{ik}. In the study of the statistical properties of bodies, the metrical properties of space time can, in a certain sense, be regarded as the "external conditions" in which these bodies are situated. The assumption that after a long enough interval of time a closed system must eventually reach a state of equilibrium depends obviously on the external conditions remaining constant. But the metric tensor g_{ik} is, generally speaking, a function not only of the co-ordinates but of time as well, so that the "external conditions" are by no means constant. It is important to note with this that the gravitational field cannot itself be counted as part of the closed system because in that case the conservation laws, which, as we have seen, are the very foundation of statistics, would become simply identities. As a result of this, in the general theory of relativity the universe as a whole must be regarded not as a closed system, but as one which is in a variable gravitational field. In this case the application of the law of increase of entropy does not imply the necessity of statistical equilibrium.

Thus, in the part we have discussed of the problem of the universe as a whole, the physical roots of the apparent contradictions are clear. But there exist still more difficulties in understanding the physical foundations of the law of increase of entropy.

Classical mechanics, as is known, is completely symmetrical as regards the direction of time. That is to say, the equations of motion remain unaltered if t is replaced by $-t$: hence if these equations permit some motion, then they must permit the reverse motion, when the mechanical system passes through the same configurations in the reverse order. Naturally the same symmetry must be preserved in the statistics which is based on classical mechanics. Hence, if a certain process is possible in a closed macroscopic system which is accompanied by an increase in entropy, then the reverse process ought also to be possible in which the entropy of the system will decrease. The above formulation of the law of increase of entropy does not in itself contradict this symmetry as it only speaks of the most probable consequence of a macroscopically described state. In other words, given a non-equilibrium macroscopic state then the law of increase of entropy asserts only that of all the microscopic states satisfying the given macroscopic description, the overwhelming majority will lead subsequently to an increase in entropy.

But a contradiction, a very deep one, arises if one looks at a different aspect of the problem. When formulating the law of increase of entropy we talked about the most probable result of some macroscopic state which was given at a certain moment of time. However, this state must itself have arisen from some other state as the result of some process occurring in nature. The symmetry with regard to both directions of time means that for any arbitrarily chosen macroscopic state at time $t = t_0$ one can assert not only that there is an overwhelming probability that its consequence at $t > t_0$ will be an increase in entropy, but also that it is overwhelmingly probable that it arose itself from a state with greater entropy. In other words there is an overwhelming probability that the moment $t = t_0$, at which we arbitrarily chose the macroscopic state, is a minimum of entropy as a function of time.

Quite obviously this assertion is in no way equivalent to the law of increase of entropy according to which, in all closed systems which actually exist in nature, the entropy never decreases (apart from quite negligible fluctuations). It is this general formulation of the law of increase of entropy which is completely confirmed by all events which actually occur. It must be emphasised that it is in no way equivalent to the formulation given at the beginning of this section, as might seem apparent. To get one formulation from the other we have to introduce the concept of an observer who artificially "prepares" a closed system at a certain moment of time so that the question of its previous existence altogether disappears; such a connection between physical laws and the attributes of an observer is obviously quite inadmissible.

It is quite uncertain at present whether one can deduce the law of increase of entropy formulated in such a way on the basis of classical mechanics. We note that in view of the invariance of the equations of classical mechanics under time reversal we can only speak about a deduction of the monotonic change of entropy. To obtain the law of its monotonic increase we have to define the future as the direction of time in which entropy increases. The problem of the proof of the equivalence of such a definition of past and future with its quantum mechanical definition (see below) would also arise.

It is more natural to think of the origin of the law of increase of entropy in its general formulation given above as being bound up with the quantum mechanical effects. The basic equation of quantum mechanics, Schrödinger's equation, is itself symmetrical under time reversal (provided Ψ, Ψ^* are interchanged at the same time). This means that if at a certain moment of time $t = t_1$ the wave function is given as $\Psi = \Psi(t_1)$ and according to Schrödinger's equation at another moment of time $t = t_2$ it must be $\Psi(t_2)$, then the transformation from $\Psi(t_1)$ to $\Psi(t_2)$ is reversible: in other words, if at time $t = t_1$ $\Psi = \Psi^*(t_2)$ then at $t = t_2$ it would be $\Psi = \Psi^*(t_1)$.

Notwithstanding this symmetry, quantum mechanics does implicitly involve the non-equivalence of the two directions of time. This non-equivalence appears in connection with the process, which is basic in quantum mechanics, of the interaction of a quantum mechanical object with a system which obeys classical mechanics to a sufficient degree of accuracy. It appears in that if two processes of interaction take place consecutively with a given quantum object (let us call them A and B) then the assertion that the probability of some result of process B is determined by the results of process A can be true only if process A takes place before process B.

Thus the two directions of time are not physically equivalent in quantum mechanics and it is possible that the "macroscopic" expression of this is the law of increase of entropy. However, up to now no one has been able to prove convincingly that such a connection actually exists. If, however, the origin of the law of increase of entropy is in fact of this nature then there must exist a quantum inequality involving the quantum constant which justifies this law and which is actually satisfied in nature (mostly probably by a large margin).

To sum up let us repeat the general formulation of the law of increase of entropy: in all closed systems which are possible in nature, the entropy never decreases; it increases or, in the extreme, remains constant. Corresponding to these two possibilities it is usual to divide all processes occurring in macroscopic bodies into irreversible and reversible. By the first we understand processes accompanied by an increase in entropy of the whole closed system; the reverse processes cannot occur as they would involve a decrease in entropy. Processes in which the entropy of the whole closed system remains constant† and which can, therefore, also take place in the opposite direction, are called reversible processes. A strictly reversible process represents, of course, an ideal, limiting, case; processes actually occurring in nature can only be reversible to a greater or less degree of accuracy.

---

† We must emphasise that in this case entropies of the separate parts of the system need not also remain constant.

CHAPTER II

THERMODYNAMIC QUANTITIES

§9. Temperature

THE physical quantities which describe macroscopic states are called thermo-dynamic. Some of these have a purely mechanical significance as well as a thermodynamic one, for example energy and volume. There are, however, quantities of another kind, the result of purely statistical regularities alone, which have no meaning when applied to non-macroscopic systems; entropy, for instance, is of this kind.

We shall derive below a number of relations between thermodynamic quantities which hold generally, i.e. independently of the particular nature of the bodies to which they refer. Such relations we shall call thermodynamic.

In practice, the negligible fluctuations of thermodynamical quantities are usually of no interest. Accordingly we shall follow the normal usage and completely disregard such fluctuations, regarding thermodynamic quantities as constant except for changes in the macroscopic state of the body.†

Consider two bodies in thermal equilibrium with each other, the bodies together forming a closed system. Then the entropy σ of this system will have its maximum possible value (for a given value, E, of the energy of the system). The energy E is the sum of the energies E_1 and E_2 of the separate bodies: $E = E_1 + E_2$. The same applies to σ, the entropy of the system, and the entropy of each body is a function of its energy; $\sigma = \sigma_1(E_1) + \sigma_2(E_2)$. Since $E_2 = E - E_1$, where E is a constant, σ is actually a function of one independent variable only and the necessary condition for a maximum can be written

$$\frac{d\sigma}{dE_1} = \frac{d\sigma_1}{dE_1} + \frac{d\sigma_2}{dE_2}\frac{dE_2}{dE_1} = \frac{d\sigma_1}{dE_1} - \frac{d\sigma_2}{dE_2} = 0,$$

whence

$$\frac{d\sigma_1}{dE_1} = \frac{d\sigma_2}{dE_2}.$$

This result can be easily generalised to the case of an arbitrary number of bodies in equilibrium with each other.

Thus if the system is in a state of thermodynamic equilibrium, then the derivative of entropy with respect to energy is the same for all of its parts,

---

† Fluctuations of thermodynamical quantities will be considered in Chapter XII, especially devoted to them.

i.e. is a constant for the system. The inverse of the derivative of the entropy σ of the body with respect to its energy E is called its *absolute temperature*, or simply temperature, Θ:

$$\frac{d\sigma}{dE} = \frac{1}{\Theta}. \tag{9.1}$$

The temperatures of two bodies in equilibrium with each other are equal:

$$\Theta_1 = \Theta_2.$$

Temperature, like entropy, is clearly a quantity of purely statistical character, having a meaning only for macroscopic bodies.

Consider next two bodies, together composing a closed system, but which are not in equilibrium with each other. Their temperatures Θ_1 and Θ_2 are different. In time equilibrium will be set up between the bodies, and their temperatures will gradually equalise. Their common entropy must be increasing while this takes place, i.e. its time derivative must be positive:

$$\frac{d\sigma}{dt} = \frac{d\sigma_1}{dt} + \frac{d\sigma_2}{dt} = \frac{d\sigma_1}{dE_1}\frac{dE_1}{dt} + \frac{d\sigma_2}{dE_2}\frac{dE_2}{dt} > 0.$$

Since the total energy is conserved,

$$\frac{dE_1}{dt} + \frac{dE_2}{dt} = 0,$$

so that

$$\frac{d\sigma}{dt} = \left(\frac{d\sigma_1}{dE_1} - \frac{d\sigma_2}{dE_2}\right)\frac{dE_1}{dt} = \left(\frac{1}{\Theta_1} - \frac{1}{\Theta_2}\right)\frac{dE_1}{dt} > 0.$$

Let the temperature of the second body be higher than that of the first ($\Theta_2 > \Theta_1$). Then $1/\Theta_1 - 1/\Theta_2 > 0$ and we see that

$$\frac{dE_1}{dt} > 0.$$

(Similarly, $dE_2/dt < 0$.) In other words the energy of the second body decreases while that of the first body increases. This property of temperature can be formulated as follows: energy passes from a body with higher temperature to those with lower temperatures.

Entropy is a dimensionless quantity. Hence from the definition (9.1) it follows that the temperature Θ has the dimensions of energy, for example ergs. In practice, however, it is usual to measure temperature in special units called degrees Kelvin, or simply degrees. If Θ represents the temperature measured in ergs, and T that measured in degrees then there is the following relation between them

$$\Theta = kT \tag{9.2}$$

where the coefficient of proportionality k, i.e. the number of ergs in a degree, is called BOLTZMANN's constant and its value is†

$$k = 1 \cdot 380 \times 10^{-16} \text{ ergs/degree.}$$

If one uses the temperature T measured in degrees, then the constant k occurs in thermodynamic relations. To avoid this it is convenient to introduce the factor k into the definition of entropy by introducing the quantity S, defined as

$$S = k\sigma \tag{9.3}$$

and also referred to as entropy. Then the definition of temperature becomes

$$\frac{dS}{dE} = \frac{1}{T}. \tag{9.4}$$

§10. Macroscopic motion

Motions in which the separate macroscopic parts of a body take part as a whole are called macroscopic to distinguish them from microscopic motion. Let us examine the possibility of macroscopic motion in a state of thermodynamical equilibrium.

Divide the body into a large number of small (but macroscopic) parts and let M_a, E_a, $\mathbf{P}_a$ denote the mass, energy, and momentum of the ath part. The entropy S_a of each part is a function of its internal energy, i.e. of the difference between its total energy E_a and its kinetic energy of macroscopic motion $\mathbf{P}_a^2/2M_a$.‡ Hence the total entropy of the body can be written in the form

$$S = \sum_a S_a\left(E_a - \frac{P_a^2}{2M_a}\right). \tag{10.1}$$

Assume that the body is *closed*. Then its total momentum and angular momentum are conserved as well as its energy:

$$\sum_a \mathbf{P}_a = \text{const}, \qquad \sum_a \mathbf{r}_a \times \mathbf{P}_a = \text{const.} \tag{10.2}$$

---

† For future reference note that the conversion factor between degrees and electron volts is 1 eV = 11,606 degrees.

‡ The entropy of every body is a function of its internal energy only. This follows directly from the fact that by the Galilean principle of relativity, the number of quantum states, and hence the statistical weight (whose logarithm is the entropy) must be the same for all inertial frames of reference, in particular that in which the body is at rest.

($\mathbf{r}_a$ are the radius vectors of the parts of the body). In the equilibrium state, the entropy of the body as a function of the momenta $\mathbf{P}_a$ is a maximum subject to these additional conditions. Using the well-known method of Lagrange's undetermined multipliers, the conditions for a maximum are obtained by equating to zero the derivative with respect to $\mathbf{P}_a$ of the sum

$$\sum_a \{S_a + \mathbf{a} . \mathbf{P}_a + \mathbf{h} . (\mathbf{r}_a \times \mathbf{P}_a)\}, \tag{10.3}$$

where $\mathbf{a}$ and $\mathbf{b}$ are constant vectors. Owing to the definition of temperature, differentiation of S_a with respect to $\mathbf{P}_a$† gives:

$$\frac{\partial}{\partial \mathbf{P}_a} S_a\left(E_a - \frac{P_a{}^2}{2M_a}\right) = -\frac{\mathbf{P}_a}{M_a}\frac{1}{T} = -\frac{\mathbf{v}_a}{T}$$

($\mathbf{v}_a = \mathbf{P}_a/M_a$ is the velocity of the ath part of the body). Hence by differentiating (10.3) we obtain:

$$-\frac{\mathbf{v}_a}{T} + \mathbf{a} + (\mathbf{h} \times \mathbf{r}_a) = 0.$$

or

$$\mathbf{v}_a = \mathbf{u} + (\mathbf{\Omega} \times \mathbf{r}_a) \tag{10.4}$$

where $\mathbf{u} = T\mathbf{a}$, $\mathbf{\Omega} = T\mathbf{b}$ are constant vectors.

This result has a simple physical significance. If the velocities of all parts of the body are given by (10.4) with $\mathbf{u}$ and $\mathbf{\Omega}$ the same for all the parts then it means that we are dealing with translation of the body as a whole with a constant velocity and its rotation as a whole with constant angular velocity $\mathbf{\Omega}$. Thus we have obtained an important result: a closed system in thermodynamic equilibrium can perform only uniform translation and rotation as a whole; internal macroscopic motion is impossible in a state of equilibrium.

In future, we shall usually consider bodies at rest; in this case the energy E represents the internal energy of the body.

So far we have used only the necessary condition for the entropy (as a function of the momenta) to be a maximum, but not the sufficient conditions to be imposed on its second derivatives. It is easy to see that the latter lead to the most important conclusion that temperature can only be positive: $T > 0$.‡ For this it is not even necessary actually to calculate the second derivative, but we use the following argument.

Consider the body to be at rest as a whole. If the temperature were negative, then the entropy would decrease as a function of its argument. Since entropy tends to increase, the separate parts of the body would fly apart (in such a way as to keep $\sum \mathbf{P}_a = 0$) so that the argument of each S_a in the

---

† The derivative of a scalar with respect to a vector is a vector whose components are the derivatives of the scalar with respect to the corresponding components of the first vector.

‡ Temperature $T = 0$ (absolute zero) is situated at $-273 \cdot 16°$ on the centigrade scale.

sum (10.1) may become as small as possible. In other words, for $T < 0$ bodies in equilibrium cannot exist.

We may, at this stage, already note the following fact. Although the temperature of the body or of any of its separate parts can never be negative, partial equilibria are possible in which the temperature corresponding to a definite part of the degrees of freedom of the body is negative. (For greater detail see §70.)

§11. Adiabatic processes

Changes in the external conditions in which a body is situated form a special class of the external influences to which the body is subject. Broadly speaking, by external conditions we understand different external fields. In practice the external conditions most frequently take the form of a prescribed volume for the body. In some sense this can be regarded as a special kind of external field, as the walls bounding the volume act in the same way as an infinitely high potential barrier preventing molecules of the body from passing it.

If the body is not subject to any other influences than the change in external conditions, the body is said to be in thermal isolation. It must be emphasised that although a thermally isolated body does not interact directly with other bodies, in general it is not closed and its energy can vary with time.

From a purely mechanical point of view, a thermally isolated body differs from a closed one only in that its Hamiltonian function (energy) depends explicitly on time, owing to the existence of a changing external field: $E = E(p, q, t)$. If he body also interacted directly with other bodies then it would not, itself, have a Hamiltonian function, because the interaction would depend on the co-ordinates not only of the molecules of the given body, but on those of other bodies as well.

As a consequence, the law of increase of entropy holds for thermally isolated systems as well as for closed ones. For here we actually consider the external field as a uniquely defined function of position and time, neglecting in particular the reaction of the body on the field. In other words the field here is a purely mechanical and not a statistical object. In this sense its entropy can be said to be zero and thus the above assertion follows.

Assume that the body is thermally isolated and that its external conditions change sufficiently slowly. Such a process is called *adiabatic*. We may show that in an adiabatic process the entropy of the body remains constant, i.e. it is reversible.

Specify the external conditions by some parameters which are given functions of time. Suppose, for example, we have just one such parameter which we shall denote by λ. The derivative of entropy with respect to time, dS/dt, will depend somehow on the rate of change, $d\lambda/dt$, of the parameter λ. Provided $d\lambda/dt$ is small we can expand dS/dt as a power series in $d\lambda/dt$. The zero-order term of this expansion, which does not contain $d\lambda\, dt$, must vanish, since if $d\lambda/dt = 0$, dS/dt must also be equal to zero, for the entropy of a closed system in thermodynamic equilibrium with constant external conditions must remain constant. But the first-order term proportional to $d\lambda/dt$ will also vanish, as this term changes its sign with $d\lambda/dt$, whereas from the law of increase of entropy dS/dt must always be positive. From this it follows that the expansion begins with second-order terms, i.e. for small $d\lambda/dt$ we have:

$$\frac{dS}{dt} = A\left(\frac{d\lambda}{dt}\right)^2,$$

whence

$$\frac{dS}{d\lambda} = A\frac{d\lambda}{dt}.$$

Hence as $d\lambda/dt$ tends to zero, so does $dS/d\lambda$, which proves the reversibility of an adiabatic process.

It must be stressed that although an adiabatic process is reversible, by no means every reversible process is adiabatic. The reversibility of a process requires only that the total entropy of the whole closed system should be constant, while the entropies of its separate parts can both increase and decrease. An adiabatic process satisfies a more restrictive condition; the entropy of the given body, which is itself only part of a closed system, also remains constant.

We defined an adiabatic process above as a sufficiently slow one. To be more exact we can say that the external conditions must change so slowly that at every instant the body can be considered to be in the equilibrium state corresponding to the external conditions at that moment. In other words, the process must be slow compared with the process of establishing equilibrium in the given body.†

We can deduce a formula which allows us to calculate a whole range of mean values by a purely thermodynamic method. To do this, assume that the body is undergoing an adiabatic process and define the derivative of its energy with respect to time, dE/dt. By definition the thermodynamic energy $E = \overline{E(p, q; \lambda)}$ where $E(p, q; \lambda)$ is the Hamiltonian function of the body, depending on the parameter λ. We know from mechanics that the total time derivative of the Hamiltonian function is equal to its partial time

---

† In reality this condition may be very weak; a "slow" adiabatic process may in fact be rather "fast". Thus, for example, in the expansion of a gas (say by a piston moving out of a cylinder) the velocity of the piston must only be small compared with the velocity of sound in the gas, i.e. in practice it can be very large.

In physics courses adiabatic expansion (or compression) is often defined as "sufficiently fast". This deals with the other side of the question; the process must occur so fast that there is no time for heat to be exchanged with the surrounding medium. This is a condition which ensures in practice the thermal isolation of the body, and it is implicitly understood that the condition of slowness in comparison with the setting up of equilibrium is satisfied.

derivative†

$$\frac{dE(p,q;\lambda)}{dt} = \frac{\partial E(p,q;\lambda)}{\partial t}.$$

In the given case $E(p, q; \lambda)$ depends explicitly on time with $\lambda(t)$, and hence we can write

$$\frac{dE(p,q;\lambda)}{dt} = \frac{\partial E(p,q;\lambda)}{\partial \lambda}\frac{d\lambda}{dt}.$$

Since the order in which the operations of averaging over the statistical distribution and time differentiation are performed is obviously arbitrary we have

$$\frac{dE}{dt} = \frac{\overline{dE(p,q;\lambda)}}{dt} = \frac{\overline{\partial E(p,q;\lambda)}}{\partial \lambda}\frac{d\lambda}{dt} \tag{11.1}$$

(where $d\lambda/dt$ is a given function of time and may be taken out from underneath the averaging sign).

A very important fact is that because the process is adiabatic the mean value of the derivative $\partial E(p, q; \lambda)/\partial \lambda$ in (11.1) can be interpreted as a mean over a statistical distribution corresponding to the equilibrium state with the given value of the parameter, i.e. with the external conditions which occur at the given instant.

The derivative dE/dt can also be expressed in another form, by considering the thermodynamic quantity E as a function of the entropy S of the body and the external parameter λ. Since the entropy S remains constant in an adiabatic process we have:

$$\frac{dE}{dt} = \left(\frac{\partial E}{\partial \lambda}\right)_S \frac{d\lambda}{dt}, \tag{11.2}$$

where the subscript to the bracket indicates that the derivative is taken for constant S.

Comparing (11.1) with (11.2) we find:

$$\frac{\overline{\partial E(p,q;\lambda)}}{\partial \lambda} = \left(\frac{\partial E}{\partial \lambda}\right)_S. \tag{11.3}$$

---

† Indeed we have

$$\frac{dE}{dt} = \frac{\partial E}{\partial t} + \sum_i \left(\frac{\partial E}{\partial p_i}\dot{p}_i + \frac{\partial E}{\partial q_i}\dot{q}_i\right)$$

but in accordance with Hamilton's equations

$$\dot{p}_i = -\frac{\partial E}{\partial q_i}, \qquad \dot{q}_i = \frac{\partial E}{\partial p_i}$$

and hence the terms under the summation sign cancel out.

This is the required formula. It allows us to calculate, by thermodynamic methods, the mean values of quantities of the type $\partial E(p, q; \lambda)/\partial\lambda$ (over an equilibrium statistical distribution). Such quantities often occur when one studies the properties of macroscopic bodies and so formula (11.3) plays a very important part in statistics. Amongst these are the calculations of different forces acting on the body (when the parameters λ are the co-ordinates of one or other part of the body; see the next section about pressure), calculations of the electric or magnetic moment of the body (where the parameters are the intensities of the electric or magnetic fields), etc.

All the arguments which we have been using here for classical mechanics apply entirely to quantum theory, except that instead of the energy $E(p, q; \lambda)$ we must everywhere use the Hamiltonian $\hat{H}$. Formula (11.3) becomes

$$\overline{\frac{\partial\hat{H}}{\partial\lambda}} = \left(\frac{\partial E}{\partial\lambda}\right)_S \tag{11.4}$$

where the bar implies complete statistical averaging (which includes automatically quantum mechanical averaging).

§12. Pressure

The energy E of the body as a thermodynamic quantity is additive: the energy of the body is equal to the sum of the energies of its separate (macroscopic) parts.† The same is true of the entropy, the other thermodynamic quantity.

The additivity of energy and entropy leads us to the following very important conclusion. If a body is in thermal equilibrium then we can assert that its entropy, for a given value of its energy (or its energy, for a given value of its entropy) depends only on its *volume* but not on its shape.‡ The change of shape of a body can really be considered as the displacement of its various parts and thus the energy and entropy, being additive quantities, do not change. In this case, certainly, we assume that the body is not in an external field of force, so that the displacement of parts of the body is not connected with the change in their energies.

Thus the macroscopic state of a stationary body in equilibrium is completely defined by only two quantities, for example its volume and energy. All other thermodynamic quantities can be expressed as functions of these two. Because of this interdependency of different thermodynamic quantities one can use any other pair of them as independent variables.

---

† Provided we neglect the interaction energies of these parts; this cannot be done if we are concerned with those particular phenomena which are explicitly connected with the existence of bounding surfaces between different bodies (Chapter XV is devoted to the study of these phenomena).

‡ It should be mentioned that this assertion applies in fact to liquids and gases but not to solid bodies. A change of shape (deformation) of a solid body requires the expenditure of some work, i.e. the energy of the body is changed by it. This is connected with the fact that the deformed state of a solid body is, strictly speaking, a partial thermodynamic equilibrium (but the relaxation time for achieving total equilibrium is so large that in many respects the deformed body behaves like one in equilibrium).

We now find the force with which a body acts on the surface bounding its volume. From the well-known formulae of mechanics we obtain the force acting on a given element of surface d**s** as

$$F = -\frac{\partial E(p,q;\mathbf{r})}{\partial \mathbf{r}}$$

where $E(p, q; \mathbf{r})$ is the energy of the body as a function of the co-ordinates and momenta of its particles and the radius vector of the given surface element, in this case acting as an external parameter. Averaging this equation, and applying formula (11.3) we have

$$\bar{F} = -\overline{\frac{\partial E(p,q;\mathbf{r})}{\partial \mathbf{r}}} = -\left(\frac{\partial E}{\partial \mathbf{r}}\right)_S = -\left(\frac{\partial E}{\partial V}\right)_S \frac{\partial V}{\partial \mathbf{r}}$$

where V is the volume. Since the change in volume is equal to d**s** . d**r** where d**s** is the element of surface, $\partial V/\partial \mathbf{r} = $ d**s** and hence

$$\bar{F} = -\left(\frac{\partial E}{\partial V}\right)_S d\mathbf{s}.$$

From this we see that the mean force acting on a surface element is directed along the normal to it and is proportional to its area (*Pascal's Law*). The absolute value of the force acting on the unit element of surface is equal to

$$P = -\left(\frac{\partial E}{\partial V}\right)_S. \tag{12.1}$$

This quantity is called the *pressure*.

When temperature was defined by formula (9.1) we were really discussing a body not directly in contact with any other bodies and, in particular, not surrounded by any external medium. In these circumstances it was possible to talk about the change of energy and entropy of the body without being more precise about the nature of the process. In the general case of a body in an external medium (or surrounded by the walls of a vessel) formula (9.1) must be made more precise. Actually, if the volume of the given body is changed during some process this is bound to have some effect on the condition of the bodies in contact with it. Thus for the definition of temperature we ought to consider simultaneously all the bodies in contact (for example the body together with the vessel containing it). If we want to define temperature in terms of the thermodynamic quantities of the given body alone, then, obviously, we have to assume that the volume of this body remains constant. In other words the temperature will be defined as the derivative of the energy of the body with respect to its entropy taken at constant volume:

$$T = \left(\frac{\partial E}{\partial S}\right)_V.$$

Eqs. (12.1–2) can be written down as follows in the form of a relation between the differentials

$$dE = T \, dS - P \, dV. \tag{12.3}$$

This is called the *Thermodynamic Identity* and is one of the most important thermodynamic relations.

Bodies which are in equilibrium with each other have equal pressures. This follows directly from the fact that thermal equilibrium itself presupposes the existence of mechanical equilibrium; in other words the forces with which any two of these bodies act on each other (over the surface of their common boundary) must balance, i.e. their absolute values must be the same and their directions opposite.

The equality of pressure of bodies in equilibrium can also be deduced from the condition that the entropy should be a maximum, as we deduced the equality of temperature in §9. To do this, consider two parts of a closed system which are in contact. One of the necessary conditions for the entropy to be a maximum is that it should be a maximum with respect to a change in the volumes V_1 and V_2 of these two parts, the states of all the other parts remaining unchanged. The latter means that in particular the sum $V_1 + V_2$ also remains unchanged. If S_1 and S_2 are the entropies of these parts then we have

$$\frac{\partial S}{\partial V_1} = \frac{\partial S_1}{\partial V_1} + \frac{\partial S_2}{\partial V_2}\frac{\partial V_2}{\partial V_1} = \frac{\partial S_1}{\partial V_1} - \frac{\partial S_2}{\partial V_2} = 0.$$

But from the thermodynamic identity (12.3), rewritten in the form

$$dS = \frac{1}{T} \, dE + \frac{P}{T} \, dV,$$

we can see that $\partial S/\partial V = P/T$ and we find that $P_1/T_1 = P_2/T_2$. Since the temperatures T_1 and T_2 are equal for equilibrium we obtain from this the required equality of pressures.

It should be borne in mind that in reaching thermal equilibrium, the equality of pressure (i.e. mechanical equilibrium) occurs much faster than the equality of temperature, and hence we often meet cases where the pressure is constant throughout the body although the temperature is not constant. The point is that variation of pressure s connected with the existence of unbalanced forces which produce macroscopic motion, which in turn equalises the pressure much more quickly than the temperature whose equalisation is not connected with macroscopic motion.

It is easy to see that in any equilibrium state the pressure of the body must be positive. In fact when $P > 0$ we have $(\partial S/\partial V)_E > 0$ and the entropy of the body could increase only if the body expanded, which, however, is prevented by the surrounding bodies. On the other hand for $P < 0$ we would have $(\partial S/\partial V)_E < 0$ and the body would tend to contract spontaneously because that would lead to an increase in entropy.

There is, however, an important difference between the condition that the temperature should be positive and the condition that the pressure should. Bodies with negative temperature would be completely unstable and quite incapable of existing in nature. However, non-equilibrium states with negative pressure could exist in nature with a limited stability. The fact is that the spontaneous contraction of the body involves its "detachment" from the walls of the vessel or the creation of cavities inside it, i.e. the creation of a new surface; this gives rise to the possibility of negative pressures in so-called metastable states.†

§13. Work and quantity of heat

An external force applied to a body can do *work* on it, defined by the general laws of mechanics as the product of the force and the displacement produced by it. This work can be used to bring the body into a state of macroscopic motion (in general to change its kinetic energy) or to displace the body in an external field (for instance, to raise it against gravity). We shall mainly be interested in the case when the volume of the body changes as a result of the work done on it (i.e. the external forces compress the body leaving it, as a whole, stationary).

We shall in future count work R done by the external forces on the body as positive. Negative work, $R < 0$ will then mean that the body does work (equal to $|R|$) on some external objects (for instance by its expansion).

Bearing in mind that the force acting on a unit element of surface of the body is the pressure and that the product of the element of surface of the body with its displacement is the volume described by this element, we find that the work done on the body (per unit time) by a change of volume is

$$\frac{dR}{dt} = -P\frac{dV}{dt}. \tag{13.1}$$

(For a contraction of the body $dV/dt < 0$ so that $dR/dt < 0$). This formula applies both to reversible and irreversible processes, subject to only one condition; during the entire process, the body must be in a state of mechanical equilibrium, i.e. at all instants the pressure must be constant throughout the body.

If the body is thermally isolated then the change in its energy is entirely due to the work done on it. In the general case of a non-thermally isolated body energy is acquired (or lost) by means of direct transmission from other bodies in contact with it, as well as through work. This part of the change in energy is called the quantity of *heat*, Q, received by the body. Thus the change of energy of the body (per unit time) can be written in the form

$$\frac{dE}{dt} = \frac{dR}{dt} + \frac{dQ}{dt}. \tag{13.2}$$

---

† For the definition of metastable states see §21, for negative pressures see also §79.

As in the case of work we shall count as positive the heat received by the body from external sources.

Generally speaking, the energy E in (13.2) must be understood as the total energy if the body including the kinetic energy of macroscopic motion. However, we shall usually consider work concerned with the change in volume of a stationary body. In this case the energy reduces to the internal energy of the body.

In the case where the work is defined by formula (13.1), we have, for the quantity of heat:

$$\frac{dQ}{dt} = \frac{dE}{dt} + P\frac{dV}{dt}. \tag{13.3}$$

Assume that during the entire process the body can be considered at any given instant to be in the state of thermal equilibrium which corresponds to the values of its energy and volume at that instant. (It must be stressed that this does not mean that the process must necessarily be reversible, as the body is not necessarily in equilibrium with its surroundings.) Then from the thermodynamic identity† (12.3) we can write:

$$\frac{dE}{dt} = T\frac{dS}{dt} - P\frac{dV}{dt}.$$

comparing this with (13.2) we obtain for the quantity of heat

$$\frac{dQ}{dt} = T\frac{dS}{dt}. \tag{13.4}$$

The work dR and quantity of heat dQ gained by the body in an infinitesimal change of its state are not total differentials.‡ Only the sum $dQ+dR$, i.e. the change in energy dE, is a total differential. Hence one can speak of the energy E in a given state but one cannot, for instance, talk of the quantity of heat possessed by a body in a given state. In other words the energy of the body cannot be split into heat energy and mechanical energy. This division is possible only if one refers to a change of energy. The change in energy due to the transition of the body from one state to another can be divided into the quantity of heat gained (or lost) by the body, and the work done on it (or by it on other bodies). This subdivision is not uniquely determined by the initial and final states of the body but depends on the actual nature of the process. In other words the work and quantity of heat are functions of the process undergone by the body, and not only of its initial and final states. This is particularly easy to see in the case when the body undergoes a cyclic process beginning and ending with the same state. In

---

† The thermodynamic identity defines the differential of the function $E(S, V)$; the energy of the body in the equilibrium state.

‡ In this sense the notations dR and dQ are not strictly rigorous, and hence we shall avoid using them.

this case the actual change in energy is zero, while the body may have gained (or lost) a certain amount of heat (or work). Mathematically it is expressed by saying that the integral round a closed contour of the total differential dE is zero, while the integrals of dQ and dR, not total differentials, are different from zero.

The quantity of heat which, when added to a body, raises its temperature by one unit of temperature (for instance one degree) is called its *specific heat*. It is obvious that the specific heat of a body depends on the circumstances in which it is warmed up. It is usual to distinguish the specific heat C_v at constant volume and the specific heat C_p at constant pressure. It is clear that

$$C_v = T\left(\frac{\partial S}{\partial T}\right)_V, \tag{13.5}$$

$$C_p = T\left(\frac{\partial S}{\partial T}\right)_P. \tag{13.6}$$

Let us conclude with the cases where formula (13.4) for the quantity of heat does not apply but where, at the same time, it becomes possible to establish some inequalities for this quantity. There exist processes in which the body is not in thermal equilibrium although the temperature (and pressure) are constant throughout the body. Amongst these are chemical reactions in a homogeneous mixture of interacting substances. Owing to the existence in the body itself of an irreversible process (the chemical reaction) the entropy of the body increases independently of the heat taken in by it, so that the following inequality must hold:

$$\frac{dQ}{dt} < T\frac{dS}{dt}. \tag{13.7}$$

Another case in which a similar inequality can be obtained is an irreversible process taking the body from one equilibrium state to another close to it, but during which the body is not in equilibrium.† Then between the quantity of heat δQ received by the body, and the change δS of its entropy, there is the inequality

$$\delta Q < T\,\delta S. \tag{13.8}$$

§14. The heat function

If the volume of the body remains constant during the process, then $dQ = dE$, i.e. the quantity of heat gained by the body is equal to the change in its energy. If the process takes place at constant pressure then the quantity of heat can be written down as the differential

$$dQ = d(E+PV) = dW. \tag{14.1}$$

---

† An example is the so-called Joule-Thomson process (see §18) with a small pressure change.

of a certain quantity

$$W = E + PV \qquad (14.2)$$

which is called the *heat function* of the body.† The change in the heat function during a process at constant pressure is thus equal to the heat gained by the body.

It is easy to find an expression for the total differential of the heat function. By substituting $dE = T\,dS - P\,dV$ in $dW = dE + P\,dV + V\,dP$ we find:

$$dW = T\,dS + V\,dP,$$

whence it follows that

$$T = \left(\frac{\partial W}{\partial S}\right)_P, \qquad V = \left(\frac{\partial W}{\partial P}\right)_S. \qquad (14.4)$$

If the body is thermally isolated (remember this does *not* mean that it is closed) then $dQ = 0$ and from (14.1) it follows that for processes taking place in a thermally isolated body at constant pressure

$$W = \text{const}, \qquad (14.5)$$

i.e. its heat function is conserved.

From the identity $dE = T\,dS - P\,dV$ we can write the specific heat C_v in the form

$$C_v = \left(\frac{\partial E}{\partial T}\right)_V. \qquad (14.6)$$

Similarly for the specific heat C_p we have:

$$C_p = \left(\frac{\partial W}{\partial T}\right)_P. \qquad (14.7)$$

We thus see that the heat function acts, at constant pressure, like the energy does at constant volume.

§15. The free energy and thermodynamic potential

The work done on the body in an infinitesimal, isothermal reversible change in its state can be written as the differential of a certain quantity

$$dR = dE - dQ = dE - T\,dS = d(E - TS)$$

or

$$dR = dF \qquad (15.1)$$

where

$$F = E - TS \qquad (15.2)$$

_____

† It is also called the "enthalpy" or the "heat content".

is a new function of the state of a body called its *free energy*.† Thus the work done on the body in an isothermal, reversible process is equal to the change in its free energy.

Let us construct the thermodynamic identity for the free energy. Substituting $dE = T\,dS - P\,dV$ in $dF = dE - T\,dS - S\,dT$, we obtain:

$$dF = -S\,dT - P\,dV. \tag{15.3}$$

From this we can easily see that

$$S = -\left(\frac{\partial F}{\partial T}\right)_V, \qquad P = -\left(\frac{\partial F}{\partial V}\right)_T. \tag{15.4}$$

Using the relation $E = F + TS$ we can express the energy in terms of the free energy in the form:

$$E = F - T\left(\frac{\partial F}{\partial T}\right)_V = -T^2\left(\frac{\partial}{\partial T}\frac{F}{T}\right)_V. \tag{15.5}$$

The formulae (12.1–2; 14.4; 15.4) show that given any one of the quantities E, W, or F (as functions of the appropriate two variables) one can, by constructing its partial derivatives, obtain all the other thermodynamic quantities. Because of this, the quantities E, W, and F are sometimes called the thermodynamic potentials (by analogy with mechanical potential) or characteristic functions: the energy E, with respect to the variables S, V; the heat function W, with respect to S, P; the free energy F, with respect to V, T.

So far we lack a thermodynamic potential related to the variables P, T. To obtain it we substitute in (15.3) $P\,dV = d(PV) - V\,dP$ and taking $d(PV)$ over to the left-hand side we get:

$$d\Phi = -S\,dT + V\,dP, \tag{15.6}$$

in which we introduce the new quantity

$$\Phi = E - TS + PV = F + PV = W - TS, \tag{15.7}$$

called the *thermodynamic potential* (in the narrow sense of the word) or the Gibbs free energy.

From (15.6) we obviously obtain

$$S = -T\left(\frac{\partial \Phi}{\partial T}\right)_P, \qquad V = \left(\frac{\partial \Phi}{\partial P}\right)_T. \tag{15.8}$$

The heat function is expressed in terms of Φ just as E is in terms of F:

$$W = \Phi - T\left(\frac{\partial \Phi}{\partial T}\right)_P = -T^2\left(\frac{\partial}{\partial T}\frac{\Phi}{T}\right)_P. \tag{15.9}$$

---

† Also called the Helmholtz free energy.

If apart from the volume there exist other parameters λ_i defining the state of the system, then to the thermodynamic identity must be added terms proportional to the differentials $d\lambda_i$:

$$dE = T\,dS - P\,dV + \sum_i \Lambda_i\,d\lambda_i, \qquad (15.10)$$

where Λ_i are some functions of the state of the body. Since the transformation of the identity for other potentials does not affect the variables λ_i it is clear that the same terms will be added to the thermodynamical identities for F, Φ, and W:

$$dF = -S\,dT - P\,dV + \sum_i \Lambda_i\,d\lambda_i,$$

etc. Hence the quantities Λ_i can be obtained by differentiating any one of the potentials with respect to Λ_i (but with different variables considered constant in the differentiation). Remembering also formula (11.3) we can write a similar relation

$$\overline{\frac{\partial E(p,q;\lambda)}{\partial \lambda}} = \left(\frac{\partial F}{\partial \lambda}\right)_{T,V} \qquad (15.11)$$

which expresses the mean value of the derivative of the Hamiltonian of a body with respect to some parameter in terms of the derivative of the free energy with respect to that parameter. (Similarly in terms of the derivatives of Φ or W.)

Note the following fact. If the values of the parameters λ_i change only slightly, then E, F, W, and Φ also change only by a small amount. It is obvious that these changes will always be equal to one another if every one of them is considered with the appropriate pair of quantities constant:

$$(\delta E)_{S,V} = (\delta F)_{T,V} = (\delta W)_{S,P} = (\delta \Phi)_{T,P}. \qquad (15.12)$$

The free energy and thermodynamic potential have an important property which determines the sign of their change during various irreversible processes. Starting from inequality (13.7) and substituting in it dQ/dt from (13.3) we obtain

$$\frac{dE}{dt} + P\frac{dV}{dt} < T\frac{dS}{dt}. \qquad (15.13)$$

Assuming that the process takes place isothermally and at constant volume ($T = $ const, $V = $ const) then this inequality can be written in the form:

$$\frac{d(E-TS)}{dt} = \frac{dF}{dt} < 0. \qquad (15.14)$$

Thus an irreversible process at constant temperature and volume results in a decrease in the free energy of the body.

Similarly for $P = $ const, $T = $ const the inequality (15.13) takes the form

$$\frac{d\Phi}{dt} < 0, \qquad (15.15)$$

i.e. irreversible processes at constant temperature and pressure result in a decrease of thermodynamic potential.†

Hence in a state of thermal equilibrium the free energy and thermodynamic potential of the body are minimal: the first with respect to changes of state at constant T and V, and the second with respect to changes of state at constant T and P.

PROBLEM

How can one calculate the mean kinetic energy of the particles of a body, given the formula for its free energy?

SOLUTION. The Hamiltonian function (Hamiltonian operator in the quantum case) can be written in the form $E(p, q) = U(q)+K(p)$ where $U(q)$ is the potential energy of interaction of the particles of the body and $K(p)$ their kinetic energy. The latter is a quadratic function of the momenta inversely proportional to the mass m of the particles (for a body made up of equal particles). Thus taking m as a parameter:

$$\frac{\partial E(p, q; m)}{\partial m} = -\frac{1}{m}\kappa(p).$$

So applying formula (15.11) we obtain the mean kinetic energy $K = K(p)$:

$$K = -m\left(\frac{\partial F}{\partial m}\right)_{T,V}.$$

§16. Relations between the derivatives of thermodynamic quantities

In practice, the most convenient pairs of thermodynamic quantities, and the most often used, are T, V and T, P. In this connection we may need to transform derivatives of thermodynamic quantities with respect to each other to other variables, some dependent, some independent.

If one uses V and T as independent variables then the results of the transformation can be conveniently expressed in terms of the pressure P and specific heat C_v (as functions of V and T). The equation connecting volume, pressure and temperature is called the *equation of state* of the body. Thus the formulae which we are considering must enable us to calculate different derivatives of thermodynamic quantities in terms of the equation of state and the specific heat C_v.

---

† Remember here that we are speaking in both cases of processes (for instance chemical reactions) during which the body is not in equilibrium, so that its state is not uniquely defined by its volume (or pressure) and temperature.

Similarly when P and T are chosen as basic variables the results of the transformation must be expressed in terms of V and C_p (as functions of P and T).

It should be borne in mind that the dependence of C_v on V or C_p on P (but not on temperature) can itself be found directly from the equation of state. In fact it is easily seen that the derivative $(\partial C_p/\partial V)_T$ can be transformed to a form in which it is determined by the function $P(V, T)$. Using the fact that $S = -(\partial F/\partial T)_V$, we have:

$$\left(\frac{\partial C_v}{\partial V}\right)_T = T\frac{\partial^2 S}{\partial V \partial T} = -T\frac{\partial^3 F}{\partial V \partial T^2} = -T\frac{\partial^2}{\partial T^2}\left(\frac{\partial F}{\partial V}\right)_T,$$

and as $(\partial F/\partial V)_T = -P$ we obtain the required expression

$$\left(\frac{\partial C_v}{\partial V}\right)_T = T\left(\frac{\partial^2 P}{\partial T^2}\right)_V. \tag{16.1}$$

Similarly we can show that

$$\left(\frac{\partial C_p}{\partial P}\right)_T = -T\left(\frac{\partial^2 V}{\partial T^2}\right)_P. \tag{16.2}$$

(By transforming by means of formula (15.8).)

We now proceed to show how some of the most frequently used thermodynamic derivatives may be transformed.

The derivative of entropy with respect to volume or pressure can be calculated from the equation of state by means of the following formulae which follow immediately from the thermodynamic identities.

We have:

$$\left(\frac{\partial S}{\partial V}\right)_T = -\frac{\partial}{\partial V}\left(\frac{\partial F}{\partial T}\right)_V = -\frac{\partial}{\partial T}\left(\frac{\partial F}{\partial V}\right)_T,$$

or

$$\left(\frac{\partial S}{\partial V}\right)_T = \left(\frac{\partial P}{\partial T}\right)_V. \tag{16.3}$$

Similarly

$$\left(\frac{\partial S}{\partial P}\right)_T = -\frac{\partial}{\partial P}\left(\frac{\partial \Phi}{\partial T}\right)_P = -\frac{\partial}{\partial T}\left(\frac{\partial \Phi}{\partial P}\right)_T,$$

or

$$\left(\frac{\partial S}{\partial P}\right)_T = -\left(\frac{\partial V}{\partial T}\right)_P. \tag{16.4}$$

The derivative $(\partial E/\partial V)_T$ is calculated from the identity $dE = T\,dS - P\,dV$ as

$$\left(\frac{\partial E}{\partial V}\right)_T = T\left(\frac{\partial S}{\partial V}\right)_T - P$$

or, by substituting in (16.3),

$$\left(\frac{\partial E}{\partial V}\right)_T = T\left(\frac{\partial P}{\partial T}\right)_V - P. \tag{16.5}$$

Similarly one can obtain the following formulae:

$$\left(\frac{\partial E}{\partial P}\right)_T = -T\left(\frac{\partial V}{\partial T}\right)_P - P\left(\frac{\partial V}{\partial P}\right)_T, \tag{16.6}$$

$$\left(\frac{\partial W}{\partial V}\right)_T = T\left(\frac{\partial P}{\partial T}\right)_V + V\left(\frac{\partial P}{\partial V}\right)_T \qquad \left(\frac{\partial W}{\partial P}\right)_T = V - T\left(\frac{\partial V}{\partial T}\right)_P, \tag{16.7}$$

$$\left(\frac{\partial E}{\partial T}\right)_P = C_p - P\left(\frac{\partial V}{\partial T}\right)_P \qquad \left(\frac{\partial W}{\partial T}\right)_V = C_v + V\left(\frac{\partial P}{\partial T}\right)_V. \tag{16.8}$$

Lastly we show how the specific heat C_v can be calculated from the specific heat C_p and the equation of state using T, P as basic variables. Since $C_v = T(\partial S/\partial T)_V$, we have to transform the derivative $(\partial S/\partial T)_V$ to other independent variables. Such transformations are carried out most simply by means of the Jacobian.†

---

† The Jacobian $\partial(u, v)/\partial(x, y)$ is defined as the determinant

$$\frac{\partial(u,v)}{\partial(x,y)} = \begin{vmatrix} \dfrac{\partial u}{\partial x} & \dfrac{\partial u}{\partial y} \\ \dfrac{\partial v}{\partial x} & \dfrac{\partial v}{\partial y} \end{vmatrix}. \tag{I}$$

It has the following obvious properties

$$\frac{\partial(v,u)}{\partial(x,y)} = -\frac{\partial(u,v)}{\partial(x,y)} \tag{II}$$

$$\frac{\partial(u,y)}{\partial(x,y)} = \left(\frac{\partial u}{\partial x}\right)_y. \tag{III}$$

Furthermore the following relations are satisfied

$$\frac{\partial(u,v)}{\partial(x,y)} = \frac{\partial(u,v)}{\partial(t,s)}\frac{\partial(t,s)}{\partial(x,y)}, \tag{IV}$$

$$\frac{d}{dt}\left(\frac{\partial(u,v)}{\partial(x,y)}\right) = \frac{\partial\left(\dfrac{du}{dt},v\right)}{\partial(x,y)} + \frac{\partial\left(u,\dfrac{dv}{dt}\right)}{\partial(x,y)}. \tag{V}$$

We write

$$C_v = T\left(\frac{\partial S}{\partial T}\right)_V = T\frac{\partial(S,V)}{\partial(T,V)}$$

$$= T\frac{\dfrac{\partial(S,V)}{\partial(T,P)}}{\dfrac{\partial(T,V)}{\partial(T,P)}} = T\frac{\left(\dfrac{\partial S}{\partial T}\right)_P\left(\dfrac{\partial V}{\partial P}\right)_T - \left(\dfrac{\partial S}{\partial P}\right)_T\left(\dfrac{\partial V}{\partial T}\right)_P}{\left(\dfrac{\partial V}{\partial P}\right)_T}$$

$$= C_p - T\frac{\left(\dfrac{\partial S}{\partial P}\right)_T\left(\dfrac{\partial V}{\partial T}\right)_P}{\left(\dfrac{\partial V}{\partial P}\right)_T}.$$

Substituting in this from (16.4) we obtain the required formula:

$$C_p - C_v = -T\frac{\left(\dfrac{\partial V}{\partial T}\right)_P^2}{\left(\dfrac{\partial V}{\partial P}\right)_T}. \tag{16.9}$$

Similarly, transforming $C_p = T(\partial S/\partial T)_P$ to variables T, V, we obtain the formula:

$$C_p - C_v = -T\frac{\left(\dfrac{\partial P}{\partial T}\right)_V^2}{\left(\dfrac{\partial P}{\partial V}\right)_T}. \tag{16.10}$$

The derivative $(\partial P/\partial V)_T$ is always negative, i.e. when a body is isothermally expanded its pressure always drops. (In §21 this fact will be proved rigorously). From (6.10) it hence follows that for all bodies

$$C_p > C_v. \tag{16.11}$$

In an adiabatic expansion (or contraction) of a body its entropy remains constant. Hence the relation between the temperature, volume and pressure of a body during an adiabatic process is defined by various derivatives taken with the entropy constant. We shall derive formulae allowing us to calculate these derivatives from the equation of state of the body and its specific heat.

For the derivative of temperature with respect to volume we have, transforming to independent variables V, T:

$$\left(\frac{\partial T}{\partial V}\right)_S = \frac{\partial(T,S)}{\partial(V,S)} = \frac{\dfrac{\partial(T,S)}{\partial(V,T)}}{\dfrac{\partial(V,S)}{\partial(V,T)}} = -\frac{\left(\dfrac{\partial S}{\partial V}\right)_T}{\left(\dfrac{\partial S}{\partial T}\right)_V} = -\frac{T}{C_v}\left(\frac{\partial S}{\partial V}\right)_T,$$

or, substituting in (16.3)

$$\left(\frac{\partial T}{\partial V}\right)_S = -\frac{T}{C_v}\left(\frac{\partial P}{\partial T}\right)_V. \tag{16.12}$$

Similarly we obtain the formula

$$\left(\frac{\partial T}{\partial P}\right)_S = \frac{T}{C_p}\left(\frac{\partial V}{\partial T}\right)_P. \tag{16.13}$$

From these formulae we can see that if the coefficient of thermal expansion $(\partial V/\partial T)_P$ is positive (negative) then in an adiabatic expansion the temperature of the body will fall (rise)†.

In addition, we may calculate the adiabatic compressibility of the body. We write

$$\left(\frac{\partial V}{\partial P}\right)_S = \frac{\partial(V,S)}{\partial(P,S)} = \frac{\dfrac{\partial(V,S)}{\partial(V,T)}}{\dfrac{\partial(P,S)}{\partial(P,T)}}\frac{\partial(V,T)}{\partial(P,T)} = \frac{\left(\dfrac{\partial S}{\partial T}\right)_V}{\left(\dfrac{\partial S}{\partial T}\right)_P}\left(\frac{\partial V}{\partial P}\right)_T$$

or

$$\left(\frac{\partial V}{\partial P}\right)_S = \frac{C_v}{C_p}\left(\frac{\partial V}{\partial P}\right)_T. \tag{16.14}$$

Owing to the inequality $C_p > C_v$ it thus follows that the absolute value of an adiabatic compressibility is always smaller than that of an isothermal compressibility.

Using (16.9–10) we can derive from (16.14) the relations

$$\left(\frac{\partial V}{\partial P}\right)_S = \left(\frac{\partial V}{\partial P}\right)_T + \frac{T}{C_p}\left(\frac{\partial V}{\partial T}\right)_P^2, \tag{16.15}$$

$$\left(\frac{\partial P}{\partial V}\right)_S = \left(\frac{\partial P}{\partial V}\right)_T - \frac{T}{C_v}\left(\frac{\partial P}{\partial T}\right)_V^2. \tag{16.16}$$

§17. The thermodynamic scale of temperature

We now show how one can construct, in principle at least, a thermodynamic scale of temperature using an arbitrary body whose equation of state we assume to be initially unknown. In other words the problem is to establish, by means of this body, a relation $T = T(\tau)$ between the absolute scale of temperature T and some purely empirical scale τ defined by a "thermometer" graduated in an arbitrary way.

---

† In §21 it will be shown rigorously that $C_v > 0$ and hence $C_p > 0$ always.

To do this we start from the following relation (in which all quantities refer to the given body):

$$\left(\frac{\partial Q}{\partial P}\right)_T = T\left(\frac{\partial S}{\partial P}\right)_T = -T\left(\frac{\partial V}{\partial T}\right)_P,$$

using (16.4). Since τ and T are uniquely related the derivative is the same at constant τ as at constant T. We may rewrite the derivative $(\partial V/\partial T)_P$ in the form:

$$\left(\frac{\partial V}{\partial T}\right)_P = \left(\frac{\partial V}{\partial \tau}\right)_P \frac{d\tau}{dT}.$$

Then we have:

$$\left(\frac{\partial Q}{\partial P}\right)_\tau = -T\left(\frac{\partial V}{\partial \tau}\right)_P \frac{d\tau}{dT},$$

or

$$\frac{d\log T}{d\tau} = -\frac{\left(\dfrac{\partial V}{\partial \tau}\right)_P}{\left(\dfrac{\partial Q}{\partial P}\right)_\tau}. \tag{19.1}$$

Both the quantities on the right-hand side of the equation can be measured directly as functions of the empirical temperature τ; $(\partial Q/\partial P)_\tau$ is determined by the quantity of heat which must be supplied to the body to keep its temperature constant when it expands, and $(\partial V/\partial \tau)_P$ is determined by the change in volume of the body when it is heated. Thus formula (17.1) solves the problem in question, enabling us to determine the required relation, $T = T(\tau)$.

At the same time it should be borne in mind that the integration of the relation (17.1) determines $\log T$ to within an additive constant. Hence the temperature is determined to within an arbitrary constant factor. Obviously this should be so; the choice of a unit of absolute temperature remains arbitrary, which is equivalent to the existence of an arbitrary constant factor in the relation $T = T(\tau)$.

§18. The Joule-Thomson process

Consider the following process. A gas, (or liquid) at pressure P_1 is steadily transferred to a vessel where the pressure is P_2 $(P_2 < P_1)$. The steadiness of the process means that P_1 and P_2 remain constant throughout the entire process. Such a process can be imagined as the transfer of gas through a porous partition (a in Fig. 1) where the pressure on each side of the partition is kept constant by suitably moving pistons. If the openings in the partition are sufficiently small we may consider the macroscopic velocity of the gas to be zero. We shall also assume that the gas is thermally isolated from any external medium.

The process we have described is known as a Joule-Thomson process. We must emphasise that this process is irreversible. This is clear because of the presence of the partition with small holes, which destroys the velocity of the gas by setting up large frictional forces.

Let a certain quantity of gas with volume V_1 at pressure P_1 pass (in thermal isolation) to the region at pressure P_2 acquiring volume V_2. The change in

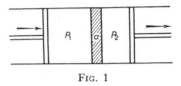

Fig. 1

energy E_2-E_1 of this gas will be equal to the work done on it to remove it from volume V_1 (which will equal P_1V_1) minus the work done by the gas itself to occupy volume V_2 at pressure P_2 (which will equal P_2V_2). Thus we have

$$E_2-E_1 = P_1V_1-P_2V_2$$

i.e. $$E_1+P_1V_1 = E_2+P_2V_2$$

or $$W_1 = W_2. \tag{18.1}$$

Thus the heat function of the gas is conserved in a Joule-Thomson process.

The change of temperature with a small change in pressure as the result of a Joule-Thomson process is given by the derivative $(\partial T/\partial P)_W$ taken at constant heat function. We may transform this derivative changing to independent variables P, T. We have

$$\left(\frac{\partial T}{\partial P}\right)_W = \frac{\partial(T,W)}{\partial(P,W)} = \frac{\dfrac{\partial(T,W)}{\partial(P,T)}}{\dfrac{\partial(P,W)}{\partial(P,T)}} = -\frac{\left(\dfrac{\partial W}{\partial P}\right)_T}{\left(\dfrac{\partial W}{\partial T}\right)_P}$$

whence, using (14.7) and (16.7), we obtain

$$\left(\frac{\partial T}{\partial P}\right)_W = \frac{1}{C_p}\left[T\left(\frac{\partial V}{\partial T}\right)_P - V\right]. \tag{18.2}$$

The change of entropy is given by the derivative $(\partial S/\partial P)_W$. From the identity $dW = T\,dS + V\,dP$ which we may write in the form

$$dS = \frac{dW}{T} - \frac{V}{T}\,dP,$$

we have:

$$\left(\frac{\partial S}{\partial P}\right)_W = -\frac{V}{T}. \tag{18.3}$$

This quantity is always negative, as it should be, the transferring of the gas to a lower pressure by means of the irreversible Joule-Thomson process is accompanied by an increase in entropy.

We add a remark about the process in which the gas is initially in one of the two connected vessels and expands into the other; clearly this is not a steady process, and the pressures in both vessels will change until they become equal. In such an expansion of a gas into a vacuum, its energy, E is conserved. If, after the expansion, the total volume has changed only slightly, then the change of temperature is given by the derivative $(\partial T/\partial V)_E$. Transforming this derivative to independent variables V, T we obtain the formula

$$\left(\frac{\partial T}{\partial V}\right)_E = \frac{1}{C_v}\left[P - T\left(\frac{\partial P}{\partial T}\right)_V\right]. \tag{18.4}$$

For the change in entropy we have:

$$\left(\frac{\partial S}{\partial V}\right)_E = \frac{P}{T}. \tag{18.5}$$

As we should expect, the entropy increases during the expansion, i.e. with an increase in V.

§19. Maximum work

Consider a thermally isolated system consisting of several bodies which are not in thermal equilibrium with each other. During the setting up of equilibrium the system can do work (on some external objects). The transition to equilibrium can, however, be carried out in different ways, in which the final equilibrium states of the system (in particular, its energy and entropy) will certainly be different.

Correspondingly, the total amount of work which can be obtained from the non-equilibrium system will depend on the way in which equilibrium is set up and the question arises as to which way of reaching equilibrium will produce the maximum possible work. Here we are only interested in the work produced due to the system not being in equilibrium. This means that we must ignore the work which might be done by a general expansion of the system—work which could also be done by the system, which is itself in equilibrium. To do this we shall assume that the total volume remains constant.

Let the initial energy of the system be E_0, and the energy in an equilibrium state, as a function of the entropy of the system in this state, be $E(S)$. Owing to the thermal isolation of the system the work done by it is simply equal to the change in energy $|R| = E_0 - E(S)$. (We write $|R|$ in accordance with our convention that $R < 0$, if the work is performed by the system.)

Differentiating $|R|$ with respect to the entropy S of the final state we have:

$$\frac{\partial |R|}{\partial S} = -\left(\frac{\partial E}{\partial S}\right)_V = -T,$$

where T is the temperature of the final state. We see that this derivative is negative, i.e. $|R|$ decreases as S increases. But the entropy of a thermally isolated system cannot decrease. Hence the maximum possible $|R|$ will be obtained if S remains constant during the entire process.

Thus we conclude that the work done by the system is a maximum when its entropy remains constant, i.e. when the transition to an equilibrium state is a reversible one.

Let us find the maximum amount of work which can be done in the exchange of a small quantity of energy between two bodies at different temperatures T_1 and T_2; $T_2 > T_1$. First of all we must emphasise that if the transfer of energy were to be brought about by direct contact of the bodies, then no work at all would be done. The process would be irreversible (the entropy of the bodies would increase by $\delta E(1/T_1 - 1/T_2)$ where δE is the amount of energy transferred). Hence to bring about a reversible transfer of energy, and thus obtain the maximum work, it is necessary to introduce some auxiliary body ("working body") which performs a certain, reversible, cyclic process. This process must take place in such a way that bodies between which a direct exchange of energy takes place are at the same temperature. That is to say, the working body at temperature T_2 is brought into contact with the body at temperature T_2 and isothermally gains from it a certain energy. Then it is adiabatically cooled to temperature T_1 and gives up this energy at this temperature to the body at temperature T_1 and finally returns adiabatically to its initial state. During the expansions associated with this process the working body does work on external objects. The cyclic process we have described is called the *Carnot Cycle*.

Turning now to the calculation of the resulting maximum work we note that the working body need not be considered, since it returns to its initial state. Suppose the hotter second body loses energy $-\delta E_2 = -T_2\,\delta S_2$ and the first body will then gain energy $\delta E_1 = T_1\,\delta S_1$. Owing to the reversibility of the process, the sum of the entropies of the two bodies remains constant, i.e. $\delta S_1 = \delta S_2$. The work done is equal to the decrease in the total energy of both bodies, i.e.

or

$$|\delta R|_{\max} = -\delta E_1 - \delta E_2 = -T_1\,\delta S_1 - T_2\,\delta S_2 = -(T_2 - T_1)\,\delta S_2,$$

$$|\delta R|_{\max} = \frac{T_2 - T_1}{T_2}|\delta E_2|. \tag{19.1}$$

The ratio of the work done to the quantity of energy used is called the *efficiency* η. The maximum efficiency of the transfer of energy from a warmer to a colder body is, from (19.1)

$$\eta_{max} = \frac{T_2 - T_1}{T_2}. \tag{19.2}$$

A more convenient quantity is the so-called *coefficient of utility n* defined as the ratio of the work done to the maximum work which could be obtained in the given conditions. It is obvious that

$$n = \frac{\eta}{\eta_{max}}. \tag{19.3}$$

§20. The maximum work done by a body in an external medium

We shall now consider the problem of maximum work in a different situation. Suppose the body is in an external medium whose temperature T_0 and pressure P_0 differ from those of the body (T and P). The body can do work on some object which is understood to be thermally isolated from both the medium and the given body. The medium, together with the body in it and the object on which work is done, forms a closed system. The volume and energy of the medium are so large that changes in them due to processes taking place in the body do not produce any significant change in the temperature and pressure of the medium; these may, therefore, be considered to be constant.

If the medium were not there, then the work done by the body on a thermally isolated object for a given change in state of the body (i.e. given initial and final states) would be a uniquely defined quantity equal to the change in the energy of the body. The presence of the medium also involved in the process makes the result no longer unique, and the question arises as to what is the maximum work a body can do for a given change in state.

If, in a transition from one state to another, the body does work on an external object, than in an inverse transition from the second state to the first, some external source must do work on the body. To a direct transition, in which the body does the maximum work $|R|_{max}$ there corresponds an inverse transition which requires the external source to supply the minimum work R_{min}. It is evident that the amounts $|R|_{max}$ and $|R|_{min}$ are identical so that the problems of their calculation are equivalent and in future we shall consider the work done on the body by an external, thermally isolated source of work.

During the process, the body can exchange heat and work with the medium. Such work done on the body must be excluded from the total work done on the body, since we are only interested in the work which is done by the given external object. Thus the total change ΔE in the energy of the body for some (not necessarily small) change of state is made up of three parts: the work R

done on the body by the external source, the work done by the medium, and the heat received from the medium. As was pointed out above, owing to the great size of the medium its temperature and pressure may be considered to be constant; hence the work done by it on the body is $P_0 \Delta V_0$ and the heat given out by it is $-T_0 \Delta S_0$ (letters with subscripts refer to the medium and those without a subscript to the body). Thus we have

$$\Delta E = R + P_0 \Delta V_0 - T_0 \Delta S_0.$$

Since the volume of the medium and the body together remains constant $\Delta V_0 = -\Delta V$. Furthermore, in accordance with the law of increase of entropy we have $\Delta S + \Delta S_0 \geqslant 0$ (the entropy of the thermally isolated source of work does not change at all); thus $\Delta S_0 \geqslant -\Delta S$. Hence from $R = \Delta E - P_0 \Delta V_0 + T_0 \Delta S_0$ we obtain:

$$R \geqslant \Delta E - T_0 \Delta S + P_0 \Delta V. \tag{20.1}$$

Equality is attained for a reversible process. Thus we again conclude that the transition occurs with the minimum expenditure of work (and hence the inverse transition with the maximum work done) if it is reversible. The value of the minimum work is given by the formula

$$R_{\min} = \Delta(E - T_0 S + P_0 V) \tag{20.2}$$

(T_0 and P_0, being constant, can be taken under the Δ), i.e. this work is equal to the change in the quantity $E - T_0 S + P_0 V$. For maximum work the formula must obviously be rewritten with the opposite sign

$$|R|_{\max} = -\Delta(E - T_0 S + P_0 V) \tag{20.3}$$

since the initial and final states are interchanged.

If, at each instant during the process, the body is in an equilibrium state (but not, of course, in equilibrium with the medium), then for an infinitesimal change of state (20.2) may be written in a different form; substituting $dE = T \, dS - P \, dV$ into $dE_{\min} = dE - T_0 \, dS + P_0 \, dV$, we find:

$$dR_{\min} = (T - T_0) \, dS - (P - P_0) \, dV. \tag{20.4}$$

There are two important special cases. If the volume and the temperature of the body remain constant, and the latter is equal to that of the medium, then from (20.2) we have $R_{\min} = \Delta(E - TS)$, or

$$R_{\min} = \Delta F \tag{20.5}$$

i.e. the minimum work is equal to the change in the free energy of the body. If the temperature and pressure are constant, and $T = T_0$, $P = P_0$ we have:

$$R_{\min} = \Delta \Phi \tag{20.6}$$

i.e. the work done by the external source is equal to the change in the thermodynamic potential of the body.

It must be stressed that in both the special cases one must consider a body which is not in equilibrium and hence its state is not defined by T and V (or P) alone; otherwise the constancy of these quantities would mean that no process could take place at all. One can discuss, for example, a chemical reaction in a mixture of two interacting substances, the process of solution, etc.

Now assume that the body in the external medium is left to itself and that no work is done on it. In this body spontaneous, irreversible processes will occur which bring it into equilibrium. In the relation (20.1) we must put $R = 0$ and hence it will become:

$$\Delta(E - T_0 S + P_0 V) \leqslant 0. \tag{20.7}$$

This means that as a result of processes undergone by the body the quantity $E - T_0 S + P_0 V$ will decrease so that at equilibrium it will be a minimum.

In particular, during spontaneous processes at constant temperature $T = T_0$ and constant pressure $P = P_0$ the thermodynamic potential Φ of the body decreases, and during processes at constant temperature $T = T_0$ and volume its free energy F decreases. These results were already obtained by a different approach in §15. Note that the deduction given here does not assume that the temperature and the volume (or pressure) of the body remain constant for the whole of the process: it can be asserted that the thermodynamic potential (or free energy) of the body decrease in every process in which the temperature and pressure (or volume) are the same (and are equal to those of the medium) at the beginning and the end, even if they were changing at some stage in the process.

Yet another thermodynamic meaning can be given to the minimum work. Let S_t be the total entropy of the body together with the medium. If the body is in equilibrium with the medium then S_t is a function of their total energy E_t

$$S_t = S_t(E_t).$$

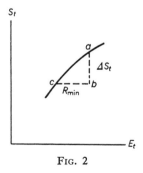

Fig. 2

If the body is not in equilibrium with the medium then their total entropy (for the same value of their total energy E_t) differs from the value $S_t(E_t)$ by some quantity $\Delta S_t < 0$. In Fig. 2 the solid line represents the function

$S_t(E_t)$ and the vertical line ab the quantity $-\Delta S_t$. The horizontal line bc is the change in the total energy during the transition from the state of equilibrium with the medium to the state represented by the point. In other words, this line represents the minimum work an external source must do to bring the body from a state of equilibrium with the medium to the given state. The state of equilibrium we are referring to (the point C in Fig. 2) obviously does not coincide with the state of equilibrium corresponding to the given value E_T (the point a).

Since the body represents only a very small part of the whole system, the processes taking place in it lead to relatively insignificant changes in the total energy and entropy. From the graph in Fig. 2 it thus follows that

$$\Delta S_t = -\frac{\mathrm{d}S_t(E_t)}{\mathrm{d}E_t}R_{\min},$$

but the derivative $\mathrm{d}E_t/\mathrm{d}S_t$ is the equilibrium temperature of the system, i.e. the temperature T_0 of the medium. Thus,

$$\Delta S_t = -\frac{R_{\min}}{T_0} = -\frac{1}{T_0}(\Delta E - T_0\,\Delta S + P_0\,\Delta V). \qquad (20.8)$$

This relation expresses how much the entropy of the closed system (body and medium) differs from its maximum possible value if the body is not in equilibrium with the medium, where ΔE, ΔS, and ΔV are the differences between the energy, entropy, and volume of the body and their values in the state of total equilibrium.

§21. The thermodynamic inequalities

In obtaining the conditions for thermal equilibrium from the condition of maximum entropy, we have so far considered only its first derivatives. Requiring the derivatives with respect to energy and volume to be zero, we had (§9, 12) for equilibrium, the condition that the temperatures and pressures should be the same at all parts of the body. However, the vanishing of the first derivatives is only a necessary condition for an extremum and does not ensure that the entropy is always a maximum. To obtain conditions for a maximum we are obliged to investigate the second derivatives of the function.

It is more convenient, however, to carry out this investigation not starting directly from the condition that the entropy should be a maximum but from another, equivalent, condition.† We select from the body under consideration a small (but macroscopic) part. In relation to this part, the rest of the body can be considered as an external medium. Then, from the results of the

---

† In considering the dependence of entropy on the momenta of macroscopic motion we already investigated the conditions satisfied by both the first and second derivatives (§10). We saw that this implied absence of internal macroscopic motion and a positive temperature.

previous section, we know that for equilibrium the quantity

$$E - T_0 S + P_0 V$$

is a minimum, where E, S, V are the energy, entropy and volume of the given part of the body and T_0 and P_0 are the temperature and pressure of the external medium, i.e. of the other parts of the body. Obviously T_0 and P_0 are equally the temperature and pressure of the part under consideration in its equilibrium state.

Thus for every small deviation from equilibrium, the quantity $E - T_0 S + P_0 V$ must be positive, i.e.

$$\delta E - T_0\, \delta S + P_0\, \delta V > 0. \tag{21.1}$$

In other words, one can say that the minimum work which must be done to transform a body from an equilibrium state to a neighbouring state is positive. In future we shall omit the subscript zero from all the coefficients of variations of thermodynamic quantities from their equilibrium values, it being understood that the coefficients refer to equilibrium values.

Expanding δE in a Taylor series (considering E as a function of S and V) we get, to second order,

$$\delta E = \frac{\partial E}{\partial S}\, \delta S + \frac{\partial E}{\partial V}\, \delta V + \frac{1}{2}\left(\frac{\partial^2 E}{\partial S^2}\, \delta S^2 + 2\frac{\partial^2 E}{\partial S \partial V}\, \delta S\, \delta V + \frac{\partial^2 E}{\partial V^2}\, \delta V^2 \right).$$

But $\partial E/\partial S = T$, $\partial E/\partial V = P$, so that the first-order terms are equal to $T\, \delta S - P\, \delta V$ and cancel when we substitute δE into (21.1). Thus we have the condition

$$\frac{\partial^2 E}{\partial S^2}\, \delta S^2 + 2\frac{\partial^2 E}{\partial S\, \partial V}\, \delta S\, \delta V + \frac{\partial^2 E}{\partial V^2}\, \delta V^2 > 0. \tag{21.2}$$

It is known that for this inequality to hold, two conditions must be satisfied.[†]

$$\frac{\partial^2 E}{\partial S^2} > 0 \tag{21.3}$$

$$\frac{\partial^2 E}{\partial S^2}\frac{\partial^2 E}{\partial V^2} - \left(\frac{\partial^2 E}{\partial S\, \partial V} \right)^2 > 0. \tag{21.4}$$

For $\partial^2 E/\partial S^2$ we have:

$$\frac{\partial^2 E}{\partial S^2} = \left(\frac{\partial T}{\partial S} \right)_V = \frac{T}{C_v}.$$

Hence condition (21.3) requires the ratio T/C_v to be positive and as $T > 0$

---

† The special case, when there is equality in (21.4) will be considered below in §80.

this means

$$C_v > 0,$$

i.e. the specific heat at constant volume is always positive.

The condition (21.4) can be written in terms of a Jacobian

$$\frac{\partial\left[\left(\frac{\partial E}{\partial S}\right)_V, \left(\frac{\partial E}{\partial V}\right)_S\right]}{\partial(S, V)} > 0$$

or

$$\frac{\partial(T, P)}{\partial(S, V)} < 0.$$

Changing to variables T and V, we have:

$$\frac{\partial(T, P)}{\partial(S, V)} = \frac{\dfrac{\partial(T, P)}{\partial(T, V)}}{\dfrac{\partial(S, V)}{\partial(T, V)}} = \frac{\left(\dfrac{\partial P}{\partial V}\right)_T}{\left(\dfrac{\partial S}{\partial T}\right)_V} = \frac{T}{C_v}\left(\frac{\partial P}{\partial V}\right)_T < 0.$$

Since $C_V > 0$ this is equivalent to the condition

$$\left(\frac{\partial P}{\partial V}\right)_T < 0, \tag{21.6}$$

i.e. an increase of volume at constant temperature always results in a decrease of pressure.

Conditions (21.5) and (21.6) are called *thermodynamic inequalities*. States in which these conditions are not satisfied are unstable and cannot exist in nature.

In §16 we already noted that owing to inequality (21.6) and formula (16.9) $C_p > C_v$ always. From (21.5) we may hence conclude that also

$$C_p > 0 \quad \text{always.} \tag{21.7}$$

C_v and C_p being positive means that the energy is a monotonic increasing function of temperature at constant volume, and that the heat function is a similar function of temperature but at constant pressure. Entropy increases monotonically with temperature both at constant volume and constant pressure.

The conditions (21.5, 21.6) derived for any small part of a body are also certainly valid for the body as a whole provided it is homogeneous (so far we have considered only such bodies). The necessity of the latter condition must be stressed. Consider for example a body whose particles are held together by gravitational forces; such a body would clearly be inhomogeneous—it would be denser towards the centre. The specific heat of such a body as a whole may be less than zero, i.e. the body may get hotter when its energy decreases. Note that this does not contradict the fact that the specific heat is positive for each small part of the body since the energy of the whole body in such conditions is not the sum of the energies of its parts—there is the additional energy of the gravitational interactions of these parts.

The inequalities which we have derived are conditions for equilibrium. However, they are not sufficient for the equilibrium to be completely stable.

Actually, there can exist states for which, for infinitely small deviations, the entropy decreases and the body subsequently returns to its initial state, while for some finite deviations the entropy can be larger than that in the initial state. After such a finite deviation the body will not return to its initial state but on the contrary will tend to go into some other equilibrium state with a higher maximum of entropy than that in the initial state. As a result of this possibility one must distinguish between those equilibrium states which we call *metastable* and *stable* states. If a body is in a metastable state, then after a sufficiently large deviation from it the body cannot return to its initial state. Although a metastable state is stable within certain limits, sooner or later the body is bound to pass from it to another, stable, state. The latter corresponds to the greatest possible maximum of entropy; a body removed from such a state will sooner or later return to it.

§22. Le Chatelier's principle

Consider a closed system consisting of a medium and a body surrounded by it. Let S be the total entropy of the system and y some quantity relating to the body such that the condition that S is a maximum with respect to it; i.e.

$$\frac{\partial S}{\partial y} = 0$$

implies that the body is itself in an equilibrium state, though not necessarily in equilibrium with the medium. Further, let x be another thermodynamic quantity relating to the same body such that if

$$\frac{\partial S}{\partial x} = 0,$$

as well as $\partial S/\partial y = 0$, then the body is not only in internal equilibrium but also in equilibrium with the medium.

We introduce the notation

$$X = -\frac{\partial S}{\partial x}, \qquad Y = -\frac{\partial S}{\partial y}. \tag{22.1}$$

For total thermodynamic equilibrium the entropy S must be a maximum.

For this not only must

$$X = 0, \qquad Y = 0, \tag{22.2}$$

but also we must have

$$\left(\frac{\partial X}{\partial x}\right)_y > 0 \qquad \left(\frac{\partial Y}{\partial y}\right)_x > 0 \tag{22.3}$$

and

$$\left(\frac{\partial X}{\partial x}\right)_y\left(\frac{\partial Y}{\partial y}\right)_x - \left(\frac{\partial X}{\partial y}\right)_x^2 > 0. \tag{22.4}$$

Assume that by means of some small external influence the equilibrium of the body with the medium is disturbed, the quantity x is slightly changed and the condition $x = 0$ upset; we assume that y is not directly affected by the given disturbance.

Let Δx be the change in x; then the change in X at the moment of the disturbance will be

$$(\Delta X)_y = \left(\frac{\partial X}{\partial x}\right)_y \Delta x.$$

The change in x at constant y certainly breaks the condition $Y = 0$, i.e. the internal equilibrium of the body. After this equilibrium has been re-established the quantity $X \equiv \Delta X$ will have the value

$$(\Delta X)_{Y=0} = \left(\frac{\partial X}{\partial x}\right)_{Y=0} \Delta x,$$

where the derivative is taken for constant Y.

Let us compare the two values of ΔX. Making use of the properties of Jacobians we have

$$\left(\frac{\partial X}{\partial x}\right)_{Y=0} = \frac{\partial(X, Y)}{\partial(x, Y)} = \frac{\dfrac{\partial(X, Y)}{\partial(x, y)}}{\dfrac{\partial(x, Y)}{\partial(x, y)}} = \left(\frac{\partial X}{\partial x}\right)_y - \frac{\left(\dfrac{\partial X}{\partial y}\right)_x^2}{\left(\dfrac{\partial Y}{\partial y}\right)_x}.$$

The denominator of the second term in this expression is positive, by (22.3). Making use also of (22.4) we find that

$$\left(\frac{\partial X}{\partial x}\right)_y > \left(\frac{\partial X}{\partial x}\right)_{Y=0} > 0 \tag{22.5}$$

or

$$|(\Delta X)_y| > |(\Delta X)_{Y=0}|. \tag{22.6}$$

The inequalities (22.5) and (22.6) comprise the so-called *Le Chatelier's principle*.

Consider the change Δx of the quantity x as a measure of the external influence on the body and ΔX as a measure of the change in the properties of the body as a result of this influence. The inequality (22.6) shows that when the internal equilibrium of the body is restored after the external influence disturbs it, ΔX is decreased. Hence Le Chatelier's principle may be formulated as follows:

An external influence, disturbing the equilibrium of a body, induces in it processes tending to weaken the effects of this influence.

Some examples will illustrate what has been said above. To start with, it is convenient to alter slightly the definition of the quantities X and Y. Using formula (20.8), according to which the change in entropy of the system (medium and body) is given by $-R_{min}/T_0$ where T_0 is the temperature of the medium and R_{min} the minimum work necessary to bring the body from a state of equilibrium with the medium to the given state, we can write:

$$X = \frac{1}{T_0}\frac{\partial R_{min}}{\partial x}, \qquad Y = \frac{1}{T_0}\frac{\partial R_{min}}{\partial y}. \tag{22.7}$$

For an infinitesimal change of state of the body we have (see (20.4)):

$$dR_{min} = (T-T_0)\,dS - (P-P_0)\,dV;$$

all quantities without a subscript referring to the body and those with subscript 0 to the medium.

If x is the entropy S of the body then $X = (T-T_0)/T_0$. The equilibrium condition $X = 0$ gives $T = T_0$, i.e. equality of temperature between the body and the medium. Inequalities (22.5) and (22.6) become:

$$\left(\frac{\partial T}{\partial S}\right)_y > \left(\frac{\partial T}{\partial S}\right)_{Y=0} > 0 \tag{22.8}$$

$$|(\Delta T)_y| > |(\Delta T)_{Y=0}|. \tag{22.9}$$

The interpretation of these inequalities is as follows. A change in the quantity x—the entropy of the body—means that the body gains (or loses) a certain amount of heat. As a result, the equilibrium of the body itself is disturbed and in particular its temperature changes (by an amount $(\Delta T)_p$). Re-establishment of equilibrium in the body will have the effect of reducing the absolute value of the change in its temperature (which becomes equal to $(\Delta T)_{y=0}$), i.e. it acts so as to weaken the effects of the external influence. In other words the heating (cooling) of the body stimulates processes tending to lower (raise) its temperature.

Now let x be the volume V of the body. Then $X = -(P-P_0)/T_0$. For equilibrium $X = 0$, i.e. $P = P_0$. Inequalities (22.5) and (22.6) become

$$\left(\frac{\partial P}{\partial V}\right)_y < \left(\frac{\partial P}{\partial V}\right)_{Y=0} < 0, \tag{22.10}$$

$$|(\Delta P)_y| > |(\Delta P)_{Y=0}|. \tag{22.11}$$

If the body is disturbed from equilibrium so as to change its volume (at constant temperature), then its pressure changes. Re-establishment of equilibrium in the body will lead to a reduction in the absolute value of the change in pressure. Bearing in mind that a reduction in volume of the body increases its pressure (and vice versa), we can say that a decrease (increase) in the volume of the body stimulates processes tending to decrease (increase) its pressure.

Later on we shall meet many applications of these results (to solutions, chemical reactions, etc.).

Note that if, in the inequality (22.8), for the quantity y we take the volume of the body we will have:

$$\left(\frac{\partial T}{\partial S}\right)_y = \left(\frac{\partial T}{\partial S}\right)_V = \frac{T}{C_v}, \qquad \left(\frac{\partial T}{\partial S}\right)_{Y=0} = \left(\frac{\partial T}{\partial S}\right)_P = \frac{T}{C_p},$$

since the condition $Y = 0$ means in this case $P = P_0$, i.e. constant pressure. Thus we again obtain the already familiar inequality

$$C_p > C_v > 0.$$

Similarly if, in (22.10), we take the entropy of the body for y then the condition $Y = 0$ will imply constant temperature and we shall find

$$\left(\frac{\partial P}{\partial V}\right)_S < \left(\frac{\partial P}{\partial V}\right)_T < 0,$$

a result we already know.

§23. Nernst's theorem

The fact that the specific heat C_v is positive means that the energy is a monotonic increasing function of temperature. Conversely, as the temperature falls the energy decreases monotonically, and hence at the lowest temperature possible, i.e. absolute zero, the body must be in the state with the lowest possible energy. Considering the energy of the body to be the sum of the energies of the parts into which we can mentally divide it, then we can assert that each of these parts will be in the state in which it has the minimum possible energy; it is clear that for the sum to take its minimum value, each term must be at its minimum value.

Thus at absolute zero, any part of the body must be in a definite quantum state—namely the ground state. In other words the statistical weights of these parts are all equal to unity and hence their product, i.e. the statistical weight of the macroscopic state of the body, as a whole, is also equal to unity, and the entropy of the body—the logarithm of its statistical weight—is equal to zero. Hence we reach the following important conclusion: the entropy of any body vanishes at absolute zero (this is called *Nernst's Theorem*).†

---

† To avoid confusion we must stress that we are talking about temperature tending to zero subject to some otherwise unchanged conditions, e.g. constant volume and constant pressure. If, for example, the temperature of a gas tends to zero simultaneously with its density, then the entropy need not tend to zero.

We must emphasise that this theorem is deduced from quantum statistics and depends on the concept of discrete quantum states. It cannot be derived from purely classical statistics in which entropy is only defined to within an arbitrary additive constant (see §7).

Nernst's Theorem also allows us to reach conclusions about the behaviour of other thermodynamic quantities as $T \to 0$.

It is easy to see that at $T = 0$ the specific heats C_p and C_v vanish.

$$C_p = C_v = 0 \quad \text{at} \quad T = 0. \tag{23.1}$$

This follows directly from the definition of specific heat in the form

$$C = T\frac{\partial S}{\partial T} = \frac{\partial S}{\partial \ln T}.$$

As $T \to 0$ we have $\log T \to -\infty$ and since S tends to a constant limit (zero), the given derivative clearly tends to zero.

Also the coefficient of thermal expansion vanishes,

$$\left(\frac{\partial V}{\partial T}\right)_P = 0 \quad \text{at} \quad T = 0 \tag{23.2}$$

since this derivative is equal to the derivative $-(\partial S/\partial P)_T$ (see (16.4)), which vanishes at $T = 0$ since $S = 0$ at $T = 0$ and arbitrary pressure. Similarly we also see that

$$\left(\frac{\partial P}{\partial T}\right)_V = 0 \quad \text{at} \quad T = 0. \tag{23.3}$$

Usually entropy tends to zero as $T \to 0$ following a power law, i.e. $S = aT^n$ where a is a function of pressure or volume. Obviously in this case the specific heats, and the quantities $(\partial V/\partial T)_P$, $(\partial P/\partial T)_V$ tend to zero according to the same law (with the same n).

Finally we see that the difference $C_p - C_v$ tends to zero more rapidly than the specific heats themselves, i.e.

$$\frac{C_p - C_v}{C_p} = 0 \quad \text{at} \quad T = 0. \tag{23.4}$$

For instance, let $S = aT^n$. Then from formula (16.9) we see that $C_p - C_v \sim T^{2n+1}$ and therefore $(C_p - C_v)/C_p \sim T^{n+1}$. (It must be borne in mind that the compressibility $(\partial V/\partial P)_T$ in general remains finite at $T = 0$.)

If the specific heat of the body is known over the whole range of the change in temperature, then the entropy can be calculated by means of integration. Thus the dependence of entropy on temperature for a given pressure will be given by the formula

$$S = \int_0^T \frac{C_p}{T}\,dT. \tag{23.5}$$

For the heat function the corresponding formula is

$$W = W_0 + \int\limits_0^T C_p \, dT, \qquad (23.6)$$

where W_0 is the value of the heat function at $T = 0$. For the thermodynamic potential $\Phi = W - TS$ we have, correspondingly,

$$\Phi = W_0 + \int\limits_0^T C_p \, dT - T \int\limits_0^T \frac{C_p}{T} \, dT. \qquad (23.7)$$

§24. The dependence of thermodynamic quantities on the number of particles

Besides energy and entropy, the other thermodynamic quantities, such as F, Φ, W are also additive (as follows directly from their definitions, taking into account the fact that pressure and temperature are constant throughout a body in an equilibrium state). This property allows us to reach certain conclusions as to the way all these quantities depend on the number of particles in the body. We shall consider here bodies made up of identical particles (molecules); all the results can be directly generalised to bodies consisting of different particles, i.e. mixtures (see §83).

The additivity of a quantity means that when the amount of the substance (and with it the number N of particles) is changed by a certain factor, the quantity will change by the same factor. In other words an additive thermodynamic quantity must be a homogeneous function of first order in additive variables.

We may express the energy of the body as a function of entropy and volume and also of the number of particles. Since S and V are themselves additive, this function must be of the form

$$E = Nf\left(\frac{S}{N}, \frac{V}{N}\right) \qquad (24.1)$$

which is the most general homogeneous function of first order in N, S and V.

The free energy F is a function of N, T and V. Since the temperature is constant throughout the body and the volume is additive, we can say in the same way that

$$F = Nf\left(\frac{V}{N}, T\right). \qquad (24.2)$$

Analogously, for the heat function W, expressed as a function of N, S

and P, we obtain

$$W = Nf\left(\frac{S}{N}, P\right) \tag{24.3}$$

and lastly, for the thermodynamic potential as a function of N, P, T, we have:

$$\Phi = Nf(P, T). \tag{24.4}$$

Up till now, we have actually regarded the number of particles as a parameter having a given constant value for each body. Now let us regard N formally as another independent variable, when terms proportional to dN must be added to the thermodynamic identities. For example, for the total differential of the energy we write

$$dE = T\, dS - P\, dV + \mu\, dN \tag{24.5}$$

where μ stands for the partial derivative

$$\mu = \left(\frac{\partial E}{\partial N}\right)_{S, V}. \tag{24.6}$$

The quantity μ is called the *chemical potential* of the body. Similarly, the differentials for F, Φ and W are now

$$dW = T\, dS + V\, dP + \mu\, dN \tag{24.7}$$

$$dF = -S\, dT - P\, dV + \mu\, dN \tag{24.8}$$

$$d\Phi = -S\, dT + V\, dP + \mu\, dN \tag{24.9}$$

with the same μ. From these formulae it follows that

$$\mu = \left(\frac{\partial W}{\partial N}\right)_{S,P} = \left(\frac{\partial F}{\partial N}\right)_{T,V} = \left(\frac{\partial \Phi}{\partial N}\right)_{P,T}, \tag{24.10}$$

i.e. the chemical potential can be obtained by differentiating any of the quantities E, W, F, Φ with respect to the number of particles, although in each case it will be expressed in terms of different variables.

Differentiating Φ in the form (24.4) we find that

$$\mu = \frac{\partial \Phi}{\partial N} = f(P, T),$$

i.e. $\Phi = N\mu$ \tag{24.11}

Thus the chemical potential of a body (consisting of identical particles) is simply its thermodynamic potential per molecule. Expressed in terms of P and T the chemical potential does not depend on N. For the differential of the chemical potential we can thus immediately write the following expression

$$d\mu = -s\,dT + v\,dP, \tag{24.12}$$

where s and v are the entropy and volume per molecule.

If we consider (as we usually have done so far) a definite amount of the substance, then the number of particles in it is a given constant, and its volume is variable. Now let us take a definite volume inside a body and consider the substance contained in this volume; in this case the variable will be the number of particles N, and the volume will be constant. Then, for example, the identity (24.8) will reduce to

$$dF = -S\,dT + \mu\,dN.$$

the independent variables here being T and N. Now let us introduce a new thermodynamic function such that the second independent variable will be μ and not N. To do this we substitute

$$\mu\,dN = d(\mu N) - N\,d\mu$$

and we get

$$d(F - \mu N) = -S\,dT - N\,d\mu,$$

but $\mu N = \Phi$ and $F - \Phi = PV$; thus the new thermodynamic function (which we shall denote by the letter Ω) is simply

$$\Omega = -PV. \tag{24.13}$$

and

$$d\Omega = -S\,dT - N\,d\mu. \tag{24.14}$$

The number of particles is obtained by differentiating Ω with respect to the chemical potential at constant temperature and volume.

$$N = -\left(\frac{\partial\Omega}{\partial\mu}\right)_{T,V} = V\left(\frac{\partial P}{\partial\mu}\right)_{T\,V}. \tag{24.15}$$

In the same way as we deduced the equality of small changes in E, W, F, and Φ (with corresponding constant quantities; see (15.12)), it is easy to show that the change $(\delta\Omega)_{T\mu V}$ at constant T, μ, V has the same value. In other words

$$(\delta E)_{S,V,N} = (\delta F)_{T,V,N} = (\delta\Phi)_{T,P,N} = (\delta W)_{S,P,N} = (\delta\Omega)_{T,\mu\,V}. \tag{24.16}$$

Finally, just as was done in §§ 15 and 20 for free energy and thermodynamic potential, one can show that the work done in a reversible process taking place at constant T, V, and μ is equal to the change in the function Ω. In a state of thermal equilibrium, the function Ω is at a minimum with respect to changes of state at constant T, V, μ.

PROBLEM

Obtain an expression for the specific heat C_v in terms of the variables T, μ, V.

SOLUTION: We transform the derivative $C_v = T(\partial S/\partial T)_{V,N}$ to variables T, V, μ; for this we write (taking V as constant throughout):

$$\left(\frac{\partial S}{\partial T}\right)_N = \frac{\partial(S,N)}{\partial(T,N)} = \frac{\dfrac{\partial(S,N)}{\partial(T,\mu)}}{\dfrac{\partial(T,N)}{\partial(T,\mu)}} = \left(\frac{\partial S}{\partial T}\right)_\mu - \frac{\left(\dfrac{\partial S}{\partial \mu}\right)_T \left(\dfrac{\partial N}{\partial T}\right)_\mu}{\left(\dfrac{\partial N}{\partial \mu}\right)_T}$$

$$\text{but} \quad \left(\frac{\partial S}{\partial \mu}\right)_T = -\frac{\partial^2 \Omega}{\partial T \partial \mu} = \left(\frac{\partial N}{\partial T}\right)_\mu ; \quad \text{hence}$$

$$C_v = T\left\{ \left(\frac{\partial S}{\partial T}\right)_\mu - \frac{\left(\dfrac{\partial N}{\partial T}\right)_\mu^2}{\left(\dfrac{\partial N}{\partial \mu}\right)_T} \right\}.$$

§25. The equilibrium of a body in an external field

Consider a body in an external field which is constant (with time). Thus different parts of the body are in different external conditions and so the body will not be uniform. One of the equilibrium conditions for such a body is, as before, that the temperature should be constant throughout the body; but the pressure will now be different at different points. To derive a second condition for equilibrium consider two neighbouring volumes and require that their entropy $S = S_1 + S_2$ should be a maximum, the states of other parts of the body being given. One of the necessary conditions for a maximum will be the vanishing of the derivative $\partial S/\partial N_1$. Since the total number $N_1 + N_2$ of particles in both parts is constant, we have:

$$\frac{\partial S}{\partial N_1} = \frac{\partial S_1}{\partial N_1} + \frac{\partial S_2}{\partial N_2}\frac{\partial N_2}{\partial N_1} = \frac{\partial S_1}{\partial N_1} - \frac{\partial S_2}{\partial N_2} = 0.$$

But from the identity $dE = T\,dS - \mu\,dN$ written in the form

$$dS = \frac{dE}{T} - \frac{\mu}{T}\,dN,$$

we see that the derivative $(\partial S/\partial N)_{E,T} = -\mu/T$. Thus we have: $\mu_1/T_1 = \mu_2/T_2$. But for equilibrium $T_1 = T_2$ so that $\mu_1 = \mu_2$. Hence we conclude that for equilibrium in an external field, the condition

$$\mu = \text{const}, \tag{25.1}$$

must be satisfied; i.e. the chemical potential of all parts of the body must be the same. The chemical potential of each part is a function of its temperature and pressure, and also of the parameters specifying the external field. If there is no field, then from the uniformity of μ and T follows automatically the uniformity of pressure.

In the gravitational field the potential energy u of a molecule is a function of the co-ordinates x, y, z of its centre of gravity alone (and is independent of the distribution of atoms in the molecule). In this case the changes in the thermodynamic quantities relating to the body are simply obtained by adding to its energy the potential energy of its molecules in the field. In particular the chemical potential (thermodynamic potential per molecule) will have the form

$$\mu = \mu_0 + u(x, y, z)$$

where $\mu_0(P, T)$ is the chemical potential in the absence of the field. Thus we may write the condition for equilibrium in a gravitational field in the form

$$\mu_0(P, T) + u(x, y, z) = \text{const.} \tag{25.2}$$

In particular, in a uniform gravitational field, $u = mgz$ (m the mass of a molecule, g the gravitational acceleration, and z the vertical co-ordinate).

Differentiating (25.2) with respect to the co-ordinate z at constant temperature, we get

$$v\, dP = -mg\, dz,$$

where $v = (\partial \mu_0 / \partial P)_T$ is the specific volume. For small changes of pressure v can be considered to be constant. Introducing the density $\rho = m/v$ and integrating we obtain:

$$P = \text{const} - \rho g z,$$

i.e. the usual formula for the hydrostatic pressure of an incompressible fluid.

§26. Rotating bodies

In a state of thermal equilibrium, as we saw in §10, uniform translations and rigid-body rotations are the only possible motions. Uniform translation needs no special treatment as, from the Galilean principle of relativity, it does not affect the mechanical properties of the body nor, therefore, its thermodynamic properties. The thermodynamic quantities relating to the body change only in that the kinetic energy of the body is added to its energy.

Consider a body rotating uniformly about a fixed axis with angular velocity Ω. Let $E(p, q)$ be the energy of the body in a fixed co-ordinate system and $E'(p, q)$ be the energy relative to a co-ordinate system rotating with the body. We know from mechanics that these quantities are connected by the relation

$$E'(p,q) = E(p,q) - \mathbf{\Omega} \cdot \mathbf{M}(p,q) \tag{26.1}$$

where $\mathbf{M}(p, q)$ is the angular momentum of the body.†

In this way the energy $E'(p, q)$ depends on the angular velocity $\mathbf{\Omega}$ as a parameter, and

$$\frac{\partial E'(p,q)}{\partial \mathbf{\Omega}} = -\mathbf{M}(p,q).$$

Averaging this equation over the statistical distribution and using formula (11.3) we obtain

$$\left(\frac{\partial E'}{\partial \mathbf{\Omega}}\right)_S = -\mathbf{M}, \tag{26.2}$$

where $E' = \overline{E'(p, q)}$, $\mathbf{M} = \overline{\mathbf{M}(p, q)}$ are the mean (thermodynamic) energy and angular momentum of the body.

On the basis of this relation we can write the thermodynamic identity for

---

† See, for example, *Mechanics*, Moscow 1958, §39, or H. Goldstein: *Classical Mechanics* (Addison-Wesley Publishing Company Inc., Cambridge, Mass., 1953) §4–8.

The velocity $\mathbf{v}$ of the particle relative to the fixed co-ordinate system is related to the velocity $\mathbf{v}'$ in the rotating system by $\mathbf{v} = \mathbf{v}' + \mathbf{\Omega} \times \mathbf{r}$ where $\mathbf{v}$ is the position vector of the particle. Hence the Lagrangian function of the rotating body is

$$L = \tfrac{1}{2} \Sigma\, mv^2 - U = \tfrac{1}{2} \Sigma\, mv'^2 + \Sigma\, m\mathbf{v}' \cdot (\mathbf{\Omega} \times \mathbf{r}) + \tfrac{1}{2} \Sigma\, m(\mathbf{\Omega} \times \mathbf{r})^2 - U$$

(the summation being over all particles of the body, and U being the potential energy of their interaction). The momentum of a single particle relative to the rotating system is

$$\mathbf{p}' = \frac{\partial L}{\partial \mathbf{v}'} = m\mathbf{v}' + m(\mathbf{\Omega} \times \mathbf{r}) = m\mathbf{v} = \mathbf{p}, \tag{1}$$

i.e. it equals the momentum relative to the fixed system. The energy (the Hamiltonian function) in the rotating system is given by the formula

$$E' = \Sigma\, \mathbf{p} \cdot \mathbf{v}' - L = \tfrac{1}{2} \Sigma\, mv'^2 - \tfrac{1}{2} \Sigma\, m(\mathbf{\Omega} \times \mathbf{r})^2 + U, \tag{2}$$

where the velocities $\mathbf{v}'$ are to be expressed in terms of $\mathbf{p}'$; this gives

$$E' = \sum \frac{p'^2}{2m} + U - \mathbf{\Omega} \cdot \mathbf{M} \tag{3}$$

where $\mathbf{M} = \Sigma\, \mathbf{r} \times \mathbf{p}$ is the angular momentum of the body which, by (1), is the same in both systems of co-ordinates. From the same relation, $\mathbf{p} = \mathbf{p}'$, the energy in the fixed system is seen to be

$$E = \sum \frac{p^2}{2m} + U = \sum \frac{p'^2}{2m} + U,$$

and substituting in (3) we obtain the desired result (26.1).

We have here carried out the calculation for classical mechanics; in quantum mechanics the same relation holds between the operators of the corresponding quantities. Hence all the thermodynamic relations derived below hold whichever type of mechanics is used to describe the motion of the body.

a rotating body with a given volume in the form

$$dE' = T\,dS - \mathbf{M}\cdot d\mathbf{\Omega}. \tag{26.3}$$

For the free energy $F' = E' - TS$ (in the rotating system of co-ordinates) we have, similarly,

$$dF' = -S\,dT - \mathbf{M}\cdot d\mathbf{\Omega}. \tag{26.4}$$

Averaging the identity (26.1), we see

$$E' = E - \mathbf{M}\cdot\mathbf{\Omega}. \tag{26.5}$$

Differentiating this identity and substituting in (26.3) we get the thermo-dynamic identity for the energy in the fixed system of co-ordinates:

$$dE = T\,dS + \mathbf{\Omega}\cdot d\mathbf{M}. \tag{26.6}$$

Similarly, for the free energy, we have

$$dF = -S\,dT + \mathbf{\Omega}\cdot d\mathbf{M}. \tag{26.7}$$

Thus in these identities the independent variable is not the angular velocity but the angular momentum and

$$\mathbf{\Omega} = \left(\frac{\partial E}{\partial \mathbf{M}}\right)_S = \left(\frac{\partial F}{\partial \mathbf{M}}\right)_T. \tag{26.8}$$

As we know from mechanics, uniform rotation is, in a sense, equivalent to the appearance of two fields of force—the centrifugal and Coriolis forces. The centrifugal force is proportional to the dimensions of the body (it in-volves the distance from the axis of rotation), while the Coriolis force is completely independent of the size of the body. Owing to this, the influence of the latter on the thermodynamic properties of a rotating macroscopic body is quite insignificant compared with the effects of the former, and it can usually be completely neglected.† Hence the condition for thermal equilibrium of a rotating body will be found by substituting the centrifugal energy of the particles into (25.2) in place of $u(x, y, z)$:

$$\mu_0(P, T) - \frac{m\Omega^2 r^2}{2} = \text{const} \tag{26.9}$$

where μ_0 is the chemical potential of the stationary body, m is the mass of the molecule and r is its distance from the axis of rotation.

For the same reason, the total energy E of a rotating body can be written as the sum of its internal energy (which we denote here by E_{int}) and its kinetic energy of rotation:

$$E = E_{int} + \frac{M^2}{2I} \tag{26.10}$$

---

† It can be shown that in classical statistics the Coriolis forces have no effect at all on the statistical properties of the body. See §34.

where I is the moment of inertia of the body about the axis of rotation. It should be borne in mind that rotation, in general, changes the distribution of mass in the body and hence the moment of inertia and the internal energy of the body depend, in general, on Ω (or on M). Only if the rotation is sufficiently slow can these quantities be considered to be constant and independent of Ω.

Consider an isolated, uniformly rotating solid body with a given distribution of mass. Since the entropy of the body is a function of its internal energy we have, in this case,

$$S = S\left(E - \frac{M^2}{2I}\right).$$

owing to the isolation of the body, its total energy and angular momentum are conserved and its entropy must be a maximum for the given values of M and E. Hence we conclude that the equilibrium rotation of the body takes place about the axis about which the moment of inertia is a maximum. This automatically ensures that the axis of rotation is a principal axis of the body. This fact, however, is already obvious for the following reasons: if the body rotates about an axis other than a principal one then, as we know from mechanics, the axes will themselves be rotating (precessing) in space; in other words, the rotation will be non-uniform, and hence not in equilibrium.

§27. Thermodynamic relations in the relativistic region

Relativistic mechanics leads to a number of changes in the usual thermodynamic relations. We shall here examine the most interesting of those changes.

If the microscopic motion of the particles becomes relativistic, then the general thermodynamic relations do not change, but the application of relativity theory to this case allows us to obtain an important inequality between the pressure and the energy of the body:

$$P < \frac{E}{3V} \tag{27.1}$$

where E is the energy of the body including the rest energy of its particles.†

The most interesting are the changes introduced by the general theory of relativity in the conditions for thermal equilibrium, when the gravitational field of the body itself is taken into account. Consider a stationary macroscopic body; its gravitational field will obviously be static.‡ In a constant gravitational field one must distinguish the conservable energy

---

† For the derivation of this inequality see L. LANDAU and E. LIFSCHITZ, *The Classical Theory of Fields*, Addison Wesley Press, 1951, §7.10.

‡ Remember that a gravitational field is said to be static if one can choose a frame of reference in which the metric tensor g_{ik} does not depend on the time co-ordinate x^0 (see *ibid.*, § 10.10).

E_0 of a small part of the body from the energy E measured by an observer at a particular point. These two quantities are connected by the relation†

$$E_0 = E\sqrt{(-g_{00})},$$

where g_{00} is the time component of the metric tensor.‡ But from the very meaning of the proof given in §9 of the uniformity of temperature throughout a body in equilibrium, it is clear that it is the quantity obtained by differentiating the entropy with respect to the conservable energy E_0 which must be constant throughout the body. The temperature T measured by an observer at a given point of space is obtained by differentiating the entropy with respect to the energy E and will hence be different at different points of the body.

To obtain a quantitative relation we note that entropy, from its very definition, depends exclusively on the internal state of the body, and hence does not change on the appearance of a gravitational field, (provided that the field does not affect the internal state of the body, a condition which in practice is always satisfied). Hence the derivative of the conservable energy E_0 with respect to entropy will be equal to $T(\sqrt{-g_{00}})$ and thus one of the conditions for thermal equilibrium of the body will be that this quantity should be constant throughout the body:

$$T\sqrt{(-g_{00})} = \text{const.} \tag{27.2}$$

The second condition, that of constant chemical potential, changes similarly. Chemical potential is defined as the derivative of energy with respect to the number of particles. Since the number of particles is obviously unchanged by the gravitational field, the chemical potential measured at each given point must satisfy the same relation as the temperature

$$\mu\sqrt{(-g_{00})} = \text{const.} \tag{27.3}$$

Note that the relations (27.2–3) may be written in the form

$$T = \text{const}\frac{dx^0}{ds}, \qquad \mu = \text{const}\frac{dx^0}{ds} \tag{27.4}$$

allowing us to consider the body not only in the frame of reference in which it is at rest but also in those in which it moves (rotating as a whole). Then the derivative dx^0/ds must be taken along the world line described by a given point of the body.

In a weak (Newtonian) gravitational field $g_{00} = -1-(2\phi/c^2)$ where ϕ is the gravitational potential.‖ Substituting this expression into (27.2) and

---

† See L. LANDAU E. LIFSCHITZ, *The Classical Theory of Fields.*, §10.10.
‡ In the absence of a gravitational field (Galilean metric) $g_{00} = -1$. We define the metric tensor by the expression for an interval written in the form $ds^2 = -g_{ik}\,dx^i\,dx^k$.

‖ See for instance, *ibid.* §10.8.

extracting the square root we get, to the same degree of approximation

$$T = \text{const}\left(1 - \frac{\phi}{c^2}\right). \tag{27.5}$$

Bearing in mind that $\phi < 0$ we find that at equilibrium the temperature is higher in those parts of the body where $|\phi|$ is greater, i.e. deep inside the body. In the limiting case of the transition to non-relativistic mechanics $(c \to \infty)$ (27.5) transforms, as it ought, to $T = \text{const}$.

Similarly one can transform condition (27.3), but it must be borne in mind that the relativistic chemical potential transforms, in the limit, not directly to the usual (non-relativistic) expression for the chemical potential in the absence of a field, here denoted by μ_0 but into $\mu_0 + mc^2$ where mc^2 is the rest energy of one of the constituent particles of the body. Hence we have

$$\mu\sqrt{(-g_{00})} \cong (\mu_0 + mc^2)\left(1 + \frac{\phi}{c^2}\right) \cong \mu_0 + mc^2 + m\phi,$$

so that the condition (27.3) transforms to

$$\mu_0 + m\phi = \text{const},$$

which coincides, as it should, with (25.2).

Lastly we shall give a useful relation which is a direct corollary of conditions (27.2) and (27.3). Dividing one by another we find that $\mu/T = \text{const}$, whence it follows that

$$\frac{d\mu}{\mu} = \frac{dT}{T}.$$

On the other hand, in accordance with the thermodynamic identity (24.12), for constant (unit) volume, we have:

$$dP = S\,dT + N\,d\mu$$

where S, N are the entropy and number of particles per unit volume of the body. Substituting $dT = (T/\mu)\,d\mu$ and noting that $\mu N + ST = \Phi + ST = \epsilon + P$ (ϵ being the energy per unit volume) we obtain the desired relation.†

$$\frac{d\mu}{\mu} = \frac{dP}{\epsilon + P}. \tag{27.6}$$

---

† In the non-relativistic case, this relation reduced to a trivial identity; putting $\mu \cong mc^2$, $\epsilon \cong \rho c^2$ $\gg P$ (ρ being the density) we get $d\mu = v\,dP$ ($v = m/\rho$ is the volume per particle) as one would expect for $T = \text{const}$.

CHAPTER III

THE GIBBS DISTRIBUTION

§28 The Gibbs distribution

WE now turn to the problem posed in Chapter I—to find the distribution function for a subsystem, i.e. a small macroscopic part of a large closed system. The most convenient and most general method of attacking this problem is based on applying the microcanonical distribution to the whole system.

Separating the body in which we are interested from the rest of the closed system, we consider the system as made up of two parts: the given body and all the other parts, which we shall call the "medium" as opposed to the body. The microcanonical distribution (6.6) then takes the form

$$dw = \text{const } \delta(E+E'-E^{(0)})\, d\Gamma d\Gamma' \tag{28.1}$$

where E, $d\Gamma$ and E', $d\Gamma'$ relate to the body and the medium respectively, and $E^{(0)}$ is the given value of the energy of the closed system; the sum of E and E' (the energies of the body and the medium) must be equal to $E^{(0)}$.

Our object will be to find the probability w_n that the whole system should be in a state in which the body is in some particular quantum state (with energy E_n), i.e. in a state described in a microscopic manner. We are not interested in the microscopic state of the medium, i.e. we take it to be in some macroscopically described state. Let $\Delta\Gamma'$ be the statistical weight of the macroscopic state of the medium; let us also denote by $\Delta E'$ the range of values of the energy of the medium corresponding to the range $\Delta\Gamma'$ of quantum states in the sense indicated in §7.

The required probability w_n can be found by replacing $d\Gamma$ by unity in (28.1), putting $E = E_n$ and integrating with respect to $d\Gamma'$:

$$w_n = \text{const} \int \delta(E_n+E'-E^{(0)})\, d\Gamma'.$$

Let $\Gamma'(E')$ be the total number of quantum states of the medium with energy less than or equal to E'. Since the integrand depends on E' alone, we can transform to integration with respect to dE' by putting:

$$d\Gamma' = \frac{d\Gamma'(E')}{dE'}\, dE'.$$

The derivative $d\Gamma'/dE'$ can be replaced (see §7) by the fraction

$$\frac{d\Gamma'}{dE'} = \frac{e^{S'(E')/k}}{\Delta E'},$$

where $S'(E')$ is the entropy of the medium as a function of its energy ($\Delta E'$ is also certainly a function of E'). In this way

$$w_n = \text{const} \int \frac{e^{S'/k}}{\Delta E'} \delta(E' + E_n - E^{(0)}) \, dE'.$$

Owing to the presence of the δ-function the integration is reduced to substituting $E^{(0)} - E_n$ for E' and we obtain:

$$w_n = \text{const} \left(\frac{e^{S'/k}}{\Delta E'} \right)_{E' = E^{(0)} - E_n}.$$

We now take into account the fact that since the body is small its energy E_n is small compared with $E^{(0)}$. The quantity $\Delta E'$ changes relatively very little with small changes in E'; hence in it we may simply replace E' by $E^{(0)}$, so that it becomes a constant independent of E_n. In the exponential $e^{S'/E}$ we must expand $S'(E^{(0)} - E_n)$ in powers of E_n and keep the linear term as well:

$$S'(E^{(0)} - E_n) = S'(E^{(0)}) - E_n \frac{dS'(E^{(0)})}{dE^{(0)}}.$$

But the derivative of the entropy S' with respect to the energy is simply $1/T$ where T is the temperature of the system (the temperature of the body is the same as that of the medium, since the system is supposed to be in a state of equilibrium).

Thus we finally obtain the following expression for w_n

$$w_n = A e^{-E_n/kT} \tag{28.3}$$

where A is a normalisation constant independent of E_n. This is one of the most important formulae in statistical physics; it gives the statistical distribution of any macroscopic body which is a small part of some large closed system. The distribution (28.3) is called the *Gibbs distribution* or *canonical distribution* (it was obtained by Gibbs for classical statistics in 1901).

The normalisation constant A is determined by the relation $\Sigma w_n = 1$ whence

$$\frac{1}{A} = \sum_n e^{-E_n/kT}. \tag{28.4}$$

The mean value of any physical quantity relating to the given body can be calculated with the aid of the Gibbs distribution from the formula

$$f = \Sigma w_n f_{nn} = \frac{\Sigma f_{nn} e^{-E_n/kT}}{\sum_n e^{-E_n/kT}}. \tag{28.5}$$

In classical statistics an expression exactly corresponding to formula (28.3) is obtained for the distribution function in phase space:

$$\rho(p, q) = A e^{-E(p,q)/kT}, \tag{28.6}$$

where $E(p, q)$ is the energy of the body as a function of the co-ordinates and momenta of its particles.† The normalisation constant A is determined by the condition

$$\int \rho\, dp\, dq = A \int e^{-E(p,q)/kT}\, dp\, dq = 1. \tag{28.7}$$

In practice, cases often arise in which not the whole microscopic motion of the particles is quasi-classical, but only the motion corresponding to some of the degrees of freedom, while the motion corresponding to the remaining degrees of freedom is quantised. (For instance, one can have quasi-classical translational motion of the molecules while the motion of the atoms within the molecules is quantised). In such a case the energy levels of the body can be written as functions of the quasi-classical co-ordinates and momenta: $E_n = E_n(p, q)$ where n is the set of quantum numbers specifying the "quantum part" of the motion, for which the values of p, q play the part of parameters. The expression for the Gibbs distribution will then take the form

$$dw_n(p, q) = A e^{-E_n(p,q)/kT}\, dp_{cl}\, dq_{cl} \tag{28.8}$$

where $dp_{cl}\, dq_{cl}$ is the product of the differentials of the "quasi-classical" co-ordinates and momenta.

Lastly it is necessary to make the following remark about the range of problems for whose solution the Gibbs distribution can be used. We have all the time been talking about the latter as the statistical distribution for a subsystem as, in fact, it is. Nevertheless, it is important to realise that the same distribution can also be used with complete success to give the basic statistical properties of closed bodies. In fact, such properties of a body as the values of its thermodynamic quantities, or the probability distribution for the co-ordinates and velocities of its particles, are obviously independent of whether we consider it closed or placed in an imaginary thermostat (§7). In the latter case, however, the body becomes a "subsystem" and the Gibbs distribution is strictly applicable. In using the Gibbs distribution the difference between a closed body and a non-closed one really occurs only when we consider the relatively uninteresting problem of the fluctuations of the total energy of the body. The Gibbs distribution gives, for the mean fluctuation of this quantity, a non-zero value which has a real meaning for a body in a medium, but is quite meaningless for a closed body, since, by definition, the energy of such a body is constant and does not fluctuate.

The possibility of applying the Gibbs distribution to closed bodies (in the sense indicated) is also obvious from the fact that it is almost the same as the microcanonical distribution (and at the same time is much more convenient for practical calculations). In fact the microcanonical distribution is equivalent, roughly speaking, to the assumption that all microstates of the

---

† To avoid confusion note once again that w_n (or ρ) is a monotonic function of energy and certainly cannot have a maximum at $E = \overline{E}$. Only the energy distribution function, i.e. the product of w_n with $d\Gamma(E)/dE$ has a sharp maximum at $E = \overline{E}$.

body compatible with its given total energy are equally probable. The canonical distribution is "spread" over some interval of values of the energy whose width (of the order of the mean fluctuation of the energy) is, however, negligibly small for a macroscopic body.

§29. The Maxwell distribution

The energy $E(p, q)$ in the classical form of the Gibbs distribution can always be expressed as the sum of two parts, the kinetic and potential energies. Of these, the first is a quadratic function of the momenta of the atoms,[†] while the second is a function of their co-ordinates, whose form depends on the law of interaction of the particles inside the body (and on the external field, if any). If we denote the kinetic and potential energies by $K(p)$ and $U(q)$ then $E(p, q) = K(p) + U(q)$ and the probability $dw = \rho(p, q)\,dp\,dq$ will take the form

$$dw = Ae^{-\frac{U(q)}{kT} - \frac{K(p)}{kT}}\,dp\,dq,$$

i.e. it splits up into a product of two factors, one depending only on the co-ordinates, and the other only on the momenta. This means that the probabilities for the momenta (or velocities) and those for the co-ordinates are independent of one another, in the sense that the particular values of the momenta have no effect on the probabilities of particular values of the co-ordinates and vice versa. In this way the probabilities of different values of the momenta can be written in the form

$$dw_p = ae^{-K(p)/kT}\,dp \tag{29.1}$$

and the probability distribution for the co-ordinates

$$dw_q = be^{-U(q)/kT}\,dq. \tag{29.2}$$

Since the sum of the probabilities of all possible values of the momenta (and similarly for the co-ordinates) must be equal to unity, each of the probabilities dw_p and dw_q must be normalised, i.e. their integrals over all possible values of the momenta or co-ordinates for the given body must be equal to unity. From these conditions the constants a and b in (29.1) and (29.2) can be obtained.

We proceed to investigate the probability distribution for the momenta, emphasising once again the very important fact that in classical statistics such a distribution does not depend at all on the type of interaction between the particles of the body or on the type of external field, and hence the distribution can be expressed in a form applicable to any kind of body.[‡]

---

† It is assumed that we are using cartesian co-ordinates.
‡ In quantum statistics this assumption is not, in general, valid.

The kinetic energy of the whole body is equal to the sum of the kinetic energies of each of the atoms in it, and the probability again splits up into the products of factors each depending on the momenta of one of the atoms alone. This again means that the probabilities for the momenta of different atoms are independent of each other, i.e. the momentum of one has no influence on the probability of a value of the momentum of any of the others. Hence we may write down a probability distribution for the momentum of each separate atom.

For an atom of mass m the kinetic energy equals

$$\frac{p_x^2 + p_y^2 + p_z^2}{2m}$$

where p_x, p_y, p_z are the cartesian components of the momentum, and the probability will take the form

$$dw_{\mathbf{p}} = ae^{-\frac{1}{2mkT}(p_x^2 + p_y^2 + p_z^2)} \, dp_x \, dp_y \, dp_z.$$

The constant a is determined by the normalisation condition. With the help of the well-known formula

$$\int\limits_{-\infty}^{+\infty} e^{-\alpha x^2} \, dx = \sqrt{\frac{\pi}{\alpha}}$$

we find

$$a \int\limits_{-\infty}^{+\infty}\!\!\int\!\!\int e^{-\frac{1}{2mkT}(p_x^2 + p_y^2 + p_z^2)} \, dp_x dp_y dp_z = a\left(\int\limits_{-\infty}^{+\infty} e^{-p^2/2mkT} \, dp \right)^3$$

$$= a(2\pi mkT)^{3/2} = 1.$$

Hence $a = (2\pi mkT)^{-3/2}$, and we finally get the probability distribution for the momenta in the form

$$dw_{\mathbf{p}} = \frac{1}{(2\pi mkT)^{3/2}} e^{-(p_x^2 + p_y^2 + p_z^2)/2mkT} \, dp_x \, dp_y \, dp_z. \tag{29.3}$$

Changing from momenta to velocities $(\mathbf{p} = m\mathbf{v})$, we can write the corresponding distribution for velocities:

$$dw_{\mathbf{v}} = \left(\frac{m}{2\pi kT} \right)^{3/2} e^{-m(v_x^2 + v_y^2 + v_z^2)/2kT} \, dv_x \, dv_y \, dv_z. \tag{29.4}$$

This is the so-called *Maxwell distribution* (1860). Note that it again splits up into the product of three independent factors:

$$dw_{\mathbf{v}_x} = \sqrt{\frac{m}{2\pi kT}} e^{-mv_x^2/2kT}\, dv_x, \ldots \tag{29.5}$$

each of which defines the probability distribution for a separate component of the velocity.

If the body consists of molecules (for example a polyatomic gas), then as well as the Maxwell distribution for the separate atoms, there is also the same distribution for the translational motion of the molecules as a whole. In fact, one can separate the energy of the translational motion from the kinetic energy of the molecule, of which it is an additive part, and as a result the required distribution will take the form of (29.4), where m is now the total mass of the molecule and v_x, v_y, v_z are the components of the velocity of its centre of gravity. It should be emphasised that the Maxwell distribution for the translational motion of the molecule can hold independently of the nature of the intramolecular motion of the atoms (and the rotation of the molecule) even in the case when the latter has to be described by quantum mechanics.†

Expression (29.4) is written in terms of cartesian co-ordinates in "velocity space". If from cartesian co-ordinates we change to spherical polars we obtain:

$$dw_{\mathbf{v}} = \left(\frac{m}{2\pi kT}\right)^{3/2} e^{-mv^2/2kT} v^2 \sin\theta\, d\theta\, d\phi\, dv, \tag{29.6}$$

where v is the absolute value of the velocity and θ and ϕ are the polar angle and azimuth specifying the direction of the velocity. Integrating out the angles we find the probability distribution for the absolute value of the velocity

$$dw_v = 4\pi \left(\frac{m}{2\pi kT}\right)^{3/2} e^{-mv^2/2kT} v^2\, dv. \tag{29.7}$$

Sometimes it is convenient to use cylindrical co-ordinates in velocity space. Then

$$dw_{\mathbf{v}} = \left(\frac{m}{2\pi kT}\right)^{3/2} e^{-m(v_z^2+v_r^2)/2kT} v_r\, dv_r\, dv_z\, d\phi \tag{29.8}$$

where v_z is the component of velocity along the z axis, v_r is the velocity perpendicular to the axis and ϕ is the angle giving the direction of $\mathbf{v}_r$.

Let us calculate the mean value of the kinetic energy of the atom. From the definition of mean value and using (29.5) we find for any cartesian com-

---

† The Maxwell distribution is also valid, obviously, for the so-called Brownian motion of particles suspended in a fluid.

ponent of velocity†

$$\overline{v_x^2} = \sqrt{\left(\frac{m}{2\pi kT}\right)} \int_{-\infty}^{\infty} v_x^2 e^{-mv_x^2/2kT} \, dv_x = \frac{kT}{m}; \qquad (29.9)$$

hence the mean value of the kinetic energy of the atom is $3kT/2$.

Hence we can say that the mean total kinetic energy of all the particles in the body is always equal to $3NkT/2$ in classical statistics where N is the total number of atoms.

PROBLEMS

1. Find the mean value of the nth power of the absolute value of the velocity.

SOLUTION: Using (29.7) we find:

$$\overline{v^n} = 4\pi \left(\frac{m}{2\pi kT}\right)^{3/2} \int_0^{\infty} e^{-mv^2/2kT} v^{n+2} \, dv = \frac{2}{\sqrt{\pi}} \left(\frac{2kT}{m}\right)^{n/2} \Gamma\left(\frac{n+3}{2}\right).$$

In particular if n is even ($n = 2r$) then

$$\overline{v^{2r}} = \left(\frac{kT}{m}\right)^r (2r+1)!!.$$

If $n = 2r+1$ then

$$\overline{v^{2r+1}} = \frac{2}{\sqrt{\pi}} \left(\frac{2kT}{m}\right)^{(2r+1)/2} (r+1)!.$$

---

† We shall quote here for future reference the values of integrals which are often met in dealing with the Maxwell distribution

$$I_n = \int_0^{\infty} e^{-\alpha x^2} x^n \, dx.$$

Substituting $\alpha x^2 = y$ gives:

$$I_n = \tfrac{1}{2} \alpha^{-(n+1)/2} \int_0^{\infty} e^{-y} y^{(n-1)/2} \, dy = \tfrac{1}{2} \alpha^{-(n+1)/2} \Gamma\left(\frac{n+1}{2}\right)$$

where $\Gamma(x)$ is the gamma function. In particular if $n = 2r$, $r > 0$ then

$$I_{2r} = \frac{(2r-1)!!}{2^{r+1}} \sqrt{\frac{\pi}{\alpha^{2r+1}}}$$

where $(2r-1)!! = 1.3.5 \ldots (2r-1)$. If $r = 0$ then

$$I_0 = \frac{1}{2} \sqrt{\frac{\pi}{\alpha}}.$$

If $n = 2r+1$ then

$$I_{2r+1} = \frac{r!}{2\alpha^{r+1}}.$$

The same integral with limits $-\infty$ to $+\infty$ is equal to zero for odd n and for even n is equal to twice the integral from 0 to $+\infty$.

2. Find the mean square fluctuation of the velocity.

SOLUTION: We have

$$\overline{(\Delta v)^2} = \overline{(v-\bar{v})^2} = \overline{v^2}-\bar{v}^2.$$

Using the results of example (1) for $n = 1$ and $n = 2$ we find

$$\overline{(\Delta v)^2} = \frac{kT}{m}\left(3-\frac{8}{\pi}\right).$$

3. Find the mean, mean square, and mean square fluctuation of the kinetic energy of an atom.

SOLUTION: Using the result of Example 1, we find:

$$\bar{\epsilon} = \frac{m}{2}\overline{v^2} = \frac{3kT}{2}, \quad \overline{\epsilon^2} = \frac{m^2}{4}\overline{v^4} = \frac{15}{4}(kT)^2$$

$$\overline{(\Delta\epsilon)^2} = \overline{\epsilon^2}-\bar{\epsilon}^2 = \frac{3}{2}(kT)^2.$$

4. Find the probability distribution for the kinetic energy of an atom.

SOLUTION:

$$dw_\epsilon = \frac{2}{\sqrt{(\pi k^3 T^3)}}e^{-\epsilon/kT}\sqrt{\epsilon}\,d\epsilon.$$

5. Find the probability distribution for the angular velocity of a rotating molecule.

SOLUTION: As in the case of the translational motion, one can write (in classical statistics) the probability distribution for the rotation of each molecule separately. The kinetic energy of rotation of a molecule considered as a solid body (which is justified because of the smallyness of the intramolecular oscillations of the atoms) is equal to

$$\epsilon_{rot} = \tfrac{1}{2}(I_1\Omega_1^2+I_2\Omega_2^2+I_3\Omega_3^2) = \frac{1}{2}\left(\frac{M_1^2}{I_1}+\frac{M_2^2}{I_2}+\frac{M_3^2}{I_3}\right)$$

where I_1, I_2, I_3 are the principal moments of inertia, Ω_1, Ω_2, Ω_3 are the components of the angular velocity along the principal axes of inertia and

$$M_1 = I_1\Omega_1, \quad M_2 = I_2\Omega_2, \quad M_3 = I_3\Omega_3$$

are the components of angular momenta which act as generalised momenta for the velocities Ω_1, Ω_2, Ω_3. The normalised probability distribution for the angular momentum is

$$dw_M = (2\pi kT)^{-3/2}(I_1 I_2 I_3)^{-1/2}e^{-\frac{1}{2kT}\left(\frac{M_1^2}{I_1}+\frac{M_2^2}{I_2}+\frac{M_3^2}{I_3}\right)}\,dM_1\,dM_2\,dM_3$$

and for the angular velocity is

$$dw_\Omega = (2\pi kT)^{-3/2}(I_1 I_2 I_3)^{1/2}e^{-\frac{1}{2kT}(I_1\Omega_1^2+I_2\Omega_2^2+I_3\Omega_3^2)}\,d\Omega_1\,d\Omega_2\,d\Omega_3.$$

6. Find the mean squares of the angular velocity and angular momentum of a molecule.

SOLUTION: With the help of the above distribution we get

$$\overline{\Omega^2} = kT\left(\frac{1}{I_1}+\frac{1}{I_2}+\frac{1}{I_3}\right), \qquad \overline{M^2} = kT(I_1+I_2+I_3).$$

§30. The probability distribution for an oscillator

Consider a body whose atoms undergo small oscillations about certain equilibrium positions. For example, the oscillations of an atom in a crystal or the oscillations of atoms in the molecules of a gas (in the second case the motion of the molecule as a whole does not influence the oscillation of the atoms and hence does not affect the following results).

As is known from mechanics, the Hamiltonian (energy) of a system consisting of an arbitrary number of particles undergoing small oscillations can be expressed as the sum

$$E(p, q) = \tfrac{1}{2} \sum_\alpha (p_\alpha{}^2 + q_\alpha{}^2 \omega_\alpha{}^2)$$

where q_α are the so-called normal co-ordinates of the oscillation (the equilibrium positions are $q_\alpha = 0$), $p_\alpha = \dot{q}_\alpha$, are the corresponding generalised momenta, and ω_α are the frequencies of the oscillations. In other words $E(p, q)$ splits up into the sum of independent terms, each one of which corresponds to a separate normal oscillation (or, as one says, to an "oscillator"). In quantum mechanics the same will hold for the Hamiltonian operator of a system, so that each oscillator is quantised independently, and the energy levels of a system are represented by the sums

$$\sum_\alpha n\omega_\alpha(n_\alpha + \tfrac{1}{2}).$$

(n_α integers).

Due to this, the Gibbs distribution for the system as a whole splits up into the product of independent factors, each specifying the statistical distribution for a single oscillator. On this basis we consider below a single oscillator.

We define the probability distribution for the co-ordinate q of the oscillator† (the subscript α, which labels the oscillator will, from now on, be omitted). In classical statistics the problem can be solved quite simply: since the potential energy of the oscillator is $\tfrac{1}{2}w^2q^2$ the probability distribution is given by the formula

$$dw_q = Ae^{-\omega^2 q^2 / 2kT}\, dq,$$

or, evaluating A from the normalisation condition:

$$dw_q = \frac{\omega}{\sqrt{(2\pi kT)}} e^{-\omega^2 q^2 / 2kT}\, dq. \tag{30.1}$$

(The integration with respect to dq may be taken from $-\infty$ to $+\infty$ in view of its rapid convergence).

We now turn to the solution of the problem in the quantum case. Let $\psi_n(q)$ be the wave functions of the stationary states of the oscillator

---

† The normal co-ordinate q has dimensions cm . gm$^{1/2}$.

corresponding to the energy levels

$$\epsilon_n = \hbar\omega(n+\tfrac{1}{2}).$$

If the oscillator is in the nth state, then the quantum-mechanical probability distribution for its co-ordinates is given by the square $\psi_n{}^2$ (in this case the functions ψ_n are real and hence we write simply $\psi_n{}^2$ instead of the square of the modulus $|\psi_n|^2$). The required statistical probability distribution is obtained by multiplying $\psi_n{}^2$ by the probability w_n of finding the oscillator in the nth state, and then summing over all states. In accordance with the Gibbs distribution w_n has the form

$$w_n = ae^{-\epsilon_n/kT}$$

where a is a constant. In this way we obtain the formula:

$$dw_q = a \, dq \sum_{n=0}^{\infty} e^{-\epsilon_n/kT}\psi_n{}^2 \tag{30.2}$$

which is obviously in complete agreement with the general formula (5.8).

To calculate this sum we make use of the following device. We introduce the notation $dw_q = \rho_q dq$ and construct the derivative

$$\frac{d\rho_q}{dq} = 2a \sum_{n=0}^{\infty} e^{-\epsilon_n/kT}\psi_n\frac{d\psi_n}{dq}.$$

Introducing the momentum operator $\hat{p} = -i\hbar \, d/dq$ and remembering that the momentum of the oscillator has non-zero matrix elements only for the transition $n \to n+1$[†] we write:

$$\frac{d\psi_n}{dq} = \frac{i}{\hbar}\hat{p}\psi_n = \frac{i}{\hbar}(p_{n-1,n}\,\psi_{n-1}+p_{n+1,n}\,\psi_{n+1}) = \frac{\omega}{\hbar}(q_{n-1,n}\,\psi_{n-1}-q_{n-1,n}\,\psi_{n+1}).$$

We have used the relations

$$p_{n-1,n} = -i\omega q_{n-1,n}, \qquad p_{n+1,n} = i\omega q_{n+1,n}$$

between the matrix elements of the co-ordinates and the momenta. In this way we have:

$$\frac{d\rho_q}{dq} = \frac{2a\omega}{\hbar}\left\{\sum_{n=0}^{\infty} q_{n-1,n}\,\psi_n\,\psi_{n-1}e^{-\epsilon_n/kT} - \sum_{n=0}^{\infty} q_{n+1,n}\,\psi_n\,\psi_{n+1}e^{-\epsilon_n/kT}\right\}.$$

In the first sum we change the index of summation $(n \to n+1)$ and, taking into consideration the relations

$$\epsilon_{n+1} = \epsilon_n+\hbar\omega, \qquad q_{n+1\,n} = q_{n,n+1}, \qquad q_{-1,0} = 0$$

---

† See *Quantum Mechanics*, §21.

we find:

$$\frac{d\rho_q}{dq} = -\frac{2a\omega}{\hbar}(1-e^{-\hbar\omega/kT})\sum_{n=0}^{\infty} q_{n,\,n+1}\psi_n\psi_{n+1}e^{-\epsilon_n/kT}.$$

In exactly the same way we can establish the relation

$$q\rho_q = a(1+e^{-\hbar\omega/kT})\sum_{n=0}^{\infty} q_{n,\,n+1}\psi_n\psi_{n+1}e^{-\epsilon_n/kT}.$$

Comparing the two relations we get the equation:

$$\frac{d\rho_q}{dq} = -\left(\frac{2\omega}{\hbar}\tanh\frac{\hbar\omega}{2kT}\right)q\rho_q$$

whence

$$\rho_q = \text{const}\exp\left\{-q^2\frac{\omega}{\hbar}\tanh\frac{\hbar\omega}{2kT}\right\}.$$

Evaluating the constant from the normalisation condition, we finally obtain the following formula (F. BLOCH, 1932)

$$dw_q = \left(\frac{\omega}{\pi\hbar}\tanh\frac{\hbar\omega}{2kT}\right)^{1/2}\exp\left\{-q^2\frac{\omega}{\hbar}\tanh\frac{\hbar\omega}{2kT}\right\}dq. \qquad (30.3)$$

Thus also in the quantum case the probabilities of different values of the co-ordinate of the oscillator are distributed according to a law of the form $e^{-\alpha q^2}$, but with a different value of the coefficient α from that in the classical case. In the limiting case $\hbar\omega \ll kT$, when quantisation already ceases to have any effect, formula (30.3) becomes identical with formula (30.1) as we would expect.

In the limiting case $\hbar\omega \gg kT$ formula (30.3) becomes

$$dw_q = \sqrt{\left(\frac{\omega}{\pi\hbar}\right)}\,e^{-q^2\omega/\hbar}\,dq,$$

i.e. the purely quantum probability distribution for the co-ordinate in the ground state of the oscillator.† This corresponds to the fact that when $kT \ll \hbar\omega$ the oscillations of the oscillator are practically unexcited.

The probability distribution for the momentum of the oscillator can be written down by analogy with (30.3) without repeating the calculation. The fact is that the problem of quantisation of an oscillator is completely symmetrical as regards co-ordinates and momenta and the wave functions of the oscillator in the p-representation coincide with its ordinary co-ordinate

---

† This is the square of the modulus of the wave function of the ground state of the oscillator.

wave functions (on substituting p/ω for q†). Hence the desired distribution is

$$dw_p = \left(\frac{1}{\pi\hbar\omega}\tanh\frac{\hbar\omega}{2kT}\right)^{\frac{1}{2}} \exp\left\{-\frac{p^2}{\hbar\omega}\tanh\frac{\hbar\omega}{2kT}\right\} dp. \qquad (30.4)$$

In the classical limit ($\hbar\omega < kT$) it becomes the usual Maxwell distribution

$$dw_p = (2\pi kT)^{-\frac{1}{2}} e^{-p^2/2kT} dp. \qquad (30.5)$$

§31. The free energy in the Gibbs distribution

In accordance with formula (7.9) the entropy of a body can be calculated as the mean value of the logarithm of its distribution function

$$S = -k\overline{\log w_n}.$$

Substituting in this the Gibbs distribution, we get:

$$S = -k\log A + \frac{\bar{E}}{T}$$

whence $k\log A = (\bar{E}-TS)/T$. But the mean energy $\bar{E}$ is just what is meant by energy in thermodynamics, hence $\bar{E}-TS = F$ and $k\log A = F/T$, i.e. the normalisation constant of the distribution is directly related to the free energy of the body.

Thus the Gibbs distribution may be written in the form

$$w_n = e^{(F-E_n)/kT}, \qquad (31.1)$$

in which it is most often used. Similarly in the classical case, with the help of (7.12) we get the expression

$$\rho = (2\pi\hbar)^{-s} e^{[F-E(p,\,q)]/kT}. \qquad (31.2)$$

The normalisation condition for the distribution (31.1) gives:

$$\sum_n w_n = e^{F/kT} \sum_n e^{-E_n/kT} = 1,$$

whence

$$e^{-F/kT} = \sum_n e^{-E_n/kT}$$

or, on taking logarithms:

$$F = -kT\log \sum_n e^{-E_n/kT}. \qquad (31.3)$$

This formula serves as a basis for the thermodynamic applications of the Gibbs distribution. It makes it possible, in principle, to calculate the thermodynamic functions of any body from its energy spectrum.

† See *Quantum Mechanics*, §21, problem 1.

The sum under the logarithm in (31.3) is usually called the *partition function*. It represents simply the trace of the operator $e^{-\hat{H}/kT}$, where $\hat{H}$ is the Hamiltonian of the given body.†

$$Z = \sum_n e^{-E_n/kT} = \mathrm{Tr}(e^{-\hat{H}/kT}). \tag{31.4}$$

This notation has the advantage that for the evaluation of the trace we can use any complete set of wave functions.

A corresponding formula for classical statistics is obtained from the normalisation condition for the distribution (31.2). First, however, it is necessary to take into account the following fact, which was unimportant as long as we were interested in the distribution function itself and did not connect the normalising coefficient with a quantitative property of the body (its free energy). If, for example, the positions of two identical atoms are interchanged, then, after the exchange, the microstate of the body will be represented by a different point of phase space, which is obtained from the initial one by substituting the co-ordinates and momenta of one atom for those of the other. On the other hand, since the interchanged atoms are identical, both states are physically the same. Thus a whole series of points in phase space correspond to the same physical microstate of the body. But in the integration of the distribution (31.2) each state must, obviously, be counted only once.‡ In other words we must integrate only over those regions of phase space which correspond to physically distinct states of the body: we shall denote this fact by an accent on the integral sign.

Thus we obtain the formula:

$$F = -kT \log {\int}' e^{-E(p,\,q)/kT}\, d\Gamma; \tag{31.5}$$

in this, and in all similar cases below we shall denote by $d\Gamma$ the element of phase volume divided by $(2\pi\hbar)^s$

$$d\Gamma = \frac{dp\, dq}{(2\pi\hbar)^s}. \tag{31.6}$$

Thus the quantum partition function in (31.3) is replaced by the integral in (31.5). As was shown already in §29, the classical energy $E(p, q)$ can always be written as the sum of kinetic energy $K(p)$ and potential energy $U(q)$. The kinetic energy is a quadratic function of the momenta, and the integration with respect to them can be carried out in general form. Thus

† In accordance with the general rules, $e^{-\hat{H}/kT}$ is understood as an operator whose eigenfunctions coincide with those of $\hat{H}$ and whose eigenvalues are equal to $e^{-E_n/kT}$.

‡ This fact becomes quite obvious if we consider the classical partition function as the limit of the quantum statistical one. In the latter the summation is over all different quantum states and the question does not arise (remember that owing to the quantum mechanical principle of symmetry of the wave functions, the quantum state is unchanged by the interchange of identical particles).

From the purely classical point of view the need for such an interpretation of the statistical integration is connected with the fact that otherwise the multiplicativity of the statistical weight, and hence the additivity of entropy and the other thermodynamic functions, would be destroyed.

the problem of calculating the partition function reduces in practice to that of integrating the function $e^{-U(q)/kT}$ with respect to the co-ordinates.

In practice, in calculating the partition function it is usually convenient to enlarge the region of integration by introducing an appropriate correction factor. For example, we may consider a gas consisitng of N identical atoms. Then one can integrate with respect to the co-ordinates of each atom independently—taking the integral over the whole volume occupied by the gas. The result, however, will have to be divided by the number of possible permutations of N atoms, i.e. by $N!$. In other words, the integral $\int'$ can be replaced by the integral over the whole phase space divided by $N!$:

$$\int' \ldots d\Gamma = \frac{1}{N!} \int \ldots d\Gamma. \tag{31.7}$$

Similarly it is convenient to increase the range of integration for a gas consisting of N identical molecules; with respect to the co-ordinates of the molecules as a whole (the co-ordinates of their centres of mass), we integrate over the whole volume, and with respect to the intramolecular co-ordinates of the atoms we integrate over each molecule's own "volume" (i.e. the small region in which the atoms composing the molecule have an appreciable probability of being found); the integral must then again be divided by $N!$.

PROBLEMS

1. The potential energy of interaction of the particles of a body is a homogeneous function of nth degree in their co-ordinates. From considerations of similarity, deduce the form of the free energy of the body in classical statistics.

SOLUTION: In the partition function

$$Z = \int' e^{-[K(p)+U(q)]/kT} d\Gamma$$

we replace each q by λq and each p by $\lambda^{n/2} p$ (where λ is an arbitrary constant). If, at the same time we replace T by $\lambda^n T$, then the integrand will remain unchanged. However, the limits of integration for the co-ordinates are changed: the linear dimensions of the region of integration being changed by a factor $1/\lambda$, which means that the volume is changed by a factor λ^{-3}; to leave the limits of integration unchanged, we must at the same time replace V by $\lambda^3 V$. After all these substitutions, the integral will be multiplied by a factor $\lambda^{3N(1+n/2)}$ from the transformation of the variables in $d\Gamma$ ($s = 3N$ co-ordinates and the same number of momenta if N is the number of particles). Thus we come to the conclusion that by the substitutions

$$V \to \lambda^3 V, \qquad T \to \lambda^n T$$

the change in the partition function is

$$Z \to \lambda^{3N(1+n/2)} Z.$$

The most general function $Z(V, T)$ having this property is

$$Z = T^{3N(\frac{1}{2}+\frac{1}{n})} f(V T^{-3/n})$$

where f is an arbitrary function of one variable. From this we obtain for the free energy an expression of the form

$$F = -3\left(\frac{1}{2}+\frac{1}{n}\right)NkT \ln T + NT\phi\left(\frac{VT^{-3/n}}{N}\right),\tag{1}$$

which involves only one arbitrary function of one variable (the number N is introduced into the second term of (1) in order to make it additive).

2. Deduce the virial theorem for a macroscopic body for which the interaction energy between the particles is a homogeneous function of nth degree of their co-ordinates.

SOLUTION: Using the method of deducing the virial theorem in mechanics[†] we calculate the time-derivative of the sum $\Sigma\, \mathbf{r}\cdot\mathbf{p}$ where $\mathbf{r}$ and $\mathbf{p}$ are the radius vectors and momenta for the body. Bearing in mind that $\dot{\mathbf{r}} = \partial K(p)/\partial\mathbf{p}$ and that $K(p)$ is a homogeneous function of second degree in the momenta, we find

$$\frac{d}{dt}\sum \mathbf{r}\cdot\mathbf{p} = \sum \mathbf{p}\cdot\frac{\partial K(p)}{\partial\mathbf{p}} + \sum \mathbf{r}\cdot\dot{\mathbf{p}} = 2K(p) + \sum \mathbf{r}\cdot\dot{\mathbf{p}}.$$

The particles of the body move in a bounded region of space with velocities which remain finite. Hence the quantity $\Sigma\, \mathbf{r}\cdot\mathbf{p}$ is bounded, and the mean value of its time derivative is zero, so that

$$2K + \overline{\sum \mathbf{r}\cdot\dot{\mathbf{p}}} = 0$$

(where $K = K(p)$). The derivatives $\dot{p}$ are determined by the forces acting on the particles of the body. In summing over all the particles one must take into account the forces exerted on the body (on its surface) by surrounding bodies as well as the forces of interaction between the particles:

$$\sum \mathbf{r}\cdot\dot{\mathbf{p}} = -\sum \mathbf{r}\frac{\partial U(q)}{\partial\mathbf{r}} - p\oint \mathbf{r}\cdot d\mathbf{f}$$

$$= -nU - 3PV$$

(we transform the surface integral to a volume integral and note that div $\mathbf{r} = 3$). Thus we get $2K - nu - 3PV = 0$, or, on introducing the total energy $E = U+K$:

$$(n+2)K = nE + 3PV.\tag{2}$$

This is the required theorem. It holds not only for classical mechanics but also in the quantum case. In the classical case, the mean kinetic energy $K = \frac{3}{2}nkT$ and relation (2) gives:

$$E + \frac{3}{n}PV = 3\left(\frac{1}{2}+\frac{1}{n}\right)NkT.\tag{3}$$

This formula can also be deduced from expression (1) for the free energy which we obtained in example (1).

In the case in which the interaction of the particles follows Coulomb's Law ($n = 1$) we have, from (2)

$$K = -E + 3PV.$$

This relation is the limiting case of the relativistic relation[‡]

$$E - 3PV = \sum mc^2 \Big/ \sqrt{\left(1 - \frac{v^2}{c^2}\right)},$$

in which the energy E also includes the rest energy of particles of the body.

---

† See, for example, H. GOLDSTEIN, *Classical Mechanics* §3–4; *Mechanics* §10, Moscow, 1958.
‡ See *The Classical Theory of Fields*, §7.10.

§32. Thermodynamic perturbation theory

In practice, in the calculation of thermodynamic quantities, there occur cases when the energy $E(p, q)$ includes certain relatively small terms, which can be neglected in an initial approximation. For instance the potential energy of the particles of the body in an external field can be of this nature (for the conditions which must be satisfied before we can consider terms as small, see below).

In these cases it is possible to develop a kind of "perturbation theory" to calculate thermodynamic quantities (R. E. PEIERLS, 1933). We shall first of all show how it can be done in a case in which the classical Gibbs distribution is applicable.

We write the energy $E(p, q)$ in the form

$$E(p, q) = E_0(p, q) + V(p, q) \tag{32.1}$$

where V represents the small terms. To calculate the free energy of the body we write:

$$e^{-F/kT} = \int' e^{-[E_0(p, q) + V(p, q)]/kT} \, d\Gamma$$

$$\cong \int' e^{-E_0/kT}\left(1 - \frac{V}{kT} + \frac{V^2}{2(kT)^2}\right) d\Gamma. \tag{32.2}$$

In the expansion in powers of V here and below we stop at the second-order terms, with a view to calculating only the first- and second-order corrections. Taking the logarithm and again expanding in series to the same approximation we have:

$$F = F_0 + \int'\left(V - \frac{V^2}{2kT}\right)e^{[F_0 - E_0(p, q)]/kT} \, d\Gamma +$$

$$+ \frac{1}{2kT}\left[\int' V e^{[F_0 - E_0(p, q)]/kT} \, d\Gamma\right]^2,$$

where F_0 is the "unperturbed" free energy calculated for $V = 0$.

The integrals obtained above represent the mean values of the corresponding quantities averaged over the "unperturbed" Gibbs distribution. Denoting such averaging by a bar over the symbol, and noting that $\overline{V^2} - \bar{V}^2 = \overline{(V - \bar{V})^2}$, we finally obtain

$$F = F_0 + \bar{V} - \frac{1}{2kT}\overline{(V - \bar{V})^2}. \tag{32.3}$$

Thus the first-order correction to the free energy is simply equal to the mean value of the perturbing energy V. The second-order correction is always negative and is determined by the mean square deviation of V from its mean value. In particular, if the mean value $\bar{V}$ becomes zero then the free energy decreases as a result of the perturbation.

Comparison of the second-order term with that of first order in (32.3) allows us to state the condition that the perturbation method described should be applicable. We must bear in mind that both the mean $\bar{V}$ and the mean square $\overline{(V-\bar{V})^2}$ are, roughly speaking, proportional to the number of particles (see the reference in §2 about the mean square fluctuations of thermodynamic quantities of macroscopic bodies). Hence the required condition can be expressed by saying that the perturbation energy per particle must be small compared with kT.†

Let us now carry out the corresponding calculation for the quantum case. In place of (32.1) we write the corresponding expression for the Hamiltonian operator: $\hat{H} = \hat{H}_0 \hat{V} +$. In accordance with quantum perturbation theory, the energy levels of the perturbed system, up to the second-order correction, are given by the expression:‡

$$E_n = E_n^{(0)} + V_{nn} + {\sum_m}' \frac{|V_{nm}|^2}{E_n^{(0)} - E_m^{(0)}}, \tag{32.4}$$

where $E_n^{(0)}$ are the unperturbed energy levels (assumed nondegenerate) and the accent on the summation sign means that we must omit the term with $m = n$.

This expression must be substituted into the formula

$$e^{-F/kT} = \sum_n e^{-E_n/kT}$$

and the same expansion carried out as in the case above. The simple calculations lead to the following result:

$$F = F_0 + \sum_n V_{nn}w_n + {\sum_n}{\sum_m}' \frac{|V_{nm}|^2}{E_n^{(0)} - E_m^{(0)}}w_n -$$

$$- \frac{1}{2kT}\sum_n V_{nn}^2 w_n + \frac{1}{2kT}\left(\sum_n V_{nn}w_n\right)^2, \tag{32.5}$$

where $w_n = e^{F_0 - E_n^{(0)}/kT}$ is the unperturbed Gibbs distribution. The diagonal matrix element V_{nn} is simply the mean value of the perturbing energy V in the given (nth) quantum state. Hence the sum

$$\sum w_n V_{nn}$$

is the totally averaged value of V, averaged both over the quantum states

---

† In expanding the integrand in (32.3) we expanded it strictly speaking in terms of the quantity V/kT which is proportional to the number of particles and, hence, not small. However, taking the logarithm and expanding again the large terms cancel and we get a series of powers of small quantities.

‡ See *Quantum Mechanics*, §38.

of the body and over the statistical distribution over the different quantum states. Denoting the latter averaging by a bar over the symbol, we find that the first-order correction to the free energy is equal to $\bar{V}$, a result formally agreeing with the one obtained above in the classical case.

Formula (32.5) can be presented in the equivalent form

$$F = F_0 + \bar{V}_{nn} - \frac{1}{2}\sum_n\sum_m{}'\frac{|V_{nm}|^2(w_m - w_n)}{E_n^{(0)} - E_m^{(0)}} - \frac{1}{2kT}\overline{(V_{nn} - \bar{V}_{nn})^2}. \quad (32.6)$$

All the second-order terms in this expression are negative (since $w_m - w_n$ has the same sign as $E_n^{(0)} - E_m^{(0)}$). Thus the second-order correction to the free energy is always negative in the quantum case also.

As in the classical case, the condition for applicability of this method is that the perturbation energy (per particle) should be small compared with kT. But the condition for the usual quantum perturbation theory to be applicable (giving expression (32.4) for E_n) is, as is well known, that the perturbation matrix elements should be small compared with the corresponding differences between energy levels; roughly speaking the perturbation energy must be small compared with the differences between energy levels between which transitions are allowed.†

These two conditions are by no means the same—temperature has no connection with the energy levels of the body. It can happen that the perturbation energy is small compared with kT but at the same time is not small, or is even large, compared with the relevant energy differences between levels. In such cases, "perturbation theory" for thermodynamic quantities (i.e. formula 32.6) will be applicable, while perturbation theory for the energy levels (i.e. formula 32.4) will not apply; in other words then the range of convergence of the expansion represented by (32.6) may be wider than the range of convergence of the expansion (32.4) from which it was deduced. Of course the opposite case is also possible (at sufficiently low temperatures).

Formula (32.6) simplifies considerably if not only the perturbation energy, but also the differences between energy levels are small compared with kT. Expanding $w_m - w_n$ in (32.6) in powers of $(E_n^{(0)} - E_m^{(0)})/kT$, we find, in this case:

$$F = F_0 + \bar{V}_{nn} - \frac{1}{2kT}[\sum_m{}'\overline{|V_{nm}|^2} + \overline{(V_{nn} - \bar{V}_{nn})^2}].$$

But by the laws of matrix multiplication we have:

$$\sum_m{}'|V_{nm}|^2 + V_{nn}^2 = \sum_m|V_{nm}|^2 = \sum_m V_{nm}V_{mn} = (V^2)_{nn}$$

and we get an expression formally coinciding with formula (32.3). Thus in this case the quantum mechanical formula formally transforms to the classical case.

---

† These, in general, are transitions which change the states of only a small number of particles.

§33. Expansion in powers of $\hbar$

Formula (31.5) is, in fact, the first term in the expansion in powers of $\hbar$ of the quantum mechanical expression (31.3) for the free energy in the quasi-classical case. The calculation of the next, non-vanishing term of this expansion also is of considerable interest (WIGNER, UHLENBECK and GROPPER 1932).

The problem of calculating the free energy reduces to the calculation of the partition function. To do this we use the fact that the latter represents the trace of the operator $e^{-\lambda \hat{H}}$ (see eq. 31.4); we introduce the notation $\lambda = 1/kT$ to simplify the clumsy expressions below. The calculation of the trace of an operator may be carried out with the aid of any complete orthonormal set of wave functions. For this purpose it is convenient to choose the wave functions representing the motion of N non-interacting particles in some large (but finite), volume V. These functions are of the form:

$$\psi_p = \frac{1}{V^{N/2}} e^{(i/\hbar) \sum_i p_i q_i} \tag{33.1}$$

where q_i are the cartesian co-ordinates, and p_i the corresponding momenta of the particles, labelled by the index i taking values 1, 2, ..., s, where $s = 3N$ is the number of degrees of freedom of a system with N particles.

The following calculation applies equally to a system with identical particles or different particles (atoms). To take into account in the general form possible differences in the particles, we attach to the mass of the particle the appropriate index labelling the degree of freedom: m_i (obviously the values of the three m_i relating to one particle will be the same).

The existence of identical particles in the body means that in quantum theory we ought to take into account the so-called "exchange" effects. This means, first of all, that the wave function (33.1) must be made symmetrical or antisymmetrical in the co-ordinates of the particles depending on which type of statistics the particles obey. It turns out, however, that this effect leads only to the appearance in the expression for the free energy of exponentially small terms and hence is quite uninteresting. The quantum mechanical identity of the particles also affects the way in which one carries out the summation over the momenta in the calculation of the partition function for a quantum perfect gas. This effect leads to the appearance in the expression for the free energy of terms of third order in $\hbar$ (see below) and hence this also has no influence on the terms of order $\hbar$ with which we shall be dealing. Thus in our calculation we need not take any exchange effects into account.

In each of the wave functions (33.1) the momenta p_i have specific, constant values. The set of all possible values of the p_i form a dense discrete sequence (the distance between neighbouring values being inversely proportional to the linear dimensions of the system).† Hence the summation of the matrix

---

† See *Quantum Mechanics*, §20.

elements $(e^{-\lambda\hat{H}})_{pp}$ over all possible values of the momenta can be replaced by integration with respect to $dp = dp_1\, dp_2 \ldots dp_s$ bearing in mind that the number of quantum states "allocated" to the volume $V^N dp$ of phase space (the values of all the co-ordinates of the particles in V and with momenta in the range dp) is equal to

$$\frac{V^N\, dp}{(2\pi\hbar)^s}.$$

We introduce the notation

$$I = e^{-(i/\hbar)\,\sum_i p_i q_i} e^{-\lambda\hat{H}} e^{(i/\hbar)\,\sum_i p_i q_i}. \tag{33.2}$$

The matrix elements in which we are interested are obtained by integrating with respect to the co-ordinates:

$$(e^{-\lambda\hat{H}})_{pp} = \frac{1}{V^N} \int I\, dq. \tag{33.3}$$

The desired partition function is obtained from this by integrating with respect to the momenta as well. Thus altogether we have to integrate I over the whole phase space or, more accurately, over those regions of phase space corresponding to physically distinct states of the body as was explained in §31; as we did then, we denote this by an accent on the integral sign:

$$Z = \sum_n e^{-\lambda E_n} = \int' I\, d\Gamma. \tag{33.4}$$

Let us first calculate the quantity I using the following method. We construct the derivative $\partial I/\partial\lambda$. Bearing in mind that

$$\frac{\partial}{\partial\lambda} e^{-\lambda\hat{H}} = -\hat{H} e^{-\lambda\hat{H}}$$

we find

$$\frac{\partial I}{\partial\lambda} = -e^{-(i/\hbar)\,\Sigma\, p_i q_i}\hat{H}(e^{(i/\hbar)\,\sum_i p_i q_i}I).$$

We may expand the right-hand side of the equation using the explicit expression for the Hamiltonian of the body:

$$\hat{H} = \sum_i \frac{p_i^2}{2m_i} + U = -\frac{\hbar^2}{2}\sum_i \frac{1}{m_i}\frac{\partial^2}{\partial q_i^2} + U, \tag{33.5}$$

where $U = U(q_1, q_2, \ldots, q_s)$ is the potential energy of interaction of all the particles in the body. With the aid of (33.5) we get, after a simple calculation, the following equation for I:

$$\frac{\partial I}{\partial\lambda} = -E(p,q)I + \sum_i \frac{\hbar^2}{2m_i}\left(\frac{2i}{\hbar}p_i\frac{\partial I}{\partial q_i} + \frac{\partial^2 I}{\partial q_i^2}\right),$$

where

$$E(p,q) = \sum_i \frac{p_i^2}{2m_i} + U \tag{33.6}$$

is the usual classical expression for the energy of the body. The solution to this equation must satisfy the obvious condition $I = 1$ when $\lambda = 0$. By substituting

$$I = e^{-\lambda E(p,\,q)}\chi$$

we get

$$\frac{\partial \chi}{\partial \lambda} = \sum_i \frac{\hbar^2}{2m_i}\left[-\frac{2i\lambda p_i}{\hbar}\frac{\partial U}{\partial q_i}\chi + \frac{2ip_i}{\hbar}\frac{\partial \chi}{\partial q_i} - \lambda\chi\frac{\partial^2 U}{\partial q_i^2} \right.$$
$$\left. + \lambda^2\chi\left(\frac{\partial U}{\partial q_i}\right)^2 - 2\lambda\frac{\partial \chi}{\partial q_i}\frac{\partial U}{\partial q_i} + \frac{\partial^2 \chi}{\partial q_i^2}\right] \tag{33.8}$$

with the boundary condition $\chi = 1$ when $\lambda = 0$.

With a view to obtaining an expansion in powers of $\hbar$ we solve this equation (33.8) by the method of successive approximations:

$$\chi = 1 + \hbar\chi_1 + \hbar^2\chi_2 + \dots \tag{33.9}$$

where $\chi_1 = 0$, $\chi_2 = 0$ when $\lambda = 0$. Substituting this expansion in equation (33.8) and collecting terms with the same powers of $\hbar$ we get the equations

$$\frac{\partial \chi_1}{\partial \lambda} = -i\lambda \sum_i \frac{p_i}{m_i}\frac{\partial U}{\partial q_i}$$

$$\frac{\partial \chi_2}{\partial \lambda} = \sum_i \frac{1}{2m_i}\left[-2i\lambda p_i\frac{\partial U}{\partial q_i}\chi_1 + 2ip_i\frac{\partial \chi_1}{\partial q_i} - \lambda\frac{\partial^2 U}{\partial q_i^2} + \lambda\left(\frac{\partial U}{\partial q_i}\right)^2 \right].$$

From the first equation we determine χ_1 and subsequently from the second we determine χ_2. After a simple calculation we obtain

$$\chi_1 = -\frac{i\lambda^2}{2}\sum_i \frac{p_i}{m_i}\frac{\partial U}{\partial q_i},$$

$$\chi_2 = -\frac{\lambda^4}{8}\left(\sum_i \frac{p_i}{m_i}\frac{\partial U}{\partial q_i}\right)^2 + \frac{\lambda^3}{6}\sum_i\sum_k \frac{p_i}{m_i}\frac{p_k}{m_k}\frac{\partial^2 U}{\partial q_i \partial q_k}$$

$$+ \frac{\lambda^3}{6}\sum_i \frac{1}{m_i}\left(\frac{\partial U}{\partial q_i}\right)^2 - \frac{\lambda^2}{4}\sum_i \frac{1}{m_i}\frac{\partial^2 U}{\partial q_i^2}. \tag{33.10}$$

The required partition function is equal to

$$Z = \int{}' (1+\hbar\chi_1+\hbar^2\chi_2)e^{-\lambda E(p,\, q)}\, d\Gamma. \tag{33.11}$$

It is easy to see that the first-order term in $\hbar$ in this integral vanishes, since for this term the integrand $\chi_1 e^{-nE(p,q)}$ is an odd function of the momenta ($E(p, q)$ is quadratic in the momenta while χ_1 is, from (33.10) linear in the momenta) and hence its integral with respect to the momenta vanishes. Thus rewriting (33.11) in the form

$$Z = (1+\hbar^2\bar{\chi}_2) \int{}' e^{-\lambda E(p,\, q)}\, d\Gamma,$$

where we have introduced the quantity $\bar{\chi}_2$ averaged over the classical Gibbs distribution,

$$\bar{\chi}_2 = \frac{\int{}' \chi_2 e^{-\lambda E(p,\, q)}\, d\Gamma}{\int{}' e^{-\lambda E(p,\, q)}\, d\Gamma},$$

and substituting this expression for the partition function into formula (31.3) we get for the free energy:

$$F = F_{\mathrm{cl}} - \frac{1}{\lambda}\log(1+\hbar^2\bar{\chi}_2)$$

or, to the same accuracy

$$F = F_{\mathrm{cl}} - \frac{\hbar^2}{\lambda}\bar{\chi}_2 \tag{33.12}$$

Here F_{cl} denotes the expression for the free energy in classical statistics (formula (31.5)).

Thus the next term after the classical one in the expansion of the free energy appears to be of second order in $\hbar$. This fact is not accidental. In equation (33.8), which we have solved by the method of successive approximations, the quantum constant only enters in the combination $i\hbar$; hence the expansion we obtain is also an expansion in powers of $i\hbar$. The free energy, which is a real quantity, can only contain real powers of $i\hbar$. Hence the expansion carried out above for the free energy (neglecting exchange effects) is an expansion in even powers of $\hbar$.

It remains to calculate the mean value $\bar{\chi}_2$. We saw in §29 that in classical statistics the probability distributions for the co-ordinates and for the momenta are independent. Hence one can average over the co-ordinates and momenta separately.

The mean value of the product of two different momenta is obviously equal to zero; $\overline{p_i p_k} = \bar{p}_i \cdot \bar{p}_k = 0$ and the mean square value $\overline{p_i^2}$ is equal to m_i/λ. Hence we may write

$$\overline{p_i p_k} = \frac{m_i}{\lambda} \delta_{ik}$$

where $\delta_{ik} = 1$ for $i = k$ and 0 for $i \neq k$. Averaging over the momenta with the aid of this formula we obtain for $\bar{\chi}_2$ the following expression

$$\bar{\chi}_2 = \frac{\lambda^3}{24} \sum_i \frac{1}{m_i} \overline{\left(\frac{\partial U}{\partial q_i}\right)^2} - \frac{\lambda^2}{12} \sum \frac{1}{m_i} \overline{\frac{\partial^2 U}{\partial q_i^2}}. \tag{33.13}$$

Both terms can be combined into one since the mean values involved are connected by the relation

$$\overline{\frac{\partial^2 U}{\partial q_i^2}} = \lambda \overline{\left(\frac{\partial U}{\partial q_i}\right)^2}. \tag{33.14}$$

This expression can easily be derived by noting that

$$\int \frac{\partial^2 U}{\partial q_i^2} e^{-\lambda U} \, dq_i = \frac{\partial U}{\partial q_i} e^{-\lambda U} \bigg| + \lambda \int \left(\frac{\partial U}{\partial q_i}\right)^2 e^{-\lambda U} \, dq_i.$$

In the calculation of $\overline{\partial^2 U/\partial q_i^2}$ the first term on the right-hand side will give an expression representing a surface effect; owing to the macroscopic nature of the body it can be completely neglected in comparison with the second term which gives a volume effect.

Substituting the expression thus obtained for $\bar{\chi}_2$ into formula (33.12) and replacing λ by $1/kT$ we obtain the following expression for the free energy

$$F = F_{cl} + \frac{\hbar^2}{24(kT)^2} \sum_i \frac{1}{m_i} \overline{\left(\frac{\partial U}{\partial q_i}\right)^2}. \tag{33.15}$$

We see that the correction to the classical value is always a positive quantity determined by the mean squares of the forces acting on the particles. This correction decreases with an increase in the mass of the particles and with an increase in temperature.

As explained above, the next term in this expansion would be of fourth order. This makes it possible to calculate quite independently the term of order $\hbar^3$ which appears in the free energy owing to peculiarities in the sum over the momenta due to the quantum mechanical identity of the particles. This term formally coincides with a correction term occurring in a similar calculation for a perfect gas and is given by formula (55.14)

$$F^{(3)} = \pm \frac{\pi^{3/2}}{2g} \frac{N^2\hbar^3}{V(kT)^{1/2}m^{3/2}} \tag{33.16}$$

(for a body consisting of N identical particles), the upper sign relating to Fermi statistics and the lower one to Bose-Einstein statistics, while g is the total degree of degeneracy in the direction of the momenta, both electronic and nuclear.

The formulae we have obtained also allow us to find the correction terms to the probability distribution functions for the co-ordinates and momenta of atoms of the body. In accordance with the general results obtained in §5 the probability distribution for the momenta is obtained by integrating I with respect to dq (see eq. 5.10):

$$dw_p = \text{const } dp \int I \, dq.$$

The term $\chi_1 e^{-\lambda E(p,q)}$ in I contains a total derivative with respect to the co-ordinates and when integrated with respect to them gives a quantity which represents a surface effect, and can be omitted.

We thus have:

$$dw_p = \text{const } e^{-\lambda \sum_i (p_i^2/2m_i)} \, dp \int (1+\hbar^2\chi_2)e^{-\lambda U} \, dq.$$

The third and fourth terms in the expression for χ_2 (33.10), when integrated with respect to the co-ordinates, give a small, constant term (not involving the momenta) which, to the approximation we are using, can be neglected. Absorbing the factor $\int e^{-nU} \, dq$ into the constant coefficient we have:

$$dw_p = \text{const } e^{-\lambda \sum_i (p_i^2/2m_i)} \left[1 - \hbar^2 \frac{\lambda^4}{8} \sum_i \sum_k \frac{p_i p_k}{m_i m_k} \frac{\partial U}{\partial q_i} \frac{\partial U}{\partial q_k} + \right.$$
$$\left. + \hbar^2 \frac{\lambda^3}{6} \sum_i \sum_k \frac{p_i p_k}{m_i m_k} \frac{\partial^2 U}{\partial q_i \partial q_k} \right] dp.$$

The mean values contained in this are connected by the relation

$$\overline{\frac{\partial^2 U}{\partial q_i \partial q_k}} = \lambda \overline{\frac{\partial U}{\partial q_i} \frac{\partial U}{\partial q_k}}$$

(as in (33.14)). Hence we have

$$dw_p = \text{const } e^{-\lambda \sum_i (p_i^2/2m_i)} \left[1 + \frac{\hbar^2\lambda^4}{24} \sum_i \sum_k \frac{p_i p_k}{m_i m_k} \frac{\partial U}{\partial q_i} \frac{\partial U}{\partial q_k} \right] dp. \tag{33.17}$$

This expression can be rewritten conveniently in the following form

$$dw_p = \text{const} \exp\left\{-\frac{1}{kT}\left[\sum_i \frac{p_i^2}{2m_i} - \frac{\hbar^2}{24(kT)^3}\sum_i\sum_k \frac{p_i p_k}{m_i m_k}\frac{\partial U}{\partial q_i}\frac{\partial U}{\partial q_k}\right]\right\} dp.$$

(33.18)

replacing the expression in square brackets in (33.17) by the corresponding exponential, which is correct to the required accuracy.

Thus we see that the corrected classical distribution function for the momenta is obtained by adding to the kinetic energy term in the exponent a quadratic term in the momenta whose coefficients depend on the law of interaction of the particles of the body.

If we wish to find the probability distribution for any one of the momenta p_i, we must integrate (33.17) with respect to all the other momenta. In such an integration all the terms with squares p_k^2, $k \neq i$, will give small constant terms which can be neglected compared with 1 and the terms involving products of different momenta will give zero contribution. As a result we find, again returning to the exponential form:

$$dw_{p_i} = \text{const} \exp\left\{-\frac{p_i^2}{2m_i kT}\left[1-\frac{\hbar^2}{12(kT)^3 m_i}\overline{\left(\frac{\partial U}{\partial q_i}\right)^2}\right]\right\} dp_i. \qquad (33.19)$$

We see that the distribution differs from the Maxwellian one only in the replacement of the real temperature T by some other, higher, "effective temperature".

$$dw_{p_i} = \text{const} \exp\left\{-\frac{p_i^2}{2m_i kT_{\text{eff}}}\right\} dp_i,$$

where

$$T_{\text{eff}} = T+\frac{\hbar^2}{12T^2 k^3 m_i}\overline{\left(\frac{\partial U}{\partial q_i}\right)^2}.$$

Similarly one can also calculate a corrected distribution function for the co-ordinates. It is obtained by integrating I with respect to the momenta:

$$dw_q = \text{const}\, dq \int I\, dp.$$

The same calculations, by means of which we obtain expression (33.13), lead to the following result:

$$dw_q = \text{const}\, e^{-\lambda U}\left[1+\frac{\hbar^2\lambda^3}{24}\sum_i \frac{1}{m_i}\overline{\left(\frac{\partial U}{\partial q_i}\right)^2} - \frac{\hbar^2\lambda^2}{12}\sum_i\frac{1}{m_i}\frac{\partial^2 U}{\partial q_i^2}\right] dq,$$

or, in the exponential form:

$$dw_q = \text{const} \exp\left\{-\frac{1}{kT}\left[U - \frac{\hbar^2}{24(kT)^2}\sum_i \frac{1}{m_i}\left(\frac{\partial U}{\partial q_i}\right)^2 + \right.\right.$$

$$\left.\left. + \frac{\hbar^2}{12kT}\sum_i \frac{1}{m_i}\frac{\partial^2 U}{\partial q_i^2}\right]\right\} dq. \tag{33.20}$$

§34. The Gibbs distribution for rotating bodies

The question of thermodynamic relations for rotating bodies was discussed in §26. We shall now explain how the Gibbs distribution must be formulated for rotating bodies; we shall then have completely covered the problem of their statistical properties. As was shown in §26, the effects of uniform translational motion, in accordance with the Galilean principle of relativity, influence the statistical properties of a body only in a trivial manner, and hence they need no special consideration.

In a co-ordinate system rotating with the body, the ordinary Gibbs distribution is valid; in classical statistics

$$\rho = (2\pi\hbar)^{-s} e^{[F' - E'(p,\,q)]/kT} \tag{34.1}$$

where $E'(p, q)$ is the energy of the body in this system, as a function of the co-ordinates and momenta, and F' is the free energy in the same system. The energy $E'(p, q)$ is connected with the energy $E(p, q)$ in the stationary system by the relation

$$E'(p,q) = E(p,q) - \boldsymbol{\Omega}\cdot\mathbf{M}(p,q) \tag{34.2}$$

where $\boldsymbol{\Omega}$ is the angular velocity, and $\mathbf{M}(p, q)$ the angular momentum, of the body (see §26). Substituting (34.2) into (34.1) we find the Gibbs distribution for the rotating body to be of the form†

$$\rho = (2\pi\hbar)^{-s} e^{[F' - E(p,\,q) + \boldsymbol{\Omega}\cdot\mathbf{M}(p,\,q)]/kT}. \tag{34.3}$$

In classical statistics, the Gibbs distribution for a rotating body can be expressed in a different form. To do this we make use of the following expression for the energy of the body in the rotating system of co-ordinates:

$$E' = \sum \frac{mv'^2}{2} - \frac{1}{2}\sum m(\boldsymbol{\Omega}\times\mathbf{r})^2 + U, \tag{34.4}$$

where $\mathbf{v}'$ are the velocities of the particles in the rotating system and $\mathbf{r}$ their

---

† The distribution (34.3), like the usual Gibbs distribution is in complete agreement with the results obtained in §4 starting from Liouville's Theorem (4.2): the logarithm of the distribution function is a linear function of the energy and momentum of the body.

radius vectors (see footnote on page 73, formula (2)). Let

$$E_0(\mathbf{v}, \mathbf{r}) = \sum \frac{mv'^2}{2} + U \tag{34.5}$$

denote that part of the energy independent of $\boldsymbol{\Omega}$. We obtain the Gibbs distribution in the form

$$\rho = (2\pi\hbar)^{-s} \exp\left\{\frac{F' - E_0(\mathbf{v}', \mathbf{r}) + \frac{1}{2}\sum m(\boldsymbol{\Omega}\times\mathbf{r})^2}{kT}\right\}.$$

The function ρ gives the probability associated with the element of phase space

$$dx_1\, dy_1\, dz_1 \dots dp'_{1x}\, dp'_{1y}\, dp'_{1z} \dots,$$

where $\mathbf{p}' = m\mathbf{v}' + m(\boldsymbol{\Omega}\times\mathbf{r})$ are the momenta of the particles of the body (see footnote on page 73, formula (1)). Since, in finding the differentials of the momenta, the co-ordinates must remain constant, we have $d\mathbf{p}' = m\, d\mathbf{v}'$ and we can write the probability distribution in terms of the co-ordinates and velocities of the particles:

$$dw = C \exp\left\{\frac{F'}{kT} - \frac{1}{kT}\left[E_0(\mathbf{v}', \mathbf{r}) - \sum \frac{m}{2}(\boldsymbol{\Omega}\times\mathbf{r})^2\right]\right\} \times$$
$$\times dx_1\, dy_1\, dz_1 \dots dv'_{1x}\, dv'_{1y}\, dv'_{1z}, \tag{34.6}$$

where for simplicity we use C to denote $(2\pi\hbar)^{-s}$ times the product of the masses of the particles appearing when we change from momentum to velocity differentials.

For a stationary body we would have

$$dw = Ce^{[F' - E_0(\mathbf{r}, \mathbf{r})]/kT}\, dx_1\, dy_1\, dz_1 \dots dv_{1x}\, dv_{1y}\, dv_{1z} \tag{34.7}$$

with the same expression (34.5) for $E_0(\mathbf{v}, \mathbf{r})$ as a function now of the velocities in the fixed system of co-ordinates. Thus we see that the Gibbs distribution for the co-ordinates and velocities of a rotating body differs from that for a stationary body only by the addition of a potential energy equal to

$$-\tfrac{1}{2}\sum m(\boldsymbol{\Omega}\times\mathbf{r})^2.$$

In other words, as far as the statistical properties of the body are concerned, the rotation is equivalent to the appearance of an external field corresponding to the centrifugal forces. The Coriolis forces do not affect these properties.

It must be emphasised, however, that the last result applies only to classical statistics. In the quantum case, for a rotating body the expression

$$\hat{w} = e^{(F' - \hat{H} + \boldsymbol{\Omega}\cdot\hat{\mathbf{M}})/kT} \tag{34.8}$$

gives the statistical operator analogous to (34.3). This operator can be formally reduced to a form corresponding to (34.6), when the velocities $\mathbf{v}'$

will be replaced by operators $\hat{\mathbf{v}} = (\hat{\mathbf{p}}'/m) - \mathbf{\Omega} \times \mathbf{r}$. However the components of this vector operator do not commute with each other as do those of the velocity operator $\hat{\mathbf{v}}$ in a stationary system: hence the statistical operators corresponding to expressions (34.6) and (34.7) would, generally speaking, differ fundamentally from each other, quite apart from the presence in one of them of the centrifugal energy.

§35. The Gibbs distribution for a variable number of particles

So far, we have always implicitly assumed that the number of particles in the body is a given constant quantity. In doing so we were deliberately ignoring the fact that, actually, interchange of particles can take place between different subsystems. In other words, the number of particles N, in a subsystem is bound to fluctuate about its mean value. To express precisely what we mean here by the number of particles, we define a subsystem as a part of a system included in a *specified* volume: then by N we mean the number of particles in this volume†.

Thus there arises the problem of generalising the Gibbs distribution to bodies with a variable number of particles. We shall deal below with formulae for bodies consisting of identical particles; the subsequent generalisation to systems containing different particles will be obvious (§83).

The distribution function depends now not only on the energy of the quantum state, but also on the number N of particles, in the body, and clearly the energy levels E_{nN} themselves also vary with N (this is indicated by adding the subscript N). The probability that the body contains N particles and is at the same time in the nth state will be denoted by w_{nN}.

The form of this function can be determined by exactly the same method as that by which the function w_n was obtained in §28. The difference is only that the entropy of the medium is now not only a function of its energy E' but also of the number N' of particles in it: $S' = S(E', N')$. Writing $E' = E^{(0)} - E_{nN}$ and $N' = N^{(0)} - N$ (N is the number of particles in the body, $N^{(0)}$ the number of particles in the whole closed system, which is large compared with N) we have, in accordance with (28.2):

$$w_{nN} = \text{const} \exp \left\{ \frac{1}{k} S'(E^{(0)} - E_{nN}, N^{(0)} - N) \right\}$$

(the quantity $\Delta E'$ being regarded as constant, as in §28).

We further expand S' in powers of E_{nN} and N and again restrict ourselves to linear terms. From the thermodynamic identity (24.5) written in the form

$$dS = \frac{dE}{T} + \frac{P}{T} dV - \frac{\mu}{T} dN,$$

---

† Already in deriving the Gibbs distribution in §28 we were strictly speaking considering subsystems in exactly this sense; in going from (28.2) to (28.3) we were differentiating the entropy, keeping the volume of the body (and hence also of the medium) constant.

it follows that

$$\left(\frac{\partial S}{\partial E}\right)_{V,N} = \frac{1}{T}, \qquad \left(\frac{\partial S}{\partial N}\right)_{E\,V} = -\frac{\mu}{T},$$

hence

$$S'(E^{(0)}-E_{nN},\ N^{(0)}-N) \cong S'(E^{(0)}, N^{(0)}) - \frac{E_{nN}}{T} + \frac{\mu N}{T},$$

the chemical potentials and temperatures of the body and the medium being the same because of the equilibrium conditions.

Thus we get the following expression for the distribution functions:

$$w_{nN} = Ae^{(\mu N - E_{nN})/kT}. \tag{35.1}$$

The normalisation constant A can be expressed in terms of thermodynamic quantities as in §31. We may calculate the entropy of the body:

$$S = -k\,\overline{\log w_{nN}} = -k \log A - \frac{\mu\bar{N}}{T} + \frac{\bar{E}}{T},$$

whence

$$kT \log A = \bar{E} - TS - \mu\bar{N}.$$

But $\bar{E} - TS = F$ and the difference $F - \mu N$ is the thermodynamic potential Ω. Thus $kT \log A = \Omega$ and we can rewrite (35.1) in the form

$$w_{nN} = e^{(\Omega + \mu N - E_{nN})/kT}. \tag{35.2}$$

This is the formulation of the Gibbs distribution for a variable number of particles.

The normalisation condition for the distribution (35.2) requires the sum of w_{nN}, first over all quantum states (for given N) and then over all values of N, to be equal to unity.

$$\sum_N \sum_n w_{nN} = e^{\Omega/kT} \sum_N \left(e^{\mu N/kT} \sum_n e^{-E_{nN}/kT}\right) = 1.$$

Hence we obtain the following expression for the thermodynamic potential Ω.

$$\Omega = -kT \log \sum_N \left[e^{\mu N/kT} \sum_n e^{-E_{nN}/kT}\right]. \tag{35.3}$$

This formula together with formula (31.3) can be used to calculate thermodynamic quantities of different bodies. Formula (31.3) gives the free energy of the body as a function of T, N, and V, and (35.3) gives the potential Ω as a function of T, μ and V.

In classical statistics we write the probability distribution in the form

$$dw_N = \rho_N\, dp^{(N)}\, dq^{(N)},$$

where

$$\rho_N = (2\pi\hbar)^{-s}e^{[\Omega+\mu N-E_N(p,\,q)]/kT}. \qquad (35.4)$$

The variable N is written as a subscript to the distribution function; it is also put as an index to the phase volume element emphasising that to each value of N corresponds a separate phase space (with its number of dimensions $2s$). The formula for Ω can thus be written in the form

$$\Omega = -kT \log\{ \sum_N e^{\mu N/kT} \int' e^{-E_N(p,\,q)/kT} \, d\Gamma_N\}. \qquad (35.5)$$

Lastly we shall say a few words about the relation between the Gibbs distribution deduced above for a variable number of particles (35.2) and the previous distribution (31.1). First of all it is clear that for the determination of all the statistical properties of the body, apart from fluctuations of the total number of particles in it, the two distributions are completely identical. If we neglect fluctuations in N we get $\Omega+\mu N = F$ and the distribution (35.2) completely coincides with (31.1).

The relation between the distributions (31.1) and (35.2) is in some sense similar to the relation between the microcanonical and canonical distributions. The description of a subsystem by means of the microcanonical distribution is equivalent to disregarding fluctuations in its total energy, and the canonical distribution in its usual form (31.1), takes this fluctuation into account. At the same time the latter does not take into account the fluctuation in the number of particles; one might say that it is "microcanonical with respect to the number of particles". The distribution (35.2) is "canonical" both as regards energy and also the number of particles. It is usually called the "grand canonical distribution".

Thus all three distributions, microcanonical, canonical and grand canonical, are applicable, in principle, to the determination of the thermodynamic properties of a body. The difference, from this point of view, is only a matter of mathematical convenience. In fact the microcanonical is the most inconvenient and is never used in practice. The most convenient is usually the grand canonical Gibbs distribution.

§36. The deduction of the thermodynamic identity from the Gibbs distribution

Since the Gibbs distribution plays such a fundamental part in the whole of statistics we shall give here another method of obtaining it. We have seen in §4 and §6 that the application of Liouville's theorem (together with the assumption of the multiplicativity of the distribution functions of subsystems) enabled us to reach the conclusion that the logarithm of the distribution function of a subsystem must be a linear function of its energy.

$$\log w_n = \alpha + \beta E_n \tag{36.1}$$

where the coefficients β are the same for all subsystems of a given closed system (see (6.4) or in the classical case the analogous relation (4.5)). Hence

$$w_n = e^{\alpha + \beta E_n};$$

if one introduces purely formally the notation

$$\beta = -\frac{1}{kT}, \qquad \alpha = \frac{F}{kT}$$

then this expression coincides formally with the Gibbs distribution (31.1). It remains to show that from the Gibbs distribution itself, i.e. in a purely statistical way, one can deduce the basic thermodynamic identity.

We have already seen that the quantity β (or T), and hence kT also, must be the same for all the particles of a system in equilibrium. Furthermore, it is obvious that we must have $\beta < 0$, i.e. $T > 0$ otherwise the normalisation sum Σw_n would certainly diverge (since, owing to the kinetic energy of the particles the energy can have an arbitrarily large value). All these properties coincide with the basic properties of thermodynamic temperature.

To deduce a quantitative relation we must start from the normalisation condition

$$\sum_n e^{(F-E_n)/kT} = 1.$$

Let us differentiate this equation regarding its left-hand side as a function of T and some parameters $\lambda_1, \lambda_2 \dots$, specifying the external conditions in which the body is situated; these parameters can, for instance, determine the shape and size of the volume occupied by the body. The energy levels E_n depend on the values of $\lambda_1, \lambda_2, \dots$, as parameters.

Differentiating, we write

$$\sum \frac{w_n}{kT}\left[dF - \frac{\partial E_n}{\partial \lambda} d\lambda - \frac{F-E_n}{T} dT \right] = 0$$

(for simplicity we shall consider here only one external parameter λ). Hence

$$dF \sum_n w_n = d\lambda \sum_n w_n \frac{\partial E_n}{\partial \lambda} + \frac{dT}{T}\left(F - \sum_n w_n E_n \right).$$

On the left-hand side of the equation $\Sigma w_n = 1$, and on the right

$$\sum_n w_n E_n = \bar{E}, \qquad \sum_n w_n \frac{\partial E_n}{\partial \lambda} = \overline{\frac{\partial E_n}{\partial \lambda}}.$$

Taking into account the fact that $F - \bar{E} = -TS$ and that†

$$\frac{\overline{\partial E_n}}{\partial \lambda} = \frac{\overline{\partial \hat{H}}}{\partial \lambda},$$
(36.2)

we finally obtain:

$$dF = -S\,dT + \frac{\overline{\partial \hat{H}}}{\partial \lambda}\,d\lambda.$$

This is the general form of the thermodynamic identity for the free energy.

In the same way one can also get the Gibbs distribution with a varying number of particles. If one regards the number of particles as a dynamical variable then it is clear that it is (for a closed system) an "integral of motion" and, in fact, an additive one. Hence one must write:

$$\log w_{nN} = \alpha + \beta E_n + \gamma N$$
(36.3)

where γ, like β, must be the same for all parts of the system in equilibrium. Putting

$$\alpha = \frac{\Omega}{kT}, \qquad \beta = -\frac{1}{kT}, \qquad \gamma = \frac{\mu}{kT},$$

we obtain the distribution in the form (35.2) after which a method similar to the one used above enables one to obtain the thermodynamic identity for the potential Ω.

---

† If the Hamiltonian $\hat{H}$ (and with it its eigenvalues E_n) depends on some parameter λ then

$$\frac{\partial E_n}{\partial \lambda} = \left(\frac{\partial \hat{H}}{\partial \lambda}\right)_{nn}$$

(see *Quantum Mechanics*, eq. 72.2) whence, after statistical averaging, we obtain formula (36.2).

CHAPTER IV

THE PERFECT GAS

§37. The Boltzmann distribution

ONE of the most important systems to be studied in statistical physics is the so-called *perfect gas*. By this we mean a gas in which the interaction between the particles (molecules) is so weak that it can be neglected. This approximation is physically justified either when the interaction is small, whatever the distance between the particles, or when the gas is sufficiently rarefied. In the latter, more important, case the molecules are almost always sufficiently far apart for the interaction forces to be negligible.

The absence of the intermolecular interaction reduces the quantum mechanical problem of determining the energy levels E_n of the gas as a whole, to the determination of the energy levels of a single molecule. We shall denote these levels by ϵ_k where the suffix k conventionally denotes the set of quantum numbers specifying the state of the molecule. The energy E_n will then represent the sum of the energies of all the molecules.

It must be borne in mind, however, that even in the absence of any direct dynamic interaction there exist certain peculiar quantum mechanical effects of the particles on one another which are connected with the identity of the particles (the so-called exchange effects). Thus if the particles "obey Fermi statistics" then this effect appears in that no more than one particle can be in each quantum state at a given time;† a similar effect acting in a different way takes place for particles "obeying Bose statistics".

We shall denote by n_k the number of particles in the gas which are in the kth quantum state; the numbers n_k are sometimes called the "occupation numbers" of the different quantum states. We consider the problem of calculating the mean values $\bar{n}_k$ of these numbers. We examine first in detail the extremely important case when, for all the numbers n_k

$$\bar{n}_k \ll 1 \tag{37.1}$$

Physically this case corresponds to the gas being sufficiently rarefied. Later on we shall establish criteria for this condition to be satisfied, but we may mention here that it is satisfied in practice for all the usual molecular and atomic gases. The condition would only be violated at densities which are so high that the substance could in no way be regarded as a gas.

---

† It must be emphasised that, when we speak of the quantum state of a separate particle, we shall always have in mind states completely defined by a set of values of all the quantum numbers (including the orientation of its angular momentum, if any). They must not be confused with the quantum energy levels—to the same energy level can correspond a series of different quantum states (if the level is degenerate).

The condition $\bar{n}_k \ll 1$ for the mean occupation numbers means that, at any moment of time, no more than one particle is in fact in each quantum state. As a result of this one can neglect not only the direct forces of interaction between the particles, but also the quantum mechanical effects mentioned above. This fact, in turn, enables us to apply the Gibbs distribution to the separate molecules.

We had actually derived the Gibbs distribution for bodies which were comparatively small, but macroscopic, parts of some large closed system. The fact that the bodies were macroscopic enabled us to regard them as quasi-closed, i.e. in a certain sense to neglect their interaction with other parts of the system. In the case which we are considering the separate molecules of the gas are quasi-closed, although they are certainly not macroscopic bodies.

By applying the formulae of the Gibbs distribution to the gas molecules we can assert that the probability that a molecule is in the kth state, and hence also the mean number $\bar{n}_k$ of molecules in this state is proportional to $e^{-\epsilon_k/kT}$, i.e.

$$\bar{n}_k = ae^{-\epsilon_k/kT}, \tag{37.2}$$

where a is a constant determined by the normalisation condition

$$\sum_k \bar{n}_k = N \tag{37.3}$$

(N is the total number of molecules in the gas). The distribution of the molecules of a perfect gas over different states given by formula (37.2) is called the Boltzmann distribution (it was discovered for classical statistics by BOLTZMANN in 1877).

The constant coefficient in (37.2) can be expressed in terms of the thermodynamic functions of the gas. To do this we shall give another derivation of the formula based on the application of the Gibbs distribution to the set of all particles of the gas in the given quantum state. We can do this (even if the numbers n_k are not small) for there is no direct interaction between these and all other particles (which is the case for all the particles of a perfect gas) and the quantum mechanical exchange effects take place only for particles which are in the same state. Assuming the general formula for the grand canonical distribution (35.2) with $E = n_k\epsilon_k$, $N = n_k$ and giving a suffix k to the quantity Ω, we obtain the probability distribution for the different values of n_k in the form

$$w_{nk} = e^{[\Omega_k + n_k(\mu - \epsilon_k)]/kT}. \tag{37.4}$$

In particular $w_0 = e^{\Omega_k/kT}$ is the probability that there should be no particle in the kth state. In the case in which we are interested, when $\bar{n}_k \ll 1$ the probability w_0 is near unity and hence in the expression

$$w_1 = e^{(\Omega_k + \mu - \epsilon_k)/kT}$$

for the probability that there is one particle in the kth state, we may put

$e^{\Omega_k/kT} = 1$, neglecting high powers of small quantities. Then

$$w_1 = e^{(\mu - \epsilon_k)/kT}.$$

As far as the probabilities of values of $n_k > 1$ are concerned we may take them to be zero to the same approximation. Hence:

$$\bar{n}_k = \Sigma\, w_{n_k} n_k = w_1.1$$

and we obtain the Boltzmann distribution in the form

$$\bar{n}_k = e^{(\mu - \epsilon_k)/kT}. \tag{37.5}$$

In this way the coefficient in formula (37.2) is expressed in terms of the chemical potential of the gas.

§38. The Boltzmann distribution in classical statistics

If the motion of the gas molecules (and of the atoms inside them) were governed by classical mechanics, we could introduce in place of the distribution over quantum states, a distribution of the molecules in phase space, i.e. over momenta and co-ordinates. Let dN be the average number of molecules "enclosed" in the volume element of phase space for a molecule, $dp\, dq = dq_1 \ldots dq_r\, dp_1 \ldots dp_r$ (r is the number of degrees of freedom of the molecule). We write this in the form

$$dN = n(p,q)\, d\tau, \qquad d\tau = \frac{dp\, dq}{(2\pi\hbar)^r} \tag{38.1}$$

and we shall call $n(p, q)$ the "density in phase space" (although $d\tau$ differs by a factor $(2\pi\hbar)^{-r}$ from the volume element in phase space). We now obtain in place of (37.5)

$$n(p,q) = e^{[\mu - \epsilon(p, q)]/kT} \tag{38.2}$$

where $\epsilon(p, q)$ is the energy of a molecule as a function of the co-ordinates and momenta of the atoms inside it.

Usually, however, not all the motion of the molecule is quasi-classical, but only that motion corresponding to a part of its degrees of freedom. In particular for a gas which is not in an external field, the translational motion of the molecules is always classical and the kinetic energy of translational motion enters into the energy ϵ_k of the molecule as an independent additive quantity. The remaining part of the energy contains neither the co-ordinates x, y, z nor the momenta p_x, p_y, p_z of the centre of gravity of the molecule. This fact allows us to remove from the general formula for the Boltzmann distribution the factor determining the distribution of the molecules of the gas in terms of these particular variables. The distribution of molecules throughout the volume of the gas will obviously be just uniform and the number of molecules per unit volume with momenta in the given ranges

dp_x, dp_y, dp_z takes the form of the Maxwell distribution

$$dN_\mathbf{p} = \frac{N}{V(2\pi mkT)^{3/2}} e^{-(p_x^2+p_y^2+p_z^2)/2mkT} \, dp_x \, dp_y \, dp_z, \qquad (38.3)$$

$$dN_\mathbf{v} = \frac{N}{V}\left(\frac{m}{2\pi kT}\right)^{3/2} e^{-m(v_x^2+v_y^2+v_z^2)/2kT} \, dv_x \, dv_y \, dv_z \qquad (38.4)$$

(m the mass of a molecule) normalised for N/V particles per unit volume.

Consider next a gas which is in an external field in which the potential energy of a molecule is a function of the co-ordinates of its centre of gravity alone: $U = U(x, y, z)$ (such as, for example, the field of gravity). If the translational motion in this field is quasi-classical (as it always is in practice), then $U(x, y, z)$ enters into the energy of the molecule as an independent additive quantity. The Maxwell distribution over the velocities of the molecules clearly remains unchanged and the distribution over the co-ordinates of the centre of gravity will be given by the formula

$$dN_\mathbf{r} = n_0 e^{-u(x, y, z)/kT} \, dv. \qquad (38.5)$$

This formula gives the number of molecules in the space volume element $dV = dx \, dy \, dz$; the quantity

$$n(\mathbf{r}) = n_0 e^{-u(x, y, z)/kT} \qquad (38.6)$$

represents the density of the particles. The constant n_0 is the density at points where $u = 0$. Formula (38.6) is called the *Boltzmann Formula*.

In particular, in a uniform gravitational field directed along the z axis, $u = mgz$ and the density distribution of the gas is given by what is called the barometric formula

$$n(z) = n_0 e^{-mgz/kT}, \qquad (38.7)$$

where n_0 is the density at the level $z = 0$.

At a great distance from the earth, its gravitational field must be given by the exact Newtonian expression in which the potential energy u vanishes at infinity. In accordance with formula (38.6) the density of a gas ought to have a non-zero, finite value at infinity. However, a finite quantity of gas cannot be distributed over an infinite volume if the density vanishes nowhere. This means that in the field of gravity a gas (the atmosphere) cannot be equilibrium and must constantly be dispersed into space.†

PROBLEMS

1. Find the density of gas in a cylinder of radius R and length l rotating about its axis with angular velocity Ω (the cylinder contains N molecules).

---

† This process led to the loss of the lunar atmosphere, but for the earth, with its much larger mass, the rate of dispersal of the atmosphere is so small that this process is in practice of no importance.

SOLUTION: In §34 it was shown that the rotation of the body as a whole is equivalent to an external field with potential energy $-\frac{1}{2}m\Omega^2 r^2$ (r the distance from the axis of rotation). Hence the density of the gas is

$$n(r) = Ae^{m\Omega^2 r^2/2kT}.$$

Normalisation gives

$$n(r) = \frac{Nm\Omega^2 e^{m\Omega^2 r^2/2kT}}{2\pi kTl(e^{m\Omega^2 R^2/2kT}-1)}.$$

2. Find the momentum distribution of particles for a relativistic perfect gas.

SOLUTION: The energy of a relativistic particle is expressed in terms of its momentum as $\epsilon = c\sqrt{(m^2c^2+p^2)}$ (c the velocity of light). The normalised momentum distribution is

$$dN_{\mathbf{p}} = \frac{N}{V} \frac{\exp\left\{-\dfrac{c\sqrt{(m^2c^2+p^2)}}{kT}\right\}}{2\left(\dfrac{kT}{mc^2}\right)^2 K_1\left(\dfrac{mc^2}{kT}\right)+\dfrac{kT}{mc^2}K_0\left(\dfrac{mc^2}{kT}\right)} \frac{dp_x\,dp_y\,dp_z}{4\pi(mc)^3}$$

where K_0, K_1 are the Bessel functions of second kind for imaginary argument.

§39. The collision of molecules

The molecules of a gas contained in a vessel collide with its walls when they move about. Let us calculate the average number of impacts of molecules of the gas on the wall per unit time.

We choose some surface element of the wall and use a co-ordinate system with the z axis perpendicular to this surface element (which can be written in the form $dx\,dy$). Only those molecules of the gas whose z-co-ordinates are not larger than the component v_z of their velocity along this axis (which must, of course, at the same time be directed towards the wall of the vessel and not in the opposite direction) will reach the wall of the vessel in unit time.

The number $d\nu_v$ of collisions of molecules per unit time (for unit surface of the wall of the vessel) for which the velocity components lie in given intervals dv_x, dv_y, dv_z will hence be obtained by multiplying the distribution (38.4) by the volume of a cylinder of base 1 cm² and of height v_z. We then obtain

$$d\nu_v = \frac{N}{V}\left(\frac{m}{2kT}\right)^{3/2} e^{-m(v_x^2+v_y^2+v_z^2)/2kT}\, v_z\,dv_x\,dv_y\,dv_z. \tag{39.1}$$

From this it is easy to calculate the total number ν of impacts of the gas molecules on unit surface of the vessel in unit time. To do this we integrate (39.1) over all velocities v_z from 0 to ∞ and over v_x and v_y from $-\infty$ to $+\infty$. (One must not integrate over v_z from $-\infty$ to 0 since for $v_z < 0$ the molecule would be flying away from the wall and hence would not hit it.)

This gives

$$v = \frac{N}{V}\sqrt{\frac{kT}{2\pi m}} = \frac{P}{\sqrt{(2\pi mkT)}} \tag{39.2}$$

(we have expressed the density of the gas in terms of its pressure according to the Clapeyron equation).

Formula (39.1) may be written in spherical co-ordinates in "velocity space", introducing, instead of v_x, v_y, v_z, the absolute value of the velocity v and the polar angles θ and ϕ defining its direction. If we take the z axis for the polar axis then $v_z = v \cos \theta$ and

$$d\nu_v = \frac{N}{V}\left(\frac{m}{2\pi kT}\right)^{3/2} e^{-mv^2/2kT} v^3 \sin \theta \cos \theta \, d\theta \, d\phi \, dv. \tag{39.3}$$

We now consider collisions of molecules with each other. To do this it is necessary to find first of all the distribution of the molecules in terms of their velocities relative to one another (the velocity in every case being that of the centre of gravity of the molecule). To do this we choose one of the gas molecules and consider the motion of all the other molecules relative to it. This is, for each molecule we consider, not the absolute velocity v (relative to the walls of the vessel) but the velocity v' relative to some other molecule. In other words, instead of dealing with separate molecules we consider each time the relative motion of a pair of molecules and are not interested in the motion of their common centre of gravity.

From mechanics we know that the energy of relative motion of two material particles (of masses m_1 and m_2) is equal to $\frac{1}{2}m'v'^2$, where $m' = m_1 m_2/(m_1+m_2)$ is their "reduced mass" and v' their relative velocity. Hence the distribution of the molecules of a gas over the relative velocities has the same form as the distribution over the absolute velocities with m replaced by the "reduced mass" m'. Provided the molecules are identical $m' = m/2$ and we obtain, for the number of molecules per unit volume whose velocities relative to the given molecule lie between v' and $v'+dv'$, the expression

$$dN_{v'} = \frac{N}{V}\frac{\pi}{2}\left(\frac{m}{\pi kT}\right)^{3/2} e^{-mv'^2/4kT} v'^2 \, dv'. \tag{39.4}$$

The collisions of molecules with each other may be accompanied by various different processes: their deflection (scattering) through a definite angle; dissociation into atoms, etc. The processes taking place in a collision are usually characterised by their "cross-sections". The "cross-section" for some process taking place in the collision of some given molecule with others is defined as the ratio of the probability of such a collision in unit time to the density of flow of the particles (the density of flow is the number of corresponding particles per unit volume multiplied by their velocity).

Hence the number of collisions (per unit time) of a given particle with the others followed by a process with cross-section σ is equal to

$$\nu' = \frac{N}{V}\frac{\pi}{2}\left(\frac{m}{\pi kT}\right)^{3/2} \int_0^\infty e^{-mv'/4kT}\sigma v'^3 \, dv'. \tag{39.5}$$

The total number of such collisions per unit time in the whole volume occupied by the gas is obviously equal to $\nu'N/2$.

PROBLEMS

1. Find the number of impacts of gas molecules on unit area of the wall per unit time, for which the angle between the direction of the velocity of the molecule and the normal to the surface lies between θ and $\theta + d\theta$.

SOLUTION:

$$d\nu_\theta = \frac{N}{V}\left(\frac{2kT}{m\pi}\right)^{1/2} \sin\theta\cos\theta \, d\theta.$$

2. Find the number of impacts of gas molecules on unit area of the wall per unit time for which the absolute value of the velocity lies between v and $v + dv$.

SOLUTION:

$$d\nu_v = \frac{N}{V}\pi\left(\frac{m}{2\pi kT}\right)^{3/2} e^{-mv^2/2kT}v^3 \, dv.$$

3. Find the total kinetic energy E_{imp} of the gas molecules striking unit area per unit time.

SOLUTION:

$$E_{\mathrm{imp}} = \frac{N}{V}\sqrt{\frac{2k^3T^3}{m\pi}} = P\sqrt{\frac{2kT}{m\pi}}.$$

4. Find the number of collisions of one molecule with the others in unit time. Assume the molecules are rigid spheres of radius r.

SOLUTION: The cross-section for the collision of molecules with one another will now be $\sigma = \pi(2r^2) = 4\pi r^2$ (since a collision occurs each time two molecules pass at a distance less than $2r$). Substituting this in (39.5), we get:

$$\nu = 16r^2\frac{N}{V}\sqrt{\frac{\pi kT}{m}} = 16r^2 P\sqrt{\frac{\pi}{mkT}}.$$

§40. The perfect gas not in equilibrium

The Boltzmann distribution can also be deduced, by quite a different method, from the condition that the entropy of the gas as a whole regarded as a closed system should be a maximum. This method is of considerable interest in itself, since it is based on a method which allows us to calculate the entropy of a gas which is in an arbitrary macroscopic state, and not necessarily in equilibrium.

Every macroscopic state of perfect gas can be characterised in the following way. We divide all the quantum states of an individual particle of the gas into groups each of which contains neighbouring states (having, in particular, neighbouring energies). The numbers of states in each group are still very large, as are the numbers of particles in them. We label these groups of states by numbers $j = 1, 2, \ldots$, and let G_j be the number of states in group j and N_j the number of particles in these states. Then the numbers N_j will completely specify the macroscopic state of the gas.

The problem of calculating the entropy of the gas is reduced to the problem of determining the statistical weight $\Delta\Gamma$ of the given macroscopic state, i.e. the number of macroscopic ways in which this state can be achieved. Regarding each group of particles as an independent system and denoting its statistical weight by $\Delta\Gamma_j$ we can write

$$\Delta\Gamma = \prod_j \Delta\Gamma_j \tag{40.1}$$

Thus the problem is reduced to the calculation of the $\Delta\Gamma_j$.

In Boltzmann statistics the mean occupation numbers of all quantum states are small compared with unity. This means that the numbers N_j of particles must be small compared with the numbers G_j of states ($N_j \ll G_j$) but, of course, still very large. As was explained in §37 the smallness of the mean occupation numbers allows us to assume that all the particles are distributed over the different states independently of each other. Putting every one of N_j particles into one of G_j states we get altogether $G_j{}^{N_j}$ distributions, but this includes some identical ones differing only by a permutation of the particles (all the particles are identical). The number of permutations of N_j particles is $N_j!$ and so the statistical weight of the distribution of N_j particles over G_j states is equal to

$$\Delta\Gamma_j = \frac{G_j{}^{N_j}}{N_j!}. \tag{40.2}$$

The entropy of the gas is calculated as the logarithm of the statistical weight:

$$S = k \log \Delta\Gamma = k \, \Sigma \log \Delta\Gamma_j$$

Substituting from (40.2) we have:

$$S = k \sum_j (N_j \log G_j - \log N_j!).$$

Bearing in mind that the numbers N_j are large we may use for $\log N_j!$

the approximation $\log N_j = N_j \log (N_j/e)$† and we get:

$$S = k \sum_j N_j \log \frac{eG_j}{N_j}. \tag{40.3}$$

This formula solves our problem by defining the entropy of a perfect gas in an arbitrary macroscopic state determined by a set of numbers N_j. Let us rewrite it introducing the numbers $\bar{n}_j$, the average number of particles in each of the quantum states of group j:

$$\bar{n}_j = \frac{N_j}{G_j}. \tag{40.4}$$

Then

$$S = k \sum G_j \bar{n}_j \log \frac{e}{\bar{n}_j}. \tag{40.5}$$

If the motion of the particles is quasi-classical then one can transform this to the distribution of particles over phase space. We divide the phase space of the particles into cells $\Delta p^{(j)} \Delta q^{(j)}$, each of which is small but nevertheless contains a large number of particles. The number of quantum states "associated" with such a cell is equivalent to

$$G_j = \frac{\Delta p^{(j)} \Delta q^{(j)}}{(2\pi\hbar)^r} = \Delta\tau^{(j)} \tag{40.6}$$

(r being the number of degrees of freedom of the particle) and we shall write the number of particles in these states in the form $N_j = n(p, q)\Delta\tau^{(j)}$ where $n(p, q)$ is the density of distribution of particles in phase space. We now substitute these expressions into (40.5) and then, bearing in mind that the cells are small and their number large, we replace the summation over j by integration over the whole phase space of the particles:

$$S = k \int n \log \frac{e}{n} \, d\tau. \tag{40.7}$$

In the equilibrium state the entropy must be a maximum (in its application to the perfect gas this assertion is sometimes called the Boltzmann theorem). We now show how from this requirement one can find the distribution functions of the gas particles in a state of statistical equilibrium. The

† For large N we may approximately replace the sum $\log N! = \log 1 + \log 2 + \dots \log N$ by the integral

$$\int_0^N \log x \, dx = N \log \frac{N}{e}$$

problem consists of finding those $\bar{n}_j$ which give the sum (40.5) its maximum possible value subject to the additional conditions

$$\sum_j N_j = \sum_j G_j \bar{n}_j = N$$

$$\sum_j \epsilon_j N_j = \sum_j \epsilon_j G_j \bar{n}_j = E,$$

which express the fact that the total number of particles N and the total energy E of the gas remain constant. Following the well-known method of Lagrange's undetermined multipliers, we must equate to zero the derivatives

$$\frac{\partial}{\partial \bar{n}_j}\left(\frac{S}{k}+\alpha N+\beta E\right) = 0, \tag{40.8}$$

where α, β are some constants. After differentiating we find:

$$G_j(-\log \bar{n}_j+\alpha+\beta\epsilon_j) = 0,$$

whence $\log \bar{n}_j = \alpha + \beta\epsilon_j$, or

$$\bar{n} = e^{\alpha+\beta\epsilon_j}.$$

This is simply the Boltzmann distribution which we already know and the constants α and β are connected with T and μ by $\alpha = \mu/kT$, $\beta = -1/kT$†.

§41. The free energy of a perfect Boltzmann gas

We now apply the general formula (31.3)

$$F = -kT \log \sum_n e^{-E_n/kT} \tag{41.1}$$

to the calculation of the free energy of a gas obeying Boltzmann statistics.

When we write the energy E_n as the sum of the energies ϵ_k we can reduce the summation over all states of the gas to summation over all states of a single molecule. Every state of the gas will be specified by a set of N (N being the number of molecules in the gas) of the quantities ϵ_k which, in the Boltzmann case, can be taken to be all different (no more than one molecule in each molecular state). Writing $e^{-E_n/kT}$ as the product of factors $e^{-\epsilon_k/kT}$ for each molecule and summing independently over all states of each molecule we obtain the expression

$$\left(\sum_k e^{-\epsilon_k/kT}\right)^N. \tag{41.2}$$

---

† These values for α and β could have been foreseen: eqs. (40.8) can be written in the form of a relation between the differentials

$$dS+\alpha k\, dN+\beta k\, dE = 0$$

which must coincide with the thermodynamic identity (for constant volume) $dE = T\, dS+\mu\, dN$.

The set of possible values of ϵ_k is the same for all the molecules of the gas and so are therefore the sums $\sum_k e^{-\epsilon_k/kT}$.

It is necessary, however, to bear in mind the following fact. All the sets of ϵ_k differing only by a permutation of identical molecules of the gas amongst the levels ϵ_k correspond to the same quantum state of the gas, but in the partition function in formula (41.1) each of these states must be counted only once.[†] Hence we must divide expression (41.2) by the number of possible permutations of N molecules, i.e. by $N!$.[‡] This gives:

$$\sum e^{-E_n/kT} = \frac{1}{N!}\left(\sum_k e^{-\epsilon_k/kT}\right)^N. \tag{41.3}$$

Substituting this expression into (41.1) we obtain

$$F = -kT \log \sum_k e^{-\epsilon_k/kT} + kT \log N!$$

Since N is a very large number one can use the formula for

$$\log N! \cong N \log \frac{N}{e}$$

(see footnote on page 118). As a result we obtain the following formula:

$$F = -NkT \log\left[\frac{e}{N}\sum_k e^{-\epsilon_k/kT}\right], \tag{41.4}$$

which allows us to calculate the free energy of any gas consisting of identical particles and obeying Boltzmann statistics.

In classical statistics formula (41.4) must be written in the form

$$F = -NkT \log\frac{e}{N}\int e^{-\epsilon(p,\,q)/kT}\,d\tau, \tag{41.5}$$

where the integration is taken over the phase space of a molecule ($d\tau$ given by (38.1)).

§42. The equation of state of the perfect gas

It was already pointed out (§38) that the translational motion of the gas molecules is always quasi-classical and that the energy of a molecule may be written in the form

$$\epsilon_k(p_x, p_y, p_z) = \frac{p_x^2 + p_y^2 + p_z^2}{2m} + \epsilon_k' \tag{42.1}$$

---

† See footnote on page 90.

‡ It is important to note that in Boltzmann statistics the part played in expression (41.2) by terms containing equal ϵ_k is negligibly small.

where the first term is the kinetic energy of its translational motion and ϵ_k' are the energy levels corresponding to the rotation of the molecule and its internal motion; ϵ_k' depends neither on the velocity, nor the co-ordinates of the centre of gravity of the molecule (we assume that there is no external field present).

The partition function under the logarithm in (41.4) must now be replaced by the expression

$$\sum_k \frac{1}{(2\pi\hbar)^3} e^{-\epsilon_k'/kT} \int_V \int \int \int_{-\infty}^{+\infty} e^{-\frac{1}{2mkT}(p_x^2 + p_y^2 + p_z^2)} \, dp_x \, dp_y \, dp_z \, dV$$

$$= V \left(\frac{mkT}{2\pi\hbar^2}\right)^{3/2} \sum_k e^{-\epsilon_k'/kT}. \qquad (42.2)$$

(The integration over $dV = dx \, dy \, dz$ is taken over the whole volume of the gas V).

For the free energy we get

$$F = -NkT \log\left[\frac{eV}{N} \left(\frac{mkT}{2\pi\hbar^2}\right)^{3/2} \sum_k e^{-\epsilon_k'/kT} \right]. \qquad (42.3)$$

The sum in this expression obviously cannot be calculated in general form without any assumption about the properties of the molecules. However, it is important to note that it is a function of temperature alone. Hence the way in which the free energy depends on the volume is completely determined by formula (42.3), making it possible to obtain a series of important general results about the properties of a perfect gas (in the absence of an external field).

Isolating the volume term in (42.3) we may write this formula in the form

$$F = -NkT \log\frac{eV}{N} + Nf(T) \qquad (42.4)$$

where $f(T)$ is some function of temperature.

For the pressure of the gas we obtain from this:

$$P = -\frac{\partial F}{\partial V} = \frac{NkT}{V},$$

or

$$PV = NkT. \qquad (42.5)$$

We have obtained here, as the equation of state of a perfect gas, the well-known *Clapeyron's Equation*. It is often written in the form $PV = RT$ where R is called the *gas constant*.†

---

† For a gram-molecule of gas ($N = 6 \cdot 023.10^{23}$, Avogadro's Number) the gas constant is equal to $R = 8 \cdot 31410^7$ erg/degree $= 1 \cdot 986$ cal/degree $= 0 \cdot 08205$ l-atm/degree.

Knowing this one can also find the other thermodynamic functions. Thus the thermodynamic potential is equal to

$$\Phi = -NkT \log \frac{eV}{N} + Nf(T) + PV.$$

Substituting for V in terms of P and T from (42.5) (Φ must be expressed as a function of P and T) and introducing a new function of temperature $\chi(T) = f(T) - kT \log kT$, we obtain:

$$\Phi = NkT \log P + N\chi(T). \tag{42.6}$$

The entropy is defined as

$$S = -\frac{\partial F}{\partial T} = Nk \log \frac{eV}{N} - Nf'(T) \tag{42.7}$$

or, as a function of P and T:

$$S = -\frac{\partial \Phi}{\partial T} = -Nk \log P - N\chi'(T). \tag{42.8}$$

Lastly, the energy is equal to

$$E = F + TS = Nf(T) - NTf'(T). \tag{42.9}$$

We see that the energy is a function of the temperature of the gas only (the same applies to the heat function $W = E + PV = E + NkT$). This fact is, incidentally, obvious from the start. Since the molecules of a perfect gas are supposed not to interact with one another, a change in the average distance between them as the volume of the gas changes cannot affect the energy.

Besides the functions E and W other functions of temperature only are the specific heats $C_v = (\partial E/\partial T)_V$ and $C_p = (\partial W/\partial T)_P$. Since, for a perfect gas, $W = E = NkT$, the difference between these specific heats has the universal value

$$C_p - C_v = Nk. \tag{42.10}$$

PROBLEMS

1. Find the work done on a perfect gas in an isothermal change of volume from V_1 to V_2 (or pressure from P_1 to P_2).

SOLUTION: The amount of work in question, R, is equal to the change in the free energy of the gas. According to (42.4) we have:

$$R = F_1 - F_2 = NkT \log \frac{V_1}{V_2} = NkT \log \frac{P_2}{P_1},$$

The amount of heat absorbed during this process is

$$Q = T(S_2 - S_1) = NkT \log \frac{V_2}{V_1}.$$

The latter follows directly from the fact that $R+Q$ is the change in the energy of the perfect gas which must be zero for an isothermal process.

2.   Two identical perfect gases with the same temperature T and number of particles N, but with different pressures P_1 and P_2, are in two vessels. The vessels are then connected. Determine the change in entropy.

SOLUTION: Before the vessels are connected the entropy of the two gases was equal to the sum of their entropies; $S_0 = -Nk \log P_1 P_2 - 2N\chi'(T)$. After the vessels are connected the temperature of the gases remains the same (since the energy of the two gases remains conserved). The pressure will be determined by the equation

$$\frac{1}{P} = \frac{V_1 + V_2}{2NkT} = \frac{1}{2}\left(\frac{1}{P_1} + \frac{1}{P_2}\right).$$

The entropy now is equal to

$$S = 2Nk \log \frac{P_1 + P_2}{2P_1 P_2} - 2N\chi'(T).$$

Thus the change in entropy

$$\Delta S = Nk \log \frac{(P_1 + P_2)^2}{4P_1 P_2}.$$

3.   Calculate the energy of a perfect gas enclosed in a cylindrical vessel (radius R and length h) rotating about its axis with angular velocity Ω.

SOLUTION: From §34 the rotation is equivalent to the appearance of an external "centrifugal" field with potential energy $u = \frac{1}{2}m\Omega^2 r^2$ (r being the distance of the point from the axis of rotation). The presence of the external field requires the presence of an extra factor $e^{-u/kT}$ in the integrand in (42.2); correspondingly in the argument of the logarithm in (42.3) the volume V must be replaced by $\int e^{-u/kT} \, dV$. Hence we have the following formula

$$F = F_0 - NkT \log \frac{1}{V} \int e^{-u/kT} \, dV,$$

where F_0 is the free energy of the gas in the absence of an external field.

In our case we have, by using this formula for the free energy (in the rotating system of co-ordinates):

$$F' = F_0 - NkT \log \frac{1}{\pi R^2 h} \int_0^h \int_0^R e^{m\Omega^2 r^2/2kT} 2\pi r \, dr dz$$

$$= F_0 - NkT \log \left[\frac{2kT}{m\Omega^2 R^2}(e^{m\Omega^2 R^2/2kT} - 1) \right].$$

The angular momentum of the gas is

$$M = -\frac{\partial F'}{\partial \Omega} = -\frac{2NkT}{\Omega} + \frac{NmR^2\Omega}{1 - e^{-m\Omega^2 R^2/2kT}}.$$

The energy in the system rotating with the body is

$$E' = F' - T\frac{\partial F'}{\partial T} = E_0 - \frac{Nm\Omega^2 R^2}{2(1 - e^{-m\Omega^2 R^2/2kT})} + NkT,$$

and the energy in the stationary system (see (26.5)) is

$$E = E' + M\Omega = E_0 + \frac{Nm\Omega^2 R^2}{2(1 - e^{-m\Omega^2 R^2/2kT})} - NkT$$

(E_0 being the energy of the stationary gas).

§43. Perfect gas with constant specific heat

We shall see later on that, in a wide range of important cases, over greater or smaller temperature intervals, the specific heat of a gas remains constant, independent of temperature. Bearing this in mind we shall calculate here the thermodynamic functions for such a gas in the general case. It will be convenient, further on, to deal with the specific heats referred to one molecule. We shall denote them by small letters

$$C_v = Nc_v, \qquad C_p = Nc_p. \tag{43.1}$$

By differentiating (42.9) with respect to the energy we find that the function $f(T)$ is related to the specific heat c_v by the equation

$$-Tf''(T) = c_v.$$

By integrating this relation we obtain:

$$f(T) = -c_v T \log kT - k\zeta T + \epsilon_0$$

where the constants of integration are denoted by $k\zeta$ and ϵ_0. Substituting this expression into (42.4) we obtain for the free energy the following final expression:

$$F = N\epsilon_0 - NkT \log\frac{eV}{N} - Nc_v T \log kT - Nk\zeta T. \tag{43.2}$$

The constant ζ is called the *chemical constant* for the gas. For the energy we obtain

$$E = N\epsilon_0 + Nc_v T, \tag{43.3}$$

i.e. the energy is a linear function of temperature.

The thermodynamic potential Φ for the gas is obtained by adding to (43.2) the quantity $PV = NkT$ and then expressing the volume of the gas in terms of pressure and temperature. We obtain:

$$\Phi = N\epsilon_0 + NkT \log P - Nc_p T \log kT - Nk\zeta T. \tag{43.4}$$

The heat function $W = E + PV$ is equal to

$$W = N\epsilon_0 + Nc_pT. \tag{43.5}$$

Finally, by differentiating (43.2) and (43.4) with respect to temperature, we obtain the entropy expressed similarly in terms of T and V or T and P:

$$S = Nk \log\frac{eV}{N} + Nc_v \log kT + (k\zeta + c_v)N, \tag{43.6}$$

$$S = -Nk \log P + Nc_p \log kT + (k\zeta + c_p)N. \tag{43.7}$$

From these expressions for the entropy one can derive, in particular, the relations connecting the pressure, volume, and temperature of a perfect gas (with constant specific heat) during its adiabatic expansion or compression (the so-called Poisson adiabatic). Since in an adiabatic process the entropy remains constant, it follows from (43.7) that $-Nk \log P + Nc_p \log T = \text{const}$, whence $T^{c_p}P^{-k} = \text{const}$, o, using (42.10)

$$T^\gamma P^{1-\gamma} = \text{const}, \tag{43.8}$$

where γ stands for the constant ratio

$$\gamma = \frac{c_p}{c_v}. \tag{43.9}$$

Using also the equation of state $PV = NkT$, we obtain the relations between T and V and between P and V:

$$TV^{\gamma-1} = \text{const}, \qquad PV^\gamma = \text{const}. \tag{43.10}$$

PROBLEMS

1. Two identical perfect gases with the same pressure P and number of particles N, but with different temperatures T_1 and T_2 are in two vessels with volumes V_1 and V_2. The vessels are then connected. Find the change in entropy.

SOLUTION: Before the vessels are connected the entropy of the two gases (equal to the sum of their separate entropies) is, according to (43.7), $S_0 = -Nk \log P + Nc_p \log T_1T_2$.[†] After the vessels have been connected the temperatures of the gases equalise. The sum of the energies of the two gases remains constant. Using the expression for the energy (43.3) we find:

$$T = \tfrac{1}{2}(T_1 + T_2)$$

(T being the final temperature).

After the vessels have been connected, the gas has $2N$ particles and occupies a volume $V_1 + V_2 = Nk(T_1 + T_2)/P$. The pressure is now given by $2NkT/(V_1 + V_2) = P$, i.e. it remains the same, and the entropy is equal to

$$S = -2Nk \log P + 2Nc_p \log\frac{T_1 + T_2}{2}.$$

---

† We always omit constant terms in the entropy and energy, which are unimportant for solution of the problems.

The change in the entropy is

$$\Delta S = S - S_0 = Nc_p \log \frac{(T_1 + T_2)^2}{4 T_1 T_2}.$$

2. Find the work done on a perfect gas during an adiabatic compression.

SOLUTION: In an adiabatic process the quantity of heat $Q = 0$, so that $R = E_2 - E_1$, where $E_2 - E_1$ is the change in energy during the process. According to (43.3) we find $R = Nc_v(T_2 - T_1)$, where T_2 and T_1 are the temperatures of the gas before and after the process; R can be expressed in terms of the initial and final volumes V_1 and V_2 by using (43.10):

$$R = Nc_v T_1 \left[\left(\frac{V_1}{V_2} \right)^{\gamma-1} - 1 \right] = Nc_v T_2 \left[1 - \left(\frac{V_2}{V_1} \right)^{\gamma-1} \right].$$

3. Find the work and quantity of heat absorbed by a gas during a process occurring at constant volume (isochoric).

SOLUTION: Since in this case the work $R = 0$, we have:

$$Q = E_2 - E_1 = Nc_v T_2 \left[1 - \left(\frac{V_2}{V_1} \right)^{\gamma-1} \right].$$

4. Find the work and quantity of heat absorbed during a process occurring at constant pressure (isobaric).

SOLUTION: At constant pressure we have:

$$R = -P(V_2 - V_1), \qquad Q = (W_2 - W_1)$$

whence

$$R = Nk(T_1 - T_2), \qquad Q = Nc_p(T_2 - T_1)$$

5. Find the work done on a gas and the quantity of heat absorbed by it during a compression from volume V_1 to volume V_2 following the law $PV^n = a$ (polytropic process).

SOLUTION: The work done is

$$R = -\int_{V_1}^{V_2} P \, dV = \frac{a}{n-1} (V_2^{1-n} - V_1^{1-n}).$$

Since the sum of the quantity of heat and the work done is equal to the total change in energy we have:

$$Q = Nc_v(T_2 - T_1) - R$$

and since

$$T = PV/Nk = (a/Nk) V^{1-n},$$

we have

$$Q = a \left(\frac{c_v}{k} + \frac{1}{1-n} \right) (V_2^{1-n} - V_1^{1-n}).$$

6. Find the work which is done on a perfect gas and the quantity of heat absorbed by it when the gas undergoes a cyclic process (i.e. after the process is complete it returns to its initial state) consisting of two isochoric and two isobaric stages: gas passes from the state with pressure P_1 and volume V_1 to the state with P_1, V_2, then to state P_2, V_2, then to P_2, V_1, and finally to P_1, V_1.

SOLUTION: The change in energy during a cyclic process is equal to zero since the initial state coincides with the final one. Hence the work and quantity of heat absorbed in such a process are equal and opposite ($R = -Q$). To determine R in our case we notice that the work done during the isochoric processes is zero and the work done in the two isobaric processes in $-P_1(V_2-V_1.)$ and $-P_2(V_1-V_2)$, respectively. Thus $R = (V_2-V_1)(P_2-P_1)$.

7. The same for a cycle consisting of an isobar and two isothermals. The successive states of the gas have volume and temperature (1) V_1, T_1; (2) V_1, T_2; (3) V_2, T_2; (4) V_2, T_1; (5) V_1, T_1.

SOLUTION:

$$R = (T_2-T_1)Nk \log V_1/V_2.$$

8. The same for a cycle consisting of two isothermal and two adiabatic steps. (Successive states have entropy, temperature and pressure (1) S_1, T_1, P_1; (2) S_1, T_2; (3) S_2, T_2, P_2; (4) S_2, T_1; (5) S_1, T_1, P_1.)

SOLUTION:

$$Q = (T_2-T_1)(S_2-S_1) = (T_2-T_1)\left(Nk \log\frac{P_1}{P_2} + Nc_p \log\frac{T_2}{T_1}\right).$$

9. The same for a cycle consisting of two isobaric and two isothermal processes. (Successive states are: (1) P_1, T_1; (2) P_1, T_2; (3) P_2, P_2; (4) P_2, T_1; (5) P_1, T_1.)

SOLUTION: The work done on the gas during the isobaric processes is equal (see Problem 4) to $Nk(T_1-T_2)$ and $Nk(T_2-T_1)$, and in the isothermal processes to $NkT_2 \log P_2/P_1$ and $NkT_1 \log P_1/P_2$. Their sum is equal to

$$R = Nk(T_2-T_1) \log\frac{P_2}{P_1}.$$

10. The same for a cycle consisting of two isobaric and two adiabatic processes (successive states: (1) P_1, S_1, T_1; (2) P_1, S_2; (3) P_2, S_2, T_2; (4) P_2, S_1; (5) P_1, S_1, T_1).

SOLUTION: The temperature in the second state is $T_2(P_2/P_1)^{(1-\gamma)/\gamma}$, and in the fourth $T_1(P_1/P_2)^{(1-\gamma)/\gamma}$ (one can calculate them from T_1 and T_2 by means of eq. 43.8). The quantity of heat absorbed by the gas in the adiabatic processes is equal to zero and in the isobaric ones (see Problem 4) is

$$Nc_p\left[T_2\left(\frac{P_2}{P_1}\right)^{(1-\gamma)/\gamma} - T_1\right] \text{ and } Nc_p\left[T_1\left(\frac{P_1}{P_2}\right)^{(1-\gamma)/\gamma} - T_2\right].$$

Thus

$$Q = Nc_pT_1\left[\left(\frac{P_1}{P_2}\right)^{(1-\gamma)/\gamma} - 1\right] + Nc_pT_2\left[\left(\frac{P_2}{P_1}\right)^{(1-\gamma)/\gamma} - 1\right].$$

11. The same for a cycle consisting of an isochoric and two adiabatic processes (successive states: (1) V_1, S_1, T_1; (2) V_1, S_2; (3) V_2, S_2, T_2; (4) V_2, S_1; (5) V_1, S_1, T_1).

SOLUTION: By using the result of Problem (2) we find:

$$R = Nc_vT_2\left[1-\left(\frac{V_2}{V_1}\right)^{\gamma-1}\right] + Nc_vT_1\left[1-\left(\frac{V_1}{V_2}\right)^{\gamma-1}\right].$$

12. Determine the maximum work which one can obtain by connecting two vessels containing identical perfect gases having the same temperature T_0 and number of particles N, but different volumes V_1 and V_2.

SOLUTION: The maximum work is done when the process is reversible, i.e. the entropy remains constant. The work is equal to the difference in energies before and after the process takes place (§19). Before the vessels are connected the entropy of both gases is equal to the sum of their entropies and is, from (43.6)

$$S_0 = Nk \log \frac{e^2 V_1 V_2}{N^2} + 2Nc_v \log T_0.$$

After the vessels are connected we have a gas consisting of $2N$ particles occupying a volume $V_1 + V_2$ at some temperature T. Its entropy

$$S = 2Nk \log \frac{e(V_1 + V_2)}{2N} + 2Nc_v \log T.$$

From the condition $S_0 = S$ we find the temperature T:

$$T = T_0 \left[\frac{4 V_1 V_2}{(V_1 + V_2)^2} \right]^{(\gamma - 1)/2}.$$

The energy of both gases before the vessels are connected is $E_0 = 2Nc_v T_0$. After the connection it is $E = 2Nc_v T$. Hence the maximum work

$$R_{\max} = E_0 - E = 2Nc_v(T_0 - T)$$

$$= 2Nc_v T_0 \left[1 - \left(\frac{4 V_1 V_2}{(V_1 + V_2)^2} \right)^{(\gamma - 1)/2} \right].$$

13.   The same as in the previous problem for gases having the same pressure P_0 and different temperatures T_1 and T_2 before the vessels are connected.

SOLUTION: In a similar way to the solution of problem (12) we find

$$R_{\max} = Nc_v \left\{ T_1 + T_2 - 2^\gamma \sqrt{T_1 T_2} \left[\frac{T_1 T_2}{(T_1 + T_2)^2} \right]^{(\gamma - 1)/2} \right\}.$$

14.   Find the minimum work which must be done on a perfect gas to compress it from pressure P_1 to pressure P_2 at a constant temperature equal to that of the surrounding medium $(T = T_0)$.

SOLUTION: In accordance with (20.2) the minimum work $R_{\min} = (E_2 - E_1) - T_0(S_2 - S_1) + P_0(V_2 - V_1)$ where the suffixes 1 and 2 show that the quantities refer to the gas before and after compression. In the given case the energy E does not change (because the temperature is constant), i.e. $E_2 - E_1$. Using (43.7) we find the change in entropy when the pressure is changed from P_1 to P_2: $S_2 - S_1 = Nk \log (P_1/P_2)$, and the change in volume: $V_2 - V_1 = NkT_0(1/P_2 - 1/P_1)$. Hence we find

$$R_{\min} = NkT_0 \left[\log \frac{P_2}{P_1} + P_0 \left(\frac{1}{P_2} - \frac{1}{P_1} \right) \right].$$

15.   Determine the maximum work which one can obtain from a perfect gas by cooling it from temperature T to the temperature T_0 of the surrounding medium at constant volume.

SOLUTION: According to the general formula (20.3) we find

$$R_{\max} = Nc_v(T - T_0) + Nc_v T_0 \log \frac{T_0}{T}.$$

16.   The same for a gas cooled from temperature T to the temperature T_0 of the medium and at the same time expanding so that its pressure changes from P to the pressure P_0 of the medium.

SOLUTION:

$$R_{\max} = Nc_v(T - T_0) + NkT_0 \log\frac{P}{P_0} + Nc_pT_0 \log\frac{T_0}{T} + Nk\left(T\frac{P_0}{P} - T_0\right).$$

17. From a large, thermally insulated, reservoir of temperature T_0, gas flows into an empty insulated, vessel the pressure in the reservoir being kept constant. Find the change of the temperature of the gas in this process.

SOLUTION: The energy E of the gas in the vessel is made up of the energy E_0 which the gas had in the reservoir, and the work done on it in "ejecting" it from the reservoir. Since the state of the gas in the reservoir may be regarded as stationary we obtain the condition $W_0 = E$ (cf. §18). Hence the temperature of the gas in the vessel is

$$T = \gamma T_0.$$

§44. The law of equipartition

Before starting the detailed calculation of thermodynamic quantities of gases taking the various quantum effects into account, it is useful to consider the same problem from the purely classical point of view. Later we shall see in which cases, and to what extent, one can apply the results thus obtained to real gases.

A molecule is a configuration of atoms performing small oscillations about definite equilibrium positions which correspond to the minimum values of their interaction potential. The latter has the following form:

$$u = \epsilon_0 + \sum_{i,k=1}^{r_{\mathrm{vib}}} a_{ik}q_iq_k,$$

where ϵ_0 is the interaction energy of the atoms when all are in their equilibrium positions and the second term is a quadratic function of the co-ordinates specifying the distances of the atoms from their equilibrium position. The number r_{vib} of co-ordinates in this function is the number of vibrational degrees of freedom of the molecule.

This can be found in terms of the number of atoms in the molecule. A molecule with n atoms has $3n$ degrees of freedom. Of these, three correspond to the translational motion of the molecule as a whole and three to its rotation as a whole. If all the atoms are situated on a straight line (in particular for a diatomic molecule) then there are only two rotational degrees of freedom. Thus a non-collinear n-atomic molecule has, altogether, $(3n-6)$ vibrational degrees of freedom and a collinear one has $(3n-5)$. When $n = 1$ there are no vibrational degrees of freedom, since all three degrees of freedom are associated with the translational motion.

The total energy ϵ of the molecule is the sum of the kinetic and potential energy terms. The former is a quadratic function of all the momenta, whose number is equal to the total number $3n$ of degrees of freedom of the molecule. Hence the energy ϵ is of the form $\epsilon = \epsilon_0 + f_{\mathrm{II}}(p, q)$ where $f_{\mathrm{II}}(p, q)$ is a quadratic function of the momenta and co-ordinates. The total number of variables in this function is $l = 6n - 6$ (for a non-collinear molecule) or $l = 6n - 5$ (for a collinear one). For a monatomic gas $l = 3$, since the co-ordinates do not enter into the expression for the energy.

Substituting this expression for the energy into formula (41.5), we have:

$$F = -NkT \log \frac{e \cdot e^{-\epsilon_0/kT}}{N} \int e^{-f_{II}(p,q)/kT} \, d\tau.$$

To determine the dependence of the integral in this expression on temperature we substitute $p = p'\sqrt{T}$, $q = q'\sqrt{T}$ for all variables on which the function $f_{II}(p, q)$ depends. Since this function is quadratic we have:

$$f_{II}(p,q) = T f_{II}(p',q'),$$

and the T in the exponent of the integrand will cancel. The transformation of the differentials of the variables in $d\tau$ will give a factor $T^{l/2}$ which can be taken outside the integral and the integration over the vibrational co-ordinates, q, is taken over that range of their values which corresponds to the atoms remaining inside the molecule. Since, however, the integrand decreases rapidly with increasing q, one can take the integration over the whole range from $-\infty$ to $+\infty$, as for the momenta. The transformation of variables will, then, not change the limits of integration and the whole integral will be a temperature independent constant. Also taking into account the fact that the integration over the co-ordinates of the centre of gravity of the molecule gives the volume V occupied by the gas, we finally obtain for the free energy of the molecule an expression of the form

$$F = -NkT \log \frac{AVe^{-\epsilon_0/kT} T^{l/2}}{N}$$

(A being constant). Expanding the logarithm we obtain an expression exactly of the type (43.2) with a constant specific heat equal to

$$c_v = \frac{l}{2}k. \tag{44.1}$$

Similarly the specific heat $c_p = c_v + k$ is equal to

$$c_p = \frac{l+2}{2}k. \tag{44.2}$$

Thus we see that the purely classical ideal gas must have a constant specific heat. Formula (44.1) allows us in addition to lay down the following rule: with every variable occurring in the energy $\epsilon(p, q)$ of the molecule is associated an equal part $k/2$ of the specific heat c_v of the gas, or, in other words, an equal part $kT/2$ of its energy. This rule is called the *law of equipartition*.

Bearing in mind that only the momenta of the translational and rotational degrees of freedom enter into the energy $\epsilon(p, q)$ of a molecule we may say that each of these degrees of freedom contributes an amount $k/2$ to the specific heat. From each vibrational degree of freedom two variables (co-ordinates and momenta) enter into the energy $\epsilon(p, q)$ and its contribution to the specific heat is k.

For the model we are considering it is easy to find the energy distribution of the molecules of the gas in general form. For convenience we shall measure energies from ϵ_0, i.e. exclude this constant from the expression for $\epsilon(p, q)$. Let us consider the volume of the phase space of the molecule whose points correspond to values of $\epsilon(p, q)$ less than or equal to some given value ϵ. In other words we define the integral $\tau(\epsilon) = \int d\tau$ taken over the region $\epsilon(p, q) \leqslant \epsilon$. From what we have said above, $\epsilon(p, q)$ is a quadratic function of l variables. Instead of those l of the p, q, on which the energy depends let us introduce new variables $p' = p/\sqrt{\epsilon}$ and $q' = q/\sqrt{\epsilon}$. Then the condition $\epsilon(p, q) \leqslant \epsilon$ transforms to

$$\epsilon(p', q') \leqslant 1,$$

and $\int d\tau$ into $\epsilon^{l/2} \int d\tau'$. The integral $\int d\tau'$ obviously is independent of ϵ so $\tau = \text{const } \epsilon^{l/2}$. Hence

$$d\tau(\epsilon) = \text{const } \epsilon^{(l/2)-1} d\epsilon$$

and the probability distribution for the energy is

$$dw_\epsilon = Ae^{-\epsilon/kT}\epsilon^{(l/2)-1} d\epsilon.$$

Determining A from the normalisation condition we obtain:

$$dw_\epsilon = \frac{1}{(kT)^{l/2}\Gamma(l/2)}e^{-\epsilon/kT}\epsilon^{(l/2)-1} d\epsilon. \tag{44.3}$$

PROBLEM

Find the specific heat of a perfect gas in the extreme relativistic range. (The energies of the particles are connected with their momenta by $\epsilon = c_p$, c being the velocity of light.)

SOLUTION: From (41.5) we have

$$F = -NkT \log\frac{eV}{N(2\pi\hbar)^3} \int_0^\infty e^{-cp/kT}4\pi p^2\, dp.$$

After carrying out the integration we obtain

$$F = -NkT \log\frac{AVT^3}{N}$$

(A being a constant). Hence we obtain for the specific heat the value

$$c_v = 3k$$

which is twice the specific heat of a non-relativistic monatomic gas.

§45. The perfect monatomic gas

The complete calculation of the free energy (and, with it, the other thermo-dynamic quantities) of a perfect gas requires the actual calculation of the partition function in the argument of the logarithm in formula (42.3)

$$Z = \sum_k e^{-\epsilon'_k/kT}.$$

Here ϵ'_k represent the energy levels of the atom and molecule (the translational kinetic energy of the particle is omitted). If the summation is taken only over all different energy levels then one must take into account the fact that the level may be degenerate. In such a case the corresponding term must enter into the sum over all the states as many times as the degree of degeneracy. We denote the latter by g_k; in this connection the degree of degeneracy of a level is often called its statistical weight. Omitting the accent on ϵ'_k for the sake of convenience, we write the sum in which we are interested in the form

$$Z = \sum_k g_k e^{-\epsilon_k/kT}. \tag{45.1}$$

The free energy of the gas

$$F = -NkT \log\left[\frac{eV}{N} \left(\frac{mkT}{2\pi\hbar^2} \right)^{3/2} Z \right]. \tag{45.2}$$

Turning to the consideration of monatomic gases note first of all the following important fact. As the temperature of the gas rises, so does the number of atoms in excited states, including also states in the continuous spectrum corresponding to ionisation of the atom. At not too high temperatures the number of ionised atoms in the gas is relatively quite insignificant. It is important to note, however, that the gas is already almost completely ionised at temperatures for which kT is of the order of the ionisation energy I_{ion} (and not merely for $kT \gg I_{\text{ion}}$; see §102). Hence there is no point in studying non-ionised gases except at temperatures for which $kT \ll I_{\text{ion}}$.†

It is well known that the positions of atomic levels (excluding their fine structure) are such that the separation of the first excited state from the ground state is comparable in value with the ionisation energy. Hence for temperatures for which $kT \ll I_{\text{ion}}$ there will be not only practically no ionised atoms in the gas, but also practically no excited atoms and so we may consider all atoms to be in their ground states.

Consider first of all the simplest case of atoms which, in their ground states, possess neither orbital angular momentum nor spin ($L = S = 0$); the atoms of the noble gases are examples of this. Then the ground state is non-degenerate and the partition function reduces to one term: $Z = e^{-\epsilon_0/kT}$. For a monatomic gas we usually assume $\epsilon_0 = 0$, i.e. measure the energy

---

† For different atoms the value of the temperatures I_{ion}/k vary between $5 \cdot 10^{10}$ (atoms of the alkali metals) and $28 \cdot 10^{10}$ (helium).

from the ground state of the atom; then $Z = 1$. Expanding the logarithm in (45.2) as the sum of several terms we obtain for the free energy an expression of the form (43.2) with the constant specific heat

$$c_v = \tfrac{3}{2}k \tag{45.3}$$

and the chemical constant

$$\zeta = \frac{3}{2}\log\frac{m}{2\pi\hbar^2}, \tag{45.4}$$

The value obtained for the specific heat is entirely due to the translational degrees of freedom with $k/2$ for each degree of freedom (remember that the translational motion of the gas particles is always quasi-classical). The "electronic degrees of freedom" naturally have no effect on thermodynamic quantities in the given conditions (the absence of any excited atoms in the gas).†

The expressions we have obtained allow us to introduce a criterion for the applicability of Boltzmann statistics. In this statistics one assumes that the numbers $\bar{n}_k$ are small:

$$\bar{n}_k = e^{(\mu-\varepsilon_k)/kT} \ll 1$$

(see (37.1)). It is obviously sufficient to require that the condition

$$e^{\mu/kT} \ll 1$$

should be fulfilled.

For the chemical potential $\mu = \Phi/N$ we have from (43.4), substituting for C_v and ζ from (45.3, 4):

$$\mu = kT\log\left[\frac{P}{(kT)^{5/2}}\left(\frac{2\pi\hbar^2}{m}\right)^{3/2}\right] = kT\log\left[\frac{N}{V}\left(\frac{2\pi\hbar^2}{mkT}\right)^{3/2}\right]. \tag{45.5}$$

Hence we obtain the criterion

$$\frac{N}{V}\left(\frac{\hbar^2}{mkT}\right)^{3/2} \ll 1. \tag{45.6}$$

This condition requires, for a given temperature, a sufficiently low density for the gas. The substitution of actual numerical values shows that in practice for all atomic (and molecular) gases this condition could only

---

† The "electronic part" of thermodynamic quantities can obviously in no circumstances be considered from the classical viewpoint. Note in this connection the fact (which we have so far implicitly assumed) that in classical statistics atoms must be considered as particles which have no internal structure. The impossibility of applying statistics based on classical mechanics to intra-atomic phenomena is also clear from the absurdities into which we would be led by inserting into the classical formulae for the energy distribution the interaction energy of electrons with the atomic nucleus. The latter is of the form $-a/r$ where r is the distance of the electron from the nucleus and a is a constant. On making the substitution we would obtain a factor $e^{a/rkT}$ in the distribution, becoming infinite at $r = 0$. This would mean that in a state of thermal equilibrium the electrons would "fall" into the nucleus.

be violated at densities at which the interaction between particles of the gas begins to be important and the gas in any case could not be considered as perfect.

The following visual interpretation of the criterion we have obtained is quite useful. Since the majority of atoms have energies of the order of kT and hence momenta of the order of $\sqrt{(mkT)}$ one can say that all the atoms occupy a volume in phase space of order $V(mkT)^{3/2}$. To this volume are "allotted" $\sim V(mkT)^{3/2}/\hbar^3$ quantum states. In the Boltzmann case this number must be large compared with the number N of particles. Hence (45.6) is obtained.

Finally we make the following remark. The formulae obtained in this section contradict the Nernst theorem: neither the entropy nor the specific heat vanish at $T = 0$. It must be borne in mind, however, that, under the conditions in which the Nernst theorem is formulated, all real gases are already condensed at sufficiently low temperatures. The Nernst theorem actually requires that the entropy of the body for a given value of its volume should tend to zero as $T \rightarrow 0$. But as $T \rightarrow 0$ the vapour pressure of any substance becomes arbitrarily small, so that a given finite quantity of substance in a given finite volume cannot remain gaseous as $T \rightarrow 0$.

If we consider a model of a gas, which could exist in principle, consisting of mutually repulsive particles, then, although such a gas will never condense, nevertheless Boltzmann statistics ceases to apply at sufficiently low temperatures; the application of Fermi or Bose statistics leads, as we shall see later, to expressions which satisfy the Nernst theorem.

§46. The monatomic gas: influence of electronic angular momentum

If, in the ground state of an atom, one of the angular momenta L or S differs from zero then, as before, the ground state has no fine structure. Actually, the absence of fine structure in the ground state is always connected with the vanishing of the orbital momentum L; but the spin may be non-zero (for example in the atoms of the alkali metals).

A level with spin S is always degenerate with degree $2S+1$. The only difference, compared with the case investigated in the previous section, is that the partition function Z will now be equal to $2S+1$ (instead of 1) and as a result the chemical constant (45.4) will be increased by an amount†

$$\zeta_S = \log(2S+1). \tag{46.1}$$

If the ground state has a fine structure then it must be borne in mind that the intervals of this fine structure are, in general, comparable with kT.

---

† We shall write down for reference the formula for the chemical potential of a monatomic gas with a statistical weight (degree of degeneracy) g in the ground state:

$$\mu = kT \log\left[\frac{P}{g(kT)^{5/2}}\left(\frac{2\pi\hbar^2}{m}\right)^{3/2}\right] = kT \log\left[\frac{N}{gV}\left(\frac{2\pi\hbar^2}{mkT}\right)^{3/2}\right]. \tag{46.1a}$$

This formula is also valid for a Boltzmann gas of elementary particles. For an electron gas $g = 2$.

Hence in the partition function all the components of the fine structure must be taken into account.

The components of the fine structure differ in the values of the total angular momentum of the atom (for the same orbital angular momentum L and spin S). We may denote these levels, starting from the lowest, by ϵ_J; each level with a given J has a degree of degeneracy $2J+1$ in the orientation of the total angular momentum.† Hence the partition function takes the form:

$$Z = \sum_J (2J+1)e^{-\epsilon_J/kT}. \qquad (46.2)$$

The summation is taken over all possible values of J (for given L and S). For the free energy we obtain:

$$F = -NkT \log\left[\frac{eV}{N}\left(\frac{mkT}{2\pi\hbar^2}\right)^{3/2} \sum_J (2J+1)e^{-\epsilon_J/kT}\right]. \qquad (46.3)$$

This expression simplifies considerably in the two limiting cases. Assume that the temperature is so high that kT is large compared with all intervals of fine structure;

$$kT \gg \epsilon_J.$$

Then one can assume $e^{-\epsilon_J/kT} \simeq 1$, and Z will reduce simply to the total number of components of the fine structure $(2S+1)(2L+1)$. The expression for the free energy will contain, as before, the constant specific heat $c_v = 3/2k$ while to the chemical constant (45.4) will be added the quantity

$$\zeta_{SL} = \log(2S+1)(2L+1). \qquad (46.4)$$

The same expressions for thermodynamic quantities (with different ζ) are also obtained in the opposite limiting case, when kT is small compared with the fine structure intervals.‡ In this case in the sum (46.2) one can omit all terms except that with $\epsilon_J = 0$ (the lowest component of the fine structure, i.e. the ground level of the atom). As a result, the term additional to (45.4) for the chemical constant will be

$$\zeta_J = \log(2J+1) \qquad (46.5)$$

where J is the total angular momentum of the atom in its ground state. Thus in the presence of fine structure in the ground state of an atom, the specific heat of the gas has the same, constant, value for sufficiently high and sufficiently low temperatures, and in between depends on the temperature, passing through a maximum. One must, however, bear in mind

---

† We assume that the so-called Russell-Saunders coupling applies in the atom. See, for example, *Quantum Mechanics*, §67.

‡ For example we may point out that the quantities ϵ_J/k for the components of the normal triplet term for oxygen are 230° and 320°; those for the normal quintuplet term of iron vary from 600° to 1400° and that for the normal doublet term of chlorine is 1300°.

that for the actual gases concerned (the vapours of heavy metals, atomic oxygen, etc.) only the high temperature region is important and there the specific heat is already constant.

We have so far completely ignored the possibility of the atom possessing a non-zero nuclear spin i. It is well known that the presence of nuclear spin leads to the so-called hyperfine splitting of the atomic levels. The intervals of this structure are, however, so insignificant, that they may be considered small compared with kT at absolutely all temperatures when the gas exists as a gas.† Hence in the calculation of the partition function one can completely ignore the differences in energy between the components of the hyperfine multiplet and allow for this splitting simply as an increase in the degree of degeneracy of all levels (and hence of the sum Z) by a factor $2i+1$. Correspondingly the free energy will contain an additional "nuclear" term

$$F_{\text{nucl}} = -NkT \log(2i+1) \tag{46.6}$$

This term does not affect the specific heat of the gas (the corresponding energy $E_{\text{nucl}} = 0$) and leads only to a change in the entropy of $S_{\text{nucl}} = Nk \log(2i+1)$, i.e. a change in the chemical constant of $S_{\text{nucl}} = \log(2i+1)$.

Owing to the extreme weakness of the interaction of the nuclear spin with the electronic shell, the "nuclear" part of the thermodynamic quantities usually plays no part in the different thermal processes, cancelling in all equations. Hence we shall follow the usual practice of measuring entropy not from zero but from the value S_{nucl}, due to the nuclear spins.

§47. The diatomic gas with molecules of different atoms: rotation of molecules

Turning to the calculation of thermodynamic quantities for a diatomic gas, we must first of all point out that just as there is no sense in considering a monatomic gas except at temperatures for which kT is small compared with the ionisation energy, so one can only consider a diatomic gas as such for kT small compared with the energy of dissociation of the molecule.‡ This fact in turn implies that in the partition function we need only take into account the lowest electronic state of the molecule.

We shall begin by studying the most important case, when the gas molecule, in its lowest electronic state, possesses neither spin nor orbital angular momentum about its axis ($S = 0$, $\Lambda = 0$); such an electronic term obviously has no fine structure. In addition one must distinguish between molecules composed of different atoms (including different isotopes of the same element) and molecules composed of identical atoms. The latter case has some special peculiarities. In this paragraph we shall assume that the molecule is made up of different atoms.

---

† The temperatures corresponding to the intervals of the hyperfine structure of various atoms lie between 0·1° and 1·5°.

‡ For example the temperatures I_{diss}/k for various diatomic molecules are: H_2:52,000°; N_2: 85,000°; Cl_2: 29,000°, NO: 61,000°; CO: 98,000°.

It is well known that the energy of a level of a diatomic molecule consists, to a certain approximation, of three independent parts—the electronic energy (which also includes the Coulomb interaction energy of the nuclei in their equilibrium position, and which we shall measure from the sum of the energies of the separated atoms), the rotational energy, and the energy of vibration of the nuclei within the molecule. For the single electronic term these levels may be written in the form †

$$\epsilon_{vK} = \epsilon_0 + \hbar\omega(v+\tfrac{1}{2}) + \frac{\hbar^2}{2I}K(K+1) \tag{47.1}$$

where ϵ_0 is the electronic energy, $\hbar\omega$ the quantum of vibration, v the vibrational quantum number, K the rotational quantum number (rotational angular momentum of the molecule) and $I = m'r_0^2$ the moment of inertia of the molecule ($m' = m_1 m_2/(m_1 + m_2)$ is the reduced mass of the two atoms and r_0 the equilibrium distance between the nuclei).

By substituting (47.1) into the partition function, the latter obviously separates into three independent factors.

$$Z = e^{-\epsilon_0/kT} Z_{\text{rot}} Z_{\text{vib}} \tag{47.2}$$

where the "rotational" and "vibrational" functions are defined as

$$Z_{\text{rot}} = \sum_{k=0}^{\infty} (2K+1) e^{-(\hbar^2/2kTI)K(K+1)}, \tag{47.3}$$

$$Z_{\text{vib}} = \sum_{v=0}^{\infty} e^{-(\hbar\omega/kT)(v+1/2)}, \tag{47.4}$$

and the factor $(2K+1)$ in Z_{rot} allows for the degeneracy of the rotational levels in the direction of the angular momentum **K**. Similarly the free energy is expressed as the sum of three parts

$$F = -NkT \log\left[\frac{eV}{N}\left(\frac{mkT}{2\pi\hbar^2}\right)^{3/2}\right] + F_{\text{rot}} + F_{\text{vib}} + N\epsilon_0 \tag{47.5}$$

($m = m_1 + m_2$ is the mass of the molecule). The first term may be called the "translational" part (since it is connected with the translational degrees of freedom) and

$$F_{\text{rot}} = -NkT \log Z_{\text{rot}}, \qquad F_{\text{vib}} = -NkT \log Z_{\text{vib}} \tag{47.6}$$

the "rotational" and "vibrational" parts. The translational part is always given by an expression of the type (43.2) with constant specific heat

---

† See, for example, *Quantum Mechanics*, §79, formula (79.8).

$c_{\text{trans}} = 3/2k$ and chemical constant

$$\zeta_{\text{trans}} = \frac{3}{2}\log\frac{m}{2\pi\hbar^2}. \tag{47.7}$$

The total specific heat of the gas will be expressed as the sum of several terms:

$$c_v = c_{\text{trans}} + c_{\text{rot}} + c_{\text{vib}}, \qquad c_p = c_{\text{trans}} + c_{\text{rot}} + c_{\text{vib}} + k, \tag{47.8}$$

which are respectively due to the thermal excitation of the translational motion of the molecule, its rotation, and the vibration of atoms within it.

We proceed to calculate the rotational part of the free energy. If the temperature is so high that

$$kT \gg \frac{\hbar^2}{2I}$$

(the "rotational quantum" $\hbar^2/2I$ small in comparison with kT†) then terms with large K will play the main part in (47.3). But for large K the rotation of the molecule is quasi-classical. Hence in this case the quantum partition function Z_{rot} can be replaced by the corresponding classical one

$$Z_{\text{rot}} = \int e^{-\epsilon(\mathbf{M})/kT}\, d\tau_{\text{rot}} \tag{47.9}$$

where $\epsilon(\mathbf{M})$ is the classical expression for the rotational kinetic energy as a function of the angular momentum $\mathbf{M}$. Introducing a co-ordinate system ξ, η, ζ rotating with the molecule, with the ζ axis along the molecular axis, and bearing in mind that a diatomic molecule has two rotational degrees of freedom, and that the angular momentum of a linear mechanical system is perpendicular to its axis we may write:

$$\epsilon(\mathbf{M}) = \frac{1}{2I}(M^2{}_\xi + M^2{}_\eta).$$

The element $d\tau_{\text{rot}}$ is the product (divided by $(2\pi\hbar)^2$) of the differentials $dM_\xi\, dM_\eta$ and the differentials of the generalised co-ordinates corresponding to M_ξ, M_η i.e. the infinitesimal angles of rotation about the ξ and η axes: $d\phi_\xi\, d\phi_\eta$‡. But the product of two infinitesimal rotations about the ξ and η axes is simply an element of solid angle do_ζ for the direction of the third

---

† In practice, this condition is always satisfied for all gases with the exception of the two isotopes of hydrogen. For example the values of $\hbar^2/2kI$ for various molecules are: H_2: 85·4°; D_2:43°; HD: 64°; N_2: 2·9°; O_2: 2·1°; Cl_2: 0·36°; NO; 2·4°; HCl: 15·2°.

‡ It must be borne in mind that such a notation is in a sense symbolic since $d\phi_\xi$ and $d\phi_\eta$ are not total differentials of any functions of the position of the axis.

axis. The integration over the solid angle will give 4π. Thus we have:†

$$Z_{\text{rot}} = \frac{4\pi}{(2\pi\hbar)^2} \int\limits_{-\infty}^{+\infty}\!\!\int \exp-\left[\frac{1}{2kTI}(M_\xi^2+M_\eta^2)\right] \mathrm{d}M_\xi \mathrm{d}M_\eta = \frac{2kI}{\hbar^2}T.$$

Hence the free energy

$$F_{\text{rot}} = -NkT \log kT - NkT \log\frac{2I}{\hbar^2}. \tag{47.10}$$

Thus at sufficiently high temperatures, the rotational part of the specific heat is constant and equals $c_{\text{rot}} = k$ in agreement with the general results of the classical investigation in §44 ($k/2$ for each rotational degree of freedom). The rotational part of the chemical constant is equal to $\zeta_{\text{rot}} = \log(2I/\hbar^2)$. We shall see below that there is a considerable range of temperature over which the condition $kT \gg \hbar^2/2I$ is satisfied and at the same time the vibrational part of the free energy and, therefore, the vibrational part of the specific heat are non-existent. In this region the specific heat of a diatomic gas is $c_v = c_{\text{trans}} + c_{\text{rot}}$ i.e.

$$\left.\begin{array}{l} c_v = \tfrac{5}{2}k \\ c_p = \tfrac{7}{2}k \end{array}\right\} \tag{47.11}$$

and the chemical constant $\zeta = \zeta_{\text{trans}} + \zeta_{\text{rot}}$

$$\zeta = \log\left[\frac{2I}{\hbar^5}\left(\frac{m}{2\pi}\right)^{3/2}\right]. \tag{47.12}$$

In the opposite limiting case of low temperature

$$kT \ll \hbar^2/2I$$

we need only keep the first two terms

$$Z_{\text{rot}} = 1 + 3e^{-\hbar^2/IkT},$$

and for the free energy we obtain, to the same degree of approximation;

$$F_{\text{rot}} = -3NkTe^{-\hbar^2/IkT}. \tag{47.13}$$

Hence the entropy

$$S_{\text{rot}} = \frac{3N\hbar^2}{IT}e^{-\hbar^2/IkT}\left(1+\frac{IkT}{\hbar^2}\right). \tag{47.14}$$

---

† This value Z_{rot} can also be obtained in a different way; assuming that the numbers K in the sum (47.3) are large and replacing the summation by integration over K we find:

$$Z_{\text{rot}} \cong \int\limits_0^\infty 2Ke^{-K^2\hbar^2/2IkT}\,\mathrm{d}K = \frac{2kTI}{\hbar^2}$$

and the specific heat

$$c_{rot} = 3Nk\left(\frac{\hbar^2}{IkT}\right)^2 e^{-\hbar^2/IkT}. \tag{47.15}$$

Thus the rotational entropy and specific heat of the gas tend exponentially to zero as $T \to 0$. Hence at low temperatures a diatomic gas behaves like a monatomic gas, its specific heat and chemical constant having the same values as would a monatomic gas of mass m.

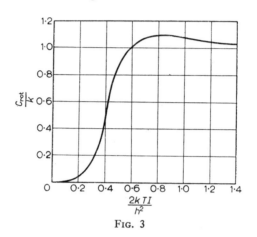

Fig. 3

In the general case, when the temperature is arbitrary, the sum of the series for Z_{rot} must be evaluated numerically. In Fig. 3 the curve shows c_{rot}/k as a function of $2kTI/\hbar^2$. The rotational specific heat rises to a maximum value of $1.1k$ for $kT = 0.81\ (\hbar^2/2I)$ and then tends asymptotically to its classical value, k.†

§48. The diatomic gas with the molecules composed of identical atoms: rotation of molecules

Diatomic molecules composed of identical atoms have certain peculiarities which necessitate changing some of the formulae obtained in the previous section.

To begin with, consider the limiting case of high temperatures, allowing a classical approximation. Since the nuclei are identical, two opposite positions of the axis of the molecule (differing simply by the interchange of the atoms) correspond to the same one physical state of the molecule.

---

† One can obtain the asymptotic expansion of thermodynamic quantities for large values of $2kTI/\hbar^2$. For the specific heat the first two terms of the expansion are

$$\frac{c_{rot}}{k} = 1 + \frac{1}{45}\left(\frac{\hbar^2}{2kTI}\right)$$

However, this gives a poor approximation for the function $c_{rot}(T)$.

Hence the classical partition function (47.9) must be divided by 2. This brings about a change in the chemical constant which now becomes

$$\zeta_{\text{rot}} = \log(I/\hbar^2). \qquad (48.1)$$

Similarly the factor 2 in the argument of the logarithm in the sum $\zeta_{\text{trans}} + \zeta_{\text{rot}}$ in (47.12) also disappears.

More important changes become necessary at temperatures requiring a quantum treatment. Since, in practice, the whole question is of interest only in its application to the two isotopes of hydrogen (H_2 and D_2) we shall below restrict ourselves to these gases. It is well known† that the condition of quantum-mechanical symmetry of the nuclei implies that in the electronic state $^1\Sigma_g^+$ (the ground state for the hydrogen molecule) rotational levels with even and odd values of K have different degrees of nuclear spin degeneracy: levels with even (odd) K appear only for even (odd) total spin of both nuclei and have respective degrees of degeneracy

$$g_g = \frac{i}{2i+1}, \qquad g_u = \frac{i+1}{2i+1}$$

when the spin is half integral or

$$g_g = \frac{i+1}{2i+1}, \qquad g_u = \frac{i}{2i+1}$$

for i integral.

For hydrogen we use the terminology that molecules in states with the larger nuclear statistical weight are called molecules of ortho-hydrogen, and those in states with smaller statistical weights are called molecules of para-hydrogen. Thus for the molecules H_2 and D_2 we have the following values for their statistical weights:

$$H_2(i = \tfrac{1}{2}) \begin{cases} \text{ortho } g_u = \tfrac{3}{4}, \\ \text{para } g_g = \tfrac{1}{4}, \end{cases} \qquad D_2(i = 1) \begin{cases} \text{ortho } g_g = \tfrac{2}{3}, \\ \text{para } g_u = \tfrac{1}{3}. \end{cases}$$

The suffix g indicates that the molecules have an even resultant nuclear spin (0 for H_2; 0 or 2 for D_2) and an even angular momentum K; the subscript u indicates odd integral nuclear spins (1 for H_2 and D_2) and odd values of K.

For molecules with different nuclei the degree of nuclear spin degeneracy was the same for all rotational levels, and hence taking it into account for them would only have led to an uninteresting change in the chemical constant. However, in this case it leads to a change in the form of the partition function itself, which must now be written in the following way‡

$$Z_{\text{rot}} = g_g Z_g + g_u Z_u, \qquad (48.2)$$

---

† See *Quantum Mechanics*, §83.
‡ The normalisation of the nuclear statistical weights (making $g_g + g_u = 1$) means that we are measuring the entropy from the value of $k \log (2i+1)^2$ in accordance with the condition assumed at the end of §46.

where

$$Z_g = \sum_{K=0,2,\dots} (2K+1)e^{-(\hbar^2/2IkT)\,K(K+1)}, \tag{48.3}$$

$$Z_u = \sum_{K=1,3,\dots} (2K+1)e^{-(\hbar^2/2IkT)\,K(K+1)}.$$

Correspondingly the free energy will be altered to

$$F_{\text{rot}} = -NkT \log(g_g Z_g + g_u Z_u) \tag{48.4}$$

and similarly for other thermodynamic quantities. At high temperatures

$$Z_g \cong Z_u \cong \tfrac{1}{2} Z_{\text{rot}} = \frac{kTI}{\hbar^2},$$

so that we obtain for the free energy the previous classical expression.

As $T \to 0$ the sum Z_g tends to unity, and Z_u tends exponentially to zero; whence at low temperatures the gas will behave like a monatomic one (the specific heat $c_{\text{rot}} = 0$) to whose chemical constant a "nuclear part" is added:

$$\zeta_{\text{nucl}} = \log g_g.$$

The above formulae obviously apply to a gas in total thermal equilibrium. For such a gas the ratio between the amounts of para- and ortho-hydrogen is a definite function of temperature which equals, according to the Boltzmann distribution

$$\left. \begin{aligned}
x_{\text{H}_2} &= \frac{N_{\text{ortho-H}_2}}{N_{\text{para-H}_2}} = \frac{g_u Z_u}{g_g Z_g} = \frac{3 Z_u}{Z_g} \\
\frac{1}{x_{\text{D}_2}} &= \frac{N_{\text{ortho-D}_2}}{N_{\text{para-D}_2}} = \frac{g_g Z_g}{g_u Z_u} = \frac{2 Z_g}{Z_u}
\end{aligned} \right\} \tag{48.5}$$

As the temperature changes from 0 to ∞ the ratio x_{H_2} goes from 0 to 3 and x_{D_2} from 0 to $\tfrac{1}{2}$ (At $T = 0$ all the molecules are in the state with lowest K, $K = 0$ corresponding to pure para-H_2 or ortho-D_2).

It must be borne in mind, however, that the probability of a change in the nuclear spin during a collision of molecules is very small. Hence the molecules of para- and ortho-hydrogen behave in practice like different modifications of hydrogen which cannot change into each other.[†] As a result in practice one has to deal not with a gas in equilibrium but with a non-equilibrium mixture of the para- and ortho- modifications of which the relative amounts have given, fixed values.[‡] The free energy of the

---

[†] In the absence of special catalysts.
[‡] For ordinary gas which has been at room temperature for a long time the ratio is equal to $x_{\text{H}_2} = 3$, $x_{\text{D}_2} = \tfrac{1}{2}$.

system is equal to the sum of the free energies of the two components. In particular, for $x = \infty$ (pure ortho-H_2 or para-D_2) we have:

$$F_{\text{rot}} = -NkT \log g_u Z_u.$$

For low temperatures $(\hbar^2/2IkT \gg 1)$ we only retain the first term in the series for Z_u, so that $Z_u = 3e^{-\hbar^2/IkT}$ and the free energy

$$F_{\text{rot}} = N\frac{\hbar^2}{I} - NkT \log 3g_u.$$

This means that the gas will behave like a monatomic one $(c_{\text{rot}} = 0)$; to the chemical constant will be added an extra term $\log 3g_u$ and to the energy the constant term $N\hbar^2/I$, due to the rotational energy of all the molecules with $K = 1$.

§49. The diatomic gas: vibration of the atoms

The vibrational parts of the thermodynamic quantities of the gas become significant at much higher temperatures than the rotational parts, since the intervals in the vibrational level scheme are large compared with the intervals in the rotational one.†

We shall assume, however, that the temperature is not high enough to excite the very high vibrational levels. The oscillations are then small (and hence harmonic) and the energy levels will be given by the usual expression $\hbar\omega (v + \frac{1}{2})$ used in (47.4).

The calculation of the vibrational partition function Z_{vib} (47.4) is quite elementary. Owing to the rapid convergence of the series we may formally extend the summation to $v = \infty$. We assume that the energy is measured from the lowest $(v = 0)$ vibrational level (i.e. we absorb $\hbar\omega/2$ into the constant ϵ_0 in (47.1)).

We then have

$$Z_{\text{vib}} = \sum_{v=0}^{\infty} e^{-(\hbar\omega/kT)v} = \frac{1}{1-e^{-\hbar\omega/kT}},$$

whence the free energy

$$F_{\text{vib}} = NkT \log(1-e^{-\hbar\omega/kT}). \tag{49.1}$$

The entropy is

$$S_{\text{vib}} = -Nk \log(1-e^{-\hbar\omega/kT}) + \frac{N\hbar\omega}{T(e^{\hbar\omega/kT}-1)}, \tag{49.2}$$

---

† As examples one may take the values of $\hbar\omega/k$ for some diatomic gases: H_2: 6100°; N_2:3340°; O_2: 2230°; NO: 2690°; HCl: 4140°.

the energy:

$$E_{\text{vib}} = \frac{N\hbar\omega}{e^{\hbar\omega/kT}-1} \qquad (49.3)$$

and the specific heat:

$$c_{\text{vib}} = k\left(\frac{\hbar\omega}{kT}\right)^2 \frac{e^{\hbar\omega/kT}}{(e^{\hbar\omega/kT}-1)^2}. \qquad (49.4)$$

The curve in Fig. 4 shows the relation between c_{vib}/k and $kT/\hbar\omega$.

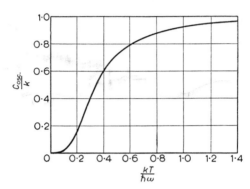

FIG. 4

At low temperatures ($\hbar\omega \gg kT$) all these quantities tend to zero exponentially:

$$F_{\text{vib}} = -NkTe^{-\hbar\omega/kT},$$
$$c_{\text{vib}} = k\left(\frac{\hbar\omega}{kT}\right)^2 e^{-\hbar\omega/kT}. \qquad (49.5)$$

On the other hand for high temperatures ($\hbar\omega \ll kT$) we have:

$$F_{\text{vib}} = -NkT \log kT + NkT \log \hbar\omega - N\frac{\hbar\omega}{2} \qquad (49.6)$$

which corresponds to a constant specific heat $c_{\text{vib}} = k$† and chemical constant $\zeta_{\text{vib}} = -\log \hbar\omega$. Adding on the values (47.11) (47.12) we find that for temperatures $kT \gg \hbar\omega$ the total specific heat of a diatomic gas is‡

$$c_v = \frac{7}{2}k, \qquad c_p = \frac{9}{2}k \qquad (49.7)$$

---

† Once more in agreement with the classical result of §44.

‡ As one can see from Fig. 4 c_{vib} actually tends to its limiting value k already for $kT = \hbar\omega$ (for $kT/\hbar\omega := 1$, $c_{\text{vib}} = 0\cdot93k$). The practical criterion for the applicability of the classical expression may be expressed as $kT \gg \hbar\omega/3$.

and the chemical constant

$$\zeta = \log\left[\frac{(2)I}{\omega\hbar^6}\left(\frac{m}{2\pi}\right)^{3/2}\right].\tag{49.8}$$

In the case of identical atoms the factor (2) must be omitted from this expression. The first two terms of the expansion for E_{vib} are equal to

$$E_{\text{vib}} = NkT - \tfrac{1}{2}N\hbar\omega.\tag{49.9}$$

The appearance of the constant term $-\tfrac{1}{2}N\hbar\omega$ is connected with the fact that we are measuring the energy from the lowest quantum level, (i.e. from the energy of "zero-point vibration") while the classical energy must be measured from the minimum of the potential energy.

The expression (49.6) for the free energy can also obviously be obtained from the classical viewpoint, since for $kT \gg \hbar\omega$ only the large quantum numbers v are important, for which the vibration is quasi-classical. The classical expression for the energy of a small vibration of frequency ω is of the form

$$\epsilon_{\text{vib}}(p,q) = \frac{p^2}{2m'} + \frac{m'\omega^2 q^2}{2}$$

(m' the reduced mass). Integration of this expression for ϵ gives, for the partition function, the value

$$Z_{\text{vib}} = \frac{1}{2\pi\hbar}\int\limits_{-\infty}^{+\infty}\!\!\int e^{-\epsilon_{\text{vib}}/kT}\, dp\,dq = \frac{kT}{\hbar\omega},\tag{49.10}$$

corresponding to (49.6).† (Owing to the rapid convergence of the integral one can extend the limits for the integration over dq to $-\infty$ and $+\infty$.)

At sufficiently high temperatures, when vibrations with large v are excited, the effects of anharmonic oscillations and interaction between the vibration and rotation of the molecule can become important. (These effects are, in principle, of the same order of magnitude). Since v is large the appropriate correction to the thermodynamic quantities can be determined classically.

Consider the molecule as a mechanical system of two particles with an interaction potential $U(r)$, in a co-ordinate system in which their centre of gravity is at rest. The energy (Hamiltonian) describing the rotation and vibration of the system in a classically exact way, is the sum of the kinetic energy (the energy of a particle of the reduced mass m') and the potential energy $U(r)$. The partition function, after integrating over the momenta, is reduced to the integral over the co-ordinates:

$$\int e^{-u(r)/kT}\, dV,$$

† The same expression can be obtained by replacing the summation over v by integration over dv.

and after integrating over the angles (in spherical polar co-ordinates) we have the integral

$$\int\limits_0^\infty e^{-u(r)/kT}\, r^2\, \mathrm{d}r.$$

The approximation corresponding to independent harmonic vibrations and rotations of the molecule is obtained if one assumes $U(r) = U_0 + \frac{1}{2}m'\omega^2 (r-r_0)^2$, and in the integration replaces the slowly varying factor r^2 by r_0^2, where r_0 is the equilibrium distance between the particles and $U_0 = U(r_0)$. To take into account anharmonic vibrations and their interaction with the rotation we now put

$$U(r) = U_0 + \frac{m'\omega^2 r_0^2}{2}(\xi^2 - \alpha\xi^3 + \beta\xi^4) \tag{49.11}$$

($\xi = (r/r_0) - 1$, α and β are constants)† and afterwards expand the whole integrand in powers of ξ taking out a factor $\exp\{-(U_0 + \frac{1}{2}m'\omega^2 r_0^2\xi^2)/kT\}$. In the expansion we retain terms only up to second order in the temperature (after integration); the integration over $\mathrm{d}\xi$ is taken from $-\infty$ to $+\infty$. The zero order term of the expansion gives the usual value of the partition function and the others give the required correction.

We omit the intermediate calculations and write down directly the final result for the correction to the free energy:

$$F_{\text{anh}} = -N(kT)^2 \frac{1}{2I\omega^2}\left[1 + 3\alpha - \frac{3}{2}\beta + \frac{15}{8}\alpha^2\right]. \tag{49.12}$$

Thus the effect of the vibration being anharmonic (and of its coupling with the rotation) leads to a correction to the free energy proportional to the square of the temperature. The corresponding correction to the specific heat is a term directly proportional to the temperature.

§50. The diatomic gas: influence of the electronic angular momentum

Some molecules (not very many, it is true) have in their lowest electronic state a non-zero orbital angular momentum or spin.

The existence of a non-zero orbital angular momentum Λ leads, as is well known, to a two-fold degeneracy of the electronic term corresponding to the two possible orientations of this angular momentum relative to the molecular axis.‡ This will affect the thermodynamic quantities of the gas with the result that owing to the doubling of the partition function the

---

† These constants can be expressed in terms of the spectroscopic constants of the molecule. See *Quantum Mechanics*, §79.

‡ Strictly speaking the term splits up into two levels (this is called a Λ-doublet) the separation of which is, however, so insignificant that we may completely neglect it here.

chemical constant will be increased by

$$\zeta_\Lambda = \log 2. \tag{50.1}$$

The presence of a non-zero spin S leads to a splitting up into $2S+1$ terms; the intervals of this fine structure are, however, so insignificant (for $\Lambda = 0$) that they may be neglected in the calculation of the thermodynamic quantities. The only effect of the presence of spin is to increase the degree of degeneracy of all terms by a factor $2S+1$. Corresponding to this, the chemical constant will be increased by

$$\zeta_S = \log(2S+1). \tag{50.2}$$

The fine structure arising when $S \neq 0$, $\Lambda \neq 0$, requires a special study. The intervals of the fine structure can in this case take values making it necessary to take them into account when calculating the thermodynamic quantities. We shall derive the formulae for the case of a doublet electronic term.† Each component of the electronic doublet has its vibrational and rotational structures, whose parameters may be considered to be identical for the two components. Hence the partition function (47.2) will contain another factor:

$$Z_{el} = g_0 + g_1 e^{-\Delta/T}$$

where g_0 g_1 are the degrees of degeneracy of the components of the doublet and Δ is their separation measured in degrees. Thus to the free energy will be added an "electronic part" equal to:

$$F_{el} = -NkT \log(g_0 + g_1 e^{-\Delta/T}). \tag{50.3}$$

We can also write down the "electronic" specific heat which must be added to the other parts of the specific heat:

$$c_{el} = k \frac{(\Delta T/)^2}{\left[1 + \dfrac{g_0}{g_1} e^{\Delta/T}\right]\left[1 + \dfrac{g_1}{g_0} e^{-\Delta/T}\right]}. \tag{50.4}$$

At both limits ($T \to 0$ and $T \to \infty$) c_{el} obviously tends to zero and it has a maximum for some temperature $T \sim \Delta$.

PROBLEM

Determine the correction to the free energy of oxygen due to the first excited electronic state of the molecule O_2 (see last footnote). The temperature is large compared with a vibrational quantum but small compared with the separation Δ between the normal term, $^3\Sigma$ and the excited one, $^1\Delta$.

† Such a case arises for NO; the lowest electronic term of the molecule NO is a doublet $\Pi_{1/2, \, 3/2}$ with a width Δ (in degrees) of 178. Both components of the doublet are doubly degenerate. An odd case arises with oxygen. The lowest electronic term of the molecule O_2 is the very narrow triplet $^3\Sigma$ whose width may be neglected. But, accidentally, the next (excited) term $^1\Delta$ (doubly degenerate) is comparatively near, at a distance $\Delta = 11\cdot300°$. It can be excited at high temperatures and thus affects the thermodynamic quantities.

SOLUTION: The partition function is

$$Z = 3 \cdot \frac{kT}{\hbar\omega} \cdot \frac{kTI}{\hbar^2} + 2e^{-\Delta/T} \cdot \frac{kT}{\hbar\omega'} \cdot \frac{kTI'}{\hbar^2}$$

where the first and second terms represent the partition functions for the ground and excited terms, each of which is the product of electronic, vibrational, and rotational factors. Hence the required correction to the free energy is

$$F_{i\Delta} = -NkT \log\left(1 + \frac{2\omega r_0'^2}{3\omega' r_0^2} e^{-\Delta/T}\right) \simeq -NkT \frac{2\omega r_0'^2}{3\omega' r_0^2} e^{-\Delta/T}$$

where ω, r_0 and ω', r_0' are the frequencies and equilibrium distances between the nuclei for the normal and excited electronic states.

§51. The polyatomic gas

The free energy of a polyatomic gas, like that of a diatomic gas, can be expressed as the sum of three parts—translational, rotational, and vibrational. The translational part, as before, is characterised by a specific heat and chemical constant equal to

$$c_{\text{trans}} = \frac{3}{2}k, \qquad \zeta_{\text{trans}} = \frac{3}{2} \log\frac{m}{2\pi\hbar^2}, \tag{51.1}$$

Owing to the large moments of inertia of polyatomic molecules (and their consequent small rotational quanta) one can always treat their rotations classically.[†] A polyatomic molecule has three rotational degrees of freedom and three (in general different) principal moments of interia I_1, I_2, I_3. Hence its kinetic energy of rotation is

$$\epsilon_{\text{rot}} = \frac{M_\xi^2}{2I_1} + \frac{M_\eta^2}{2I_2} + \frac{M_\zeta^2}{2I_3} \tag{51.2}$$

where ξ, η, ζ, are the co-ordinates in a rotating system whose axes coincide with the principal axes of the molecule (we are ignoring for the time being the special case of molecules composed of atoms lying along a straight line). This expression must be substituted into the partition function

$$Z_{\text{rot}} = \int' e^{-\epsilon_{\text{rot}}/kT} \, d\tau_{\text{rot}} \tag{51.3}$$

where

$$d\tau_{\text{rot}} = \frac{1}{(2\pi\hbar)^3} \, dM_\xi \, dM_\eta \, dM_\zeta \, d\phi_\xi \, d\phi_\eta \, d\phi_\zeta,$$

and the accent on the integral sign means, as usual, that the integration must be taken only over those orientations of the molecule which are physically distinguishable.

[†] The effects of quantisation of the rotation would only be observable for methane (CH_2) where they would appear at temperatures about 50°K (see the problem at the end of this section).

If the molecule has some axes of symmetry, certain rotations about these axes reduce to rearrangements of identical atoms. It is clear that the number of physically indistinguishable orientations of the molecule is equal to the number of permitted rotations about the axis of symmetry (including the identity transformation—rotation through 360°). Let us denote this number by σ.† We may carry out the integration in (51.3) over all orientations and at the same time divide the whole expression by σ.

In the product $d\phi_\xi\,d\phi_\eta\,d\phi_\zeta$ of the three infinitesimal rotations one can regard $d\phi_\xi\,d\phi_\eta$ as the element do_ζ of solid angle for the direction of the ζ axis. The integration over do_ζ is carried out independently of the integration over the rotation $d\phi_\zeta$ about the ζ axis itself and gives 4π. The integration over $d\phi_\zeta$ then gives another 2π. After integrating also over $dM_\xi\,dM_\eta\,dM_\zeta$ (with limits $-\infty$ to $+\infty$) we obtain the result:

$$Z_{\text{rot}} = \frac{8\pi^2}{\sigma(2\pi\hbar)^3}(2\pi kT)^{3/2}(I_1 I_2 I_3)^{1/2} = \frac{(2kT)^{3/2}(\pi I_1 I_2 I_3)^{1/2}}{\sigma\hbar^3}.$$

Hence the free energy

$$F = -\tfrac{3}{2}NkT \log kT - NkT \log\frac{(8\pi I_1 I_2 I_3)^{1/2}}{\sigma\hbar^3}. \tag{51.4}$$

Thus for the rotational specific heat we have, according to §44

$$c_{\text{rot}} = \tfrac{3}{2}k, \tag{51.5}$$

and the chemical constant is equal to

$$\zeta_{\text{rot}} = \log\frac{(8\pi I_1 I_2 I_3)^{1/2}}{\sigma\hbar^3} \tag{51.6}$$

If all the atoms in the molecule lie on the same straight line (collinear molecule), then it has, like a diatomic molecule, only two rotational degrees of freedom and one moment of inertia I. The rotational specific heat and chemical constant are, as for a diatomic gas, equal to

$$c_{\text{rot}} = k, \qquad \zeta_{\text{rot}} = \log\frac{2I}{\sigma\hbar^2} \tag{51.7}$$

where $\sigma = 1$ for an asymmetrical molecule (for example NNO) and $\sigma = 2$ for a molecule symmetrical about its centre (for example OCO).

The vibrational part of the free energy of a polyatomic gas is calculated in a similar way to the diatomic case. The difference is only that the polyatomic molecule has not one, but several vibrational degrees of freedom. In particular a (non-collinear) molecule with n atoms has obviously

---

† Thus for H_2O (isosceles triangle), $\sigma = 2$; NH_3 (regular triangular pyramid) $\sigma = 3$; CH_4 (tetrahedron) $\sigma = 12$; C_6H_6 (regular hexagon) $\sigma = 12$.

$r_{\text{vib}} = 3n-6$ vibrational degrees of freedom; for a collinear molecule with n atoms $r_{\text{vib}} = 3n-5$ (see §44). The number of vibrational degrees of freedom determines the number of so-called normal modes of vibration of the molecule each of which has its own frequency ω_α (the index α labelling the normal mode). It must be borne in mind that some of the frequencies ω_α may coincide with one another; in such cases one speaks of degenerate frequencies.

In the harmonic approximation, when we consider the vibrations to be small (considering only temperatures for which this is so) all the normal modes are independent and the vibrational energy is the sum of the energies of all the separate vibrations. Hence the vibrational partition function splits into the product of the partition functions of the separate vibrations and we obtain for the free energy F_{vib} the sum of expressions of the type (49.1).

$$F_{\text{vib}} = NkT \sum_\alpha \log(1-e^{-\hbar\omega_\alpha/kT}). \tag{51.8}$$

In this sum each frequency enters as many times as its multiplicity. One obtains similar sums for the oscillatory part of other thermodynamic quantities.

Each of the normal modes in the classical limiting case $(kT \gg \hbar\omega_\alpha)$ gives a contribution $c_{\text{vib}}^{(\alpha)} = k$ to the specific heat; for kT greater than the largest $\hbar\omega_\alpha$ we would obtain

$$c_{\text{vib}} = r_{\text{vib}}k. \tag{51.9}$$

In practice, however, this limit is never achieved, since polyatomic molecules usually break up at much lower temperatures.

The different frequencies ω_α of a polyatomic molecule are usually spread over a wide range of values. As the temperature rises, the different normal modes gradually are "included" into the specific heat. This implies that the specific heat of polyatomic gases may often be considered approximately constant over wide ranges of temperature.

We now discuss a possible peculiar transformation of vibration into rotation of which an example occurs for the molecule of ethane C_2H_6. This molecule is built up from two CH_3 groups which are a definite distance apart and are oriented relative to each other in a definite way. One of the normal modes of the molecule is a "torsional vibration" in which one CH_3 group twists relative to the other. With an increase in the energy of the vibration, the amplitude increases until ultimately, at a sufficiently high temperature, the vibration changes to free rotation. As a result the contribution of this degree of freedom to the specific heat which reaches approximately the value k when the vibration is fully excited begins to fall, for a further increase in temperature, tending asymptotically to the characteristic value for rotation, $k/2$.

Lastly we must stress that if a molecule has a non-zero spin S (for example NO_2, ClO_2) the chemical constant is increased by an amount

$$\zeta_S = \log(2S+1). \qquad (51.10)$$

PROBLEM

Find the rotational partition function for methane at low temperature.

SOLUTION: As was already pointed out in the footnote on page 148, the calculation of Z_{rot} for methane at sufficiently low temperatures must be done from the quantum standpoint.

The molecule CH_4 is in the form of a tetrahedron and rotates like a spherical top, so that its rotational levels are equal to $(\hbar^2/2I)J(J+1)$ where I is the common value of the three principal moments of inertia and J is the rotational quantum number. Since the spin of the H nucleus is equal to $i = 1/2$, and that of carbon C^{12} is equal to zero, the resultant nuclear spin of the CH_4 molecule can equal 0, 1, or 2 (with corresponding nuclear statistical weights 1, 3, and 5)[†]. For every given value of J there exists a definite number of states for each different value of the nuclear spin. In the following table are given these numbers for the first five values of J[‡].

Nuclear spin	0	1	2
$J = 0$	–	–	1
$J = 1$	–	1	–
$J = 2$	2	1	–
$J = 3$	–	2	1
$J = 4$	2	2	1

The value of the sum Z_{rot}, obtained by taking into account all the degrees of degeneracy in the direction of the rotation and of the nuclear spin, must be divided by 16, if we decide to measure the entropy from the value $k \log(2i+1)^2 = k \log 16$ (see footnote on page 141). Thus we obtain:

$$Z_{rot} = \frac{5}{16} + \frac{9}{16}e^{-\hbar^2/IkT} + \frac{25}{16}e^{-3\hbar^2/IkT} + \frac{77}{16}e^{-6\hbar^2/IkT} + \frac{117}{16}e^{-10\hbar^2/IkT} + \dots$$

---

† See *Quantum Mechanics*, §103, Example 4.
‡ Molecules with different values of resultant nuclear spin behave in practice like molecules of different modifications of methane, similarly to ortho- and para-hydrogen.

CHAPTER V

THE FERMI AND BOSE DISTRIBUTIONS

§52. The Fermi distribution

If the temperature of a perfect gas, (for given density) is sufficiently low, then Boltzmann statistics no longer applies, and a new statistics must be set up in which the mean occupation numbers of the various quantum states are not assumed to be small.

This statistics is different, however, according to which type of wave function describes the gas, which is considered as a system of N independent particles. It is well known that these functions must be either antisymmetric or symmetric with regard to the interchange of any pair of particles, and that the former applies to particles with half-integral spin and the latter to those with integral spin.

For a system of particles described by antisymmetric wave functions, the Pauli principle applies: not more than one particle can be simultaneously in any one quantum state. Statistics based on this principle is called Fermi (or Fermi-Dirac) statistics.[†]

As in §37, let us apply the Gibbs distribution to the set of all particles in the gas which are in the same quantum state; as was already pointed out in §37, we can do this even in the presence of exchange effects between the particles. Let us denote the thermodynamic potential of this system of particles by Ω; from the general formula (35.3) we then have:

$$\Omega_k = -kT \log \sum_{n_k} (e^{(\mu - \epsilon_k)/kT})^{n_k}, \tag{52.1}$$

since the energy of n_k particles in the kth state is simply $n_k \epsilon_k$. From the Pauli principle the occupation numbers of each state can only take the values 0 or 1. Hence we get:

$$\Omega_k = -kT \log(1 + e^{(\mu - \epsilon_k)/kT}).$$

The required mean number of particles in the kth quantum state will be obtained as the derivative

$$\bar{n}_k = -\frac{\partial \Omega_k}{\partial \mu} = \frac{e^{(\mu - \epsilon_k)/kT}}{1 + e^{(\mu - \epsilon_k)/kT}},$$

[†] It was invented by E. FERMI for the electron, and its relation with quantum mechanics was clarified by P. A. M. DIRAC (1926)

or, finally

$$\bar{n}_k = \frac{1}{e^{(\epsilon_k - \mu)/kT} + 1}. \tag{52.2}$$

This is the distribution function of a perfect gas obeying Fermi statistics (which we shall call, for the sake of brevity, a Fermi gas). For $e^{(\mu - \epsilon_k)/kT} \ll 1$ it transforms, as it should, into the Boltzmann function.[†]
    The Fermi distribution is normalised by the condition

$$\sum_k \frac{1}{e^{(\epsilon_k - \mu)/kT} + 1} = N \tag{52.3}$$

where N is the total number of particles in the gas. This equation determines the chemical potential as an implicit function of T and N.
    The thermodynamic potential Ω of the gas as a whole is obtained by summing Ω_k over all quantum states

$$\Omega = -kT \sum_k \log(1 + e^{(\mu - \epsilon_k)/kT}). \tag{52.4}$$

§53. The Bose distribution

    We now turn to the study of the statistics governing a perfect gas consisting of particles described by symmetric wave functions, the so-called Bose statistics (or Bose-Einstein statistics[‡]).
    The occupation numbers of quantum states for symmetric wave functions are not restricted at all and may take arbitrary values. To obtain the distribution function we proceed as in the previous section.
    We write:

$$\Omega_k = -kT \log \sum_{n_k=0}^{\infty} (e^{(\mu - \epsilon_k)/kT})^{n_k}.$$

The geometric series in this converges only for $e^{(\mu - \epsilon_k)/kT} < 1$. Since this must hold for all ϵ_k (including $\epsilon_k = 0$) it is clear that we must have

$$\mu < 0. \tag{53.1}$$

Thus in Bose statistics, the chemical potential must always be negative. Remember in this connection that in Boltzmann statistics the chemical potential always takes negative values (of large absolute value); in Fermi statistics μ can be positive or negative.

[†] In Boltzmann statistics the expression (52.1) must be expanded in powers of the small quantities $e^{(\mu - \epsilon_k)/kT}$; the first term of the expansion is $\Omega_k = -kT e^{(\mu - \epsilon_k)/kT}$, whence by differentiating with respect to μ we obtain again the Boltzmann distribution formula.
    [‡] It was introduced for light quanta by S. N. BOSE and then generalised by A. EINSTEIN (1924).

Summing the geometric series we obtain

$$\Omega_k = kT \log(1 - e^{(\mu - \epsilon_k)/kT}).$$

Hence we obtain the mean occupation numbers $\bar{n}_k = -\partial \Omega_k / \partial \mu$:

$$\bar{n}_k = \frac{1}{e^{(\epsilon_k - \mu)/kT} - 1}. \tag{53.2}$$

This is the distribution function of a perfect gas obeying Bose statistics (or a Bose gas as we shall call it). It differs from the distribution function for Fermi statistics in the sign before the 1 in the denominator. As in the previous case, for $e^{(\mu - \epsilon_k)/kT} \ll 1$ it transforms naturally to the Boltzmann distribution function. The total number of particles in the gas is given by the formula:

$$N = \sum_k \frac{1}{e^{(\epsilon_k - \mu)/kT} - 1}, \tag{53.3}$$

and the thermodynamic potential Ω of the gas as a whole is obtained by summing Ω_k over all quantum states:

$$\Omega = kT \sum_k \log(1 - e^{(\mu - \epsilon_k)/kT}). \tag{53.4}$$

§54. Non-equilibrium Fermi and Bose gases

In a similar manner to that in §40 one can also calculate the entropy of a non-equilibrium Fermi or Bose gas, and from the condition that entropy should be a maximum again obtain the Fermi and Bose distribution functions.

In the Fermi case each quantum state can contain no more than one particle but the numbers N_j are not small and quite of the same order of magnitude as the numbers G_j (all notation that of §40).

The number of possible ways of distributing N_j individual particles over G_j states (with not more than one in each) is simply the number of ways of choosing N_j out of the G_j states, i.e. the number of combinations of N_j out of G_j elements. Hence we have:

$$\Delta \Gamma_j = \frac{G_j!}{N_j! (G_j - N_j)!}. \tag{54.1}$$

Taking the logarithm of this expression and using for the logarithms of all three factorials the formula $\log N! = N \log N/e$ we find:

$$S = k \sum_j \{G_j \log G_j - N_j \log N_j - (G_j - N_j) \log (G_j - N_j)\}. \tag{54.2}$$

Introducing again the mean occupation numbers $\bar{n}_i = N_j/G_j$ we finally obtain the following expression for the entropy of a non-equilibrium Fermi gas:

$$S = -k \sum_j G_j\{\bar{n}_j \log \bar{n}_j + (1-\bar{n}_j) \log(1-\bar{n}_j)\}. \qquad (54.3)$$

From the condition that this expression should be a maximum it is easy to find from eqs. (40.8) that the equilibrium distribution is given by the formula

$$\bar{n}_j = \frac{1}{e^{\alpha+\beta\varepsilon_j}+1}$$

i.e., as we would expect, it coincides with the Fermi distribution.

Lastly in the case of Bose statistics, there can be any number of particles in each quantum state so that the statistical weight $\Delta\Gamma_j$ is the total number of ways of distributing N_j particles amongst G_j states. This number is equal to†

$$\Delta\Gamma_j = \frac{(G_j+N_j-1)!}{(G_j-1)! \, N_j!}.$$

Taking the logarithm of this expression and neglecting unity in comparison with the very large numbers G_j+N_j and G_j we obtain:

$$S = k \sum_j \{(G_j+N_j) \log(G_j+N_j) - N_j \log N_j - G_j \log G_j\}. \qquad (54.5)$$

Introducing the numbers $\bar{n}_j$ we may write the entropy of a non-equilibrium Bose gas in the form

$$S = k \sum_j G_j[(1+\bar{n}_j) \log(1+\bar{n}_j) - \bar{n}_j \log \bar{n}_j]. \qquad (54.6)$$

It is easy to see that the condition that this expression should be a maximum does indeed lead to the Bose distribution.

Both formulae for the entropy (54.2) and (54.5) go over naturally in the limiting case $N_j \ll G_j$ to the Boltzmann formula (40.3). The statistical weights (54.1) and (54.4) for Fermi and Bose statistics also go into the Boltzmann expression (40.2). (For this we must put $G_j! \cong (G_j-N_j)! \, G_j{}^{N_j}$, $(G_j+N_j-1)! \cong (G_j-1)! \, G_j{}^{N_j}$). However it must be borne in mind that to obtain this limit we neglect terms in the statistical weight of order $N_j{}^2/G_j$

---

† It is the number of ways of distributing, say, N_j identical balls into G_j boxes. Let us number the balls by a row of points placed along a line. We shall number the boxes and represent the boundaries between them by G_j-1 vertical lines in the row of points. Thus the diagram

$$\cdot \,\Big|\, \cdots \,\Big|\Big|\, \cdots \cdot \,\Big|\, \cdot\cdot$$

represents 10 balls distributed over 5 boxes with 1 ball in the first box, 3 in the second, none in the third, 4 in the fourth and 2 in the fifth. The total number of sites (containing points or lines) in this row is G_j+N_j-1. The required number of distributions of balls in the boxes is the number of ways in which one can choose G_j-1 sites for the lines, i.e. the number of combinations of G_j-1 out of (G_j+N_j-1) objects, whence we obtain the formula given in the text.

which generally speaking, are themselves not small; when we take the logarithm, however, these terms give a correction to the entropy of the comparatively small order N_j/G_j.

Lastly let us write down expressions for the entropy of a Bose gas in the important limiting case when the number of particles in each quantum state is large (so that $N_j \gg G_j$, $\bar{n}_j \gg 1$). It is well known from quantum mechanics that this case corresponds to the classical wave picture of a field. The statistical weight takes the form

$$\Delta\Gamma_j = \frac{N_j^{G_j-1}}{(G_j-1)!} \tag{54.7}$$

and the entropy

$$S = k \sum_j G_j \log \frac{eN_j}{G_j}. \tag{54.8}$$

We shall make use of this formula in §65.

§55. Fermi and Bose gases of elementary particles

Consider a gas made up of elementary particles or particles which may be considered as elementary under the given conditions. As we have already seen, one never uses the Fermi or Bose distributions for the usual atomic or molecular gases since actually these can always be described, to sufficient accuracy, by the Boltzmann distribution. All the formulae obtained in this section take a completely analogous form for both Fermi and Bose statistics, differing by one sign only. In all cases below, the upper sign applies to Fermi statistics and the lower to Bose statistics.

The energy of an elementary particle is simply the kinetic energy of its translational motion, which is always quasi-classical. Hence we have:

$$\epsilon = \frac{1}{2m}(p_x^2 + p_y^2 + p_z^2), \tag{55.1}$$

and in the distribution function we take, in the usual way, the distribution over the phase space of the particle. Here it must be remembered that, for given values of the momenta, the state of the particle is also determined by the direction of its spin. Hence the number of particles in an element of phase space $dp_x\, dp_y\, dp_z\, dV$ is obtained by multiplying the distribution (52.2) or (53.2) by

$$g\,d\tau = g\frac{dp_x\, dp_y\, dp_z\, dV}{(2\pi\hbar)^3},$$

where $g = 2S+1$ and S is the spin of the particles, i.e. it is equal to

$$dN = \frac{g\,d\tau}{e^{(\epsilon-\mu)/kT} \pm 1}. \tag{55.2}$$

By integrating over dV (which effectively means substituting the total volume V of the gas for dV) we obtain the distribution over the components p_x, p_y, p_z of the momentum of the particle. Going over to spherical polar co-ordinates in the momentum space and integrating over the angles we obtain the distribution over the absolute value of the momenta

$$dN_p = \frac{gVp^2\,dp}{2\pi^2\hbar^3(e^{(\epsilon-\mu)/kT}\pm1)},\tag{55.3}$$

(where $\epsilon = p^2/2m$) or the distribution over the energy:

$$dN_\epsilon = \frac{gVm^{3/2}}{2^{\frac12}\pi^2\hbar^3}\frac{\sqrt{\epsilon}\,d\epsilon}{e^{(\epsilon-\mu)/kT}\pm1}.\tag{55.4}$$

These formulae replace the classical Maxwell distribution.

Integrating (55.4) over $d\epsilon$, we obtain the total number of particles in the gas:

$$N = \frac{gVm^{3/2}}{2^{\frac12}\pi^2\hbar^3}\int_0^\infty\frac{\sqrt{\epsilon}\,d\epsilon}{e^{(\epsilon-\mu)/kT}\pm1}.\tag{55.5}$$

This formula determines the chemical potential implicitly as a function of the temperature T and density N/V.

Carrying out the same transition from summation to integration in formulae (52.4) (53.4), we obtain the following expression for the potential Ω:

$$\Omega = \mp\frac{VgkTm^{3/2}}{2^{\frac12}\pi^2\hbar^3}\int_0^\infty\sqrt{\epsilon}\log(1\pm e^{(\mu-\epsilon)/kT})\,d\epsilon.$$

Integrating by parts we obtain

$$\Omega = -\frac23\frac{gVm^{3/2}}{2^{\frac12}\pi^2\hbar^3}\int_0^\infty\frac{\epsilon^{3/2}\,d\epsilon}{e^{(\epsilon-\mu)/kT}\pm1}.\tag{55.6}$$

This expression coincides, except for the factor $-\frac23$, with the total energy of the gas equal to

$$E = \int_0^\infty\epsilon\,dN_\epsilon = \frac{gVm^{3/2}}{2^{\frac12}\pi^2\hbar^3}\int_0^\infty\frac{\epsilon^{3/2}\,d\epsilon}{e^{(\epsilon-\mu)/kT}\pm1}.\tag{55.7}$$

Bearing in mind also that $\Omega = -PV$ we obtain, in this way, the following relation:

$$PV = \tfrac{2}{3}E. \tag{55.8}$$

Being an exact relation, it must still be satisfied in the limiting case of a Boltzmann gas. In fact, substituting Boltzmann's value for $E = 3/2 \, NkT$, we obtain the Clapeyron equation.

From formula (55.6), making the substitution $\epsilon/kT = z$ we find that

$$\Omega = -PV = VT^{5/2}f(\mu/T), \tag{55.9}$$

where f is a function of one variable, i.e. Ω/V is a homogeneous function of μ and T of degree 5/2†. Hence:

$$\frac{S}{V} = -\frac{1}{V}\left(\frac{\partial\Omega}{\partial T}\right)_{V,\mu} \quad\text{and}\quad \frac{N}{V} = -\frac{1}{V}\left(\frac{\partial\Omega}{\partial\mu}\right)_{T,V}$$

are homogeneous functions of μ and T of degree 3/2 and their ratio is a homogeneous function of zero order, i.e. $S/N = \phi(\mu/T)$. From this we can see that in an adiabatic process ($S = $ constant) the ratio μ/T remains constant and, since $N/VT^{3/2}$ is also a function of μ/T only, then also

$$VT^{3/2} = \text{const.} \tag{55.10}$$

Then from (55.9) it follows that

$$PV^{5/3} = \text{const,} \tag{55.11}$$

and also that $T^{5/2}/P = $ const. These equations coincide with the usual Poisson adiabatic equation for a monatomic gas. Note, however, that the indices in (55.10–11) are no longer connected with the ratio of the specific heats (as it is no longer true that $C_p/C_v = 5/3$ and $c_p - c_v = k$).

Formula (55.6) rewritten in the form

$$P = \frac{g\sqrt{2}m^{3/2}(kT)^{5/2}}{3\pi^2\hbar^3}\int_0^\infty \frac{z^{3/2}\,dz}{e^{z-(\mu/kT)}\pm 1}, \tag{55.12}$$

together with formulae (55.5) determine the equation of state of the gas in parametric form (the parameter here being μ); i.e. the relations between P, V and T. In the limiting case of a Boltzmann gas (corresponding to $e^{\mu/kT} \ll 1$) these formulae lead to the Clapeyron equation, as they should. We shall show this, and also calculate the first correction term in the expansion of the equation of state.

For $e^{\mu/kT} \ll 1$ we may expand the integrand in (55.12) as a series in

---

† If one calculates the energy from (55.9) as

$$E = N\mu + TS - PV = -\mu\frac{\partial\Omega}{\partial\mu} - T\frac{\partial\Omega}{\partial T} + \Omega$$

we again get (55.8).

powers of $e^{(\mu/kT)-z}$ and, retaining the first two terms of the expansion, we obtain:

$$\int_0^\infty \frac{z^{3/2}dz}{e^{z-\mu/kT}\pm1} \cong \int_0^\infty z^{3/2}e^{(\mu/kT)-z}(1\mp e^{(\mu/kT)-z})\,dz$$

$$= \frac{3\sqrt{\pi}}{4}e^{\mu/kT}\left(1\mp\frac{1}{2^{5/2}}e^{\mu/kT}\right).$$

Substituting this into (55.12) we have

$$\Omega = -PV = -\frac{gVm^{3/2}(kT)^{5/2}}{(2\pi)^{3/2}\hbar^3}e^{\mu/kT}\left(1\mp\frac{1}{2^{5/2}}e^{\mu/kT}\right).$$

If we retain only the first term of the expansion, then we get exactly the Boltzmann value for the chemical potential of a monatomic gas (formula (45.5) for $g=1$). The next term gives the required correction so that we may write

$$\Omega = \Omega_{\text{Boltz}}\pm\frac{gVm^{3/2}(kT)^{5/2}}{16\pi^{3/2}\hbar^3}e^{2\mu/kT}. \tag{55.13}$$

But small increments to all the thermodynamic functions, expressed in terms of the corresponding variables are equal (see eq. 24.16). Hence expressing the correction to Ω in terms of T and V (which can be done to the same accuracy, making use of Boltzmann's expressions) we obtain directly the correction to the free energy

$$F = F_{\text{Boltz}}\pm\frac{\pi^{3/2}}{2g}\frac{N^2\hbar^3}{V(kT)^{1/2}m^{3/2}}. \tag{55.14}$$

Lastly, differentiating with respect to the volume we obtain the required equation of state

$$PV = NkT\left[1\pm\frac{\pi^{3/2}}{2g}\frac{N\hbar^3}{V(mkT)^{3/2}}\right]. \tag{55.15}$$

The condition that the correction term should be small naturally coincides with the condition (45.6) that Boltzmann statistics should be applicable. Thus we see that the variation of the properties of a perfect gas from the classical, arising when we lower the temperature at given density (one talks of the beginning of degeneracy) leads, in the case of Fermi statistics, to an increase in the pressure relative to its value for the ordinary gas; it may be said the quantum-mechanical exchange effects lead in this case to the appearance of an additional effective "repulsion" between the particles.

In Bose statistics the value of the pressure of the gas changes in the opposite direction; it falls below the classical value: one can say that in this case there arises an effective "attraction" between the particles.

§56. The degenerate electron gas

The study of the Fermi gas at very low temperatures is very important. As we shall see below, the temperatures we have been speaking about may, in fact, from other points of view, be considered quite high.

We talk below about an electron gas, bearing in mind the most important application of Fermi statistics. For electrons $g = 2$; however, we shall not substitute this value into the formulae so that they may be applied directly to the other cases as well.

We start by considering an electron gas at absolute zero (the so-called *completely* degenerate Fermi gas). In such a gas the electrons will be distributed over the different quantum states in such a way that the total energy of the gas has its smallest possible value. Since no more than one electron may be in any one quantum state the electrons fill all states with energies between the smallest (equal to zero) and some largest value which is determined by the number of electrons in the gas. The number of quantum states of translational motion of a particle with a momentum whose absolute value lies between p and $p + dp$ is equal to

$$\frac{4\pi p^2 \, dp \cdot V}{(2\pi\hbar)^3}.$$

Multiplying this expression by g we obtain the total number of quantum states with the momentum under consideration:

$$\frac{gVp^2 \, dp}{2\pi^2\hbar^3}. \tag{56.1}$$

The number of electrons filling all states with momenta between 0 and some p_0 is hence equal to:

$$N = \frac{gV}{2\pi^2\hbar^3} \int_0^{p_0} p^2 \, dp = \frac{gVp_0^3}{6\pi^2\hbar^3}$$

whence, for the limiting momentum p_0 we have:

$$p_0 = \left(\frac{6\pi^2}{g}\right)^{1/3} \left(\frac{N}{V}\right)^{1/3} \hbar, \tag{56.2}$$

and for the limiting energy

$$\epsilon_0 = \frac{p_0^2}{2m} = \left(\frac{6\pi^2}{g}\right)^{2/3} \frac{\hbar^2}{2m} \left(\frac{N}{V}\right)^{2/3} \tag{56.3}$$

This energy has a simple thermodynamic meaning. In accordance with what was said above, the Fermi distribution function over the quantum states,

$$\frac{1}{e^{(\epsilon-\mu)/kT} + 1} \tag{56.4}$$

tends to zero for $\epsilon > \mu$ as $T \to 0$. (In Fig. 5 this function is represented by the continuous line). From this one can see that the chemical potential of a

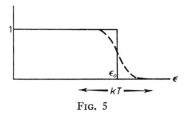

FIG. 5

gas at absolute zero coincides with the limiting energy of the electrons

$$\mu = \epsilon_0. \tag{56.5}$$

The total energy of the gas is obtained by multiplying the number of states (56.1) by $p^2/2m$ and integrating over all momenta:

$$E = \frac{gV}{4m\pi^2\hbar^3} \int_0^{p_0} p^4 \, dp = \frac{gVp_0^5}{20m\pi^2\hbar^3}$$

or, on substituting into (56.2)

$$E = \frac{3}{10}\left(\frac{6\pi^2}{g}\right)^{2/3}\frac{\hbar^2}{m}\left(\frac{N}{V}\right)^{2/3}N. \tag{56.6}$$

By means of the general relations (55.8) we finally obtain the equation of state of the gas

$$P = \frac{1}{5}\left(\frac{6\pi^2}{g}\right)^{2/3}\frac{\hbar^2}{m}\left(\frac{N}{V}\right)^{5/3}. \tag{56.7}$$

In this way the pressure of a Fermi gas at absolute zero is proportional to the 5/3 power of its density.

The formulae (56.6–7) which we have obtained can also be used as approximations for temperatures sufficiently close to absolute zero (for given density of the gas). The condition that they should be applicable (the condition of strong degeneracy of the gas) obviously requires kT to be small compared with the lowest energy ϵ_0.

$$kT \ll \frac{\hbar^2}{m}\left(\frac{N}{V}\right)^{2/3}. \tag{56.8}$$

This condition, as one would expect, is the opposite to the condition (45.6) that Boltzmann statistics should be applicable. The temperature determined by the relation $kT_0 \simeq \epsilon_0$ is called the "*degeneracy temperature*". The degenerate electron gas has the peculiar property of becoming more and more "perfect" as its density rises. This can easily be seen in the following way.

Consider a gas consisting of electrons and a corresponding number of positively charged nuclei to compensate the electronic charge (a gas of electrons only would be unstable; we have previously ignored the nuclei since the presence of the nuclei does not affect the thermodynamic quantities of the electron gas if it is assumed perfect. The Coulomb interaction energy of the electrons and nuclei is of order of magnitude Ze^2/a (reduced to one electron) where Ze is the charge on a nucleus and $a \sim (ZV/N)^{1/3}$ is the mean distance between the electrons and nuclei. The condition that the gas should be perfect is that this energy should be small compared with the mean kinetic energy of the electrons, which is of the order of magnitude of the limiting energy ϵ_0. The inequality

$$\frac{Ze^2}{a} \ll \epsilon_0,$$

after substituting $a \sim (ZV/N)^{1/2}$ into the expression (56.3) for ϵ_0, yields the condition

$$\frac{N}{V} \gg \left(\frac{e^2 m}{\hbar^2}\right)^3 Z^2 \tag{56.9}$$

We see that this condition is better satisfied when the density of the gas is greater†.

PROBLEM

Determine the number of collisions with a wall for an electron gas at absolute zero (put $g = 2$).

SOLUTION: The number of electrons (per unit volume) with momenta in the range dp travelling at an angle to the normal to the wall in the range $d\theta$ is

$$\frac{2 . 2\pi \sin\theta \, d\theta p^2 \, dp}{(2\pi\hbar)^3}$$

The required number of collisions ν (per cm² of the wall) is obtained by multiplying by $v \cos\theta(v = p/m)$ and integrating over $d\theta$ between the limits 0 and $\pi/2$ and over dp from 0 to p_0, As a result we find

$$\nu = \frac{3(3\pi^2)^{1/3}}{16} \frac{\hbar}{m} \left(\frac{N}{V}\right)^{4/3}.$$

§57. The specific heat of the degenerate electron gas

At temperatures which are low compared with the degeneracy temperature T_0, the distribution function (56.4) takes the form represented in Fig. 5

---

† The degeneracy temperature corresponding to an electron gas of density $(e^2 m/\hbar^2)^3 Z^2$ is of order of magnitude $10^6 Z^{4/3}$.

by the dotted line: it appreciably differs from zero or unity only in a narrow range of values of the energy ϵ near the limiting energy ϵ_0. The width of this so-called "border region" of the Fermi distribution is of order of magnitude kT.

Expressions (56.6–7) are the first terms in the expansion of the corresponding quantities in powers of the small ratio T/T_0. We proceed to determine the next terms of this expansion.

In (55.6) there occurs an integral of the form

$$I = \int\limits_0^\infty \frac{f(\epsilon)\,d\epsilon}{e^{(\epsilon-\mu)/kT}+1}$$

where $f(\epsilon)$ is some function of ϵ (such that the integral converges) in (55.6) $f(\epsilon) = \epsilon^{3/2}$. Let us transform this integral, making the substitution $\epsilon - \mu = kTz$:

$$I = \int\limits_{-\mu/kT}^\infty \frac{f(\mu+kTz)}{e^z+1}kT\,dz = kT\int\limits_0^{\mu/kT} \frac{f(\mu-kTz)\,dz}{e^{-z}+1} + kT\int\limits_0^\infty \frac{f(\mu+kTz)\,dz}{e^z+1}.$$

In the first integral we put

$$\frac{1}{e^{-z}+1} = 1 - \frac{1}{e^z+1}$$

and we find

$$I = \int\limits_0^\mu f(\epsilon)\,d\epsilon - kT\int\limits_0^{\mu/kT} \frac{f(\mu-kTz)\,dz}{e^z+1} + kT\int\limits_0^\infty \frac{f(\mu+kTz)\,dz}{e^z+1}.$$

In the second integral we replace the upper limit by infinity, bearing in mind that $\mu/kT \gg 1$ and that the integral converges rapidly†. Thus:

$$I = \int\limits_0^\mu f(\epsilon)\,d\epsilon + kT\int\limits_0^\infty \frac{f(\mu+kTz)-f(\mu-kTz)}{e^z+1}\,dz.$$

We now expand the numerator of the integrand as a Taylor series in powers of z and integrate term by term:

$$I = \int\limits_0^\mu f(\epsilon)\,d\epsilon + 2(kT)^2 f'(\mu)\int\limits_0^\infty \frac{z\,dz}{e^z+1} + \tfrac{1}{3}(kT)^4 f'''(\mu)\int\limits_0^\infty \frac{z^3\,dz}{e^z+1} + \ldots.$$

---

† This substitution involves neglecting exponentially small terms. It must be borne in mind that the expansion obtained below is an asymptotic and not a convergent series.

Substituting the values of the integrals,† we finally obtain:

$$I = \int\limits_0^\mu f(\epsilon)\,d\epsilon + \frac{\pi^2}{6}(kT)^2 f'(\mu) + \frac{7\pi^4}{360}(kT)^4 f'''(\mu) + \dots. \qquad (57.1)$$

---

† Integrals of this type are calculated in the following way

$$\int\limits_0^\infty \frac{z^{x-1}\,dz}{e^z+1} = \int\limits_0^\infty z^{x-1}e^{-z}\sum_{n=0}^\infty (-)^n e^{-nz}\,dz = \Gamma(x)\sum_{n=1}^\infty (-)^{n+1}\frac{1}{n^x} = (1-2^{1-x})\Gamma(x)\sum_{n=1}^\infty \frac{1}{n^x}$$

or

$$\int\limits_0^\infty \frac{z^{x-1}\,dz}{e^z+1} = (1-2^{1-x})\Gamma(x)\zeta(x) \qquad (1)$$

where $\zeta(x) = \sum_{n=1}^\infty 1/n^x$ is called the Riemann ζ-function. For $x = 1$ the expression (1) becomes indeterminate; the value of the integral

$$\int\limits_0^\infty \frac{dz}{e^z+1} = \log 2. \qquad (2)$$

For integral, even x ($x = 2n$) the ζ-function is expressed in terms of what are called the Bernoulli numbers B_n and we obtain

$$\int\limits_0^\infty \frac{z^{2n-1}}{e^z+1}\,dz = \frac{2^{2n-1}-1}{2n}\pi^{2n}B_n \qquad (3)$$

In the same way one can calculate the following integrals

$$\int\limits_0^\infty \frac{z^{x-1}\,dz}{e^z-1} = \Gamma(x)\,\zeta(x) \qquad (x > 1). \qquad (4)$$

For even integral $x = 2n$ we have

$$\int\limits_0^\infty \frac{z^{2n-1}\,dz}{e^z-1} = \frac{(2\pi)^{2n}B_n}{4n}. \qquad (5)$$

We write down for future reference some of the first Bernoulli numbers and some values of the function $\zeta(x)$.

$$B_1 = \frac{1}{6}, \quad B_2 = \frac{1}{30}, \quad B_3 = \frac{1}{42}, \quad B_4 = \frac{1}{30};$$

$$\zeta(3/2) = 2\cdot612, \quad \zeta(5/2) = 1\cdot341, \quad \zeta(3) = 1\cdot202, \quad \zeta(5) = 1\cdot037;$$

$$\Gamma(3/2) = \tfrac{1}{2}\sqrt{\pi} \quad \Gamma(5/2) = \tfrac{3}{4}\sqrt{\pi}.$$

Useful tables of functions of the type

$$F_k(\eta) = \int\limits_0^\infty \frac{z^k\,dz}{e^{z-\eta}+1}$$

are given by J. McDougall and E. C. Stoner (*Phil. Trans.* **237**, 67, 1938); A. C. Beer, M. N. Chase, P. F. Choquard (*Helv. Phys. Acta* **28**, 529, 1955); R. E. Dingle (*Appl. Sci. Res.*, Sec. B, 62 25, 1957).

The third term of the expansion is given for future reference; we shall not need it here.

Putting $f = \epsilon^{3/2}$ in formula (57.1) and substituting in (55.6) we obtain the desired next term of the expansion of the potential Ω at low temperatures:

$$\Omega = \Omega_0 - V(kT)^2 \frac{g\sqrt{2\mu}\,m^{3/2}}{12\hbar^3}. \tag{57.2}$$

By Ω_0 we denote the value of Ω at absolute zero.

Considering the second term as a small increment in Ω_0, and expressing μ in terms of T and V with the aid of the "zero approximation" (56.5), we can immediately write down for the free energy (in accordance with 24.16)

$$F = F_0 - \frac{\beta}{2}NT^2\left(\frac{V}{N}\right)^{2/3}, \tag{57.3}$$

where we have introduced for simplicity the notation

$$\beta = \left(\frac{g\pi}{6}\right)^{2/3}\frac{mk^2}{\hbar^2}. \tag{57.4}$$

Hence we find the entropy of the gas:

$$S = \beta NT\left(\frac{V}{N}\right)^{2/3}, \tag{57.5}$$

its specific heat†:

$$C = \beta NT\left(\frac{V}{N}\right)^{2/3} \tag{57.6}$$

and its energy

$$E = E_0 + \frac{\beta}{2}NT^2\left(\frac{V}{N}\right)^{2/3} = E_0\left[1 + 0\cdot0713g^{4/3}\left(\frac{mkT}{\hbar^2}\right)^2\left(\frac{V}{N}\right)^{4/3}\right]. \tag{57.7}$$

Thus the specific heat of a degenerate Fermi gas at low temperature is directly proportional to the temperature.

§58. The relativistic degenerate electron gas

When the gas is compressed the average energy of the electrons rises (ϵ_0 increases); when it becomes comparable with mc^2 relativistic effects become important. We shall consider here in some detail a completely degenerate, extreme relativistic electron gas, the energy of whose particles is large

---

† We intentionally omit the suffix v or p in the specific heat since in this approximation C_v and C_p coincide. In fact we have seen in §23 that if $S \to 0$ as $T \to 0$ then the difference $(C_p - C_v) \sim T^{2n+1}$ Thus in the given case $C_p - C_v \sim T^3$.

compared with mc^2. It is well known that the energy of a particle is, in that limit, connected with its momentum by the relation

$$\epsilon = cp \tag{58.1}$$

For the number of quantum states, and hence the limiting momentum p_0 we have the previous formulae (56.1) and (56.2). The limiting energy (i.e. the chemical potential of the gas) is now equal to

$$\epsilon_0 = cp_0 = \left(\frac{6\pi^2}{g}\right)^{1/3} \hbar c \left(\frac{N}{V}\right)^{1/3}. \tag{58.2}$$

The total energy of the gas is

$$E = \frac{gcV}{2\pi^2\hbar^3} \int\limits_0^{p_0} p^3\, dp = \frac{gcp_0^4}{8\pi^2\hbar^3}V$$

or

$$E = \frac{3}{4}\left(\frac{6\pi^2}{g}\right)^{1/3} \hbar c N \left(\frac{N}{V}\right)^{1/3}. \tag{58.3}$$

The pressure of the gas can be obtained by differentiating the energy with respect to the volume (at constant entropy, equal to zero). This gives:

$$P = \frac{E}{3V} = \frac{1}{4}\left(\frac{6\pi^2}{g}\right)^{1/3} \hbar c \left(\frac{N}{V}\right)^{4/3}. \tag{58.4}$$

The pressure of the extreme relativistic electron gas is thus proportional to the 4/3 power of its density.

It must be pointed out that the relation

$$PV = \frac{E}{3} \tag{58.5}$$

in fact holds for the extreme relativistic electron gas not only at absolute zero, but also at all other temperatures. This can easily be shown by exactly the same method as we used to derive the relation (55.8), if one uses for the energy the expression $\epsilon = cp$ instead of $\epsilon = p^2/2m$. For $\epsilon = cp$ we obtain an expression for Ω from (52.4)

$$\Omega = -\frac{gkTV}{2\pi^2c^3\hbar^3} \int\limits_0^\infty \epsilon^2 \log(1 + e^{(\mu-\epsilon)/kT})\, d\epsilon,$$

whence, integrating by parts, we obtain

$$\Omega = -\frac{1}{3}\frac{gV}{2\pi^2c^3\hbar^3} \int\limits_0^\infty \frac{\epsilon^3\, d\epsilon}{e^{(\epsilon-\mu)/kT}+1} = -\frac{E}{3}. \tag{58.6}$$

Thus for the extreme relativistic Fermi gas the pressure reaches the limiting value which the pressure of any macroscopic body can have (for given E) (See §27).

Introducing $\epsilon/kT = z$ as a variable of integration we write:

$$\Omega = -\frac{gV(kT)^4}{6\pi^2c^3\hbar^3} \int_0^\infty \frac{z^3\,dz}{e^{z-(\mu/kT)}+1}.$$

We can see from this that

$$\Omega = VT^4 f(\mu/T). \tag{58.7}$$

By the same method as in §55 we find from this that for an adiabatic process the volume, pressure and temperature of an extreme relativistic Fermi gas are connected by the relations

$$PV^{4/3} = \text{const}, \quad VT^3 = \text{const}, \quad T^4/P = \text{const}. \tag{58.8}$$

These agree with the usual Poisson equation for an adiabatic with $\gamma = 4/3$. Note, however, that γ is not the ratio of the specific heats of the gas.

PROBLEMS

1. Determine the number of collisions with the wall of an extreme relativistic completely degenerate electron gas[†].

SOLUTION: The calculations are carried out as in the example in §56 but it must be remembered that the velocity of the electrons $v \cong c$. As a result we obtain:

$$\nu = \frac{c}{4}\frac{N}{V}.$$

2. Find the specific heat of a degenerate, extreme relativistic electron gas.

SOLUTION: Applying formula (57.1) to the integral in (58.6) we find:

$$\Omega = \Omega_0 - \frac{(\mu kT)^2}{6(c\hbar)^3}V.$$

Hence the entropy,

$$S = \frac{(\mu k)^2}{3(c\hbar)^3}VT = N\frac{(3\pi^2)^{2/3}k^2}{3c\hbar}T\left(\frac{V}{N}\right)^{1/3},$$

and the specific heat

$$C = N\frac{(3\pi^2)^{2/3}k^2}{3c\hbar}\left(\frac{V}{N}\right)^{1/3}T.$$

3. Determine the equation of state of a completely degenerate relativistic electron gas (the energy of the electron is connected with the momentum by $\epsilon^2 = c^2p^2+m^2c^4$).

[†] Assume in all the problems that $g = 2$.

SOLUTION: For the number of states and limiting momentum we have formulae (56.1) and (56.2) and the total energy is equal to

$$E = \frac{Vc}{\pi^2\hbar^3} \int_0^{p_0} p^2\sqrt{(m^2c^2+p^2)} \, . \, \mathrm{d}p$$

whence

$$E = \frac{cV}{8\pi^2\hbar^3}\left\{p_0(2p_0^2+m^2c^2)\sqrt{(p_0^2+m^2c^2)}-(mc)^4\,\mathrm{sh}^{-1}\frac{p_0}{mc}\right\}.$$

For the pressure

$$P = \frac{c}{8\pi^2\hbar^3}\left\{p_0(\tfrac{2}{3}p_0^2-m^2c^2)\sqrt{(p_0^2+m^2c^2)}+(mc)^4\mathrm{sh}^{-1}\frac{p_0}{mc}\right\}.$$

It is convenient to represent the formulae obtained in parametric form, introducing as a parameter the quantity

$$\xi = 4\,\mathrm{sh}^{-1}\frac{p_0}{mc}.$$

Then we obtain

$$\frac{N}{V} = \left(\frac{mc}{\hbar}\right)^3 \frac{1}{3\pi^2}\,\mathrm{sh}^3\frac{\xi}{4},$$

$$P = \frac{m^4c^5}{32\pi^2\hbar^3}\left(\frac{1}{3}\,\mathrm{sh}\,\xi-\frac{8}{3}\,\mathrm{sh}\frac{\xi}{2}+\xi\right),$$

$$\frac{E}{V} = \frac{m^4c^5}{32\pi^2\hbar^3}(\mathrm{sh}\,\xi-\xi).$$

§59. The degenerate Bose gas

At low temperatures the properties of the Bose gas have nothing in common with the properties of the Fermi gas. This is quite obvious from the fact that for the Bose gas the state of lowest energy, in which the gas is at $T = 0$, must be a state with $E = 0$ (each particle in the quantum state with $\epsilon = 0$) while the Fermi gas at absolute zero has a non-zero energy.

If, for a given density N/V of the gas, we lower its temperature, then the chemical potential μ, given by equation (55.5) (with the lower sign), will rise, i.e., since it is negative, its absolute value will decrease. It will reach the value $\mu = 0$ at a temperature determined by the relation

$$\frac{N}{V} = \frac{g(mkT)^{3/2}}{2^{\frac{1}{2}}\pi^2\hbar^3} \int_0^\infty \frac{\sqrt{z}\,\mathrm{d}z}{e^z-1}. \tag{59.1}$$

The integral is expressible in terms of the ζ-function (see footnote on page

164); denoting the required temperature by T_0, we obtain:

$$T_0 = \frac{3 \cdot 31}{g^{2/3}} \frac{\hbar^2}{mk} \left(\frac{N}{V}\right)^{2/3}. \tag{59.2}$$

For $T < T_0$ eq. (55.5) does not have any negative solutions, but in Bose statistics the chemical potential must be negative at all temperatures.

This apparent contradiction is connected with the fact that in the given conditions we are not justified in replacing the summation (in eq. 53.3) by an integration (in eq. 55.5). Indeed, in such a transition the first term of the sum (with $\epsilon_k = 0$) is multiplied by $\sqrt{\epsilon} = 0$, i.e. it drops out of the sum. But as the temperature falls the particles must collect just in this state of lowest energy until for $T = 0$ they are all there. Mathematically this is shown by the fact that in the sum (53.3) as one goes to the limit $\mu \to 0$ the sum of all the terms of the series, except the first, tends to a finite limit (determined by the integral (55.5)) and the first term (with $\epsilon_k = 0$) tends to infinity. Letting μ tend not to zero, but to some small finite value, one can, therefore, give this first term the required finite value.

Hence in actual fact for $T < T_0$ the position will be as follows. The particles with energy $\epsilon > 0$ are distributed according to formula (55.4) with $\mu = 0$;

$$dN_\epsilon = \frac{gm^{3/2}V}{2^{\frac{1}{2}}\pi^2\hbar^3} \frac{\sqrt{\epsilon}\, d\epsilon}{e^{\epsilon/kT}-1}. \tag{59.3}$$

The total number of particles with energy $\epsilon > 0$ will thus be

$$N_{\epsilon>0} = \int dN_\epsilon = \frac{gV(mkT)^{3/2}}{2^{\frac{1}{2}}\pi^2\hbar^3} \int_0^\infty \frac{\sqrt{z}\, dz}{e^z-1} = N\left(\frac{T}{T_0}\right)^{3/2},$$

and the other

$$N_{\epsilon=0} = N\left[1-\left(\frac{T}{T_0}\right)^{3/2}\right] \tag{59.4}$$

is in the lowest state, i.e. has energy $\epsilon = 0.$†

The energy of the gas for $T < T_0$ is determined, certainly, only by those particles which have $\epsilon > 0$; assuming in (55.7) $\mu = 0$ we have:

$$E = \frac{gV(mkT)^{3/2}kT}{2^{\frac{1}{2}}\pi^2\hbar^3} \int_0^\infty \frac{z^{3/2}\, dz}{e^z-1}.$$

---

† The effect of concentrating the particles in the state $\epsilon = 0$ is often called "Bose-Einstein condensation". We must emphasise that at best one might perhaps talk about "condensation in momentum space". Actual condensation certainly does not take place in the gas.

The integral reduces to $\zeta(5/2)$ (see footnote on page 164) and we obtain the energy

$$E = 0.770NkT \left(\frac{T}{T_0}\right)^{3/2} = 0.1289\frac{m^{3/2}(kT)^{5/2}}{\hbar^3}V. \tag{59.5}$$

Thus the specific heat

$$C_v = 5E/2T, \tag{59.6}$$

i.e. the specific heat is proportional to $T^{3/2}$. Integrating the specific heat we obtain the entropy:

$$S = \frac{5E}{3T}, \tag{59.7}$$

and the free energy $F = E - TS$:

$$F = -\tfrac{2}{3}E \tag{59.8}$$

The latter result is quite reasonable since, for $\mu = 0$

$$F = \Phi - PV = N\mu + \Omega = \Omega.$$

For the pressure $P = -(\partial F/\partial V)_T$ we have:

$$P = 0.0851g\frac{m^{3/2}(kT)^{5/2}}{\hbar^3}. \tag{59.9}$$

We see that for $T < T_0$ the pressure is proportional to $T^{5/2}$ and is independent of the volume. This fact is a natural consequence of the fact that the particles in the state $\epsilon = 0$ have no momentum, and thus do not contribute to the pressure.

At the actual point $T = T_0$ all the thermodynamic quantities mentioned are continuous. One can show, however, that the derivative of the specific heat with respect to temperature has a discontinuity at this point (see the problem at the end of this section). The curve of the specific heat itself as a function of the temperature has a kink at $T = T_0$, and at this point the specific heat is a maximum (and is equal to $1.28 \cdot 3/2Nk$).

PROBLEM

1. Determine the discontinuity in $(\partial C_v/\partial T)_V$ at the point $T = T_0$.

SOLUTION: To solve this problem one must determine the energy of the gas for small positive $T - T_0$. We rewrite eq. (55.5) in the form

$$N = N_0(T) + \frac{gVm^{3/2}}{2^{\frac{1}{2}}\pi^2\hbar^3} \int_0^\infty \left[\frac{1}{e^{(\epsilon-\mu)/kT}-1} - \frac{1}{e^{\epsilon/kT}-1}\right]\sqrt{\epsilon}\, d\epsilon,$$

where the function $N_0(T)$ is determined by the equation (59.1). We expand the integrand bearing in mind that μ is small near $T = T_0$. Hence the region of small ϵ is important in the integral and we find that the above integral is equal to

$$kT\mu \int_0^\infty \frac{d\epsilon}{\sqrt{\epsilon}\,(\epsilon + |\mu|)} = -\pi k T \sqrt{\mu}.$$

Substituting this value and expressing μ in terms of $N - N_0$ we obtain:

$$-\mu = \frac{2\pi^2 \hbar^6}{g^2 m^3} \left(\frac{N_0 - N}{kTV}\right)^2.$$

To the same accuracy we may now write:

$$\frac{\partial E}{\partial \mu} = -\frac{3}{2}\frac{\partial \Omega}{\partial \mu} = \frac{3}{2}N \cong \frac{3}{2}N_0,$$

whence

$$E = E_0 + \tfrac{3}{2}N_0\mu = E_0 - \frac{3\pi^2 \hbar^6}{g^2 m^3}N_0\left(\frac{N_0 - N}{kTV}\right)^2,$$

where $E_0 = E_0(T)$ denotes the energy for $\mu = 0$, i.e. the function (59.5). The second derivative of the second term with respect to the temperature clearly gives the required discontinuity in the specific heat. Performing these calculations we obtain

$$\Delta\left(\frac{\partial C_v}{\partial T}\right)_V = -\frac{6\pi^2 \hbar^6}{k^2 g^2 m^3 V^2}\left[N_0\left(\frac{1}{T}\frac{\partial N_0}{\partial T}\right)^2\right]_{T=T_0} = 3.66\frac{Nk}{T_0}.$$

The value of the derivative $(\partial C_v/\partial T)_V$ at $T = T_0 - 0$ is, according to (59.5), $+2.89\,Nk/T_0$ and thus at $T = T_0 + 0$ it is equal to $-0.77\,Nk/T_0$.

§60. Black-body radiation

The most important application of Bose statistics is to electro magnetic radiation in thermal equilibrium, called "black-body radiation".

Black-body radiation may be considered as a "gas" made up of photons. The linear nature of the electrodynamic equations indicates that photons do not interact with one another (the principle of superposition of the electromagnetic field) so that a "photon gas" is an ideal one. Since we know the angular momentum of a photon to be a whole number, this gas obeys Bose statistics.

If the radiation is not in a vacuum but in a material medium, then, for the photon gas to be ideal, the interaction of the radiation with the medium must also be small. This condition is fulfilled for gases (over the whole radiation spectrum, except at frequencies near the absorption lines of the medium); for media of high density, however, it is only true at high temperatures.

It must be borne in mind that the presence of some matter, however little, is in general necessary to enable thermal equilibrium to be set up in the radiation, since one may assume that there is no interaction between the photons†. The mechanism which brings about the establishment of

---

† Apart from the completely negligible interactions due to the possible existence of virtual electron-positron pairs.

equilibrium is, in this case, the absorption and emission of photons by the matter. This leads to a very important property peculiar to the photon gas: the number of particles N in the gas is a variable quantity and not a given constant as for the usual gas. Thus N must itself be determined from the condition of thermal equilibrium. Requiring the free energy of the gas (for given T and V) to be a minimum, we get, for one of the necessary conditions, $\partial F/\partial N = 0$, but since $(\partial F/\partial N)_{T,V} = \mu$ we find that

$$\mu = 0 \tag{60.1}$$

i.e. the chemical potential of the photon gas is equal to zero.

The distribution of the photons over the different quantum states with energies $\epsilon_k = \hbar\omega_k$, where ω_k are the eigenfrequencies of the radiation in the given volume V, is therefore given by formula (53.2) with $\mu = 0$:

$$\bar{n}_k = \frac{1}{e^{\hbar\omega_k/kT}-1}. \tag{60.2}$$

This is called the *Planck distribution*.

Assuming the volume to be sufficiently large, we can pass in the usual way† from a discrete to a continuous distribution of eigenfrequencies of the radiation. The number of modes of oscillation with the components of their wave vector $\mathbf{f}$ lying in the intervals df_x, df_y, df_z is equal to

$$\frac{V}{(2\pi)^3}\, df_x\, df_y\, df_z,$$

as is well known, and hence the number of modes with the absolute value of the wave vector in the range df is

$$\frac{V}{(2\pi)^3}4\pi f^2\, df.$$

Introducing the frequency $\omega = cf$ and multiplying by 2 (since there are two independent directions of polarisation), we obtain the number of quantum states of the photons with frequencies between ω and $\omega+d\omega$:

$$\frac{V\omega^2\, d\omega}{\pi^2 c^3}. \tag{60.3}$$

Multiplying the distribution (60.2) by this quantity we find the number of photons in the given frequency range:

$$dN_\omega = \frac{V}{\pi^2 c^3}\frac{\omega^3 d\omega}{e^{\hbar\omega/kT}-1}, \tag{60.4}$$

and multiplying once more by $\hbar\omega$ we obtain the radiation energy in this

---

† See for example, *The Classical Theory of Fields*, §6–9.

region of the spectrum:

$$dE_\omega = \frac{V\hbar}{\pi^2 c^3} \frac{\omega^3 d\omega}{e^{\hbar\omega/kT}-1},$$ (60.5)

This expression for the spectral distribution of the energy of black body radiation is called *Planck's formula* (1900). Expressed in terms of wavelengths $\lambda = 2\pi c/\omega$, it takes the form:

$$dE_\lambda = \frac{16\pi^2 c\hbar V}{\lambda^5} \frac{d\lambda}{e^{2\pi\hbar c/kT\lambda}-1}.$$ (60.6)

For small frequencies $(\hbar\omega \ll kT)$ (60.5) gives

$$dE_\omega = V\frac{kT}{\pi^2 c^3}\omega^2\,d\omega.$$

This is called the *Rayleigh-Jeans* formula. Note that it does not involve the quantum constant $\hbar$ and can be obtained by multiplying the "number of modes" (60.3) by kT: in this sense it agrees with classical statistics, where to each "oscillatory degree of freedom" corresponds an energy kT (the law of equipartition, §44).

In the opposite limiting case of high frequency $(\hbar\omega \gg kT)$ formula (60.5) becomes

$$dE_\omega = V\frac{\hbar}{\pi^2 c^3}\omega^3 e^{-\hbar\omega/kT}\,d\omega.$$ (60.8)

This is called the *Wien formula.*

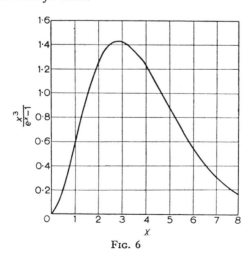

FIG. 6

Fig. 6 shows the graph of the function $x^3/(e^x -1)$, corresponding to the distribution (60.5). The derivative of the spectral distribution of the energy of black-body radiation with respect to frequency, $dE_\omega/d\omega$ has a maximum at the frequency $\omega = \omega_m$, determined by the relation

$$\frac{\hbar\omega_m}{kT} = 2{\cdot}822. \tag{60.9}$$

Thus as the temperature rises the position of the maximum of the distribution is displaced in the direction of increasing frequency proportionally to T (*Wien's displacement law*).†

We now calculate the thermodynamic quantities of black-body radiation. For $\mu = 0$ the free energy F is the same as Ω (since $F = \Phi - PV = N\mu + \Omega$). From formula (53.4) setting μ equal to zero and going over in the usual way (with the aid of (60.3)) from summation to integration we obtain:

$$F = kT\frac{V}{\pi^2 c^3} \int_0^\infty \omega^2 \log(1 - e^{-\hbar\omega/kT})\, d\omega \tag{60.10}$$

Introducing $x = \hbar\omega/kT$ as a variable of integration and integrating by parts, we obtain

$$F = -V\frac{(kT)^4}{3\pi^2\hbar^3 c^3} \int_0^\infty \frac{x^3\, dx}{e^x - 1}.$$

This integral is equal to $\pi^4/15$ (see footnote on page 164). Thus,

$$F = -V\frac{\pi^2(kT)^4}{45(\hbar c)^3} = -\frac{4\sigma}{3c}VT^4 \tag{60.11}$$

where

$$\sigma = \frac{\pi^2 k^4}{60\hbar^3 c^2} = 5{\cdot}67 \times 10^{-5} \text{ gm/sec deg}^4 \tag{60.12}$$

is called the *Stefan-Boltzmann constant*.

The entropy $S = \partial F/\partial T$ is equal to

$$S = \frac{16\sigma}{3c}VT^3, \tag{60.13}$$

and is proportional to the cube of the temperature. The total energy of the

---

† The "density" of the distribution with respect to the wavelength $dE_\lambda/d\lambda$ also has a maximum but for a different value given by

$$\frac{2\pi\hbar c}{kT\lambda_m} = 4{\cdot}965.$$

Thus the position of the maximum (λ_m) of the distribution over the wavelengths is displaced proportionally to the inverse temperature.

radiation $E = F + TS$ is equal to

$$E = \frac{4\sigma}{c} VT^4 = -3F. \tag{60.14}$$

This expression could also have been obtained by directly integrating the distribution (60.5). Thus the total energy of the black-body radiation is proportional to the 4th power of the temperature—*Boltzmann's law*. The specific heat of the radiation, $C_v = (\partial E/\partial T)_V$ is equal to

$$C_v = \frac{16\sigma}{c} T^3 V, \tag{60.15}$$

i.e. it is proportional to the cube of the temperature. Lastly the pressure

$$P = -\left(\frac{\partial F}{\partial V}\right)_T = \frac{4\sigma}{3c} T^4; \tag{60.16}$$

$$PV = \frac{E}{3}. \tag{60.17}$$

For the photon gas we obtain the same limiting expression for the pressure as for the extreme relativistic electron gas (§58), as we should; the relation (60.17) is a direct consequence of the linear dependence ($\epsilon = cp$) of the momentum of the particle in its energy.

The total number of photons in the black-body radiation is equal to

$$N = \frac{V}{\pi^2 c^3} \int_0^\infty \frac{\omega^2 \, d\omega}{e^{\hbar\omega/kT} - 1} = \frac{V(kT)^3}{\pi^2 c^3 \hbar^3} \int_0^\infty \frac{x^2 \, dx}{e^x - 1}.$$

This integral is evaluated in terms of the ζ-function of argument 3 (see footnote on page 164; $\zeta(3) = 1 \cdot 202 \ldots$). Thus

$$N = \frac{2\zeta(3)}{\pi^2} \left(\frac{kT}{\hbar c}\right)^3 V = 0 \cdot 244 \left(\frac{kT}{\hbar c}\right)^3 V. \tag{60.18}$$

In an adiabatic expansion (or compression) of a photon gas the volume and temperature are connected by the relation $VT^3 = \text{const.}$ From (60.16) the pressure and volume are connected by the relation $PV^{4/3} = \text{const.}$ Comparing this with (58.8) we see that the equation of an adiabatic for the photon gas coincides (as we would expect) with that of an adiabatic for the extreme relativistic electron gas.

Consider some body in thermal equilibrium with the black-body radiation surrounding it. The body continually reflects and absorbs the photons falling on it and at the same time radiates new ones, and in equilibrium all these processes balance one another in such a way that the distribution of the photons over the frequencies and directions remains unchanged on the average.

Since the black-body radiation is completely isotropic, energy is emitted uniformly in all directions from each element of its volume. We introduce the notation ·

$$e_0(\omega) = \frac{1}{4\pi V} \frac{dE_\omega}{d\omega} = \frac{\hbar\omega^3}{4\pi^3 c^3 (e^{\hbar\omega/kT} - 1)} \tag{60.19}$$

for the "spectral density" of the black-body radiation per unit volume and unit solid angle. Then the density of flow of energy with frequency in the interval $d\omega$ coming from every point in a direction lying in the element of solid angle do will be

$$c e_0(\omega) \, do \, d\omega$$

Hence the radiation energy (with frequency in the range $d\omega$), falling per unit time on unit surface area of the body at an angle θ to its normal will be

$$c e_0(\omega) \cos\theta \, do \, d\omega, \qquad do = 2\pi \sin\theta \, d\theta.$$

Let us denote by $A(\omega, \theta)$ the "absorbing power" of the body as a function of the frequency of the radiation and its angle of incidence; this quantity is defined as the fraction of the radiation energy in the given frequency interval incident on the surface of the body, which is absorbed by the body. This does not include radiation which passes through the body, if such is present. Then the amount of absorbed radiation (in 1 sec by 1 cm² of surface) will be:

$$c e_0(\omega) A(\omega, \theta) \cos\theta \, do \, d\omega. \tag{60.20}$$

Assume that the body does not scatter radiation and does not fluoresce; i.e. the reflection does not change the angle θ or the frequency. We shall assume that the radiation does not pass through the body, in other words, all non-reflected radiation is totally absorbed. Then the quantity of radiation (60.20) must be compensated for by radiation emitted from the body itself in the same direction and with the same frequency.

Denoting the intensity of emission (from 1 cm² of surface) by $J(\omega, \theta)$ $d\omega \, do$, and making it equal to the energy absorbed, we obtain the following relation:

$$J(\omega, \theta) = c e_0(\omega) A(\omega, \theta) \cos\theta. \tag{60.21}$$

The functions $J(\omega, \theta)$ and $A(\omega, \theta)$ are obviously different for different bodies. We see, however, that their ratio is independent of the nature of the body and is a universal function of frequency and direction

$$\frac{J(\omega, \theta)}{A(\omega, \theta)} = c e_0(\omega) \cos\theta,$$

which is determined by the energy distribution in the spectrum of a black body (at the temperature of the body). This statement is called *Kirchhoff's Law*.

If the body scatters light, then Kirchhoff's Law can only be formulated in a more limited way. Since, in this case, the reflection involves a change in the angle θ, then, starting from the equilibrium condition, one can only require that radiation absorbed from all directions must be equal to the total radiation emitted in all directions:

$$\int J(\omega, \theta) \, do = c e_0(\omega) \int A(\omega, \theta) \cos\theta \, do. \qquad (60.22)$$

The angle θ also changes, in general, in the case when the radiation can pass through the body (owing to the refraction which takes place on entering or leaving the body). In this case relation (60.22) must also be integrated over the whole surface of the body; the functions $A(\omega, \theta)$ and $J(\omega, \theta)$ depend, not only on the substance composing the body, but also on its shape and on the point of it under consideration.

Finally in the case of scattering accompanied by a change in frequency (fluorescence) Kirchhoff's Law holds only for the complete integrals over the frequencies as well as over the directions of the radiation:

$$\iint J(\omega, \theta) \, do \, d\omega = c \iint e_0(\omega) A(\omega, \theta) \cos\theta \, do \, d\omega. \qquad (60.23)$$

A body completely absorbing all energy falling on it is called *"absolutely black"*.† For such a body, by definition, $A(\omega, \theta) = 1$, and its emissive capacity is completely determined by the function

$$J_0(\omega, \theta) = c e_0(\omega) \cos\theta \qquad (60.24)$$

which is the same for all absolutely black bodies. Note that the intensity of the emission from an absolutely black body depends very simply on the direction: it is proportional to the cosine of the angle it makes with the normal to the surface of the body. The total intensity J_0 of the emission from a black body is obtained by integrating (60.24) over all frequencies and all solid angles in a hemisphere:

$$J_0 = c \int\limits_0^\infty e_0(\omega) \, d\omega \cdot \int\limits_0^{\pi/2} 2\pi \cos\theta \sin\theta \, d\theta = \frac{cE}{4V}$$

where E is defined by formula (60.14). Thus

$$J_0 = \sigma T^4, \qquad (60.25)$$

---

† Such a body may be made in the form of a cavity with highly absorbent inner walls having a small opening. Any ray falling on the opening could reach it again, and thus escape, only after many reflections from its walls. Hence, if the opening is sufficiently small, the cavity will absorb almost all the radiation falling on the opening and thus the surface of the opening will be an absolutely black body.

i.e. the total intensity of emission is proportional to the fourth power of its temperature.

Finally, let us consider radiation not in thermal equilibrium. The deviation from equilibrium can lie in the distribution over the direction as well as the spectral distribution. Let $e(\omega, \mathbf{n})\,d\omega\,do$ be the surface density of this radiation in the spectral interval $d\omega$ and with the direction of the wave vector $\mathbf{n}$ lying in the element of solid angle do. One can introduce the concept of temperature of the radiation as the temperature for which the density $e(\omega, \mathbf{n})$ is equal to the value given by Planck's formula, i.e.

$$e(\omega, \mathbf{n}) = e_0(\omega)$$

Denoting this temperature by $T_{\omega,\mathbf{n}}$ we shall have:

$$kT_{\omega,\mathbf{n}} = \frac{\hbar\omega}{\log\left\{1 + \dfrac{\hbar\omega^3}{4\pi^3 c^3}\dfrac{1}{e(\omega, \mathbf{n})}\right\}}. \tag{60.26}$$

Imagine an absolutely black body radiating into the (empty) space surrounding it. The radiation moves freely along straight rays and outside the body will no longer be in thermal equilibrium; it will not be isotropic as an equilibrium radiation must be. Since photons move in a vacuum without interacting with one another, we have the necessary basis for the strict application of Liouville's theorem to the distribution function of the photons over their phase states; i.e. over their co-ordinates and the components of of their wave vector.† In accordance with this theorem the distribution function remains constant along phase trajectories. But the distribution function coincides (to within a factor depending on the frequency) with the space density of radiation $e(\omega, \mathbf{n}, \mathbf{r})$ of the given frequency and direction. Since the frequency of the radiation also remains constant during its propagation we may formulate the following important result. In every element of solid angle in which radiation is propagated (from the given point in space) the density of the radiation $e(\omega, \mathbf{n}, \mathbf{r})$ will be the same as its density inside the black body which emitted it, i.e. equal to the density $e_0(\omega)$ of the black body radiation. However, although in equilibrium radiation this density exists for all directions, in this case it exists only for some particular direction.

Defining the temperature of non-equilibrium radiation by (60.26) we may express this result in another way by saying that the temperature $T_{\omega,\,\mathbf{n}}$ will be equal to the temperature T of the radiating black body for all directions in which radiation is being propagated (from each given point of space). If one defines the temperature of the radiation as the mean value over all directions then it will clearly be lower than that of the black body.

All the consequences of Liouville's theorem are also completely valid for

---

† If we consider the limiting case of geometrical optics we may talk of photon co-ordinates.

the case when reflecting mirrors and refracting lenses are present, in conditions when geometrical optics certainly apply. With the help of the lenses and mirrors one can focus the radiation, i.e. increase the number of directions along which rays travel (to a given point of space). By doing this one can raise the mean temperature of the radiation at this point; however, it follows from the above that one can never make it higher than the temperature of the black body by which this radiation was emitted.

CHAPTER VI

CONDENSED BODIES

§61. Solids: low temperatures

Other objects to which the statistical methods of calculating thermo-dynamic quantities can successfully be applied are solids. The characteristic property of these bodies is that the atoms in them perform only small vibrations about some equilibrium positions—the "points" of the crystal lattices. The arrangement of the lattice points which corresponds to thermal equilibrium of the body is unique, i.e. it is singled out from all other possible arrangements and hence it is regular. In other words, in thermal equilibrium the body must be a *crystal*.

Besides crystals there also exist amorphous solids whose atoms vibrate about irregularly distributed sites. From the thermodynamic point of view, such bodies are metastable and ought, in due course, to crystallise. In fact, however, their relaxation time is so large that in practice amorphous bodies behave as stable ones for unlimited times. All the following calculations apply to amorphous solids as well as crystals. The only difference is that, since amorphous bodies are not in equilibrium, the Nernst theorem does not apply to them, and as $T \to 0$ their entropy tends to a non-zero value. Hence for amorphous solids some constant S_0 must be added to the formula for the entropy (61.7) obtained below (and a corresponding term TS_0 to the free energy); this small unimportant constant (which has no effect on the specific heat of the body, for example) we shall omit in future.

A "residual" entropy not vanishing as $T \to 0$ can also be observed for crystalline solids in connection with the so-called "ordering" of crystals. If the number of sites of the crystal lattice which can be occupied by atoms of a given type is the same as the number of such atoms, then at each such site there will be one atom; in other words the probability of finding an atom near each of these sites is unity. Such crystals are called "completely ordered". There exist, however, crystals in which atoms can be not only in "their" places (i.e. places which they occupy under complete ordering) but also in some "foreign" places. In this case the number of sites in which one can find atoms of the given kind is greater than the number of these atoms, and it is obvious that the probability of finding an atom of the given kind at any of the old or new sites will be different from unity.

Thus, for instance, solid carbon monoxide is a molecular crystal in which the CO molecule can have two opposite orientations which are obtained from each other by interchanging the C and O atoms; the number of possible positions for the C (or O) atoms is in this case twice the number of these atoms.

In a state of complete thermal equilibrium at absolute zero, each crystal must be completely ordered, and the atoms of each kind must occupy completely determined positions. However, owing to the slowness with which changes in the structure of the lattice take place, in particular at low temperatures, a crystal not completely ordered at high temperatures can in fact remain thus even at very low temperatures. This "freezing" of the disorder leads to the appearance of a constant residual term in the entropy of the crystal. Thus in the above example of the crystal CO if the molecules are equally likely to take up either orientation the residual entropy will be equal to $S_0 = k \log 2$.

According to classical mechanics, all the atoms must be motionless at absolute zero and their interaction potential energy must be a minimum for equilibrium. Hence, for sufficiently low temperatures, atoms must in any case perform small vibrations only, i.e. all bodies must become solid. Actually, however, quantum effects can bring about exceptions to this rule. Such an exception is liquid helium—the only substance which remains liquid at absolute zero (at pressures below 25 atm); all other bodies solidify much earlier, before the quantum effects become apparent.†

Note that for bodies to be solid their temperature must be sufficiently low. The quantity kT must in any case be small compared with the interaction energy of the atoms (actually at higher temperatures all bodies melt or decompose chemically). This is connected with the fact that the vibrations of the atoms of solid bodies about their equilibrium positions must be small.

Let N be the number of molecules in the body and ν the number of atoms in each molecule. Then the total number of atoms is $N\nu$. From the total number $3N\nu$ of degrees of freedom we remove three corresponding to the translational, and three to the rotational motion of the body as a whole. Hence the number of vibrational degrees of freedom is $3N\nu-6$; owing, however, to the fact that the quantity $3N\nu$ is enormous, we can certainly neglect the number 6 and take the number of vibrational degrees of freedom to be simply $3N\nu$.

We must emphasize that in the study of solids we shall not here take into account the "internal" (electronic) degrees of freedom of the atoms. Hence if these degrees of freedom should become important (as can happen for metals, for example) it must be understood that the following formulae refer only to that part (the so-called "lattice part") of the thermodynamic quantities of solids connected with the vibration of the atoms. To obtain the total values of these quantities the "electronic" part (see §69) must be added to the "lattice" part.

From the mechanical point of view a system with $3N\nu$ vibrational degrees of freedom may be regarded as an ensemble of $3N\nu$ independent oscillators,

---

† The quantum effects become important when the de Broglie wavelength corresponding to the thermal motion of the atoms becomes comparable with the distances between the atoms. For liquid helium this takes place at 2–3° K.

each of which corresponds to a separate normal mode of vibration. The thermodynamic quantities connected with one vibrational degree of freedom were already calculated in §49. On this basis we may immediately write down the free energy of the solid body in the form†

$$F = N\epsilon_0 + kT \sum_\alpha \log(1 - e^{-\hbar\omega_\alpha/kT}). \tag{61.1}$$

The summation is carried out over all the $3N\nu$ normal vibrations, which are labelled by the suffix α. We have added to the sum over the vibrations a term $N\epsilon_0$ representing the interaction energy of all the atoms of the body in the equilibrium state (or, more exactly, in the state of "zero vibration"); this energy is clearly proportional to the number N of molecules in the body, so that ϵ_0 is the energy attributed to a single molecule. It must be remembered that ϵ_0 is not, in general, constant but is a function of the density, or specific volume; as the volume changes so do the interatomic distances and with them the atomic interaction energy. However ϵ_0 is independent of temperature for given volume: $\epsilon_0 = \epsilon_0(V/N)$.

The other thermodynamic quantities can be obtained in the usual way from the free energy.

Consider now the limiting case of low temperatures. For small kT only terms with low frequencies, $\hbar\omega_\alpha \sim kT$ are important in the sum over α. But low frequency vibrations are, as is well known, simply *sound waves*. The wavelength of a sound wave is connected with its frequency by the relation $\lambda = u/\omega$ where u is the velocity of sound. The wavelength of a sound wave is large compared with the lattice constant a ($\lambda \gg a$); this means that $\omega \ll u/a$. In other words, if we can regard the vibrations as sound waves, the temperature must satisfy a condition which may be written in the form

$$kT \ll \frac{\hbar u}{a}. \tag{61.2}$$

Assume that the body is isotropic (an amorphous solid). It is well known that, in an isotropic solid body, both longitudinal waves (with velocity of propagation u_l) and transverse waves with two independent directions of polarisation (both with velocity of propagation u_t) can be propagated. The frequencies of these waves are connected with the absolute value of their wave vector $\mathbf{f}$ by the linear relations $\omega = u_l f$ or $\omega = u_t f$. The number of "characteristic vibrations" in the sound wave spectrum with wave vectors whose absolute value lies in the interval df and with the given polarisation is

$$V\frac{4\pi f^2 \, df}{(2\pi)^3},$$

where V is the volume of the body. Assuming that for one of the three

---

† The quantisation of vibration was first applied to the calculation of thermodynamic quantities of solid bodies by A. EINSTEIN (1907).

independent polarisations $f = \omega/u_l$ and that for the other two $f = \omega/u_t$, we find that altogether in the interval $d\omega$ the number of vibrations is:

$$V\frac{\omega^2\,d\omega}{2\pi^2}\left(\frac{1}{u_l^3}+\frac{2}{u_t^3}\right). \tag{61.3}$$

Introducing the mean sound velocity $\bar{u}$, defined by

$$\frac{3}{\bar{u}^3} = \frac{2}{u_t^3}+\frac{1}{u_l^3},$$

then expression (61.3) will become

$$V\frac{3\omega^2\,d\omega}{2\pi^2\bar{u}^3}. \tag{61.4}$$

In this form it applies not only to isotropic bodies but also to crystals, where by $\bar{u} = \bar{u}(V/N)$ we understand the velocity of sound in the crystal averaged in a certain way. The determination of the law of averaging requires the solution of the theory of elastic propagation of sound in a crystal of the given symmetry. By means of (61.4) we carry out the change from summation to integration in (61.1) and we get

$$F = N\epsilon_0+kT\frac{3V}{2\pi^2\bar{u}^3}\int_0^\infty \log(1-e^{-\hbar\omega/kT})\omega^2\,d\omega. \tag{61.5}$$

(owing to the rapid convergence of the integral for small kT we can integrate between the limits 0 and ∞). This expression (apart from the term $N\epsilon_0$) differs from formula (60.10) for the free energy of black body radiation only by replacing the velocity of light c by the velocity of sound $\bar{u}$ and the introduction of the extra factor $3/2$. This is quite natural. Indeed, the frequency of sound vibrations is related to their wave vector by the same linear relation as for photons, and the whole numbers v_α in the energy levels $\sum_\alpha v_\alpha \hbar\omega_\alpha$ of a system of sound oscillators can be regarded as "occupation numbers" for the various "quantum states" with energies $\epsilon_\alpha = \hbar\omega_\alpha$. The value of these numbers is arbitrary, as in Bose statistics. The extra factor $3/2$ in (61.5) arises from the fact that sound oscillations have three possible directions of polarisation as compared with the photons' two.

Thus without further calculation we may use expression (60.11) obtained in §60 for the free energy of black body radiation, replacing c by $\bar{u}$ and multiplying by $3/2$. Hence the free energy of a solid is equal to:

$$F = N\epsilon_0-V\frac{\pi^2(kT)^4}{30(\hbar\bar{u})^3}, \tag{61.6}$$

and its entropy will be:

$$S = V\frac{2\pi^2 k (kT)^3}{15(\hbar\bar{u})^3},\tag{61.7}$$

its energy:

$$E = N\epsilon_0 + V\frac{\pi^2(kT)^4}{10(\hbar\bar{u})^3},\tag{61.8}$$

and specific heat:

$$C = \frac{2\pi^2 k}{5(\hbar\bar{u})^3}(kT)^3 V.\tag{61.9}$$

Thus the specific heat at low temperatures is proportional to the cube of the temperature (DEBYE, 1912)†. We write simply C for the specific heat (not distinguishing between C_p and C_v) since at low temperatures the difference $C_p - C_v$ is of a higher order than the specific heat itself (see §23; in this case $S \sim T^3$ and hence $C_p - C_v \sim T^7$).

For solid bodies with a simple crystal lattice (elements and simple compounds) the T^3 law for specific heat begins to apply at temperatures of the order of tens of degrees. For bodies with a complicated lattice one can expect adherence to this law only at considerably lower temperatures.

§62. Solids: high temperatures

We now turn to the opposite limiting case of high temperatures (of order of magnitude $kT \gg \hbar u/a$, where a is the lattice constant). In this case we may write

$$1 - e^{-\hbar\omega_\alpha/kT} \cong \hbar\omega_\alpha/kT$$

and (61.1) takes the form

$$F = N\epsilon_0 + kT \sum_\alpha \log(\hbar\omega_\alpha/kT).\tag{62.1}$$

The sum over α contains $3N\nu$ terms; we introduce the geometric mean frequency ω which is defined by

$$\log \bar{\omega} = \frac{1}{3N\nu} \sum_\alpha \log\frac{\hbar\omega_\alpha}{kT}.\tag{62.2}$$

Then we obtain, for the free energy of the solid body,

$$F = N\epsilon_0 - 3N\nu kT \log kT + 3N\nu kT \log \hbar\bar{\omega}.\tag{62.3}$$

---

† Remember that if electronic degrees of freedom are present these formulae determine only the "lattice" part of the thermodynamic quantities. However, even when an "electronic part" exists (for metals) it begins to affect the specific heat only at temperatures of about a few degrees.

The mean frequency $\bar{\omega}$ is, like $\bar{u}$, some function of the density: $\bar{\omega} = \bar{\omega}(V/N)$. From (62.3) we find the energy of the body

$$E = F - T\frac{\partial F}{\partial T},$$

i.e.

$$E = N\epsilon_0 + 3N\nu kT. \tag{62.4}$$

The high temperature case corresponds to a classical treatment of the atomic vibrations; hence it is natural that formula (62.4) should be in complete agreement with the law of equipartition (§44); with each of the $3N\nu$ vibrational degrees of freedom is associated a part kT of the energy (ignoring the constant $N\epsilon_0$).

For the specific heat we have:

$$C = Nc = 3N\nu k, \tag{62.5}$$

where $c = 3\nu k$ is the specific heat for a single molecule. We are again writing the specific heat as C bearing in mind that for solid bodies the difference between C_p and C_v is quite negligible (see end of §64).

Thus, at sufficiently high temperatures, the specific heat of a solid body is constant and depends only on the number of atoms in the body. In particular the atomic heat ($\nu = 1$) of all elements must be the same and equal to $3k$. This is called the *Dulong and Petit law*. At ordinary temperatures this law is quite well satisfied for many elements. Formula (62.5) is also satisfied at high temperatures for simple compounds; but for complex compounds this limiting value for the specific heat is never attained in general before the substances melt or disintegrate.

Substituting (62.5) into (62.3) and (62.4) we can express the free energy and energy of a solid body in the form:

$$F = N\epsilon_0 - NcT \log kT + NcT \log \hbar\bar{\omega}, \tag{62.6}$$

$$E = N\epsilon_0 + NcT. \tag{62.7}$$

The entropy $S = -\partial F/\partial T$ is equal to

$$S = Nc \log kT - Nc \log \frac{\hbar\bar{\omega}}{e}. \tag{62.8}$$

Formula (62.1) can of course also be deduced directly from classical statistics, starting from the general formula (31.5):

$$F = -kT \log \int' e^{-E(p,\,q)/kT}\, d\Gamma. \tag{62.9}$$

For the case of a solid, the integration over the co-ordinates in this interval is carried out as follows:

Each atom is considered to be in the neighbourhood of some definite lattice point and the integration over its co-ordinates is carried out only over a small volume surrounding this point; it is clear that all the points in the region of integration so defined correspond to physically different micro-states and there is no need to introduce an extra factor in the integral.†

We substitute into (62.9) the energy of the normal vibrations, expressed in terms of the co-ordinates and momenta:

$$E(p, q) = \tfrac{1}{2} \sum_\alpha (p_\alpha^2 + \omega_\alpha^2 q_\alpha^2), \tag{62.10}$$

and write $d\Gamma$ in the form

$$d\Gamma = \frac{1}{(2\pi\hbar)^{3N\nu}} \prod_\alpha dp_\alpha\, dq_\alpha.$$

Thus the integral splits into the product of $3N\nu$ identical integrals of the form:

$$\int\limits_{-\infty}^{+\infty}\!\!\int \exp\left\{-\frac{p_\alpha^2 + \omega_\alpha^2 q_\alpha^2}{2kT}\right\} dp_\alpha\, dq_\alpha = \frac{2\pi kT}{\omega_\alpha},$$

from which we obtain formula (62.1). (Owing to the rapid convergence of the integral, the integration over dq_α can be taken from $-\infty$ to $+\infty$).

At sufficiently high temperatures (provided that the solid has not yet melted or chemically decomposed) the effects of anharmonic vibrations of the atoms may become apparent. The nature of their effect on thermodynamic quantities can be found in the following way (see the analogous calculations in §49). Taking into account the next terms (after the quadratic term) of the expansion of the potential energy of the oscillation in powers of the q_α, we have:

$$E(p, q) = f_2(p, q) + f_3(q) + f_4(q) + \cdots,$$

where $f_2(p, q)$ stands for the harmonic expression (62.10) (and is quadratic in the q_α and p_α), and $f_3(q)$, $f_4(q)$, ... etc. are homogeneous functions of all the co-ordinates q_α of third, fourth, ... etc. degrees. Making the substitution $q_\alpha = q_\alpha'\sqrt{T}, p_\alpha = p_\alpha'\sqrt{T}$, in the partition function in (62.9) we obtain:

$$Z = \int' e^{-E(p,\, q)/kT}\, d\Gamma$$

$$= T^{3N\nu} \int' \exp\{-f_2(p', q') - \sqrt{T}f_3(q') - Tf_4(q') - \cdots\}\, d\Gamma.$$

We see that in the expansion of the integrand in powers of the temperature, all odd powers of $\sqrt{T}$ are multiplied by odd functions of the co-ordinates,

---

† As we had to do in the case of a gas where the integration over the co-ordinates of each particles was taken over the whole volume (see end of §31).

vanishing when integrated over the co-ordinates. Hence Z will be expressed as a series $Z = Z_0 + TZ_1 + T^2Z_2 + \ldots$, containing only integral powers of the temperature. By substituting this into (62.9) we find that the first correction term for the free energy has the form:

$$F_{anh} = AT^2, \tag{62.11}$$

i.e. it is proportional to the square of the temperature. The corresponding correction to the specific heat is of first degree in the temperature†. It should be emphasised that the expansion considered here is in powers of the ratio kT/ϵ_0, and not, of course, in powers of $kT/\hbar\bar{\omega}$, which, in this case, is large.

PROBLEMS

1. Determine the maximum work which can be obtained from two identical solids (temperatures T_1 and T_2) by equalizing their temperatures.

SOLUTION: The solution is completely analogous to the solution of problem 12 §43. We find:

$$|R|_{max} = Nc(\sqrt{T_1} - \sqrt{T_2})^2.$$

2. Determine the maximum work which can be obtained from a solid by cooling it from temperature T to the temperature T_0 of the surrounding medium (at constant volume).

SOLUTION: From formula (20.3) we find

$$|R|_{max} = Nc(T - T_0) + NcT_0 \log\frac{T_0}{T}.$$

§63. The Debye interpolation formula

We have seen that, in both the limiting cases of low and high temperatures, it is possible to carry out a sufficiently complete calculation of the thermo-dynamic quantities of a solid. However, in the intermediate temperature range such a calculation is impossible, since the sum over the frequencies in (61.1) depends to a large extent on the actual distribution of frequencies in the whole oscillatory spectrum of the given body.

Because of this it is interesting to construct a single interpolation formula, giving the correct values of thermodynamic quantities in both limiting cases. There is, of course, no unique solution to the problem of finding such a formula. One would expect, however, that an intelligently constructed interpolation formula should at least qualitatively give a correct description of the behaviour of the body also over the whole intermediate range.

The form of the thermodynamic quantities of a solid at low temperatures is determined by the frequency distribution (61.4) in its vibrational spectrum, while at high temperatures the important thing is that all vibrations are excited. Hence to construct our required interpolation formula it seems natural to begin with a model in which the frequencies are distributed over the whole length of the vibrational spectrum according to the law

---

† This correction is usually negative (corresponding to positive A in eq. 62.11).

(61.4) which, strictly speaking, only holds for the low frequencies, and the spectrum, starting from $\omega = 0$ breaks off at some finite frequency $\omega = \omega_m$. The latter is determined by the condition that the total number of oscillations should be equal to the correct number $3N\nu$:

$$\frac{3V}{2\pi^2\bar{u}^3} \int_0^{\omega_m} \omega^2 \, d\omega = \frac{V\omega^3_m}{2\pi^2\bar{u}^3} = 3N\nu.$$

whence

$$\omega_m = \bar{u}\left(\frac{6\pi^2 N\nu}{V}\right)^{1/3}. \tag{63.1}$$

Thus the frequency distribution for the model under consideration is given by the formula

$$9N\nu\frac{\omega^2 \, d\omega}{\omega^3_m} \qquad (\omega \leqslant \omega_m) \tag{63.2}$$

for the number of oscillations with frequencies lying in the interval $d\omega$ (we have expressed $\bar{u}$ in terms of ω_m).

Letting the sum in (61.1) go over into an integral we now obtain:

$$F = N\epsilon_0 + kT\frac{9N\nu}{\omega^3_m} \int_0^{\omega_m} \omega^2 \log(1-e^{-\hbar\omega/kT}) \, d\omega.$$

We introduce the so-called *Debye* or *characteristic temperature* Θ of the body defined by

$$k\Theta = \hbar\omega_m. \tag{63.3}$$

(Θ is obviously a function of the density of the body). Then

$$F = N\epsilon_0 + 9N\nu kT\left(\frac{T}{\Theta}\right)^3 \int_0^{\Theta/T} z^2 \log(1-e^{-z}) \, dz. \tag{63.4}$$

Integrating by parts, and introducing the *"Debye function"*

$$D(x) = \frac{3}{x^3} \int_0^x \frac{z^3 \, dz}{e^z-1}, \tag{63.5}$$

we may write this formula in the form

$$F = N\epsilon_0 + N\nu kT[3 \log(1-e^{-\Theta/T}) - D(\Theta/T)]. \tag{63.6}$$

For the energy $E = F - T(\partial F/\partial T)$ we hence obtain

$$E = N\epsilon_0 + 3N\nu kTD(\Theta/T), \tag{63.7}$$

and for the specific heat:

$$C = 3N\nu k\{D(\Theta/T) - (\Theta/T)D'(\Theta/T)\}. \tag{63.u}$$

The curve in Fig. 7 shows how $C/3N\nu k$ depends on T/Θ.

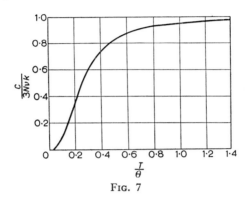

Fig. 7

Formulae (63.6–8) comprise the required formulae for the thermodynamic quantities of a solid. (Debye, 1912.)

It is easy to see that in both the limiting cases these formulae do give correct results. For $T \ll \Theta$ (low temperatures) the argument Θ/T of the Debye function is large. As a first approximation we replace x by ∞ as the upper limit of the integral in the definition of the Debye function (63.5); the definite integral thus obtained is equal to $\pi^4/15$ so that†

$$D(x) \cong \frac{\pi^4}{5x^3} \qquad (x \gg 1).$$

Substituting this into (63.8) we obtain

$$c = \frac{12N\nu k\pi^4}{5}\left(\frac{T}{\Theta}\right)^3, \tag{63.9}$$

which agrees with (61.9). For high temperatures ($T \gg \Theta$) the argument

---

† Replacing $\int_0^x$ by $\int_0^\infty - \int_x^\infty$, expanding $(e^z - 1)^{-1}$ in the second integrand in powers of e^{-z}, and integrating by parts we find that for $x \gg 1$

$$D(x) = \frac{\pi^4}{5x^3} - 3e^{-x}\left\{1 + 0\left(\frac{1}{x}\right)\right\}.$$

Hence the value given in the text is correct apart from exponentially small terms.

of the Debye function is small; for $x \ll 1$ to the first approximation $D(x) \cong 1$[†] and from (63.8) we have $C = 3Nvk$, again in complete agreement with the result previously obtained (62.5).[‡]

It is useful to note that the actual behaviour of the function $D(x)$ shows that the criterion for applying the limiting expression for the specific heat is the relative value of T and $\Theta/4$; the specific heat may be considered constant for $T \gg \Theta/4$ and proportional to T^3 for $T \ll \Theta/4$.[||]

According to Debye the specific heat is some universal function of the ratio Θ/T. In other words, according to this formula, bodies which are, as one says, "in corresponding states", (i.e. have the same Θ/T), have the same specific heat.

The Debye formula gives a good description (as good as one would expect from an interpolation formula) of the variation of specific heat with temperature only for a series of bodies with simple crystal lattices—most elements and some simple compounds (the halide salts, for example). It is not applicable to bodies of a more complicated structure; this is quite natural since such bodies have very complicated vibrational spectra.

In particular, the Debye formula is completely inapplicable to highly anisotropic crystals. The structure of such crystals may be of the "layer" or "chain" type, and the potential energy of the interaction of atoms within one "layer" or "chain" is then considerably larger than that linking different ones. Correspondingly their vibration spectrum is characterised not by one characteristic temperature, but by several, Θ_1, Θ_2, ... , of different orders of magnitude. The T^3 law for the specific heat is then valid only for temperatures which are small compared to the smallest of the Θ_i, whereas in the region between the different Θ_i new limiting laws arise. This problem has been studied in detail by E. M. LIFSHITZ.[¶]

§64. The thermal expansion of solids

The term proportional to T^4 in the free energy (61.6) can be regarded as a small increment to $F_0 = N\epsilon_0(V/N)$. On the other hand a small correction

---

[†] For $x \ll 1$ direct expansion of the integrand in powers of x and integration by parts gives

$$D(x) = 1 - \frac{3}{8}x + \frac{1}{20}x^2 - \ldots .$$

[‡] Taking into account the next term in the expansion, the specific heat at high temperatures is given by the formula

$$c = 3Nvk\left\{1 - \frac{1}{20}\left(\frac{\Theta}{T}\right)^2\right\}.$$

[||] We give as examples some values of Θ for various substances obtained from data about their specific heats: Pb: 90°; Ag: 210°; Al: 400°; KBr: 180°; NaCl: 280°; for diamond Θ has a particularly high value: $\sim 2000°$.

[¶] *J. Exper. Theor. Phys. U.S.S.R.* **22**, 471, 1952.

to the free energy (for given V and T) is equivalent to a small correction to the thermodynamic potential Φ (for given P and T; see eq. 15.12). Hence we can immediately write

$$\Phi = \Phi_0(P) - \frac{\pi^2(kT)^4 V_0(P)}{30(\hbar\bar{u})^3} \qquad (64.1)$$

where $\Phi_0(P)$ is the temperature independent part of the thermodynamic potential, $V_0(P)$ is the volume expressed as a function of pressure by means of $P = \partial F_0/\partial V = -N(d\epsilon_0/dV)$ and $\bar{u} = \bar{u}(P)$ is the mean sound velocity expressed in terms of the pressure by means of the same relation. The relation between the volume of the body and the temperature is determined by $V = \partial\Phi/\partial P$:

$$V = V_0(P) - \frac{\pi^2(kT)^4}{30\hbar^3}\frac{d}{dP}\left(\frac{V_0}{\bar{u}^3}\right). \qquad (64.2)$$

The coefficient of thermal expansion $\alpha = 1/V(\partial V/\partial T)_P$ is equal to

$$\alpha = -\frac{2\pi^2 k(kT)^3}{15\hbar^3 V_0}\frac{d}{dP}\left(\frac{V_0}{\bar{u}^3}\right). \qquad (64.3)$$

We see that at low temperatures it is proportional to the cube of the temperature. This is, however, immediately obvious from the Nernst theorem and the T^3 law for the specific heat.

Similarly at high temperatures we consider the second and third terms of (62.6) as a small correction to the first (for the body to be solid it must in any case have $kT \ll \epsilon_0$) and we obtain:

$$\Phi = \Phi_0(P) - NcT \log kT + NcT \log \hbar\bar{\omega}(P). \qquad (64.4)$$

Hence

$$V = V_0(P) + \frac{NcT}{\bar{\omega}}\frac{d\bar{\omega}}{dP}. \qquad (64.5)$$

The coefficient of thermal expansion is

$$\alpha = \frac{Nc}{V_0\bar{\omega}}\frac{d\bar{\omega}}{dP}. \qquad (64.6)$$

It does not depend on the temperature.

As the pressure increases, the atoms of the solid approach one another, and the amplitude of their vibrations (for the same energy) decreases; in other words the frequency increases. Hence $d\bar{\omega}/dP > 0$, so that $\alpha > 0$ also, i.e. solids expand with an increase in temperature. Similar considerations show that the coefficient of (64.3) is also positive.

Lastly we make use of the law of corresponding states set out at the end of the last section. The statement that the specific heat is a function of the ratio T/Θ only is equivalent to the statement that, for instance, the thermo-dynamic potential is a function of the form:

$$\Phi = \Phi_0(P) + \Theta f\left(\frac{T}{\Theta}\right). \tag{64.7}$$

From this the volume is

$$V = \frac{\partial\Phi}{\partial P} = V_0(P) + \frac{d\Theta}{dP}\left(f - \frac{T}{\Theta}f'\right),$$

and the coefficient of thermal expansion is

$$\alpha = -\frac{T}{V_0\Theta^2}\frac{d\Theta}{dP}f''.$$

Similarly we find the heat function $W = \Phi - T(\partial\Phi/\partial T)$ and specific heat $C = \partial W/\partial T$:

$$C = \frac{T}{\Theta}f''.$$

Comparing the two expressions (for C and α) we obtain the following relation:

$$\frac{\alpha}{C} = \frac{1}{\Theta V_0(P)}\frac{d\Theta}{dV_0(P)}. \tag{64.8}$$

Thus within the limits of applicability of the law of corresponding states the ratio of the coefficient of thermal expansion and the specific heat is independent of the temperature (Grüneisen's law).

We have already pointed out that the difference between the specific heat C_p and C_v is quite insignificant for solids. At low temperatures this is a general consequence of the Nernst theorem which applies to all bodies. For high temperatures we have, using the thermodynamic relation (16.9)

$$C_p - C_v = -T\frac{(\partial V/\partial T)_P^2}{(\partial V/\partial P)_T} = -T\frac{\alpha^2 V_0^2}{dV_0/dP}.$$

where $\alpha = \alpha(P)$ is the coefficient of thermal expansion (64.6). We see that the difference $C_p - C_v$ is proportional to T. This really means that its expansion in powers of kT/ϵ_0 begins with the first order term, whereas the expansion of the specific heat itself begins with a constant term. Hence it follows that for high temperatures as well $C_p - C_v \ll C$.

§65. Phonons

In the last section we considered the thermal motion of the atoms of a solid as a set of small, normal vibrations of the crystal lattice. We now study the properties of these vibrations in greater detail.

Generally there are several atoms in each unit cell of the crystal. Thus to specify an atom we must give the cell in which it is situated and the number n of the atom in the cell. The position of the unit cell can be specified by the radius vector r_s of some particular corner of the cell; these radius vectors take the values

$$r_s = s_1 a_1 + s_2 a_2 + s_3 a_3, \tag{65.1}$$

where s_1, s_2, s_3 are integers and a_1, a_2, a_3 are the lattice vectors (i.e. the edges of a unit cell).

Let us denote the atomic displacements during the vibration by $u_n{}^s$, where the suffix s numbers the unit cell, and n indicates both the particular atom in the cell, and the co-ordinate axis (x, y or z) along which the displacement is taken; the suffix n therefore takes $3r$ values, if there are r atoms in the unit cell.

The vibration takes place under the influence of the forces exerted on each atom by the others in the lattice. These forces are functions of the displacements; in view of the smallness of the displacements they may be expanded in powers of the $u_n{}^s$, retaining only the linear terms. This expansion contains no terms of zero order, since for $u_n{}^s = 0$ all atoms are in equilibrium, and the forces acting on them must vanish.

Hence the equations of motion of the atoms in the lattice are of the form

$$\ddot{u}_n{}^s = - \sum_{n', s'} \lambda_{n, n'}^{s'-s} u_{n'}{}^{s'} \tag{65.2}$$

The constant coefficients λ depend only on the difference between the suffixes s and s', since the force between two atoms evidently can depend only on the relative position of the lattice cells to which they belong, but not on their absolute position in space†.

We look for a solution of (65.2) in the form of a "monochromatic plane wave"

$$u_n{}^s = u_n e^{i(f \cdot r_s - \omega t)}. \tag{65.3}$$

The (complex) amplitude u_n depends only on the suffix n, i.e. differs only for different atoms in the same cell, but not for similar atoms in different cells.

Inserting (65.2) in (65.3) we find

$$\omega^2 u_n e^{if r_s} = \sum_{n', s'} \lambda_{n, n'}^{s'-s} u_{n'} e^{if \cdot r_{s'}}$$

Dividing both sides of this equation by $e^{if \cdot r_s}$, introducing the vector $r_\sigma = r_s - r_{s'}$ with the suffix $\sigma = s - s'$, and replacing the summation over s' by

---

† The coefficients $\lambda_{n, n'}^{s-s'}$ are related to each other by certain relations. These are consequences of the fact that if we simply displace or rotate the lattice as a whole, the force on each atom still remains zero. We shall not write down these relations.

the equivalent summation over σ, we obtain:

$$\sum_{n,\sigma} \lambda^{\sigma}_{n,\,n'} e^{i\mathbf{f}\cdot\mathbf{r}_{\sigma}} u_{n'} - \omega^2 u_n = 0 \tag{65.4}$$

This system of linear homogeneous equations for the amplitudes has a non-vanishing solution only if the determinant vanishes:

$$\left| \sum_{\sigma} \lambda^{\sigma}_{n,\,n'} e^{i\mathbf{f}\cdot\mathbf{r}_{\sigma}} - \omega^2 \delta_{nn'} \right| = 0 \tag{65.5}$$

Since the suffixes n,n' take $3r$ values, the determinant is of $3r$th order, and eq. (65.5) is an algebraic equation of $3r$th degree for ω^2.

Each of the $3r$ solutions of this equation determines the frequency ω as a function of the wave vector $\mathbf{f}$. Thus for each given value of the wave vector $\mathbf{f}$ the frequency ω can take, in general, $3r$ different values. In other words we may say that the frequency $\omega = \omega(\mathbf{f})$ is a many valued function of the wave vector with $3r$ "branches".

Amongst these $3r$ branches must be some which, for large wavelengths (compared with the interatomic distances), correspond to the usual elastic (i.e. sound) waves in the crystal. It is well known from the theory of elasticity that in a crystal, considered as a continuous medium, three types of wave can be propagated with different relations between ω and $\mathbf{f}$. For each of the three ω is a single-valued linear function of the components of the vector $\mathbf{f}$ and vanishes at $\mathbf{f} = 0$. Thus amongst the $3r$ "branches" of the function $\omega(\mathbf{f})$ there must exist three for which the frequency vanishes with $\mathbf{f}$ and is, for small $\mathbf{f}$, a single-valued linear function of the components of $\mathbf{f}$, i.e. has the form:

$$\omega = \alpha(\mathbf{n})f$$

where $\alpha(\mathbf{n})$ is some function of the direction of the vector $\mathbf{f}$ ($\mathbf{n}$ being a unit vector in this direction). These three types of wave are called *elastic* or *acoustic* waves; their characteristic property is that the lattice vibrates like a continuous medium. In the limiting case of infinitely long waves these vibrates simply become parallel displacements of the lattice.

In the remaining $3(r-1)$ types of wave the frequency does not vanish at $\mathbf{f} = 0$ but, on the contrary, tends to a constant limit as $\mathbf{f} \to 0$. These vibrations are called *optical*. In this case atoms in the same cell move relative to one another and in the limiting case $\mathbf{f} = 0$ the centre of gravity of the cell remains stationary. It is clear that if each cell contains only one atom then there cannot be any optical vibrations at all.

Note that the $3r-3$ limiting frequencies (frequencies at which $\mathbf{f} = 0$) of the optical vibrations need not necessarily be different from one another. For crystals with certain symmetries the limiting frequencies of some of the branches of the optical vibrations may coincide. We shall not examine this problem in greater detail at this point.

If the limiting frequency of one of the optical branches does not coincide with that of another branch then the frequency $\omega(\mathbf{f})$ in this branch may be expanded near $\mathbf{f} = 0$ in powers of the components f_i of the vector $\mathbf{f}$. It is easy to see that the expansion can contain only even powers of the f_i. Indeed, owing to the symmetry of the mechanical equations of motion under time reversal, if the propagation of some wave (65.3) is possible then so is the propagation of the same wave in the opposite direction. But such a change in direction is equivalent to a change in the sign of $\mathbf{f}$. Hence the functions $\omega(\mathbf{f})$ must be even: $\omega(-\mathbf{f}) = \omega(\mathbf{f})$, whence the above statement follows. Hence the relation between the frequency of the optical vibration and the wave vector near $\mathbf{f} = 0$ has the form

$$\omega = \omega_0 + \sum_{i,k=x,y,z} \alpha_{ik} f_i f_k, \tag{65.6}$$

where ω_0 is the limiting frequency and the α_{ik} are constants.

If the limiting frequencies of several of the branches coincide, then the frequencies $\omega(\mathbf{f})$ of these branches cannot in general be expanded in powers of $\mathbf{f}$ since the point $\mathbf{f} = 0$ is, for them, a singular point, (branch point) and near such a point a function cannot be expanded in series. One can only state that near $\mathbf{f} = 0$ the difference $\omega - \omega_0$ will be a homogeneous function of either first or second order (depending on the symmetry of the crystals).

The wave vector $\mathbf{f}$ of a lattice vibration has the following important property. The vector $\mathbf{f}$ enters into expression (65.2) only in the exponential factor $e^{i\mathbf{f}\cdot\mathbf{r}_s}$. But this factor remains completely unchanged when we add to the vector $\mathbf{f}$ any vector of the form

$$2\pi\mathbf{b}, \quad \mathbf{b} = p_1\mathbf{b}_1 + p_2\mathbf{b}_2 + p_3\mathbf{b}_3$$

where $\mathbf{b}$ is any vector of the reciprocal lattice (see §128), $\mathbf{b}_1$, $\mathbf{b}_2$, $\mathbf{b}_3$, are the basic vectors of the reciprocal lattice, and p_1, p_2, p_3 are integers.

We thus arrive at the result that the wave vector of a lattice vibration is only determined up to the addition of any vector of the reciprocal lattice multiplied by 2π.

Hence in each branch of the function $\omega(\mathbf{f})$ it is sufficient to consider values of the wave vector lying in some definite interval. That is, if one chooses the co-ordinate axes (oblique, in the general case) along the three basic reciprocal lattice vectors, then it is sufficient to consider values of the three components of the wave vector lying in the intervals

$$-\pi b_1 \leqslant f_x \leqslant \pi b, \quad -\pi b_2 \leqslant f_y \leqslant \pi b_2, \quad -\pi b_3 \leqslant f_z \leqslant \pi b_3. \tag{65.7}$$

In other words, for the vector $\mathbf{f}/2\pi$ one must consider all possible values lying in one cell of the reciprocal lattice. This result applies, of course, both to the acoustic and the optical vibrations.

It is important to remember that the discussion given applies only in the so-called "harmonic approximation" in which only terms quadratic in the displacements $\mathbf{u}_n{}^s$ are taken into account in the potential energy of the oscillating particles. It is only in this approximation that the different mono-chromatic waves (65.3) do not interact with one another and propagate freely through the lattice. When one takes into account the succeeding "anharmonic" terms a new kind of process appears: the scattering of these waves by one another.

In addition, it has been assumed that the periodicity of the lattice is ideal. It must be borne in mind that the ideal periodicity is broken to some extent, even without allowing for possible impurities, and other lattice defects, if the crystal contains atoms of different isotopes distributed unevenly. This disturbance, however, is comparatively small if the relative difference in the atomic weights of the isotopes is small, or if one isotope is in a considerable majority. In these cases, with which one usually deals, the picture given above still applies in the first approximation, and in higher approximations there appear different types of "scattering processes" of the waves by the "inhomogeneities" of the lattice.

Now we turn to the question of the quantum aspect of the lattice oscillations.

Instead of the waves (65.3) in which the atoms undergo a definite displacement at each instant, in quantum theory we introduce the concept of the so-called *"sound quanta"* or *"phonons"*, as "quasi-particles" propagated through the lattice with definite energies and directions of motion. Since the energy of an oscillator in quantum mechanics is an integral multiple of $\hbar\omega$ (where ω is the frequency of the classical wave) the energy of the phonon is related to the frequency ω by

$$\epsilon = \hbar\omega \tag{65.8}$$

in the same way as for light quanta, or photons. As for the wave vector $\mathbf{f}$ it is determined by the so-called "quasi-momentum" $\mathbf{p}$ of the phonon:

$$\mathbf{p} = \hbar\mathbf{f}. \tag{65.9}$$

This is a quantity in many ways analogous to the ordinary momentum, but at the same time differing from it in several important ways.[†] These are basically connected with the fact that the quasi-momentum is a quantity determined only to within the addition of a constant vector of the type $2\pi\hbar\mathbf{b}$; values of $\mathbf{p}$ differing by such a quantity are physically equivalent.

The velocity of a phonon is determined by the group velocity of the corresponding classical waves, i.e. $\mathbf{v} = \partial\omega/\partial\mathbf{f}$. This formula may also be written in the form

$$\mathbf{v} = \frac{\partial\epsilon(\mathbf{p})}{\partial\mathbf{p}} \tag{65.10}$$

which is completely analogous to the usual relation between the energy, momentum and velocity of the particles.

---

† The properties of the quasi-momentum of a phonon are completely analogous to the properties of the quasi-momentum of an electron in a periodic field; for the latter see *Quantum Mechanics*, §104.

Everything said above about the relationship between the frequency and wave vector of the waves can be completely applied to the relationship between the energy of the phonons and their quasi-momentum. In particular the function $\epsilon = \epsilon(\mathbf{p})$ has, in general, $3r$ different branches. Amongst these are three "kinds" of phonons whose energy, for sufficiently small values of the quasi-momentum, is a homogeneous function of first degree in the components of $\mathbf{p}$. The velocity of such phonons for small $\mathbf{p}$ has a value depending only on the direction of $\mathbf{p}$ but not on its magnitude. This velocity is obviously simply the corresponding velocity of sound in the crystal.

To the free propagation of the waves (65.2) in the harmonic approximation there corresponds, in the quantum case, the free motion of completely non-interacting phonons, i.e. phonons which do not "collide" with one another. In the next approximation, however, there appear various effects of the elastic and inelastic collisions of the phonons with one another. These collisions also provide the mechanism which brings about thermal equilibrium of the "phonon gas", i.e. the setting up of equilibrium for the thermal motion of the lattice.

In the collision of two (or more) phonons the law of conservation of energy must be satisfied, and also the law of conservation of quasi-momentum. The latter, however, requires the conservation of the sum of the quasi-momenta of the colliding phonons only apart from the addition of any vector of the form $2\pi\hbar\mathbf{b}$, which is due to the many-valuedness of the quasi-momentum. Thus the quasi-momenta of two phonons before a collision $(\mathbf{p}_1, \mathbf{p}_2)$ and after $(\mathbf{p}_1', \mathbf{p}_2')$ must be connected by a relation of the form

$$\mathbf{p}_1 + \mathbf{p}_2 = \mathbf{p}_1' + \mathbf{p}_2' + 2\pi\hbar\mathbf{b}. \tag{65.11}$$

In the lattice any number of identical phonons can be excited at the same time. In other words any number of phonons can be in any phonon quantum state. This means that the phonon gas obeys Bose statistics. Since, in addition, the total number of "particles" in this gas is not given, but is itself determined by the equilibrium condition, its chemical potential is equal to zero (see §60). Hence the mean number of phonons in a given quantum state (with quasi-momentum $\mathbf{p}$ and energy ϵ) is determined, for thermal equilibrium, by the Planck function

$$\bar{n}_\mathbf{p} = \frac{1}{e^{\epsilon(\mathbf{p})/kT} - 1}. \tag{65.12}$$

Note that for high temperatures $(kT \gg \epsilon)$ this expression becomes

$$\bar{n}_\mathbf{p} = kT/\epsilon \tag{65.13}$$

i.e. the number of phonons in the given state is proportional to the temperature.

By means of the concept of phonons one can describe the non-equilibrium states of a solid as one does for an ideal gas. That is, every non-equilibrium macroscopic state of a solid is determined by some non-equilibrium distribution of phonons over their quantum states. The entropy of the body in such a state can be calculated with the help of the formulae obtained in §54 (for the Bose gas). In particular, in the case in which there are many phonons in each state, the entropy is equal to

$$S = k \sum_j G_j \log\frac{eN_j}{G_j}$$

where N_j is the number of phonons in the group of G_j neighbouring states (see (54.8)). This case corresponds to high temperatures $(T \gg \Theta)$.

We may rewrite this formula in an integral form corresponding to the classical wave picture of thermal oscillations. The number of phonon states (each of $3r$ "kinds") "allotted" to the range $df_x\, df_y\, df_z$ of values of the wave vector in an element dV of the space volume is

$$d\tau = \frac{dp_x\, dp_y\, dp_z\, dV}{(2\pi\hbar)^3} = \frac{df_x\, df_y\, df_z\, dV}{(2\pi)^3}.$$

Let $U(\mathbf{r}, \mathbf{f})\, d\tau$ be the energy of the thermal oscillations in the volume dV with wave vectors in $df_x\, df_y\, df_z$. The corresponding number of phonons is

$$\frac{U(\mathbf{r}, \mathbf{f})}{\hbar\omega(\mathbf{f})}\, d\tau.$$

Using this expression for G_j and N_j and going over to integration, we obtain the following formula for the entropy of a solid with a given non-equilibrium distribution of energy in the spectrum of the thermal oscillations:

$$S = k \sum \int \log\frac{eU(\mathbf{r}, \mathbf{f})}{\hbar\omega(\mathbf{f})}\, d\tau.$$

The summation is taken over the $3r$ branches of the functions $\omega(\mathbf{f})$.

§66. Quantum liquid: Bose type spectrum

Unlike solids and gases, liquids do not allow a general calculation of their thermodynamic quantities or even their temperature dependence. The reason for this is the presence of strong interactions between the molecules of the liquid without having at the same time the smallness of the vibrations which makes the thermal motion of solids so simple. The high intensity of the molecular interaction makes it important to know, when calculating thermodynamic quantities, the actual law of interaction, which varies for different liquids. The only thing which can be done in general form is the study of the properties of liquids near absolute zero.† The principles involved

---

† The results of §§66–68 are due to L. Landau.

in this question are of considerable interest although in practice there exists only one substance (helium) which can remain liquid down to absolute zero.† Remember in this connection (see §61) that according to classical mechanics *all* bodies ought to be solid at absolute zero. Owing to the particular weakness of the interaction of its atoms, helium remains liquid down to temperatures at which quantum effects become important (the quantum liquid) after which solidification need no longer take place.

The calculation of thermodynamic quantities requires a knowledge of the energy spectrum of the given body. We must emphasise that for a system of strongly interacting particles, such as a quantum liquid, only levels corresponding to quantum-mechanical stationary states of the liquid as a whole can be considered, and on no account those corresponding to states of separate atoms. In calculating the partition function for temperatures near absolute zero one must take into account only weak excited energy levels of the liquids, i.e. states situated not too high above the ground state.

All the arguments below depend on the following fact. Every weakly excited state of a macroscopic body can, in quantum mechanics, be considered as a set of separate *"elementary excitations"*. These elementary excitations themselves behave like "quasi-particles" moving in the volume occupied by the body and having definite energies and momenta.‡

In so far as the number of the elementary excitations is sufficiently small they do not "interact" with one another (i.e. their energies combine simply additively) so that the assembly may be regarded as an ideal gas.

One of the possible types of energy spectrum for the weakly excited states of a quantum liquid (which we may call the "Bose" type spectrum) is characterised by the fact that the elementary excitations can appear or disappear one by one. But the angular momentum of every quantum system (in this case the whole liquid) can change only by a whole number. Hence an elementary excitation which occurs singly must have an integral angular momentum and hence must obey Bose statistics. Every liquid consisting of particles which obey Bose statistics must have an energy spectrum of this type.

For small momenta p (i.e. large wavelengths $\hbar/p$) these excitations correspond to normal sound waves in the liquid, i.e. are phonons. This means that the energy $\epsilon(p)$ of elementary excitations with small p is a linear function of the momentum:

$$\epsilon = up, \tag{66.1}$$

where u is the velocity of sound in the liquid. It must be emphasised, however, that the momentum of an elementary excitation in a liquid is a real

---

† Or rather, two substances: the isotopes He^3 and He^4.

‡ Thus, for example, the excited states of a solid in which the atoms perform small oscillations about their equilibrium positions may be considered as a set of phonons moving inside the body.

momentum and not a "quasi-momentum" as for a phonon in the periodic crystalline lattice of a solid.

As the momentum increases, the curve $\epsilon = \epsilon(p)$ of course deviates from a straight line; its further shape depends on the particular interaction law of the molecules in the liquid and hence cannot be determined in the general case.† It must be remembered that for sufficiently large momenta the function $\epsilon(p)$ cannot exist at all since elementary excitations with too large momenta are unstable and decompose into several excitations with smaller momenta (and energies); the determination of the properties of the spectrum near the "end point" of the curve $\epsilon = \epsilon(p)$ presents a problem which is still unsolved.

A knowledge of the function $\epsilon(p)$ for small p allows us to calculate the thermodynamic quantities of the liquid at temperatures near enough to absolute zero for all the elementary excitations in the liquid to have small energies, i.e. be phonons.‡ The appropriate formulae can be written down without further calculation by using directly the expressions obtained in §61 for the thermodynamic quantities of a solid at low temperatures. The difference is only that instead of the three possible directions of polarisation for the sound waves in the solid (one longitudinal and two transverse) there exists for the liquid only one longitudinal one; hence all expressions for thermodynamic quantities must be divided by three. Thus, for the free energy of the liquid, we have:

$$F = F_0 - V\frac{\pi^2(kT)^4}{90(\hbar u)^3} \tag{66.2}$$

where F_0 is the free energy of the liquid at absolute zero. The energy of the liquid is equal to

$$E = E_0 + V\frac{\pi^2(kT)^4}{30(\hbar u)^3}, \tag{66.3}$$

and the specific heat,

$$C = \frac{2\pi^2 k}{15(\hbar u)^3}V(kT)^3. \tag{66.4}$$

is proportional to the cube of the temperature.

As we have already pointed out, an energy spectrum of the type just considered occurs in liquid helium (isotope He⁴). An analysis of the experimental data about its various thermodynamic quantities shows that they can be accounted for completely if one assumes that in this case the curve $\epsilon(p)$

---

† Liquid helium (He⁴) has an energy spectrum of the type considered here (this follows from its experimentally found property, superfluidity—see below).

‡ For liquid helium this holds for temperatures below about 0·8° K.

has the form shown in Fig. 8: after an initial linear rise it reaches a maximum, then decreases and, for a particular value p_0 of the momentum, passes through a minimum.† In thermal equilibrium the elementary excitations found in the liquid are mostly close to the minimum energy, i.e. in the region of small ϵ (the region near $\epsilon = 0$) and in the region near the value $\epsilon(p_0)$.

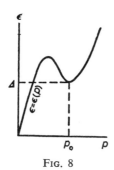

FIG. 8

Therefore just these regions are of particular importance. Near $p = p_0$, the functions $\epsilon(p)$ can be expanded in a series of powers of $p - p_0$. The linear term is absent, and up to terms of the second order we have

$$\epsilon = \Delta + \frac{(p-p_0)^2}{2\mu} \tag{66.5}$$

where $\Delta = \epsilon(p_0)$ and μ is a constant. For elementary excitations of this type the name "*rotons*" has become customary.

The empirical values of the constants Δ, p_0, μ are:

$$\Delta = 8 \cdot 9°\text{K}, \quad p_0 = 2 \cdot 1 . 10^{-19}\text{gcm/sec}, \quad \mu = 1 \cdot 72 . 10^{-24}\text{g}.$$

Since the roton energy always contains the quantity Δ, which is large compared to kT (at temperatures low enough to allow one to speak of a "roton gas"), one may in their description replace the Bose distribution, with sufficient accuracy, by the Boltzmann distribution.

PROBLEM

Determine the "roton" part of the thermodynamic functions of liquid helium.

SOLUTION: As the temperature rises there arise, besides the "phonon" parts of the thermodynamic quantities, contributions from the presence of rotons. According to eq. (41.5) we have for the free energy of a gas of N particles in a volume V:

$$F = -NkT \log\frac{eV}{N(2\pi\hbar)^3} \int e^{-\epsilon/kT} \, d^3p.$$

The number of particles in the roton gas is not a given number, but varies with the temperature and is determined by the condition that the free energy be a minimum. Equating

---

† A qualitative theory of an energy spectrum of this type has been given by R. P. FEYNMAN, *Phys. Rev.* **74**, 262, 1954.

$\partial F/\partial N$ to zero, we find for the roton number:

$$N_r = \frac{V}{(2\pi\hbar)^3} \int e^{-\epsilon/kT} \, d^3p.$$

The corresponding value of the free energy is:

$$F_r = -\frac{VkT}{(2\pi\hbar)^3} \int e^{-\epsilon/kT} \, d^3p.$$

Here we must now insert (66.5). Since $p_0^2 \gg \mu kT$, we may, in the integration over dp, replace the factor p^2 outside the exponential to sufficient accuracy by p_0^2. In integrating the exponential factor we may take the limits as $-\infty$ and $+\infty$. We finally obtain

$$N_r = \frac{2(\mu kT)^{1/2} p_0^2 V}{(2\pi)^{3/2} \hbar^3} e^{-\Delta/kT}$$

$$F_r = -kTN_r$$

Hence the roton contributions to the entropy and specific heat:

$$S_r = kN_r \left(\frac{3}{2} + \frac{\Delta}{kT} \right)$$

$$C_r = kN_r \left[\frac{3}{4} + \frac{\Delta}{kT} + \left(\frac{\Delta}{kT} \right)^2 \right]$$

We see that the temperature dependence of the roton part of the thermodynamic quantities is essentially exponential. Therefore at sufficiently low temperatures the roton part is less than the phonon part, whereas at higher temperatures the position is reversed and the roton part exceeds the phonon part.

§67. Superfluidity

A quantum liquid with an energy spectrum of the type described must possess the remarkable property of *superfluidity*, the ability to flow through narrow capillaries or slits without showing any signs of viscosity.†

We start by considering a liquid at absolute zero; at this temperature the liquid is in its ground, or unexcited state.

Consider a liquid flowing through a capillary with constant velocity **v**. The effect of the presence of viscosity would be that, owing to the friction with the walls of the tube and within the liquid itself, the kinetic energy of the liquid would be dissipated and the flow would gradually slow down.

It will be more convenient for us to study the flow in a co-ordinate system moving with the liquid. In this system the helium is stationary and the capillary walls move with velocity ($-\mathbf{v}$). When viscosity is present the stationary helium ought also to start to move. It is physically obvious that the drag on the liquid by the walls of the vessel cannot immediately cause motion

---

† This property was discovered in helium II (liquid helium at temperatures below $2\cdot19°$ K) by P. L. KAPITZA (1938).

of the liquid as a whole. Motion can only appear after the gradual excitation of internal motions, i.e. the appearance in the liquid of "elementary excitations".

Assume that there appears in the liquid one elementary excitation of momentum $\mathbf{p}$ and energy $\epsilon(\mathbf{p})$. Then the energy E_0 of the liquid (in the co-ordinate system in which it was at first stationary) will be equal to the energy ϵ of this excitation and its momentum $\mathbf{P}_0$ will be the momentum $\mathbf{p}$. Let us now return to the co-ordinate system in which the capillary is stationary. According to the well known mechanical transformation rules for energy and momentum we have for the energy E and momentum $\mathbf{P}$ of the liquid in this system:

$$E = E_0 + \mathbf{P} \cdot \mathbf{v} + \frac{Mv^2}{2}, \quad \mathbf{P} = \mathbf{P}_0 + M\mathbf{v}, \tag{67.1}$$

where M is the mass of the liquid. Substituting ϵ, $\mathbf{p}$ for E_0, $\mathbf{P}_0$ we can write:

$$E = \epsilon + \mathbf{p} \cdot \mathbf{v} + \frac{Mv^2}{2}.$$

The term $\tfrac{1}{2}Mv^2$ represents the initial kinetic energy of the moving liquid and the expression $\epsilon + \mathbf{p} \cdot \mathbf{v}$ is the change in the energy due to the appearance of the excitation. This change must be negative, since the energy of the moving liquid must decrease:

$$\epsilon + \mathbf{p} \cdot \mathbf{v} < 0.$$

For a given value of p the quantity on the left hand side of the inequality has its minimum value when $\mathbf{p}$ and $\mathbf{v}$ are antiparallel; hence we certainly must have $\epsilon - \mathbf{p} \cdot \mathbf{v} < 0$, i.e.

$$v > \frac{\epsilon}{p}. \tag{67.2}$$

This inequality must be satisfied for at least some values of the momentum p of the elementary excitation. Hence the final condition making possible the appearance of excitations in the liquid moving along the capillary will be obtained when we find the minimum value of the quantity ϵ/p. Geometrically, the ratio ϵ/p is the tangent of the angle of slope of the straight line drawn from the origin (in the p, ϵ plane) to some point on the curve $\epsilon = \epsilon(p)$. Its minimum value will obviously be determined by the point at which the straight line drawn from the origin is a tangent to the curve. If this minimum value differs from zero, then for small velocities of flow excitations cannot appear in the liquid. This means that it will not slow down, i.e. the liquid will exhibit the property of superfluidity.

The condition for the presence of superfluidity which we have obtained reduces simply to the requirement that the curve $\epsilon = \epsilon(p)$ should not touch the abscissal axis at the origin (neglecting the unlikely possibility that it might touch this axis further along). Hence, in fact, superfluidity will occur for every spectrum in which sufficiently small excitations are phonons.

Now consider the same liquid at temperatures other than absolute zero (although near to it). In this case the liquid is not in its ground state and contains excitations. The above considerations apply in themselves since they do not involve directly the fact that the liquid was initially in its ground state. If the given condition is satisfied, then the motion of the liquid relative to the walls of the tube cannot lead to the appearance of new elementary excitations in the liquid. It is necessary, however, to find out what effect the excitations already present in the liquid have.

To do this we carry out the following calculations. Imagine that "the gas of elementary excitations" moves as a whole with velocity **v** relative to the liquid. The distribution function of the gas moving as a whole is obtained from the distribution function $n(\epsilon)$ of a stationary gas by replacing the energy ϵ of a particle by the quantity $\epsilon - \mathbf{p} \cdot \mathbf{v}$, where **p** is the momentum of the particle.[†] Thus the total momentum of the gas (referred to unit volume) is

$$\mathbf{P} = \int \mathbf{p} n(\epsilon - \mathbf{p} \cdot \mathbf{v}) \frac{\mathrm{d}^3 p}{2\pi \hbar^3}$$

(where the symbol $\mathrm{d}^3 p$ denotes $\mathrm{d}p_x \, \mathrm{d}p_y \, \mathrm{d}p_z$). Assume that the velocity **v** is small, and expand the integrand in powers of $\mathbf{p} \cdot \mathbf{v}$. The zero order term disappears when integrated over the directions of the vector **p** and we have as a result:

$$\mathbf{P} = -\int \mathbf{p}(\mathbf{p} \cdot \mathbf{v}) \frac{\mathrm{d}n(\epsilon)}{\mathrm{d}\epsilon} \frac{\mathrm{d}^3 p}{(2\pi \hbar)^3}.$$

Integrating over the directions of the vector **p** we obtain:

$$\mathbf{P} = -\mathbf{v} \frac{4\pi}{3(2\pi \hbar)^3} \int_0^\infty p^4 \frac{\mathrm{d}n(\epsilon)}{\mathrm{d}\epsilon} \, \mathrm{d}p. \tag{67.3}$$

---

† For an ordinary gas this fact is a direct consequence of the Galilean principle of relativity and is proved simply by changing from one co-ordinate system to another. In the given case this does not apply directly, as the "excitation gas" moves, not in a vacuum, but "through the liquid". Nevertheless the statement remains true as can be seen from the following considerations. Let the excitation gas move with velocity **v**. Consider the co-ordinate system in which the gas as a whole is stationary, and the liquid thus moves with velocity $(-\mathbf{v})$ (system K). According to the transformation rules (67.1) the energy E of the liquid in system K is connected with its energy E_0 in the system in which the liquid is stationary (system K_0) by the relation

$$E = E_0 - \mathbf{P}_0 \cdot \mathbf{v} + \frac{Mv^2}{2}.$$

Suppose an elementary excitation with energy $\epsilon(p)$ (in system K_0) appears in the liquid. Then the additional energy of the liquid in system K will be $\epsilon - \mathbf{p} \cdot \mathbf{v}$ which proves the statement.

For phonons $\epsilon = up$† and integrating by parts we find that:

$$\mathbf{P} = -\mathbf{v}\frac{4\pi}{3}\int_0^\infty p^4\frac{dn(p)}{dp}\,dp = \mathbf{v}\frac{16\pi}{3u(2\pi\hbar)^3}\int_0^\infty p^3 n(p)\,dp.$$

But the integral

$$\frac{1}{(2\pi\hbar)^3}\int_0^\infty upn(p)\cdot4\pi p^2\,dp = \int \epsilon n(\epsilon)\frac{d^3p}{2\pi\hbar^3}$$

is simply the energy E_{ph} per unit volume, of the phonon gas, so that we have, finally:

$$\mathbf{P} = \mathbf{v}\frac{4E_{ph}}{3u^2}. \tag{67.4}$$

First of all we see that the motion of the excitation gas is accompanied by the transfer of some mass; the effective mass of unit volume of the gas is determined by the coefficient of proportionality between the momentum $\mathbf{P}$ and velocity $\mathbf{v}$ in (67.3) or (67.4). On the other hand as the liquid flows, say, along a capillary, nothing stops the "particles" of the gas colliding with the walls of the tube and exchanging momentum with them. As a result, the excitation gas will be stopped as would any ordinary gas flowing through the capillary.

Thus we reach the following conclusion. At temperatures differing from zero, part of the mass of the liquid behaves like a normal viscous liquid "sticking" to the walls of the vessel; the remaining part of the mass of the liquid behaves as a non-viscous superfluid liquid. It is very important here to note that there is "no friction" between these two parts of the liquid moving "through each other", i.e. there is no transfer of momentum from one to the other. Indeed, the very existence of such movement of one part of the mass of the liquid relative to the other was found by considering the statistical equilibrium of a uniformly moving excitation gas. But if any relative motion can take place in a state of statistical equilibrium, then it cannot be accompanied by friction.

We must emphasise that the idea of a liquid as a "mixture" of normal and

---

† For phonons the function $n(\epsilon)$ is the Bose distribution function with the chemical potential equal to zero. Hence

$$n(\epsilon - \mathbf{p}\cdot\mathbf{v}) = \frac{1}{e^{(\epsilon-\mathbf{p}.\mathbf{v})/kT}-1}.$$

Note that the condition for superfluidity ($v < \epsilon/p$) coincides exactly with the condition that this expression should be positive and finite for all energies.

superfluid "parts" is only a way of speaking convenient for the description of the processes occurring in a quantum liquid. Like all descriptions of quantum processes in classical terminology it is somewhat inadequate. To be correct one must say that in a quantum liquid two motions can take place simultaneously, to each of which is ascribed a corresponding "effective mass" (such that the sum of these two masses is equal to the total real mass of the liquid). One of the motions is "normal", i.e. it has the same properties as the motion of a normal viscous liquid; the other is superfluid. Both of these motions take place without any transfer of momentum from one to the other. It must be specially emphasised that there is no division of real particles of the liquid into superfluid ones and normal ones. In a certain sense one can talk about the superfluid and normal masses of the liquid but this does not in the least mean that there is a possibility of the liquid actually dividing into two parts.

Formula (67.4) determines the normal part of the mass of the liquid at temperatures low enough for all the elementary excitations to be considered as phonons. Substituting expression (66.3) for the energy of the phonon gas we find for the normal part of the density of the liquid.

$$\rho_n = \frac{2\pi^2}{45\hbar^3 u^5}(kT)^4. \tag{67.5}$$

As the temperature increases, an increasing part of the mass of the liquid becomes normal. At the point where the whole mass of the liquid becomes normal, the property of superfluidity completely disappears. This is the so-called λ-point of the liquid (2.19° K for helium) which is a phase transition point of the second kind (Chapter XIV).

PROBLEM

1. Find the roton part of the normal density of liquid helium.

SOLUTION: For the Boltzmann distribution $\partial n/\partial \epsilon = -n/kT$ and therefore (67.3) gives

$$(\rho_n)_r = \frac{4\pi}{3kT(2\pi\hbar)^3} \int p^4 n\, dp = \frac{1}{3kT} \int \frac{p^2 n\, d^3p}{(2\pi\hbar)^3} = \frac{\overline{p^2}}{3kT}\frac{N_r}{V}.$$

Since $p_0^2 \gg \mu kT$, we may, with sufficient accuracy take $\overline{p^2} = p_0$; inserting also for N_r from the problem in §66, we find finally

$$(\rho_n)_r = \frac{p_0^2 N_r}{3kTV} = \frac{2\mu^{1/2}p_0^4}{3(2\pi)^{3/2}(kT)^{1/2}\hbar^3}e^{-\Delta/kT}. \tag{1}$$

The phonon and roton parts of ρ_n become equal for a temperature of about 0·6° K.

The part of the $\rho_n(T)$ curve close to the λ point cannot, of course, be calculated accurately. Because of the very steep rise of ρ_n according to (1) one may, nevertheless, expect that the value of the temperature of the λ point may be obtained approximately by putting $\rho_n/\rho = 1$, and using (1). Such a calculation gives for the λ point a value of 2·5° K, in good agreement with the actual value of 2·19° K.

§68. Quantum liquid: Fermi type spectrum

We have already remarked in §66 that any quantum liquid consisting of particles with integral spin must have a Bose type spectrum. A liquid consisting of particles with spin one half can have a different sort of spectrum (which may be called a "Fermi type" spectrum); an example of such a liquid is the isotope He^3. It must be emphasised, however, that the possession of a spectrum of this type cannot be a universal property of liquids consisting of particles with half integral spin. The type of spectrum such a liquid has depends also on the nature of the interactions between its atoms. The following simple argument makes this immediately obvious: if the interaction is such that it tends to associate pairs of atoms, then in the limit we should get a molecular liquid whose particles would have integral spin, and which, therefore, would have a Bose type spectrum.

The "Fermi type" energy spectrum of a quantum liquid is constructed in a sense analogously to the spectrum of a perfect Fermi gas. The ground state of the latter corresponds to the case when all the quantum states of the separate particles with momenta ranging from zero up to some p_0 are occupied. Excited states of the gas occur when a particle makes a transition from one of the occupied zone of states to a state with $p > p_0$.

In a liquid, of course, quantum states for the separate atoms do not exist. However, as a basis for constructing this type of spectrum, we make the assumption that as the interactions between the atoms are gradually "switched on", i.e. as the transition is made from the gas to the liquid, the classification of levels remains unchanged. In this classification the "elementary excitations", whose number coincides with the number of atoms in the liquid and which obey Fermi statistics take the place of the gas particles.

Each of these "quasi-particles" has a definite momentum. (We shall come back later to the question of the validity of this assumption). Let $n(\mathbf{p})$ denote their distribution function with respect to momentum. The principle of the classification mentioned above consists in assuming that the specification of this function uniquely determines the energy E of the liquid and that the ground state corresponds to a distribution function representing the occupation of all states of the quasi-particles with momenta whose absolute values lie in some particular, bounded, range. In the simplest case this zone extends, as for the gas, from zero to some definite limiting value p_0 (a sphere in momentum space). However, another case is also possible in which, during the process of gradual transition from gas to liquid, a "cavity" appears inside this sphere, i.e. the ground state corresponds to the occupation of all states with momenta whose absolute values lie between two non-zero, finite values. Finally, in the most general case, the presence of several such "hollow spheres" (with a common centre) is possible.

For the sake of definiteness, we shall start below with the most natural case, i.e. with a solid sphere in momentum space. In other words, we shall assume that to the ground state there corresponds a "step" distribution function broken off at the value $p = p_0$. The quantity p_0 is connected with the density of the liquid by the same formula as for the gaseous case.

It is very important to note that the total energy E of the liquid by no means reduces to the sum of the energies ϵ of the quasi-particles. In other words, E represents a general functional of the distribution function, which does not reduce to the integral $\int n\epsilon \, d\tau$ (as in the case of the gas, for which the quasi-particles coincide with the actual particles).

Since it is E which is the primary notion, the question arises as to how the energy ϵ of the quasi-particles is to be defined.

We normalise the distribution function by the condition

$$\int n \, d\tau = N/V \tag{68.1}$$

where N is the number of particles in the volume V of the liquid and $d\tau$ here denotes $d^3p/(2\pi\hbar)^3$. (This condition will be made more precise below.) The change in E for an infinitesimal change in the distribution function can be written in the form

$$\frac{E}{V} = \int \epsilon \, \delta n \delta \tau. \tag{68.2}$$

The quantity $\epsilon(\mathbf{p})$ is the functional derivative of the energy with respect to the distribution function. It corresponds to the change in the energy of the system due to the addition of one quasi-particle with momentum $\mathbf{p}$ and exactly this quantity plays the part of such a quasi-particle in the field of the other particles. It is also a functional of the distribution function, i.e. the form of the function $\epsilon(\mathbf{p})$ is definite only when the distribution of all the quasi-particles in the liquid is given.

We must mention, in connection with this, that an elementary excitation, in the Fermi type spectrum can, in a sense, be regarded as an atom in the self-consistent field of the surrounding atoms. This self consistency, however, cannot be understood in the usual sense in which it is used in quantum mechanics. It is of a more fundamental nature here; in the Hamiltonian of the atom not only the effect of the distribution of the surrounding particles on the potential energy is taken into account, but also the dependence of the kinetic energy operator on the momentum operator is changed.

It is easy to see that the equilibrium distribution function of the quasi-particles is of the form of the usual Fermi distribution, with the quantity ϵ defined by (68.2) playing the part of the energy. Indeed, in view of the agreement between the classification properties of the energy levels of the liquid under consideration and those of a perfect gas, it is natural to define the entropy of the liquid by the expression

$$S = -k \int \{n \log n + (1-n) \log(1-n)\} \, d\tau. \tag{68.3}$$

(cf. eq. 54.3). By variation of this expression, subject to the auxiliary conditions that the total number of particles and total energy should be constant (variation of the latter being given by eq. 68.2), we get the required distribution

$$n = \frac{1}{e^{(\epsilon - \mu)/kT} - 1}. \tag{68.4}$$

We must emphasise, however, that notwithstanding the formal similarity between this expression and the usual Fermi distribution, it is not exactly the same in so far as the energy ϵ itself is a functional of n, so that (68.4) is strictly speaking a very complicated implicit definition of n.

In the above discussion we have so far ignored the presence of the spin of the quasi-particles. Actually, all the quantities (n, ϵ, etc.) are, in general, not only functions of the momentum, but also operational functions of the spin operator (matrix) of the quasi-particle ($\hat{s}$). If the liquid is in thermodynamic equilibrium, it is homogeneous and isotropic and the scalar quantity ϵ can depend only on scalar arguments. Hence the operator $\hat{s}$ can only occur in the form $\hat{s}^2$ or $(\hat{s} \cdot \mathbf{p})^2$ (the first power of the product $(\hat{s} \cdot \mathbf{p})$ is not admissible, since, in view of the axial nature of the spin vector, it is not a scalar but a pseudoscalar). For spin $\frac{1}{2}$ we have

$$\hat{s}^2 = \tfrac{3}{4}, \qquad (\hat{s} \cdot \mathbf{p})^2 = \tfrac{1}{4}\mathbf{p}^2$$

i.e. $\hat{s}$ disappears completely. Thus in this case the energy ϵ of the quasi-particles does not depend at all on the spin.

The independence from the spin of ϵ means that all the energy levels of the quasi-particles have a twofold degeneracy. Essentially, the assertion that the quasi-particle has a spin is the expression of the fact that this degeneracy in the levels exists. In this sense we can assert that the spin of the quasi-particles in the type of spectrum under consideration is always equal to $\frac{1}{2}$ independently of the spin of the actual particles of the liquid. Indeed, for any spin s not equal to $\frac{1}{2}$ the terms of the form $(\hat{s} \cdot \mathbf{p})^2$ would lead to the splitting of the $(2s+1)$-degenerate levels into $\frac{1}{2}(2s+1)$ of twofold degeneracy. In other words, there appear $\frac{1}{2}(2s+1)$ different branches of the function $\epsilon(\mathbf{p})$ each of which corresponds to quasi-particles "with spin $\frac{1}{2}$".

To simplify the writing of formulae we shall assume below that none of the quantities depend on the spin operator. Then the presence of the spin $\frac{1}{2}$ must be taken into account only by multiplying all integrals over phase space by a factor 2, which we assume to be included in the definition of $d\tau$:

$$d\tau = 2\frac{d^3p}{(2\pi\hbar)^3}.$$

The writing of formulae in the presence of spin dependence differs only in that integration over phase space must also be followed by taking the trace of matrix functions.

Let us now return to the assumption made above that to each quasi-particle a definite momentum can be ascribed. The condition under which such an assumption is justified requires that the uncertainty in the momentum due to the finite mean free path must be small, not only compared with the value of the momentum itself, but also compared with the breadth of the "transition" zone of the distribution (in which it differs appreciably from the "step" distribution). It is easy to see that this condition is fulfilled if the distribution $n(\mathbf{p})$ differs from the "step" distribution only by a sufficiently small deviation near the limiting momentum, i.e. near the surface of the Fermi sphere. Indeed, due to the Pauli principle only quasi-particles situated in the "transition" zone of the distribution can collide, and as a result of the scattering they must go over into free states in the same zone. Hence the collision probability is proportional the to square of the width Δp of the "transition" zone. Correspondingly, the uncertainty in the momentum connected with the collisions must also be proportional to $(\Delta p)^2$. Hence it is clear that for sufficiently small Δp the uncertainty may be small not only by comparison with p_0, but even with Δp.

Thus the method of this section applies only to excited states of the system which are described by a distribution function which differs from the "step" function only by a distortion in a small region near the upper limit. In particular, for thermodynamic equilibrium distributions only sufficiently low temperatures ($T \ll T_0$) are admissible. We may then interpret, in first approximation, the functional ϵ in (68.4) as that value which is calculated from the "step" distribution. In that case ϵ becomes a completely defined function of the magnitude of the momentum, and (68.4) reduces to the usual Fermi distribution function.

Thus, the function $\epsilon(p)$ has a direct physical sense only in the vicinity of the surface of the Fermi sphere. Here it can be expanded in powers of $p - p_0$, and then

$$\Delta\epsilon = \epsilon - \mu \cong v_0(p - p_0), \tag{68.5}$$

where

$$v_0 = \frac{\partial\epsilon}{\partial p}\bigg|_{p=p_0}$$

is the "velocity" of the quasi-particles with the limiting momentum. In a perfect Fermi gas, for which the "quasi-particles" are identical with the real particles, $\epsilon = p^2/2m$ and $v_0 = p_0/m$. By analogy we can introduce for the Fermi liquid the quantity

$$m^* = p_0/v_0 \tag{68.6}$$

and call it the effective mass of the quasi-particles[†].

[†] Note that a spectrum of the Fermi type does not admit the phenomenon of superfluidity. In the arguments of §67 we must now use $\Delta\epsilon$ instead of ϵ, and the inequality (67.2), $v > \Delta\epsilon/p$ may be satisfied for any v.

This quantity determines, in particular, the specific heat of the Fermi liquid at low temperatures. One sees easily that this is given by the same formula (57.6) as that for the gas with m replaced by m^*. This follows from the fact that the expression (68.3) for the entropy in terms of the distribution function is the same for the gas and the liquid, as is the relation between the distribution function and ϵ, and for the calculation of the integral (68.3) at low temperatures only momenta close to p_0 are of importance.

We shall denote by $\delta\epsilon$ the change in the energy of the quasi-particles which is caused by a small deviation of the distribution function from the step function. This must have the form of a linear functional:

$$\delta\epsilon(\mathbf{p}) = \int f(\mathbf{p},\mathbf{p}')\delta n'\,d\tau'. \tag{68.7}$$

The function $f(\mathbf{p}, \mathbf{p}')$ is a second functional derivative of E, and is therefore symmetric in the variables $\mathbf{p}$ and $\mathbf{p}'$. It plays an essential part in the theory of a Fermi liquid. (In the approximation of a perfect gas we have to put $f \equiv 0$).

The function f depends in general not only on the momenta, but also on the spins. If the basis distribution n is isotropic, the function f will in general contain terms of the form $\phi_{ik}(\mathbf{p}, \mathbf{p}')\hat{s}_i\hat{s}_k$. In particular exchange interactions between the quasi-particles will give rise to terms of the form $\phi(\mathbf{p}, \mathbf{p}')\,\hat{\mathbf{s}} \cdot \hat{\mathbf{s}}'$.

For simplicity we shall, however, assume in the following that the function f does not depend on the spins.

If there is no external field acting on the liquid its momentum per unit volume is then equal to the density of mass transport; this is known to be a direct consequence of the Galilean relativity principle. The velocity of a quasi-particle is $\partial\epsilon/\partial\mathbf{p}$, so that the flux of quasi-particles is given by the integral

$$\int n\,\frac{\partial\epsilon}{\partial\mathbf{p}}\,d\tau.$$

Since the number of quasi-particles in the liquid is the same as the number of real particles, it is clear that to obtain the net transport of mass by quasi-particles one must multiply their number transport by the mass m of the real particle. In this way we find the following equality:

$$\int \mathbf{p} n\,d\tau = \int m\frac{\partial\epsilon}{\partial\mathbf{p}}n\,d\tau. \tag{68.8}$$

Varying both sides of (68.8) and using (68.7), we obtain

$$\int \mathbf{p}\delta n\,d\tau = m\int \frac{\partial\epsilon}{\partial\mathbf{p}}\delta n\,d\tau + m\int\int \frac{\partial f(\mathbf{p},\mathbf{p}')}{\partial\mathbf{p}}n\delta n'\,d\tau d\tau'$$

$$= m\int \frac{\partial\epsilon}{\partial\mathbf{p}}\delta n\,d\tau - m\int\int f(\mathbf{p},\mathbf{p}')\frac{\partial n'}{\partial\mathbf{p}'}\delta n\,d\tau d\tau'.$$

(in the second integral on the right we interchange the variables of integration and integrate by parts). Since δn is arbitrary, it follows that

$$\frac{\mathbf{p}}{m} = \frac{\partial \epsilon}{\partial \mathbf{p}} - \int f \frac{\partial n'}{\partial \mathbf{p}'} \, d\tau'. \tag{68.9}$$

We now apply this relation for momenta close to the edge of the Fermi distribution. At the same time we replace the distribution function by the "step" function on the right-hand side. The energy ϵ is then a function of the momentum for which we may use the expression (68.5) and the derivative $\partial n/\partial \mathbf{p}$ is essentially a δ function:

$$\frac{\partial n}{\partial \mathbf{p}} = -\frac{\mathbf{p}}{p}\delta(p - p_0).$$

This allows us to carry out the integration in (68.9) with respect to magnitude of the momentum:

$$\int f \frac{\partial n'}{\partial \mathbf{p}'} \frac{2p'^2 \, dp' \, do'}{(2\pi\hbar)^3} = -\frac{2p_0}{(2\pi\hbar)^3} \int f \mathbf{p}'_0 \, do'.$$

In the function $f(\mathbf{p}, \mathbf{p}')$ both arguments are taken equal in magnitude, since f depends in fact only on the angle θ between $\mathbf{p}_0$ and $\mathbf{p}_0'$. Inserting this result for the integral in (68.9), multiplying both sides by $\mathbf{p}_0$ and then dividing by p_0^2, we find the following relation between the real mass of the particles, and the effective mass of the quasi-particles:

$$\frac{1}{m} = \frac{1}{m^*} + \frac{p_0}{2(2\pi\hbar)^3} 4 \int f \cos\theta \, do'. \tag{68.10}$$

Finally we calculate the compressibility of the Fermi liquid (at absolute zero) or, what amounts to the same, its sound velocity, which equals the square root of the compressibility.† The density of the liquid is $\rho = mN/V$ and the square of the sound velocity is

$$u^2 = \frac{\partial P}{\partial (mN/V)} = -\frac{V^2}{mN} \frac{\partial P}{\partial V}.$$

(At $T = 0$ also $S = 0$, so there is no need to distinguish between the isothermal and adiabatic compressibilities). For the calculation of this derivative, it is convenient to express it in terms of the derivative of the chemical potential. Since the latter depends on N and V only through the ratio N/V, we have:

$$\frac{\partial \mu}{\partial N} = -\frac{V}{N} \frac{\partial \mu}{\partial V} = -\frac{V^2}{N^2} \frac{\partial P}{\partial V}$$

---

† One must, however, bear in mind that actually, if the temperature is rigorously zero, no ordinary sound can be propagated in a Fermi liquid since its viscosity increases indefinitely as $T \to 0$.

(for $T = \text{const} = 0$: $d\mu = -V dP/N$). Thus

$$u^2 = \frac{N}{m}\frac{\partial \mu}{\partial N}. \tag{68.11}$$

Since $\mu = \epsilon(p_0) \equiv \epsilon_0$, the change $\delta\mu$ due to a change δN in the total number of particles is

$$\delta\mu = \int f\delta n'\, d\tau' + \frac{\partial \epsilon_0}{\partial p_0}\delta p_0. \tag{68.12}$$

The second term is due to the fact that a change in the total number of particles also alters the value of the limiting momentum: δN and δp_0 are connected by the relation:

$$\frac{2 \cdot 4\pi p_0^2 \delta p_0 V}{(2\pi\hbar)^3} = \delta N.$$

Since $\delta n'$ is appreciably different from zero only when $p \cong p_0$, we may write, in evaluating the integral in (68.12):

$$\int f\delta n'\, d\tau' \cong \int f\, do' \int \delta n' \frac{d\tau'}{4\pi} = \int f\, do' \frac{\delta N}{4\pi V}.$$

Substituting the result in (68.12) and introducing m^* by the relation $\partial\epsilon_0/\partial p_0 = p_0/m^*$, we find

$$\frac{\partial \mu}{\partial N} = \frac{1}{4\pi V}\int f\, do' + \frac{(2\pi\hbar)^3}{8\pi p_0 m^* V}.$$

Finally we insert for m^* from (68.10), and multiply by

$$\frac{N}{m} = \frac{2 \cdot 4\pi p_0^3}{3(2\pi\hbar)^3}\frac{V}{m}$$

this gives the result

$$u^2 = \frac{p_0^2}{3m^2} + \frac{1}{6m}\left(\frac{p_0}{2\pi\hbar}\right)^3 4\int f(1-\cos\theta)\, do'. \tag{68.13}$$

If the function f depends on the spins of both particles, the factors 4 before the integrals in (68.10) and (68.13) are to be replaced by taking the traces over both spin variables.

§69. The electronic spectra of solid dielectrics[†]

The concept of elementary excitations is also necessary for the description of the electronic spectra of solids. The electronic shells of the atoms of

---

[†] There have recently been considerable developments in the problem of the electronic energy spectra of metals. Since these could not be incorporated here, the whole subject is omitted in this edition.

solids interact strongly with one another, as a result of which one cannot speak of the energy levels of separate atoms, but only about the energy levels of the set of electronic shells of all the atoms as a whole. In speaking of the electronic spectrum of the solid we consider all the nuclei to be stationary and in their equilibrium positions, the nodes of the crystal lattice.

The character of the electronic spectrum differs for different types of solids. Consider first of all the energy spectrum of a dielectric nonparamagnetic crystal. (The question was first studied by J. FRENKEL in 1931.) Its main peculiarity is that already the first excited level is at a finite distance from the ground state; in other words, between the ground state and the spectrum of the excited levels there is an "energy gap". The presence of this gap (for normal dielectrics of the order of several electron-volts) results in the "electronic parts" of thermodynamic quantities being exponentially small (proportional to $e^{-\Delta/kT}$, where Δ is the width of the gap).

An elementary excitation in the spectrum we are considering can usually be described as an excited state of an individual atom which, however, one cannot associate with any definite atom; it is "collectivised" and is propagated in the crystal in the form of an "excitation wave" as if it jumped from one atom to another. Similarly, in the other cases these excitations may be considered as "particles" called, in this case, *excitons* having definite energies and quasi-momenta. Like all excitations which can appear singly, excitons have integral angular momentum and obey Bose statistics.

For a given value of the quasi-momentum $\mathbf{p}$ the energy of the exciton can run through a series of discrete values. Labelling these values by the suffix n we can write the energy of the exciton in the form $\epsilon_n(\mathbf{p})$. The components of the quasi-momentum, as we know, take a continuous series of values in the finite intervals (65.5). For every value of n the function $\epsilon_n(\mathbf{p})$ gives a certain "band" of values of the energy of the exciton; different bands may partially overlap. The minimum possible value of the functions $\epsilon_n(\mathbf{p})$, i.e. the smallest possible energy of the exciton, is non zero, as was already pointed out.

As well as the exciton, an excitation of a different kind can also exist in a dielectric. They may be regarded as appearing as the result of the ionisation of separate atoms. Each such ionisation leads to the appearance in the dielectric of two independently propagating "particles": an electron and a "hole". The latter by itself represents the "lack" of one electron by an atom and hence behaves like a positively charged particle. We must emphasise that in speaking of the motion of an electron and a hole in the crystal, we have in mind some "collective" excitation states of the electrons of the dielectric accompanied (unlike the excitation states) by the transfer of a positive or negative elementary charge.

The electrons and the holes have half integral spins and obey Fermi statistics. This, however, does not mean that the electron-hole spectrum of a dielectric has the same character as the Fermi-type spectrum described in §68. A characteristic of the latter is the existence of the limiting value of momentum p_0; in the given case there is nothing at all corresponding to this quantity and an electron and hole appearing simultaneously can have quite arbitrary quasi-momenta.

The electron and hole interact according to the Coulomb law. It is well known that the eigenvalue spectrum of two particles attracting one another by the Coulomb law consists of a discrete series of negative levels getting denser nearer the value zero, where a continuous spectrum of positive values begins. In the given case the discrete levels correspond to the excitation of excitons ("bound" electrons and holes) and the continuous ones to free electrons and holes. Hence we may say that (for a given value of the quasi-momentum) the possible values of the energy of an exciton form a discrete series which becomes denser as the energy increases and then becomes a continuous series of values corresponding to a freely moving electron and hole. In all these considerations we separate the electron spectrum from the motion of the atomic nuclei, which are assumed fixed at the points of the crystal lattice. This is by no means always justified. The interaction between the electrons and the lattice vibrations may be so strong that the proposed method of analysis becomes impossible. In a dielectric the interaction of an electron with the vibrations of the lattice leads to a deformation of the lattice near the position of the electron. This affects, of course, the motion of the electron substantially. (An electron, together with the lattice deformation which it causes, is called a polaron; this concept was introduced by S. I. PEKAR in 1946).

§70. Negative temperatures

We consider now some peculiar phenomena associated with the properties of paramagnetic dielectrics. The latter are characterised by their atoms having more or less freely oriented angular momenta (together with their magnetic moments). The mutual interaction of these angular momenta (exchange or magnetic depending on their distance) leads to the appearance of a new "magnetic" spectrum, superimposed on the normal dielectric spectrum.

This whole spectrum is obviously contained in a finite energy interval, in an interval of the order of magnitude of the interaction energy of the magnetic moments of all the atoms of the body situated at definite distances from each other at the lattice points of the crystal. Referred to one atom, this energy can range, as was stated above, from one tenth to hundreds of degrees. In this respect the magnetic energy spectrum differs fundamentally from the usual spectra which, owing to the presence of the kinetic energy of the particles, go up to arbitrarily large energy values.

In connection with this property we can consider the range of temperatures for which kT is large compared with all admissible values of the energy per atom. The free energy F_{mag} connected with the magnetic part of the spectrum is calculated just as in §32.

Let E_n be the energy levels of the system of interacting angular momenta.

Then we have, for our partition function:

$$Z_{\text{mag}} = \sum_n e^{-E_n/kT} \cong \sum_n \left(1 - \frac{E_n}{kT} + \frac{1}{2(kT)^2}E_n^2\right).$$

Here, as in §32 the formal expansion into a series of powers of the quantity E_n/kT, which is not small in general, gives, when we take the logarithm, an expansion in terms of the small quantity $\sim E_n/NkT$ where N is the number of atoms. The total number of levels in the spectrum under consideration is obviously equal to the number of possible combinations of the orientations of the magnetic moments; so that if they are all identical this number is g^N where g is the number of possible orientations of a single magnetic moment relative to the lattice. Denoting the arithmetic mean of a quantity by a bar over it we can rewrite Z_{mag} in the form

$$Z_{\text{mag}} = g^N \left(1 - \frac{1}{kT}\bar{E_n} + \frac{1}{2(kT)^2}\bar{E_n^2}\right).$$

Finally, taking the logarithm and again expanding in a series to the same accuracy, we obtain the following expression for the free energy.

$$F_{\text{mag}} = -kT \log Z_{\text{mag}} = -NkT \log g + \bar{E_n} - \frac{1}{2kT}\overline{(E_n - \bar{E_n})^2}. \tag{70.1}$$

Hence the entropy is

$$S_{\text{mag}} = Nk \log g - \frac{1}{2kT^2}\overline{(E_n - \bar{E_n})^2}, \tag{70.2}$$

the energy:

$$E_{\text{mag}} = \bar{E_n} - \frac{1}{kT}\overline{(E_n - \bar{E_n})^2} \tag{70.3}$$

and the specific heat:

$$C_{\text{mag}} = \frac{1}{kT^2}\overline{(E_n - \bar{E_n})^2}. \tag{70.4}$$

Consider the set of magnetic moments, fixed at the lattice points and interacting with each other, as an isolated system, ignoring its interaction with the oscillations of the lattice, which is normally very weak. Formulae (70.1–4) determine the thermodynamic quantities of this system at high temperatures.

The proof given in §10 that the temperature must be positive was based on the condition of stability of the system against the appearance of internal macroscopic motion in it. But the system of magnetic moments considered here is, by its very nature, incapable of macroscopic motion and hence the given considerations do not apply. The proof based on the normalisation condition given there for the Gibbs distribution (§36) also does not apply, since in this case the system possesses only a finite number of energy levels and thus the normalisation sum converges for any value of T.

Thus we arrive at the curious result that a system of interacting magnetic moments can have both positive and negative temperatures. Let us examine the properties of the system at different temperatures.

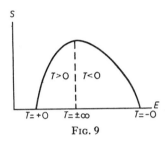

Fig. 9

At $T = 0$ the system is in its lowest quantum state and the entropy is equal to zero. As the temperature increases the energy and entropy of the system also increase monotonically. At $T = +\infty$ the energy is $\bar{E}_n$ and the entropy reaches its maximum value $Nk \log g$. These values correspond to the distribution with all states equally probable to which the Gibbs distribution tends as $T \to \infty$.

The temperature $T = -\infty$ is physically identical with the temperature $T = +\infty$; both these values give identical distributions, and identical values of thermodynamic quantities of the system. A further increase in the energy of the system corresponds to an increase in the temperature beyond $T = -\infty$ and as the temperature is negative its absolute value decreases. The entropy is then monotonically decreasing (Fig. 9)†. Finally at $T = -0$ the energy reaches its maximum and the entropy becomes zero; the system is then in its highest quantum state.

Thus the negative temperature region is not "below absolute zero" but "above infinite temperature". In this sense one can say that negative temperatures are "higher" than positive ones. Connected with this is the fact that if the system with a negative temperature interacts with a system whose temperature is positive (the oscillation of the lattice) then energy must be transferred from the first to the second, which is easily seen using the same method as in §9 where the exchange of energy between bodies of different temperatures was studied.

States of negative temperature can actually be realized in the paramagnetic system of the nuclear moments of a crystal in which the relaxation time t_2 for the mutual interaction of the nuclear spins is very small compared to the relaxation time t_1 for the interaction between the spins and the lattice (E. M. Purcell, R. V. Pound, 1951). Let the crystal be magnetised in a

---

† Near its maximum the curve $S = S(E)$ is symmetrical but it general there is no symmetry far away from this point.

strong magnetic field; the field direction is then reversed so quickly that the spins do not "have time" to follow. This will leave the system in a non-equilibrium state with an energy obviously higher than $\overline{E_n}$. During a time of the order t_2 it will reach an equilibrium state of the same energy. If, subsequently, the field is removed adiabatically, the system is left in an equilibrium state which will obviously have a negative temperature. The further exchange of energy between the spin system and the lattice, with equalisation of their temperatures, takes place over a time of the order of t_1.

CHAPTER VII

REAL GASES

§71. Deviations of gases from perfect behaviour

The equation of state of a perfect gas can in very many cases be applied to real ones with sufficient accuracy. This approximation may, however, be insufficient, and one must then take into account deviations of the behaviour of a real gas from that of a perfect gas, connected with the interaction of the molecules which compose it.

We shall do so here, however, considering the density of the gas to be so low that we may neglect triple, quadruple, etc. collisions of molecules and assume that they only interact by collisions of pairs of molecules.

To simplify the derivation of the formulae consider first a monatomic real gas. The motion of its particles may be considered classically so that its energy can be written in the form:

$$E(p, q) = \sum_{a=1}^{N} \frac{p_a^2}{2m} + U \qquad (71.1)$$

where the first term is the kinetic energy of the atoms of the gas and U is the energy of their interaction. For a monatomic gas U is a function only of the distances between the atoms. The partition function $\int e^{-E(p,q)/kT} \, d\Gamma$ splits up into the product of an integral over the momenta and an integral over the co-ordinates. The latter has the form

$$\int \cdots \int e^{-U/kT} \, dV_1 \, dV_2 \ldots dV_N,$$

where the integration over each $dV_a = dx_a \, dy_a \, dz_a$ is taken over the total volume V of the gas. For an ideal gas $U = 0$ and this integral would simply be V^N. Hence it is clear that in calculating the free energy by the general formula (31.5) we obtain:

$$F = F_p - kT \log \frac{1}{V^N} \int \cdots \int e^{-U/kT} \, dV_1 \ldots dV_N, \qquad (71.2)$$

where F_p is the free energy of the perfect gas.

Adding unity to the integrand and then subtracting it and remembering that $\int dV_1 \ldots dV_N = V^N$ we may rewrite (71.2) in the form

$$F = F_p - kT \log \left\{ \frac{1}{V^N} \int \cdots \int (e^{-U/kT} - 1) \, dV_1 \ldots dV_N + 1 \right\}, \qquad (71.3)$$

To carry out further calculations we shall make use of the following formal device. We assume that the gas is not only of sufficiently low density but that there is a sufficiently small quantity of it for us to assume that not more than one pair of particles collide at the same time. Such an assumption in no way affects the general validity of the formulae thus obtained since, owing to the additivity of the free energy, we know that it must be of the form $F = Nf(T, V/N)$, (see §24) and hence formulae obtained for small quantities of the gas are automatically true for any quantity of it.

The interaction between the atoms is appreciable only when the two atoms in question are situated very near to each other, i.e. practically collide. Hence the integrand in (71.3) differs appreciably from zero only when some two atoms are very close together. According to the assumption we have made this condition can be satisfied by not more than one pair of atoms at the same time. This pair can be chosen from the N atoms in $\frac{1}{2}N(N-1)$ ways. Owing to this the integral in (71.3) may be written in the form

$$\frac{N(N-1)}{2} \int \ldots \int (e^{-U_{12}/kT}-1)\, dV_1 \ldots dV_N$$

where U_{12} is the interaction energy of two atoms (which two is unimportant, as they are all the same); U_{12} already depends only on the co-ordinates of two atoms. Hence one can integrate over all the others, which will give V^{N-2}. In addition one can certainly replace $N(N-1)$ by N^2 since N is a very large number; substituting the resulting expression into (71.3) in place of the integral there and using the fact that $\log(1+x) \approx x$ for $x \ll 1$ we have†

$$F = F_p - \frac{kTN^2}{2V^2} \int\int (e^{-U_{12}/kT}-1)\, dV_1 dV_2,$$

where $dV_1\, dV_2$ is the product of the elements of the co-ordinates of the two atoms.

However, U_{12} is a function only of the distance between the two atoms, i.e. of the differences between their co-ordinates. Hence if one introduces, instead of the co-ordinates of each of the atoms, the co-ordinates of their common centre of gravity and their relative co-ordinates, then U_{12} will depend only on the latter (the product of whose differentials we denote by dV). Thus one can integrate over the co-ordinates of the common centre of gravity giving again the volume V. Finally we obtain:

$$F = F_p + \frac{N^2 kTB(T)}{V}, \tag{71.4}$$

---

† We shall see below that the first term in the logarithm in (71.3) is proportional to N^2/V. Hence the expansion we have made is connected with our assumption that not only the density of the gas is small but that there is not much of it.

where

$$B(T) = \tfrac{1}{2} \int (1 - e^{-U_{12}/kT}) \, dV. \tag{71.5}$$

Hence we find the pressure $P = -\partial F/\partial V$:

$$P = \frac{NkT}{V}\left(1 + \frac{NB(T)}{V}\right). \tag{71.6}$$

(since $-\partial F_p/\partial V = P_p = NkT/V$). This is the equation of state of the gas in the approximation we are considering.

As we know (§15) changes in the free energy and thermodynamic potential for small changes in the surrounding medium or properties of the body are equal to each other, one being taken at constant volume and the other at constant pressure.

If one considers the deviation from a perfect gas to be such a change, then from (71.4) we can directly find Φ. To do this we only need to express the volume in terms of pressure in the correction term in (71.4) using the Clapeyron formula:

$$\Phi = \Phi_p + NBP. \tag{71.7}$$

Hence one can express the volume in terms of the pressure

$$V = \frac{NkT}{P} + NB. \tag{71.8}$$

All we have said above refers to a monatomic gas. It is easy to see, however, that the same formulae apply also for polyatomic gases. In this case the interaction potential of the molecules depends not only on their separation but also on their relative orientation. If (as nearly always is the case) one can consider the rotations of the molecules classically, then one may say that U_{12} is a function of the co-ordinates of the centres of gravity of the molecules and some rotational co-ordinates (angles) specifying their orientation in space. It is easily seen that the only difference from the monatomic case will be reduced to the fact that now dV_a must be understood as the product of the differentials of all the co-ordinates of the molecule we have mentioned. But the rotational co-ordinates can always be chosen in such a way that the integral $\int dV_a$ is equal, as before, to the volume V of the gas. Indeed the integration over the co-ordinates of the centre of gravity gives the volume V and the integration over the angles gives a constant; the angles can always be so normalised that this constant is unity. Hence all the formulae derived in this section have the same form for polyatomic gases as well, the only difference being that in (71.5) dV is now the product of the differentials of the co-ordinates determining the distance between the molecules and also their relative orientations.†

---

† If the particles of the gas possess spin, then the form of the function U_{12} depends, in general, on the direction of the spin. In this case summation over the direction of spin is added to the integration over dV.

All the formulae obtained only make sense, clearly, if the integral (71.5) converges. A necessary condition for this is that the interaction between the molecules should decrease sufficiently rapidly with distance. If at large distances U_{12} decreases as $\sim r^{-n}$ then n must be greater than 3.†

If this condition is not satisfied, then a gas consisting of such particles cannot exist at all as a homogeneous body. In this case each element of the substances will be acted on by very strong forces due to distant particles of the gas. Hence regions near to and far from the boundary of the volume occupied by the gas will be in very different conditions and as a result the homogeneity of the gas will be destroyed.

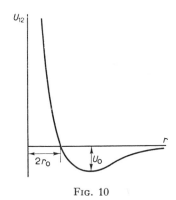

FIG. 10

For monatomic gases the function $U_{12}(r)$ has the form of the curve in Fig. 10; along the abscissa is plotted the distance r between the atoms. For small distances U_{12} increases for a decrease in distance, corresponding to repulsive forces between the atoms. Starting approximately at the point where the curve crosses the axis it rises steeply so that U_{12} soon becomes extremely large, corresponding to mutual "impenetrability" of the atoms. (For this reason the distance r_0 is sometimes called the "radius" of the atom.) For large distances U_{12} slowly increases, asymptotically approaching zero. The increase of U_{12} with distance corresponds to mutual attraction of the atoms. The minimum of U_{12}, i.e. the point at which the derivative dU_{12}/dV vanishes, is a point of "stable" equilibrium. The absolute value of the energy at this point, U_0, is generally not large (U_0/k is of the order of the critical temperature of the given substance).

In the case of the polyatomic gas the interaction energy behaves similarly, although it cannot be represented in the form of the curve in Fig. 10 since it is a function of a larger number of variables.

This knowledge about the nature of the function U_{12} is sufficient for

---

† For all atomic and molecular gases this condition is always satisfied. The interaction between electrically neutral atoms or molecules (including dipoles) falls off at large distances approximately as $U_{12} \sim 1/r^6$. See *Quantum Mechanics*, §86.

determining the sign of $B(T)$ in the limiting cases of high and low temperatures. For high temperatures $(kT \gg U_0)$ for the whole region $r > 2r_0$ we have $|U_{12}|/kT \ll 1$ and the integrand in $B(T)$ (71.5) is near zero. Hence the value of the integral is mainly determined by the region $r < 2r_0$ for which U_{12}/kT is large and positive. Hence in this region the integrand is positive and hence the whole integral is positive. Thus at very high temperatures $B(T)$ is positive.

On the other hand, for low temperatures $(kT \ll U_0)$ the main contribution to the integral comes from the region $r > 2r_0$ for which now U_{12}/kT is large and negative. Hence at sufficiently low temperatures $B(T)$ must be negative and the relation between $B(T)$ and temperature is roughly given by the exponential $-e^{-U_0/kT}$.

Being positive at high temperatures and negative at low temperatures $B(T)$ must pass through zero at some temperature.

Finally, consider a Joule-Thomson process taking place in a real gas. The change of temperature in this process is determined by the derivative

$$\left(\frac{\partial T}{\partial P}\right)_W = \frac{1}{C_p}\left[T\left(\frac{\partial V}{\partial T}\right)_P - V\right]$$

(see (18.2)). For a perfect gas this derivative naturally vanishes. For a gas with equation of state (71.8) we get:

$$\left(\frac{\partial T}{\partial P}\right)_W = \frac{N}{C_p}\left(T\frac{dB}{dT} - B\right) = \frac{N}{2C_p}\int\left[e^{-U_{12}/kT}\left(1 - \frac{U_{12}}{kT}\right) - 1\right]dV. \quad (71.9)$$

As for $B(T)$ it is easy to see that for high temperatures we must have $(\partial T/\partial P)_W < 0$, i.e. the transfer of the gas from a higher to a lower pressure in the Joule-Thomson process leads to an increase in the temperature of the gas. For low temperatures $(\partial T/\partial P)_W > 0$, i.e. the temperature of the gas falls with the pressure. For a definite temperature for each gas the Joule-Thomson effect must change sign (this is called the inversion effect).

PROBLEMS

1. Determine $B(T)$ for a gas whose particles repel each other according to the law $U_{12} = \alpha/r^n$ $(n > 3)$.

SOLUTION: In (71.5) we put $dV = 4\pi r^2 dr$, and integrate by parts with respect to dr (from 0 to ∞); then by the substitution $\alpha r^{-n} = x$ the integral reduces to a Γ-function and we obtain

$$B(T) = \frac{2\pi}{3}\left(\frac{\alpha}{kT}\right)^{3/n}\Gamma\left(1 - \frac{3}{n}\right).$$

2. The volatility of a gas is the pressure P^* which it would have, for given values of the temperature and chemical potential, if it were so diffuse that it could be considered perfect. Determine the volatility of a gas with thermodynamic potential (71.7).

SOLUTION: The chemical potential of the gas is ($\mu_p{}'$ found from (42.6)):

$$\mu = \mu_p + BP = kT\log P + \chi(T) + BP.$$

Making this equal to the expression $kT \log P^* + \chi(T)$, by definition of volatility, we obtain (to the same accuracy as (71.7)):

$$P^* = P\left(1 + \frac{BP}{kT}\right) = \frac{NkT}{V}\left(1 + \frac{2NB}{V}\right).$$

§72. Expansion in powers of the density

The equation of state (71.6) obtained in the last section is essentially the first two terms of the expansion of the pressure in powers of $1/V$:

$$P = \frac{NkT}{V}\left(1 + \frac{NB(T)}{V} + \frac{N^2 C(T)}{V^2} + \dots\right). \tag{72.1}$$

The first term of the expansion corresponds to a perfect gas, i.e. to the absence of molecular interaction. The second term is obtained by taking into account the interaction of pairs of molecules and in succeeding terms interactions of three, four, etc. molecules take part.† The coefficients B, C, ... etc. in the expansion (72.1) are called the second, third, etc. "virial coefficients". For the determination of these quantities it is convenient to start with the calculation, not of the free energy, but of the potential Ω. Once again considering the monatomic gas and starting from the general formula (35.5) applied to a gas consisting of identical particles we have:

$$e^{-\Omega/kT} = \sum_{N=0}^{\infty} \frac{1}{N!} e^{\mu N/kT} \int e^{-E_N(p,q)/kT} \, d\Gamma_N, \tag{72.2}$$

We have introduced the factor $1/N!$, after which the integration is simply carried out over the whole phase space of the system of N particles (see (31.7)).

In the succeeding terms of the sum over N, the energy $E_N(p, q)$ has the following form. For $N = 0$ obviously $E_0(p, q) = 0$. For $N = 1$ it is simply the kinetic energy of a single atom

$$E_1(p, q) = p^2/2m.$$

For $N = 2$ it is the sum of the kinetic energy of two atoms and their interaction energy

$$E_2(p, q) = \sum_{a=1}^{2} \frac{p_a^2}{2m} + U_{12},$$

Analogously

$$E_3(p, q) = \sum_{a=1}^{3} \frac{p_a^2}{2m} + U_{123},$$

where U_{123} is the interaction energy of three atoms (not, in general, equal to the sum $U_{12} + U_{23} + U_{13}$), etc.

---

† The dimensionless small parameter in terms of which the expansion is carried out, is actually the ratio Nv_0/V of the "volume" v_0 of one molecule to the volume of gas V/N per molecule.

We substitute these expressions into (72.2) and introduce the notation

$$\xi = \frac{e^{\mu/kT}}{(2\pi\hbar)^3} \int e^{-p^2/2mkT}\, d^3p = \left(\frac{mkT}{2\pi\hbar^2}\right)^{3/2} e^{\mu/kT}. \tag{72.3}$$

We shall see below that this expression is simply

$$\xi = P_P/kT,$$

where P_p is the pressure of a perfect gas for the given T and V. We obtain

$$\Omega = -kT \log\Big\{1 + \xi V + \frac{\xi^2}{2!} \int\int e^{-U_{12}/kT}\, dV_1 dV_2 +$$

$$+ \frac{\xi^3}{3!} \int\int\int e^{-U_{123}/kT} dV_1\, dV_2\, dV_3 + \ldots \Big\}.$$

Each of U_{12}, U_{123}, ... is a function only of the distances between the atoms; hence, introducing co-ordinates relative to the first atom, say, we reduce the number of integrations by one, thus obtaining an extra factor V:

$$\Omega = -PV = -kT \log\Big\{1 + \xi V + \frac{\xi^2 V}{2!} \int e^{-U_{12}/kT}\, dV_2 +$$

$$+ \frac{\xi^3 V}{3!} \int\int e^{-U_{123}/kT}\, dV_2\, dV_3 + \ldots \Big\}.$$

Lastly we expand this expression in powers of ξ; the resulting series can be represented in the form

$$P = kT \sum_{n=1}^{\infty} \frac{J_n}{n!} \xi^n, \tag{72.4}$$

where

$$J_1 = 1, \quad J_2 = \int (e^{-U_{12}/kT} - 1)\, dV_2, \left.\vphantom{\int\int}\right\} \tag{72.5}$$

$$J_3 = \int\int (e^{-U_{123}/kT} - e^{-U_{12}/kT} - e^{-U_{13}/kT} - e^{-U_{23}/kT} + 2)\, dV_2 dV_3$$

etc. The integrals J_n are constructed in an obvious way; the integrand in J_n is appreciably different from zero only if n atoms are close to one another, i.e. during collisions of n atoms.

Differentiating (72.4) with respect to μ we obtain the number of particles in the gas as

$$N = -\left(\frac{\partial\Omega}{\partial\mu}\right)_{TV} = V\left(\frac{\partial P}{\partial\mu}\right)_{T,V}.$$

Bearing in mind that from the definition (72.3) $\partial\xi/\partial\mu = \xi/kT$ we obtain:

$$N = V \sum_{n=1}^{\infty} \frac{J_n}{(n-1)!}\xi^n. \qquad (72.6)$$

The two equations (72.4) and (72.6) determine the relation between P, V, T in parametric form (with parameter ξ), i.e. they determine the equation of state of the gas. Eliminating ξ from them, one can obtain the equation of state in the form of the series (72.1) to any number of terms required.†

§73. Van der Waals' equation

In gases, the molecular interaction is very weak. As this interaction increases, the properties of the gas deviate further and further from those of a perfect gas and eventually the gas becomes a condensed body, that is, a liquid. In the latter the molecular interaction is strong and the properties of this interaction (and hence the properties of the liquid) depend to a large extent on the precise nature of the liquid. For this reason it is impossible, as we already pointed out, to establish any general formula which will quantitatively describe the properties of liquids.

One can, however, find an *interpolation formula*, qualitatively describing the transition from gas to liquid. This formula must give the correct results in two cases. For dilute gases it must transform to the formula describing the perfect gas, and with an increase in density as the gas approaches the liquid state, it must take into account the limited compressibility of the substance. Such a formula would then qualitatively describe the behaviour of the gas in the intermediate region.

To derive such a formula, we begin by studying in more detail the deviation from perfect behaviour at high temperatures. As in the previous sections we shall first of all consider a monatomic gas; for the same reasons as before all the formulae we obtain will apply to a polyatomic gas.

The nature of the interaction of the atoms of the gas described in §71 (see Fig. 9) allows us to determine the form of the first terms of the expansion of $B(T)$ in powers of the inverse temperature; we shall assume here that

---

† To the first approximation $P = kT\xi$, $N = V\xi$, whence $P = NkT/V = P_p$. The second approximation gives

$$P = kT\xi\left(1 + \frac{J_2}{2}\xi\right), \qquad N = V\xi(1 + J_2\xi).$$

Eliminating ξ from this equation we obtain (to the same accuracy)

$$P = \frac{NkT}{V} - \frac{N^2kT}{2V^2}J_2$$

which agrees with (71.6).

the ratio U_0/kT is small:

$$\frac{U_0}{kT} \ll 1. \tag{73.1}$$

Bearing in mind that U_{12} is a function only of the distance between the atoms we write $dV = 4\pi r^2\, dr$ in the integral (71.5). Splitting up the range of integration over dr into two parts we write:

$$\int (1-e^{-U_{12}/kT})\, dV = 4\pi \int_0^{2r_0} (1-e^{-U_{12}/kT})r^2\, dr + 4\pi \int_{2r_0}^{\infty} (1-e^{-U_{12}/kT})r^2\, dr.$$

But when r lies between 0 and $2r_0$ the potential energy U_{12} is in general very large. Thus in the first integral one can neglect the quantity $e^{-U_{12}/kT}$ compared with unity. This integral is then equal to $2b$, where

$$b = \frac{16}{3}\pi r_0^3.$$

If one regards r_0 as the "radius" of an atom, then b is four times its "volume". (For polyatomic gases the constant b is not necessarily equal to four times the "volume" of the molecule.)

In the second integral the absolute value of U_{12} is never larger than U_0 (Fig. 9); thus U_{12}/kT in this integral is always small compared with unity; even when $U_{12} = -U_0$. Hence we can expand $e^{-U_{12}/kT}$ as a power series in U_{12}/kT, keeping only the first two terms of the expansion. The second integral is then equal to

$$\frac{1}{kT} \int_{2r_0}^{\infty} 4\pi U_{12}r^2\, dr.$$

Since, in the whole range of integration, U_{12} is negative, the whole integral is also negative; we shall write it in the form $-2a/kT$ where a is a positive constant.

We thus find that

$$B(T) = b - a/kT. \tag{73.2}$$

Substituting this into (71.4) we find the free energy of the gas in the form

$$F = F_{\mathrm{p}} + \frac{N^2}{V}(kTb - a). \tag{73.3}$$

Substituting it into (71.7) we find the thermodynamic potential:

$$\Phi = \Phi_{\mathrm{p}} + NP(b - a/kT). \tag{73.4}$$

The required interpolation formula can be obtained from (73.3), which does not itself satisfy the necessary conditions, since it does not take into account the limits of compressibility of the gas. We substitute into (73.3) the expression for F_p from (42.2). We then obtain

$$F = Nf(T) - NkT \log\frac{e}{N} - NkT\left(\log V - \frac{Nb}{V}\right) - \frac{N^2 a}{V}. \tag{73.5}$$

In deriving formula (71.4) for the free energy of the gas we have assumed that, although the density of the gas is not so low that it can be considered perfect, yet it has an extremely large volume (so that one can neglect triple, quadruple, etc. collisions of molecules) i.e. the distances between the molecules are much larger than their diameters. We may say that the volume of the gas is certainly considerably larger than Nb. Hence $Nb/V \ll 1$, and making use of the fact that for $x \ll 1$ we may write $\log(1+x) \cong x$, we find that

$$\log(V - Nb) = \log V + \log\left(1 - \frac{Nb}{V}\right) = \log V - \frac{Nb}{V}.$$

Hence (73.5) may be written in the form

$$F = Nf(T) - NkT \log\frac{e}{N}(V - Nb) - \frac{N^2 a}{V}$$

$$= F_p - NkT \log\left(1 - \frac{Nb}{V}\right) - \frac{N^2 a}{V}. \tag{73.6}$$

In this form the formula satisfies the conditions stated above, since for large V it goes over to the formula for the free energy of the perfect gas and for small V it ensures the impossibility of unlimited condensation of the gas (for $V < Nb$ the argument of the logarithm becomes negative).

Knowing the free energy, we can determine the pressure of the gas

$$P = -\frac{\partial F}{\partial V} = \frac{NkT}{V - Nb} - \frac{N^2 a}{V^2}$$

or

$$\left(P + \frac{N^2 a}{V^2}\right)(V - Nb) = NkT. \tag{73.7}$$

This is the required interpolation equation of state for a real gas. It is called *Van der Waals' equation.*

Obviously the Van der Waals formula is just one of the endless number of possible interpolation formulae satisfying the given conditions and there is no physical reason for preferring any particular one. The Van der Waals formula is just the simplest and most convenient.†

---

† Applying this formula in practice one must choose values of the coefficients a and b giving the best agreement with experiment. The constant b in this case can in no way be regarded as four times the "molecular volume", even for a monatomic gas.

From (73.6) one can find the entropy of the gas

$$S = S_{\mathrm{p}} + Nk \log\left(1 - \frac{Nb}{V}\right), \tag{73.8}$$

and then its energy

$$E = E_{\mathrm{p}} - \frac{N^2 a}{V}. \tag{73.9}$$

We can see from this that the specific heat $C_v = (\partial E/\partial T)_V$ of a Van der Waals gas coincides with that of a perfect gas. It depends only on the temperature and in a particular case may be constant. But the specific heat C_p can easily be seen (see Problem 1) to depend not only on temperature but also on volume, and thus cannot be reduced to a constant.

The second term in (73.9) is associated with the interaction energy of the gas molecules; naturally it is negative, since on the average the net forces between the molecules are attractive.

PROBLEMS

1. Find $C_p - C_v$ for a real gas obeying Van der Waals' equation.

SOLUTION: With the help of (16.10) and Van der Waals' equation we find that

$$C - C_v = \frac{Nk}{1 - \dfrac{2Na}{kTV^3}(V - Nb)^2}.$$

2. Find the equation of an adiabatic process for a Van der Waals gas with constant specific heat C_v.

SOLUTION: Substituting $S_{\mathrm{p}} = Nk \log V + Nc_v \log T$ into (73.8) (omitting the unimportant constants) and equating S to a constant, we find the relation

$$(V - Nb)T^{c_v/k} = \text{const.}$$

It differs from the corresponding equation for an ideal gas by replacing V by $V - Nb$.

3. Find, for the same gas, the change in temperature during its expansion into a vacuum from volume V_1 to volume V_2.

SOLUTION: In an expansion into a vacuum the energy of the gas remains constant. Hence from (73.9) (with $E_{\mathrm{p}} = Nc_v T$) we find:

$$T_2 - T_1 = \frac{Na}{c_v}\left(\frac{1}{V_2} - \frac{1}{V_1}\right).$$

§74. The completely ionised gas

The method used in §§71–73 to calculate thermodynamic quantities of real gases is not suitable for a gas consisting of ionised particles with Coulomb interaction, since in this case the integrals entering in the formulae diverge. Thus such a gas requires special study.

Consider a completely ionised gas and denote the charges on its particles by $z_a e$ where the suffix a is used to distinguish different kinds of ions (e the elementary charge, z_a positive and negative integers). Let n_{a0} be the number of type a in unit volume of the gas. The gas as a whole is obviously electrically neutral, i.e.

$$\sum_a z_a n_{a0} = 0. \tag{74.1}$$

We shall assume that the behaviour of the gas deviates slightly from the perfect gas. To ensure this it is necessary that the mean energy of the Coulomb interaction of two ions ($\sim (ze)^2/r$, where $r \sim n^{-1/3}$ is the average distance between ions) must be small compared with the mean kinetic energy of the ions ($\sim kT$). Thus we must have $(ze)^2 n^{1/3} \ll kT$, or

$$n \ll \left(\frac{kT}{z^2 e^2}\right)^3. \tag{74.2}$$

To calculate thermodynamic quantities of such a gas one must begin by determining the increase E_{Coul} in its energy (compared with the energy of the perfect gas) due to the Coulomb interaction of its particles.[†]

It is well known from electrostatics that the energy of the electrical interaction of a system of charged particles can be written down as half the sum of the products of each charge with its potential in the field of all the other charges. In the given case

$$E_{\text{Coul}} = V \cdot \tfrac{1}{2} \sum_a e z_a n_{a0} \phi_a, \tag{74.3}$$

where ϕ_a is the field potential acting on an ion of type a due to all the other charges. To calculate these potentials we proceed in the following way.

Each of the ions creates around itself an inhomogeneously charged (on the average spherically symmetrical) *ion cloud*. In other words, if one chooses some ion of the gas and considers the density of distribution of the other ions relative to the given one then this density will depend only on the distance r from its centre. We denote the density of distribution of ions (of type a) in this ion cloud by n_a. The potential energy of each ion of type a in the electric field surrounding it is $z_a e\phi$ where ϕ is the potential of this field. Hence, in accordance with the Boltzmann formula we have

$$n_a = n_{a0} e^{-z_a e\phi / kT}. \tag{74.4}$$

The constant coefficient is put equal to n_{a0} since at a great distance from the centre (as $\phi \to 0$) the density of the ion cloud must become the mean ionic density for the gas.

The potential ϕ of the field in the ionic cloud is related to the charge

---

[†] The method set out in the text was used by DEBYE and HÜCKEL for the calculation of thermodynamic quantities of strong electrolytes.

density in it (equal to $\sum\limits_a ez_a n_a$) by Poisson's electrostatic equation:

$$\Delta\phi = -4\pi e \sum_a z_a n_a. \tag{74.5}$$

Because of the assumption we made about the relative weakness of the ionic interaction, the energy $ez_a\phi$ is small compared with kT and formula (74.4) may be written approximately in the form

$$n_a = n_{a0} - \frac{n_{a0}ez_a}{kT}\phi. \tag{74.6}$$

Substituting this expression into (74.5) and bearing in mind the condition (74.1) that the gas as a whole should be neutral, we obtain the equation

$$\Delta\phi - \kappa^2\phi = 0 \tag{74.7}$$

where we have introduced the notation

$$\kappa^2 = \frac{4\pi e^2}{kT} \sum_a n_{a0}z_a^2. \tag{74.8}$$

The quantity κ has the dimensions of an inverse length.

The spherically symmetric solution of equation (74.7) is

$$\phi = \text{const}\, \frac{e^{-\kappa r}}{r}.$$

In the immediate neighbourhood of the centre the field must become the pure Coulomb field of the given charge (whose value we denote by $z_b e$). In other words, for sufficiently small r we must have $\phi \simeq ez_b/r$; hence one can see that we must make the constant equal to $z_b e$, so that the required potential distribution is given by

$$\phi = ez_b\frac{e^{-\kappa r}}{r}. \tag{74.9}$$

Hence we can see that the field becomes very small for distances large compared with $1/\kappa$. Thus the length $1/\kappa$ may be regarded as determining the size of the ion cloud produced by the given ion (it is also called the *Debye-Hückel* radius. All the calculations we carry out here assume that this "radius" is large compared with the distances between ions. (This condition obviously is the same as (74.2)).

Expanding the potential (74.9) as a series we find that for small κr,

$$\phi = \frac{ez_b}{r} - ez_b\kappa + \dots$$

The omitted terms vanish at $r = 0$. The first term is the Coulomb field of the given ion itself. The second is obviously the potential due to all other ions of the "cloud" at the position of the given ion; this is the quantity which must be substituted into (74.3): $\phi_a = -ez_a\kappa$.

Thus we obtain the following expression for the "Coulomb part" of the energy of the gas

$$E_{\text{Coul}} = -\frac{V}{2}\kappa e^2 \sum_a n_{a0}z_a^2 = -Ve^3\left(\frac{\pi}{kT}\right)^{\frac{1}{2}} (\sum_a n_{a0}z_a^2)^{3/2}, \qquad (74.10)$$

or, introducing the total number of different ions in the gas, $N_a = n_{a0}V$:

$$E_{\text{Coul}} = -e^3\left(\frac{\pi}{kTV}\right)^{\frac{1}{2}} (\sum_a N_a z_a^2)^{3/2}. \qquad (74.11)$$

Thus this energy is inversely proportional to the temperature and the volume of the gas.

Integrating the thermodynamic relation $E/T^2 = -(\partial/\partial T)(F/T)$ we can obtain from E_{Coul} the corresponding addition to the free energy

$$F = F_p - \frac{2e^3}{3}\left(\frac{\pi}{kTV}\right)^{\frac{1}{2}} (\sum_a N_a z_a^2)^{3/2} \qquad (74.12)$$

(the constant of integration must be put equal to zero since $F \to F_p$ as $T \to \infty$). Hence we obtain the pressure

$$P = \frac{kT}{V} \sum N_a - \frac{e^3}{3V^{3/2}}\left(\frac{\pi}{kT}\right)^{\frac{1}{2}} (\sum_a N_a z_a^2)^{3/2}. \qquad (74.13)$$

The thermodynamic potential is obtained from F just as in §71 (i.e. by treating the second term of (74.12) as a small correction to F_p)

$$\Phi = \Phi_p - \frac{2e^3}{3kT}\left(\frac{\pi P}{\sum N_a}\right)^{\frac{1}{2}} (\sum_a N_a z_a^2)^{3/2}. \qquad (74.14)$$

We must make the following remark about the formulae we have obtained. Although they were derived on the assumption that the relative motion of the interacting particles was quasi-classical, nevertheless they still hold when (for sufficiently large velocities of the particles) the motion becomes quantised. The reason for this is that the greatest contribution to E_{Coul} comes from the interaction of particles comparatively far from one another. The relative motion of distant particles is associated with large values of their orbital angular momentum and hence is always quasi-classical.

Lastly let us deal with the question of how the formulae we have obtained must be changed in the case when the electrons in the gas must be regarded as a Fermi gas. Let $n_a(\mu_a)$ be the density of particles of type a as a function of their chemical potential, according either to the Fermi or the Bose distribution. In the presence of an external electric field the density distribution in space will be obtained by changing the function of μ_a to that of $\mu_{a0} - z_a e\phi$ where μ_{a0} is the value of the chemical potential when $\phi = 0$. Expanding in powers of ϕ we obtain the approximate equation

$$n_a = n_{a0} - z_a e \phi \frac{\partial n_{a0}}{\partial \mu_a}. \tag{74.15}$$

taking the place of (74.6) (for a Boltzmann gas $n_a \sim e^{\mu/kT}$ and eq. 74.15 becomes eq. 74.6).

Repeating all the above calculations with this expression we obtain a constant

$$\kappa^2 = 4\pi e^2 \sum_a z_a^2 \frac{\partial n_{a0}}{\partial \mu_a} \tag{74.16}$$

and the following expression for the Coulomb interaction potential of the gas particles:

$$U_{\text{Coul}} = -e^3 \left(\frac{\pi}{V}\right)^{\frac{1}{2}} (\Sigma_a N_a z_a^2) \left(\Sigma_a z_a^2 \frac{\partial N_a}{\partial \mu_a}\right)^{\frac{1}{2}}. \tag{74.17}$$

We write here U_{Coul} instead of E_{Coul} as in (74.11) since, in the Fermi distribution, in taking account of the interaction of the particles the kinetic energy also changes and thus (74.17) does not give the total correction to the energy of the gas.

The free energy can be calculated directly from U_{Coul} without first calculating the total energy. To do this we note that in the Hamiltonian for the gas, $E(p, q) = K(p) + U(q)$, the Coulomb interaction potential energy $U(q)$ is proportional to the square of the charge, e^2, hence considering e^2 as a parameter we may write:

$$U(q) = e^3 \frac{\partial U(q)}{\partial(e^2)} = e^2 \frac{\partial E(p, q)}{\partial(e^2)}.$$

Averaging this equation, and making use of (15.11) (with e^2 as the parameter λ), we obtain:

$$U_{\text{Coul}} = e^2 \left(\frac{\partial F}{\partial(e^2)}\right)_{T,V}$$

where U_{Coul} is given by (74.17). From this, by a simple integration, we obtain:

$$F = F_{\text{p}} - \frac{2e^3}{3} \left(\frac{\pi}{V}\right)^{\frac{1}{2}} (\Sigma_a N_a z_a^2) \left(\Sigma_a z_a^2 \frac{\partial N_a}{\partial \mu_a}\right)^{\frac{1}{2}}. \tag{74.18}$$

In this form this formula can be applied for any statistics.

We must point out that for the strongly degenerate electron gas the derivative $\partial N_a/\partial \mu_a$ is small compared with its value (N_a/kT) for a non-degenerate gas. Hence the presence of a degenerate electron gas does not, to the first approximation, affect the value of the Debye-Hückel radius.

The Debye-Hückel method explained above has the advantage of simplicity and transparency. Its main disadvantage, on the other hand, is the fact that it cannot be generalised to include higher-order approximations in respect of the concentration. We whall therefore also review briefly another method (proposed by N. N. Bogolyubov, 1946) which is more complicated but allows in principle the calculation of the thermodynamic functions to any degree of accuracy.

This method starts from the consideration of the so-called correlation functions between the simultaneous positions of several atoms at given space points. The simplest and most fundamental of these is the binary correlation function w_{ab}, which is proportional to the probability of finding simultaneously two particles (ions) in given space points $\mathbf{r}_a$ and $\mathbf{r}_b$. (The kinds of ions a and b may be different or identical.) Because of the isotropy and uniformity of the gas, this function depends, of course, only on $r = |\mathbf{r}_b - \mathbf{r}_a|$. We choose the normalisation factor in the function w_{ab} in such a way as to make it tend to unity as $r \to \infty$; then

$$w_{ab}\, dV_a\, dV_b = V^2.$$

If the function w_{ab} is known, the required energy E_{Coul} can be found by integration, using the obvious formula:

$$E_{\text{Coul}} = \frac{1}{2V^2} \sum_a \sum_b N_a N_b \iint u_{ab} w_{ab}\, dV_a dV_b \qquad (74.19)$$

where the summation over a, b extends over all the kinds of ions, and u_{ab} is the Coulomb potential for a pair of such ions at distance r.

According to Gibbs' distribution formula the function w_{ab} is given by the following expression:

$$w_{ab} = \frac{1}{V^{N-2}} \int \exp\left\{\frac{F - F_{\text{p}} - U}{kT}\right\} dV_1 dV_2 \ldots dV_{N-2} \qquad (74.20)$$

where U is the mutual Coulomb interaction energy of all ions, and the integration extends over the co-ordinates of all ions except the two given ones. To evaluate this integral approximately, we use the following device.

We differentiate equation (74.20) with respect to the co-ordinates of ion b. This gives

$$\frac{\partial w_{ab}}{\partial \mathbf{r}_b} = -\frac{w_{ab}}{kT} \frac{\partial u_{ab}}{\partial \mathbf{r}_b} - \frac{1}{kTV} \sum_c N_c \int \frac{\partial u_{bc}}{\partial \mathbf{r}_b} w_{abc}\, dV_c \qquad (74.21)$$

where the summation in the last term on the right goes over all kinds of ions, and w_{abc} is the ternary correlation function, defined by

$$w_{abc} = \frac{1}{V^{N-3}} \int \exp\left\{\frac{F - F_{\text{p}} - U}{kT}\right\} dV_1 dV_2 \ldots dV_{N-3}$$

in analogy with (74.20).

Assuming the gas sufficiently dilute, and considering only terms of first order, we may express the ternary correlation function in terms of the binary one. Indeed, neglecting the possibility of all three ions being close to each other, we may write

$$w_{abc} = w_{ab}w_{bc}w_{ac}.$$

To the same approximation we may assume that even the pairs of particles are not so close that the function w_{ab} is appreciably different from unity. Introducing the small quantity

$$\omega_{ab} = w_{ab} - 1 \tag{74.22}$$

and neglecting higher powers of this than the first, we may write:

$$w_{abc} = \omega_{ab} + \omega_{bc} + \omega_{ac} + 1. \tag{74.23}$$

If we insert this in the integral on the right-hand side of (74.21) there remains only the term in ω_{ac}; the other terms are identically zero because of the isotropy of the gas. In the first term on the right it is sufficient to assume $w_{ab} = 1$. Thus:

$$\frac{\partial \omega_{ab}}{\partial \mathbf{r}_b} = -\frac{1}{kT}\frac{\partial u_{ab}}{\partial \mathbf{r}_b} - \frac{1}{kTV}\sum_c N_c \int \omega_{ac} \frac{\partial u_{bc}}{\partial \mathbf{r}_b}\, dV_c.$$

We now operate on both sides of this equation with the operation div, remembering that

$$u_{ab} = \frac{z_a z_b e^2}{r}, \quad \mathbf{r} = \mathbf{r}_b - \mathbf{r}_a$$

and using the well-known formula

$$\Delta\frac{1}{r} = -4\pi\delta(\mathbf{r}).$$

The integration on the right is now trivial because of the δ-function in the integrand, and we obtain the result:

$$\Delta\omega_{ab}(\mathbf{r}) = \frac{4\pi z_a z_b e^2}{kT}\delta(\mathbf{r}) + \frac{4\pi e^2 z_b}{kTV}\sum_c N_c z_c \omega_{ac}(\mathbf{r}).$$

The solution of this system of equations may be written in the form

$$\omega_{ab}(\mathbf{r}) = z_a z_b \omega(\mathbf{r}) \tag{74.24}$$

which reduces the system to the single equation

$$\Delta\omega(\mathbf{r}) = \frac{4\pi e^2}{kT}\delta(\mathbf{r}) + \frac{4\pi e^2}{kTV}\sum_c N_c z_c^2.\omega(\mathbf{r}). \tag{74.25}$$

This final equation is of the same form as the eq. (74.7) in the Debye-Hückel method. (The term with the δ-function represents the boundary condition imposed there on the function $\phi(r)$ for $r \to 0$.) It is easy to see that we obtain the previous result for the energy E_{Coul}.

In the next approximation the calculations become much more laborious (nobody has so far carried them out). In particular, the assumption (74.24) is now insufficient, and one has to introduce a ternary correlation which can no longer be reduced to the binary one. For this one finds an equation which is analogous to (74.21) and contains now quadruple correlations (reducible, in the second-order approximation, to the ternary one).

§75. Quantum-mechanical calculation of the virial coefficients

In calculating the virial coefficients in §§71–3 we started from classical statistics, which is always justified in practice. However, the calculation of these coefficients in the quantum case also presents a certain interest; in actual fact it may apply to helium at sufficiently low temperatures. We shall show how one can calculate the second virial coefficient taking into account the quantisation of the interaction of pairs of gas particles (BETH and UHLENBECK, 1937). We shall consider a monatomic gas whose atoms have no resultant electronic angular momentum; bearing in mind the case of helium, we shall also assume for the sake of definiteness that the atomic nuclei have no spin and that the atoms obey Bose statistics.

To the approximation we are interested in, it is sufficient to retain only the first three terms in the sum with respect to n in formula (35.3):

$$\Omega = -kT \log\{1 + \sum_n e^{\mu - E_{1n}/kT} + \sum_n e^{2\mu - E_{2n}/kT}\}. \tag{75.1}$$

Here E_{1n} denotes the energy levels of a single atom, and E_{2n} the energy levels of a system of two interacting atoms. Our object is to calculate only those correction terms to thermodynamic quantities which are connected with the direct interaction of atoms; the corrections connected with the quantum-mechanical exchange effects which already exist in the ideal gas are determined by formula (55.15) according to which the "exchange" part of the second virial coefficient is equal (in the case of Bose statistics) to

$$B_{\mathrm{exch}} = -\frac{1}{2}\left(\frac{\pi \hbar^2}{mkT}\right)^{3/2}. \tag{75.2}$$

Thus our problem reduces to the calculation of the sum

$$Z^{(2)} = \sum_n e^{2\mu - E_{2n}/kT}$$

but we must subtract from this the expression which would be obtained for two noninteracting atoms.

The energy levels E_{2n} are made up from the kinetic energy of the motion of the centre of gravity of the two atoms ($p^2/4m$ where $\mathbf{p}$ is the momentum of this motion and m is the atomic mass) and the energy of their relative motion. We denoted the latter by ϵ; this being the energy level of a particle of mass $m/2$ (the reduced mass of the two atoms) moving in the central field $U_{12}(r)$ (U_{12} the potential energy of the interacting atoms). The motion of the centre of gravity is always quasi-classical and carrying out in the usual way the integration over its co-ordinates and momenta (cf. §42) we obtain

$$Z^{(2)} = Ve^{2\mu/kT}\left(\frac{mkT}{\pi\hbar^2}\right)^{3/2}\sum e^{-\epsilon/kT}.$$

If we denote by Z_{int} that part of the sum $Z^{(2)}$ due to the interaction of the particles then we may write Ω in the form

$$\Omega = \Omega_{\text{p}} - kTVe^{2\mu/kT}\left(\frac{mkT}{\pi\hbar^2}\right)^{3/2}Z_{\text{int}}.$$

Considering the second term as a small increment to the first and expressing it in terms of T, V, and N (using formula 45.5 for the chemical potential of a perfect gas) we obtain for the free energy the expression

$$F = F_{\text{p}} - kT\frac{8N^2}{V}\left(\frac{\pi\hbar^2}{mkT}\right)^{3/2}Z_{\text{int}}.$$

Differentiating with respect to V, we obtain the pressure, and the part of the virial coefficient due to the interaction of the atoms, which we are interested in becomes:

$$B_{\text{int}}(T) = -8\left(\frac{\pi\hbar^2}{mkT}\right)^{3/2}Z_{\text{int}}. \tag{75.3}$$

The spectrum of the energy levels ϵ consists of a discrete spectrum of negative values (associated with restricted relative motion of the atoms) and a continuous spectrum of positive values (free motion). We denote the first by ϵ_n; the second can be written in the form f^2/m where $\mathbf{p}$ is the momentum of relative motion of the atoms at a great distance from one another. The sum,

$$\sum_n e^{|\epsilon_n|/kT}$$

over the discrete spectrum is included as a whole in Z_{int}, but one must separate from the integral over the continuous spectrum the part corresponding to the free motion of noninteracting particles. To do this we use the following device.

For large distances r, the wave function of the stationary state with orbital angular momentum l and positive energy p^2/m has the asymptotic form[†]

$$\psi = \frac{\text{const}}{r} \sin\left(\frac{p}{\hbar}r - \frac{l\pi}{2} + \delta_l\right)$$

where the phase shift $\delta_l = \delta_l(p)$ depends on the actual form of the field $U_{12}(r)$. We finally assume that the range of variation of the distance r is bounded by the large, but still finite value R. Then the momentum p can take only a discrete set of values, determined by the boundary condition that ψ should vanish at $r = R$:

$$\frac{p}{\hbar}R - \frac{l\pi}{2} + \delta_l = s\pi$$

where s is an integer. But for large R this series of values is very dense and the sum

$$\sum_p e^{-p^2/mkT}$$

can be replaced by an integral. To do this, for given l we multiply the sum by

$$ds = \frac{1}{\pi}\left(\frac{R}{\hbar} + \frac{d\delta_l}{dp}\right)dp$$

and integrate with respect to dp. The result must again be multiplied by $2l+1$ (the degree of degeneracy in the direction of the orbital angular momentum), and summed over l:

$$\sum_p e^{-p^2/mkT} = \frac{1}{\pi}\sum_l (2l+1)\int_0^\infty \left(\frac{R}{\hbar} + \frac{d\delta_l}{dp}\right)e^{-p^2/mkT}\,dp.$$

For particles obeying Bose statistics and having no spin the co-ordinate wave functions must be symmetrical; this means we can have only even values of l, so that the summation over l is carried out only over all even numbers.

For free motion all the phase shifts $\delta_l = 0$. Hence the expression which remains for $\delta_l = 0$ is that part of the sum which must be discarded, since it is not connected with the interaction of the atoms. Thus we obtain for the required Z_{int} the following expression:

$$Z_{\text{int}} = \sum_n e^{|\epsilon|/kT} + \frac{1}{\pi}\sum_l \int_0^\infty (2l+1)\frac{d\delta_l}{dp}e^{-p^2/mkT}\,dp, \tag{75.4}$$

† See *Quantum Mechanics*, §33, formula (33.16).

and the virial coefficient $B = B_{exch} + B_{int}$ is equal to:

$$B(T) = -\frac{1}{2}\left(\frac{\pi\hbar^2}{mkT}\right)^{3/2}(1+16Z_{int}).\tag{75.5}$$

It is well known that the phase shifts δ_l determine the amplitude of scattering of particles moving in the field $U_{12}(r)$ according to the formula†

$$f(\theta) = \frac{\hbar}{2ip}\sum_l(2l+1)(e^{2i\delta_l}-1)P_l(\cos\theta),$$

where P_l are Legendre polynomials, θ is the angle between the directions of incidence and scattering; the summation in this case is taken over all even values of l. Because of this, it is possible to express the integral in (75.4) in terms of the scattering amplitude. It is easily verified by direct substitution of the expression for $f(\theta)$ that the following relation holds:

$$\sum_l(2l+1)\frac{d\delta_l}{dp} = \frac{1}{2\hbar}\frac{d}{dp}\{p[f(0)+f^*(0)]\}+\frac{1}{4\pi\hbar^2}\int p^2\left(f\frac{\partial f^*}{\partial p}-f^*\frac{\partial f}{\partial p}\right)do.$$

The sum on the left is simply the integrand in (75.4) and when we substitute this (and integrate one of the terms by parts) we obtain

$$Z_{int} = \sum_n e^{|\epsilon_n|/kT}+\frac{1}{\pi\hbar mkT}\int_0^\infty p^2e^{-p^2/mkT}[f(0)+f^*(0)]\,dp+$$

$$+\frac{1}{(2\pi\hbar)^2}\int\int p^2e^{-p^2/mkT}\left(f\frac{\partial f^*}{\partial p}-f^*\frac{\partial f}{\partial p}\right)dp\,do.\tag{75.6}$$

If, for a particle in the field $U_{12}(r)$ there exist discrete levels, then for sufficiently low temperatures the dependence of $B(T)$ on temperature will mainly be determined by the sum over the discrete levels, which increases exponentially as the temperature decreases. The discrete levels may, however, be entirely absent; then the virial coefficient will depend on T according to some power law (if one takes into account the fact that as $p \to 0$ the scattering amplitude tends to a constant limit, then it is easily seen that for sufficiently low temperatures B will mainly be determined by the term B_{exch}).

We note that in the case of weak interactions, when the collisions between the particles can be described by Born approximation, the scattering amplitude is small, and the third term in (75.6), which is quadratic in this amplitude, may be neglected. For weak interaction there are no bound states, and therefore the first term in (75.6) is absent. Using the familiar expression for the scattering amplitude $f(0)$ in Born approximation, which is proportional to

---

† See, for example, *Quantum Mechanics*, §105. The scattering cross-section into the element of solid angle do is $|f(\theta)|^2do$.

the integral $\int U_{12}(r)r^2 dr$, one sees easily that the expression for F then agrees exactly with eq. (32.3) (without the quadratic term) as it should do in this case.

PROBLEM

1. Determine the quantum correction (of order $\hbar^2$) to the quasi-classical value for the virial coefficient $B(T)$ for a monatomic gas.

SOLUTION: The correction to the classical free energy is given by formula (33.15). Taking into account the fact that in our case only pair interactions of atoms occur, and that U_{12} is a function only of the distance between the atoms we find that:

$$B_{\mathrm{qu}} = \frac{\pi \hbar^2}{6m(kT)^3} \int\limits_0^\infty \left(\frac{dV_{12}}{dr} \right)^2 e^{-U_{12}/kT} r^2 \, dr.$$

This expression gives the correction to the usual classical value given by (71.4). Note that $B_{\mathrm{qu}} > 0$.

§76. The degenerate "nearly perfect" gas

We proceed now to the problem of the thermodynamical properties of a "nearly perfect", strongly degenerate gas (in contrast to the slightly degenerate gas, discussed in the preceding section). This question has no direct physical meaning, since the real gases existing in nature are condensed at temperatures near absolute zero. In view of the considerable theoretical interest of the problem it is, however, worth while to consider a formal model of a gas of particles, interacting in such a way as to avoid the condensation.

The condition for the gas to be "nearly perfect" is that the molecular "interaction radius" a should be small compared with the mean distance between the particles $R \sim (V/N)^{1/3}$. This condition can be formulated also as

$$fa \ll 1 \tag{76.1}$$

where $f \sim p/\hbar$ is the wave vector of a particle; this is clear already since in a strongly degenerate gas R is the only characteristic length, which can determine the de-Broglie wavelength of its particles†.

We shall take here into account only collisions of pairs of particles (and shall use in this section the notation u for the interaction energy of two particles instead of the U_{12} used above). Our ultimate aim consists in calculating the first terms in the expansion of the thermodynamical quantities in powers of a/R, using some form of quantum-mechanical perturbation theory. The difficulty consists in the fact that due to a rapid increase of u at small distances, perturbation theory (the Born approximation) is invalid for the actual molecular collisions. However, this difficulty can be overcome in the following way.

In the Born approximation the effective scattering cross-section for the collision of two particles of mass m is given by the squared modulus $|a|^2$

---

† For a degenerate Fermi-gas it is seen directly from (56.2) that the boundary momentum $p_0 \sim \hbar(N/V)^{1/3}$.

of the "scattering amplitude"

$$a = \frac{m}{4\pi\hbar^2} \int u e^{i\mathbf{f}.\mathbf{r}} dV$$

$\hbar\mathbf{f}$ being the momentum transfer in the collision†. Under condition (76.1), i.e. for "slow" collisions, we have $\mathbf{f}r \ll 1$, in the entire region which is important in the integration, so that

$$a = \frac{m}{4\pi\hbar^2} u_0, \qquad u_0 = \int u \, dV. \tag{76.2}$$

Since this quantity completely determines the collision properties, the same must hold if the Born approximation is valid) for the thermodynamical properties of the gas.

Hence it is possible to use the following artificial device: we formally replace the actual interaction u by another one, which gives the same value of the scattering amplitude, but allows the use of perturbation theory. In so far as the final result of the calculations contains u only through the scattering amplitude, this result will be identical with the one which would be obtained with the correct function u.

A. Bose gas.

The energy spectrum of the weakly excited states of a nearly perfect Bose gas can be calculated by means of perturbation theory using the second quantisation formalism (N. N. Bogolyubov, 1947). We suppose the gas particles to have zero spin.

The Hamiltonian of a system of N particles interacting in pairs formalism in the second quantisation is‡

$$\hat{H} = \sum_{\mathbf{p}} \frac{p^2}{2m} \hat{A}_{\mathbf{p}}^+ \hat{A}_{\mathbf{p}} + \frac{1}{2} \sum u_{\mathbf{p_1 p_2}}^{\mathbf{p_1' p_2'}} \hat{A}_{\mathbf{p_1'}}^+ \hat{A}_{\mathbf{p_2'}}^+ \hat{A}_{\mathbf{p_2}} \hat{A}_{\mathbf{p_1}} \tag{76.3}$$

Here $\hat{A}_{\mathbf{p}}^+$ and $\hat{A}_{\mathbf{p}}$ are the "creation" and "annihilation" operators of a free particle with a momentum $\mathbf{p}$, i.e. in a state described (in a volume V) by the wave function

$$\psi_{\mathbf{p}} = \frac{1}{\sqrt{V}} e^{i\mathbf{p}.\mathbf{r}/\hbar}.$$

The first term in (76.3) corresponds to the kinetic, and the second—to the potential energy of the particles. In the latter the summation is performed

---

† We use $a = f(\theta)$ in this section; cf. *"Quantum Mechanics"*, §110. The scattering cross-section in the solid angle element do (in the centre of mass system) is $d\sigma = |a|^2 do$, if one does not take into account the quantum-mechanical identity of the colliding particles. Taking account of this identity the cross-section is $d\sigma = 4|a|^2 do$, it being necessary to integrate over a half sphere (and not over the complete sphere) in order to obtain the total cross-section.

‡ See *Quantum Mechanics*, §62.

over all values of the momenta of the particle pairs consistent with momentum conservation in the collisions:

$$p_1 + p_2 = p_1' + p_2'.$$

It is only under this condition that the matrix elements have non-zero values:

$$u_{p_1 p_2}^{p_1' p_2'} = \frac{1}{V^2} \int \int \exp\left\{\frac{i}{\hbar}(p_1 - p_1') \cdot r_1 + \frac{i}{\hbar}(p_2 - p_2') \cdot r_2\right\} u(r_2 - r_1) dV_1 dV_2$$

$$= \frac{1}{V} \int e^{i p \cdot r / \hbar} u(r) dV \tag{76.4}$$

$(p = p_2 - p_2' = -(p_1 - p_1'))$ is the change in momentum of a particle in the collision). Since in our case the momenta of the particles are supposed (according to (76.1)) to be small, we can insert for the matrix elements in all the essential terms of the sum their value for $p = 0$. We have then:

$$\hat{H} = \sum_p \frac{p^2}{2m} \hat{A}_p^+ \hat{A}_p + \frac{1}{2V} u_0 \sum \hat{A}_{p_1'}^+ \hat{A}_{p_2'}^+ \hat{A}_{p_2} \hat{A}_{p_1} \tag{76.5}$$

The starting point for the application of perturbation theory to the Hamiltonian (76.5) is the following consideration. In the ground state of a perfect Bose gas all the particles are in the zero energy state: $n_0 = N$, $n_p = 0$ ($p \neq 0$). Hence in the weakly excited (and in the ground) states of a nearly perfect gas the occupation numbers n_p are non-zero, but very small compared with n_0. The fact, that the quantity $\hat{A}_0^+ \hat{A}_0 = n_0 \simeq N$ is large compared with that unity, implies the expression

$$\hat{A}_0 \hat{A}_0^+ - \hat{A}_0^+ \hat{A}_0 = 1$$

is small compared with $\hat{A}_0^+$, $\hat{A}_0$ themselves. Hence we can consider the latter as ordinary numbers (equal to $\sqrt{n_0}$), neglecting their noncommutability.

The application of perturbation theory consists now in expanding the quadruple sum in (76.5) in powers of the small quantities $\hat{A}_p$, $\hat{A}_p^+$ ($p \neq 0$). The zero-order term of the expansion is

$$\hat{A}_0^+ \hat{A}_0^+ \hat{A}_0 \hat{A}_0 = \hat{A}_0^4 \tag{76.6}$$

The first-order terms are absent (since such terms cannot take account of the momentum conservation). The second-order terms are

$$A_0^2 \sum_{p \neq 0} (\hat{A}_p \hat{A}_{-p} + \hat{A}_p^+ \hat{A}_{-p}^+ + \hat{A} 4_p^+ \hat{A}_p) \tag{76.7}$$

To second order accuracy, we can replace $A_0^2 = n_0$ in (76.7) by the total number N of the particles. However, in the term (76.6) it is necessary to use the more exact relation

$$A_0^2 + \sum_{\mathbf{p} \neq 0} \hat{A}_{\mathbf{p}}^+ \hat{A}_{\mathbf{p}} = N$$

As a result the sum of the terms (76.6) and (76.7) turns out to be equal to

$$N^2 + N \sum_{\mathbf{p} \neq 0} (\hat{A}_{\mathbf{p}} \hat{A}_{-\mathbf{p}} + \hat{A}_{\mathbf{p}}^+ \hat{A}_{-\mathbf{p}}^+ + 2\hat{A}_{\mathbf{p}}^+ \hat{A}_{\mathbf{p}})$$

and inserting this into (76.5) we obtain the following expression for the Hamiltonian

$$H = \frac{N^2}{2V} u_0 + \frac{N}{2V} u_0 \sum_{\mathbf{p} \neq 0} (\hat{A}_{\mathbf{p}} \hat{A}_{-\mathbf{p}} + \hat{A}_{\mathbf{p}}^+ \hat{A}_{-\mathbf{p}}^+ + 2\hat{A}_{\mathbf{p}}^+ \hat{A}_{\mathbf{p}}) +$$

$$+ \sum_{\mathbf{p}}' \frac{p^2}{2m} \hat{A}_{\mathbf{p}}^+ \hat{A}_{\mathbf{p}}. \tag{76.8}$$

The integral u_0 is to be expressed in terms of a real physical quantity—the scattering amplitude. In the second-order terms in (76.8) (which are the only ones necessary for determination of the energy spectrum) we can directly use (76.2). This latter formula is, however, not sufficiently exact to be used in the first-order term (which is essential for the calculation of the ground state energy).

Formula (76.2) corresponds to the first approximation of perturbation theory. We can obtain a more exact relation by noting that if the probability of a certain quantum transition of the system under the influence of a constant perturbation $\hat{V}$ is determined in the first approximation by the matrix element V_0^0, then in the second approximation V_0^0 must be replaced by

$$V_0^0 + \sum_{n}' \frac{V_n^0 V_0^n}{E_0 - E_n},$$

the summation being performed over all the states of the unperturbed system†. In the present case we deal with a collision process in a system of two particles and the part of V_0^0 is played by

$$u_{00}^{00} = \frac{1}{V} \int u \, dV.$$

Making use also of the other matrix elements (76.4) we find that for passing

---

† See *Quantum Mechanics* §43.

from the first to the second approximation we must replace u_0 by

$$u_0 + \frac{1}{V}\sum_{\mathbf{p}\neq 0}\frac{|\int u^{i\mathbf{p}.\mathbf{r}/\hbar}dV|^2}{-p^2/m} \cong u_0 - \frac{u_0{}^2}{V}\sum_{\mathbf{p}\neq 0}\frac{m}{p^2}$$

or again substituting u_0 for all the integrals (as in (76.5)):†

$$u_0\left(1 - \frac{u_0}{V}\sum_{\mathbf{p}\neq 0}\frac{m}{p^2}\right).$$

Therefore we obtain, instead of (76.2):

$$a = \frac{m}{4\pi\hbar^2}u_0\left(1 - \frac{u_0}{V}\sum_{\mathbf{p}\neq 0}\frac{m}{p^2}\right), \qquad (76.9)$$

or, to the same approximation:

$$u_0 = \frac{4\pi\hbar^2 a}{m}\left(1 + \frac{y\pi\hbar^2 a}{V}\sum_{\mathbf{p}\neq 0}\frac{1}{p^2}\right).$$

By inserting this expression into (76.8) we find the final Hamiltonian:

$$\hat{H} = \frac{2\pi\hbar^2}{m}a\frac{N^2}{V}\left(1 + \frac{4\pi\hbar^2 a}{V}\sum_{\mathbf{p}\neq 0}\frac{1}{p^2}\right) +$$

$$+ \frac{2\pi\hbar^2}{m}a\frac{N}{V}\sum_{\mathbf{p}\neq 0}(\hat{A}_{\mathbf{p}}\hat{A}_{-\mathbf{p}} + \hat{A}_{\mathbf{p}}^{+}\hat{A}_{-\mathbf{p}}^{+} + 2\hat{A}_{\mathbf{p}}^{+}\hat{A}_{\mathbf{p}}) + \sum_{\mathbf{p}\neq 0}\frac{p^2}{2m}\hat{A}_{\mathbf{p}}^{+}\hat{A}_{\mathbf{p}}. \qquad (76.10)$$

For evaluation of the energy levels it is necessary to diagonalise the Hamiltonian. This is accomplished by introduction of the new operators $\hat{B}_{\mathbf{p}}$, $\hat{B}_{\mathbf{p}}^{+}$ according to the linear transformation

$$\hat{A}_{\mathbf{p}} = \frac{\hat{B}_{\mathbf{p}} + L_{\mathbf{p}}\hat{B}_{-\mathbf{p}}^{+}}{\sqrt{(1 - L^2)}}, \quad \hat{A}_{\mathbf{p}}^{+} = \frac{\hat{B}_{\mathbf{p}}^{+} + L_{\mathbf{p}}\hat{B}_{-\mathbf{p}}}{\sqrt{(1 - L_{\mathbf{p}}^2)}}, \qquad (76.11)$$

$L_{\mathbf{p}}$ being defined as

$$L_{\mathbf{p}} = \frac{mV}{4\pi a\hbar^2 N}\left\{\epsilon(\mathbf{p}) - \frac{p^2}{2m} - \frac{4\pi a\hbar^2}{m}\frac{N}{V}\right\} \qquad (76.12)$$

---

† As a result of this substitution we obtain a sum which is divergent (for large $\mathbf{p}$). This fact is of no consequence for our present aims, since after the subsequent insertion in the Hamiltonian we shall get an expression which is still convergent, large $\mathbf{p}$ making no contribution to it.

with the notation

$$\epsilon(\mathbf{p}) = \sqrt{\left\{\frac{4\pi a\hbar^2}{m}\frac{N}{V}\frac{p^2}{m} + \left(\frac{p^2}{2m}\right)^2\cdot\right\}} \tag{76.13}$$

This is readily verified by inserting (76.11) into (76.10), which in fact leads to

$$\hat{H} = E_0 + \sum_{\mathbf{p} \neq 0} \epsilon(\mathbf{p})\hat{B}_{\mathbf{p}}^+\hat{B}_{\mathbf{p}} \tag{76.14}$$

with

$$E_0 = \frac{N^2}{2V}\frac{4\pi\hbar^2 a}{m} + \frac{1}{2}\sum_{\mathbf{p} \neq 0}\left\{\epsilon(\mathbf{p}) - \frac{p^2}{2m} - \frac{N}{V}\frac{4\pi\hbar^2 a}{m} +\right.$$

$$\left. + \frac{N^2}{V^2}\left(\frac{4\pi\hbar^2 a}{m}\right)^2\frac{m}{p^2}\right\}. \tag{76.15}$$

It is also easy to see that from the commutation rules

$$\hat{A}_{\mathbf{p}}\hat{A}_{\mathbf{p}'} - \hat{A}_{\mathbf{p}'}\hat{A}_{\mathbf{p}} = 0, \quad \hat{A}_{\mathbf{p}}\hat{A}_{\mathbf{p}'}^+ - \hat{A}_{\mathbf{p}'}^+\hat{A}_{\mathbf{p}} = \delta_{\mathbf{p}\mathbf{p}'}$$

the same rules follow for the operators $\hat{B}_{\mathbf{p}}$, $\hat{B}_{\mathbf{p}}^+$. Hence we infer that $\hat{B}_{\mathbf{p}}^+$ and $\hat{B}_{\mathbf{p}}$ are the "creation" and "annihilation" operators of quasi-particles (elementary excitations) with energy $\epsilon(\mathbf{p})$, which obey Bose statistics. The quantity

$$\hat{B}_{\mathbf{p}}^+\hat{B}_{\mathbf{p}} = N_{\mathbf{p}}$$

represents the number of quasi-particles with momentum $\mathbf{p}$, and (76.13) gives the momentum dependence of their energy. Thus we have completely determined the energy spectrum of the weakly excited states of the gas; it belongs naturally to the Bose type spectra (§66).

As for E_0, it is the energy of the ground state of the gas. By changing the summation over discrete $\mathbf{p}$ values (in the volume V) to integration over $V d^3 p/(2\pi\hbar)^3$, and performing the calculation we arrive at the following expression:

$$E_0 = \frac{2\pi\hbar^2 a}{m}\frac{N^2}{V}\left[1 + \frac{128}{15\sqrt{\pi}}\sqrt{\frac{a^3 N}{V}}\right] \tag{76.16}$$

(T. D. LEE, C. N. YANG, 1957). It represents the two first terms of the expansion in powers of $\sqrt{a^3 N/V}$. However, the method described already cannot be used for the calculation of the next term. This term would contain the volume as V^{-2}, but a quantity of this order depends not only on the double, but also on the triple collisions, and hence cannot be expressed in terms of the amplitude a only.

For large values of the momentum, the energy (76.13) of the elementary excitations tends to $\epsilon \simeq p^2/2m$, i.e. to the kinetic energy of a separate particle of the gas.

For small values of the momentum we have:

$$\epsilon \simeq p\sqrt{\frac{4\pi a\hbar^2 N}{m^2 V}}.$$

It is easy to see that the coefficient of p is identical with the sound velocity u in the gas, so that this result is in agreement with the general assertions of §66. At absolute zero the free energy coincides with the energy E and by taking the principal term of the latter we find the pressure

$$P = -\frac{\partial E}{\partial V} = \frac{2\pi\hbar^2 a}{m}\frac{N^2}{V^2};$$

the sound velocity is $u = \sqrt{\partial P/\partial \rho}$, $\rho = mV/N$ being the density of the gas.

We note, that in the gas model considered the scattering amplitude a is necessarily positive (repulsion between the particles). This can be seen already from the formulae we have derived which would contain imaginary terms if $a < 0$. The meaning of the condition $a > 0$ is that it is necessary for the given model of the Bose gas to be thermodynamically stable (i.e. for the inequality $(\partial P/\partial V)_T < 0$ to be satisfied).

The statistical distribution of the elementary excitations, $\bar{N}_{\mathbf{p}}$, is given simply by the Bose function (with zero chemical potential)

$$\bar{N}_{\mathbf{p}} = \frac{1}{e^{\epsilon/kT} - 1}.$$

As for the distribution of the gas particles themselves, it can be readily calculated as

$$\bar{n}_{\mathbf{p}} = \hat{A}_{\mathbf{p}}^+ \hat{A}_{\mathbf{p}}.$$

Inserting (76.11)

$$\bar{n}_{\mathbf{p}} = \frac{\overline{(\hat{B}_{\mathbf{p}}^+ + L_{\mathbf{p}}\hat{B}_{-\mathbf{p}})(\hat{B}_{\mathbf{p}} + L_{\mathbf{p}}\hat{B}_{\pm\mathbf{p}}^+)}}{1 - L_{\mathbf{p}}^2}$$

and taking into account the absence of diagonal matrix elements in $\hat{B}_{-\mathbf{p}}\hat{B}_{\mathbf{p}}$ and $\hat{B}_{\mathbf{p}}^+\hat{B}_{-\mathbf{p}}^+$, we get:

$$\bar{n}_{\mathbf{p}} = \frac{\bar{N}_{\mathbf{p}} + L_{\mathbf{p}}^2(\bar{N}_{\mathbf{p}} + 1)}{1 - L_{\mathbf{p}}^2}. \tag{76.17}$$

Of course, this expression is valid only for $\mathbf{p} \neq 0$. The number of particles in the zero energy state is equal to

$$\bar{n}_0 = 1 - \sum_{\mathbf{p} \neq 0} \bar{n}_{\mathbf{p}} = 1 - \frac{V}{(2\pi\hbar)^3}\int \bar{n}_{\mathbf{p}}d^3p. \tag{76.18}$$

In particular, at absolute zero temperature $N_p = 0$ for $\mathbf{p} \neq 0$ and with the help of (76.12) we obtain from (76.17) the following distribution function:

$$\bar{n}_\mathbf{p} = \left(\frac{N}{V}\frac{4\pi\hbar^2 a}{m}\right)^2 \frac{1}{2\epsilon(\mathbf{p})\left\{\epsilon(\mathbf{p}) + \dfrac{p^2}{2m} + \dfrac{N}{V}\dfrac{4\pi\hbar^2 a}{m}\right\}}. \tag{76.19}$$

In a non-perfect Bose gas there exist, naturally, particles with non-zero energies even at absolute zero.

B. Fermi gas

We proceed to the discussion of the almost perfect degenerate Fermi gas and assume, for simplicity that the spin of the particles (which must be half-integer) is 1/2.

The state of a free particle with a non-zero spin is determined, apart from its momentum $\mathbf{p}$, by the value of its spin z-component σ. Correspondingly, we use double indices for the second quantisation operators and write, instead of (76.3):

$$\hat{H} = \sum_{\mathbf{p},\sigma} \frac{p^2}{2m}\hat{A}^+_{\mathbf{p}\sigma}\hat{A}_{\mathbf{p}\sigma} +$$

$$\tag{76.20}$$

$$+ \frac{1}{2}\sum u^{\mathbf{p}_1'\sigma_1',\mathbf{p}_2'\sigma_2'}_{\mathbf{p}_1\sigma_1,\mathbf{p}_2\sigma_2}\hat{A}^+_{\mathbf{p}_1'\sigma_1'}\hat{A}^+_{\mathbf{p}_2'\sigma_2'}\hat{A}_{\mathbf{p}_2\sigma_2}\hat{A}_{\mathbf{p}_1\sigma_1}.$$

As in (76.3), we replace all the matrix elements in the second term by their values

$$u^{0\sigma_1',0\sigma_2'}_{0\sigma_1,0\sigma_2}.$$

for zero values of the momenta. We note that in view of the anti-commutativity of the operators $\hat{A}_{\mathbf{p}_1\sigma_1}$, $\hat{A}_{\mathbf{p}_2\sigma_2}$ in Fermi statistics, their product is antisymmetric with respect to the permutation of their indices; the same holds for the product $\hat{A}^+_{\mathbf{p}_1'\sigma_1'}\hat{A}^+_{\mathbf{p}_2'\sigma_2'}$. As a result, all the terms of the second sum in (76.20) which contain identical indexes σ_1, σ_2 or σ_1', σ_2' vanish. Physically, this means that in the limiting case of slow collisions only particles with opposite spins interact with each other.

We introduce the notation†

$$\frac{u_0}{V} = u^{0+,0-}_{0+,0-} - u^{0+,0-}_{0-,0+} \tag{76.21}$$

(here and in the following the indexes $+$ and $-$ stand for $\sigma = +1/2$ and

---

† If the interaction energy of the particles does not depend on the spin variables, the second term in (76.21) is zero (the spin of each of the particles remains unchanged in the collision).

$\sigma = -1/2$ respectively), and obtain the Hamiltonian in the final form

$$\hat{H} = \sum_{\mathbf{p},\sigma} \frac{p^2}{2m} \hat{A}^+_{\mathbf{p}\sigma} \hat{A}^+_{\mathbf{p}\sigma} + \frac{u_0}{V} \sum \hat{A}^+_{\mathbf{p}_1'+} \hat{A}^+_{\mathbf{p}_2'-} \hat{A}_{\mathbf{p}_2-} \hat{A}_{\mathbf{p}_1+} \tag{76.22}$$

the summation in the second term being extended over all momenta obeying the conservation law

$$\mathbf{p}_1 + \mathbf{p}_2 = \mathbf{p}_1' + \mathbf{p}_2'.$$

We shall perform the calculation of the eigenvalues of this Hamiltonian by means of the usual quantum-mechanical perturbation theory, the second term in (76.22) (the interaction energy of the particles) being considered small in comparison with the first one (the kinetic energy). The latter is already diagonal and its eigenvalues are:

$$E^{(0)} = \sum_{\mathbf{p},\sigma} \frac{p^2}{2m} n_{\mathbf{p}\sigma}. \tag{76.23}$$

The first-order correction is given by the diagonal matrix elements of the interaction energy; they are:

$$E^{(1)} = \frac{u_0}{V} \sum_{\mathbf{p}_1,\mathbf{p}_2} n_{\mathbf{p}_1+} n_{\mathbf{p}_2-}. \tag{76.24}$$

To calculate the second-order correction we use the usual formula of perturbation theory

$$E_n^{(2)} = {\sum_m}' \frac{|V_{nm}|^2}{E_n - E_m}$$

the indices n, m labelling the unperturbed states of the whole system. A simple calculation gives†

$$\frac{2}{V^2} u_0^2 {\sum_{\mathbf{p}_1\mathbf{p}_2\mathbf{p}_1'}}' \frac{n_{p_1+} n_{p_2-}(1 - n_{p_1'+})(1 - n_{p_2'-})}{(p_1^2 + p_2^2 - p_1'^2 - p_2'^2)/2m}. \tag{76.25}$$

The structure of this expression is quite understandable: the squared matrix element of the transition $\mathbf{p}_1, \mathbf{p}_2 \rightarrow \mathbf{p}_1', \mathbf{p}_2'$ is proportional to the occupation numbers of the states $\mathbf{p}_1, \mathbf{p}_2$ and to the numbers of "vacancies" in the states $\mathbf{p}_1', \mathbf{p}_2'$.

However, the expression (76.25) does not in itself exhaust the second-order terms in the energy. A contribution of the same order of magnitude also

---

† The sum (76.25) is in itself divergent. This fact is due to the insertion of a constant value instead of all matrix elements in (76.22) and is of no importance for the subsequent calculations (compare the footnote on page 244).

arises from (76.24) after u_0 is expressed in terms of the scattering amplitude. In the same way as formula (76.9) was derived, we now get†

$$a = \frac{mu_0}{4\pi\hbar^2}\left[1 + \frac{2u_0}{V}\sum_{\mathbf{p_i}'}\frac{1}{(p_1^2+p_2^2-p_1'^2-p_2'^2)2m}\right].$$

Solving this for u_0 and inserting into (76.24), we obtain, apart from the first-order term

$$E^{(1)} = \frac{4\pi\hbar^2 a}{mV}\sum_{\mathbf{p_1p_2}}n_{\mathbf{p_1}+}n_{\mathbf{p_2}-}, \tag{76.26}$$

also terms of the second order; being added to (76.25) the latter give

$$E^{(2)} = \frac{2}{V^2}\left(\frac{4\pi\hbar^2 a}{m}\right)^2\sum_{\mathbf{p_1,p_2,p_i}'}\left\{\frac{n_{\mathbf{p_1}+}n_{\mathbf{p_2}-}[(1-n_{\mathbf{p_1}'+})(1-n_{\mathbf{p_2}'-})-1]}{(p_1^2+p_2^2-p_1'^2-p_2'^2)/2m}\right\}.$$

The term with a product of four ns in the numerator turns out to be zero: its numerator is symmetric and denominator antisymmetric with respect to the exchange of $\mathbf{p_1}$, $\mathbf{p_2}$ with $\mathbf{p_1}'$, $\mathbf{p_2}'$ and hence after performing a symmetrical summation over these variables we obtain zero. Thus:

$$E^{(2)} = -\frac{2}{V^2}\left(\frac{4\pi\hbar^2 a}{m}\right)^2\sum_{\mathbf{p_1p_2p_i}'}\frac{n_{\mathbf{p_1}+}n_{\mathbf{p_2}-}(n_{\mathbf{p_1}'+}+n_{\mathbf{p_2}'-})}{(p_1^2+p_2^2-p_1'^2-p_2'^2)/2m}. \tag{76.27}$$

With the aid of the formulae we have obtained we can, in the first place, calculate the ground state energy of the gas. To do this, we have to put $n_{\mathbf{p}\sigma} = 1$ inside the "Fermi sphere" and $n_{\mathbf{p}\sigma} = 0$ outside it‡. Noting that

$$\sum_{\mathbf{p}}n_{\mathbf{p}+} = \sum_{\mathbf{p}}n_{\mathbf{p}-} = \frac{N}{2}$$

we obtain from (76.26) the first-order correction

$$E_0^{(1)} = \frac{\pi a\hbar^2}{m}\frac{N^2}{V}.$$

---

† The quantity a is meant to be the energy independent scattering amplitude for slow collisions. On the other hand this formula apparently depends on $\mathbf{p_1}$, $\mathbf{p_2}$. However this dependence is actually confined to the imaginary part of the amplitude, which can be disregarded since we know beforehand that the final results of our calculations will be real.

‡ It is to be noted, that although in the initial Hamiltonian the quantities $\hat{A}_{\mathbf{p}\sigma}^+\hat{A}_{\mathbf{p}\sigma}$ are the occupation numbers of the real particle states after its diagonalisation with the aid of perturbation theory we deal already with the distribution function for the quasi-particles, its zero-order approximation values being those given in the text.

In (76.27) we replace the summation over the four momenta subject to the condition $\mathbf{p}_1 + \mathbf{p}_2 = \mathbf{p}_1' + \mathbf{p}_2'$ integration over

$$\frac{V^3}{(2\pi\hbar)^9}\delta(\mathbf{p}_1+\mathbf{p}_2-\mathbf{p}_1'-\mathbf{p}_2')d^3p_1\, d^3p_2\, d^3p_1'\, d^3p_2'.$$

Then

$$E_0^{(2)} = -\frac{8mV}{(2\pi\hbar)^9}\left(\frac{4\pi\hbar^2 a}{m}\right)^2\int\int\int\int\frac{\delta(\mathbf{p}_1+\mathbf{p}_2-\mathbf{p}_1'-\mathbf{p}_2')}{p_1^2+p_2^2-p_1'^2-p_2'^2}d^3p_1\, d^3p_2\, d^3p_1'\, d^3p_2'$$

the integration being performed over the region

$$p_1 \leqslant p_0, \qquad p_2 \leqslant p_0, \qquad p_1' \leqslant p_0$$

$p_0 = \hbar(3\pi^2 N/V)^{1/3}$ being the boundary momentum of the Fermi sphere. After some calculation one arrives at the following final expression for the ground state energy†

$$E_0 = \frac{3}{10}(3\pi^2)^{2/3}\frac{\hbar^2}{m}\left(\frac{N}{V}\right)^{2/3}N +$$
$$+ \frac{\pi a\hbar^2}{m}\frac{N}{V}N\left[1 + \frac{6}{35}\left(\frac{3}{\pi}\right)^{1/3}a\left(\frac{N}{V}\right)^{1/3}(11-2\log 2)\right] \tag{76.28}$$

(K. HUANG, C. N. YANG, 1957).

According to the general statements of §68, the spectrum of the elementary excitations (i.e. the function $\epsilon(\mathbf{p})$) and the function $f(\mathbf{p}, \hat{\mathbf{s}}; \mathbf{p}', \hat{\mathbf{s}}')$, which plays an essential role in the theory of the Fermi-type spectra, are determined by the first and second variations of the total energy with respect to the distribution function. If E is written in the form of a discrete sum, then, by definition:

$$\delta E = \sum_{\mathbf{p}\sigma} \epsilon(\mathbf{p}, \sigma)\delta n_{\mathbf{p}\sigma} + \frac{1}{2V}\sum_{\mathbf{p}\sigma,\mathbf{p}'\sigma'} f(\mathbf{p}, \sigma; \mathbf{p}', \sigma')\delta n_{\mathbf{p}\sigma}\delta n_{\mathbf{p}'\sigma'}$$

($n_{\mathbf{p}\sigma}$ being put equal 1 inside and 0 outside the Fermi sphere after the differentiations are performed).

However, there is no need to calculate the energy of the elementary excitations in this way, since at any rate the function $\epsilon(\mathbf{p})$ has meaning only in the vicinity of $p = p_0$ (cf. §68), where it is determined by a single parameter m^* which can be calculated in a simpler way (see below).

To calculate $f(\mathbf{p}, \sigma; \mathbf{p}', \sigma')$ we need to differentiate twice the sum of expressions (76.26) and (76.27), and then put the absolute values of $\mathbf{p}$ and $\mathbf{p}'$ equal to p_0 (see §68). Performing these simple calculations and then

---

† Actually, it is simpler to perform the calculations in another sequence, by beginning with the explicit calculation of the f-function (see below).

changing to integration instead of summation, we get

$$f(\mathbf{p},\tfrac{1}{2};\mathbf{p}',-\tfrac{1}{2}) = \frac{4\pi\hbar^2 a}{m} - \left(\frac{4\pi\hbar^2 a}{m}\right)^2 \frac{8m}{(2\pi\hbar)^3} \times$$

$$\times \int\int \left\{ \frac{\delta(\mathbf{p}+\mathbf{p}'-\mathbf{p}_1-\mathbf{p}_2)}{2p_0^2-p_1^2-p_2^2} + \frac{1}{2}\frac{\delta(\mathbf{p}+\mathbf{p}_1-\mathbf{p}'-\mathbf{p}_2)+\delta(\mathbf{p}'+\mathbf{p}_1-\mathbf{p}-\mathbf{p}_2)}{p_1^2-p_2^2} \right\} d^3p_1\, d^3p_2$$

$$f(\mathbf{p},\tfrac{1}{2};\mathbf{p}',\tfrac{1}{2}) = f(\mathbf{p},-\tfrac{1}{2};\mathbf{p}',-\tfrac{1}{2}) =$$

$$= \left(\frac{4\pi\hbar^2 a}{m}\right)^2 \frac{4m}{(2\pi\hbar)^3} \int\int \frac{\delta(\mathbf{p}+\mathbf{p}_1-\mathbf{p}'-\mathbf{p}_2)+\delta(\mathbf{p}'+\mathbf{p}_1-\mathbf{p}-\mathbf{p}_2)}{p_1^2-p_2^2} d^3p_1\, d^3p_2.$$

The integration in these expressions is performed comparatively easily due to the small number of integration variables.

The final result must be expressed in vectorial form, independant of the choice of the z-axis, on which the spins are projected. In doing so, we note that in the gas model considered the spin dependent term in $f(\mathbf{p}, \hat{\mathbf{s}}; \mathbf{p}', \hat{\mathbf{s}}')$ can be only of an exchange nature, i.e. proportional to $\hat{\mathbf{s}} \cdot \hat{\mathbf{s}}'$[†]. The final result is

$$f = \frac{2\pi a\hbar^2}{m}\left[1+2\left(\frac{3}{\pi}\right)^{1/3}a\left(\frac{N}{V}\right)^{1/3}\left(2+\frac{\cos\theta}{2\sin(\theta/2)}\log\frac{1+\sin(\theta/2)}{1-\sin(\theta/2)}\right)\right] -$$

$$(76.29)$$

$$- \frac{8\pi a\hbar^2}{m}\hat{\mathbf{s}}_1\cdot\hat{\mathbf{s}}_2\left[1+2\left(\frac{3}{\pi}\right)^{1/3}a\left(\frac{N}{V}\right)^{1/3}\left(1-\frac{1}{2}\sin\frac{\theta}{2}\log\frac{1+\sin(\theta/2)}{1-\sin(\theta/2)}\right)\right]$$

θ being the angle between $\mathbf{p}$ and $\mathbf{p}'$ (A. ABRIKOSOV and I. KHALATNIKOV, 1957)[‡].

The function f being known, the effective mass of the quasi-particles is calculated from formula (68.10) and equals:

$$\frac{m^*}{m} = 1 + \frac{8}{15}\left(\frac{3}{\pi}\right)^{2/3}(7\log 2 - 1)a^2\left(\frac{N}{V}\right)^{2/3}.$$

$$(76.30)$$

On the other hand by using (68.13) we can calculate the sound velocity in

---

[†] If the values $f(1/2;1/2), f(1/2; -1/2)$ of such a function of two spins are known (for a fixed direction of the z-axis), then it can be written as $a+b\hat{\mathbf{s}}_1\cdot\hat{\mathbf{s}}_2$ with

$$a + \frac{b}{4} = f(\tfrac{1}{2};\tfrac{1}{2}), \qquad a - \frac{b}{4} = f(\tfrac{1}{2};-\tfrac{1}{2}).$$

[‡] The function (76.29) diverges logarithmically for $\theta = \pi$. This result is due to the approximations made in the calculations; a more exact analysis shows, that although $\theta = \pi$ is really a singular point of the function, the latter tends to zero and not to infinity in this point (for $a>0$). Non-applicability of the expression (76.29) in the vicinity of the point $\theta = \pi$ is of no consequence for the subsequent applications, since the latter contain only integrals which converge at this point.

the gas; it turns out to be

$$u^2 = \pi \left(\frac{\pi}{3}\right)^{1/3} \left(\frac{N}{V}\right)^{2/3} \frac{\hbar^2}{m^2} + $$
$$+ \frac{2\pi a \hbar^2}{m^2} \frac{N}{V}\left[1 + \frac{4}{15}\left(\frac{3}{\pi}\right)^{1/3} a \left(\frac{N}{V}\right)^{1/3}(11 - 2\log 2)\right]. \tag{76.31}$$

By integrating $u^2 m/N$ over dN we find, by (68.13) the chemical potential μ (at absolute zero), and integrating once more we arrive at the expression (76.28) for the energy $E_0 = \int \mu \, dN$ of the ground state.

Formula (76.28) represents the first terms of the expansion of the gas energy in powers of $a(N/V)^{1/3}$. It would be possible, in principle, to obtain also several of the next terms by means of analogous, although much more cumbersome, calculations. The reason is that in a Fermi gas the triple collisions contribute only to the terms of comparatively higher order. At least two of the three colliding particles have the same spin projection, and the co-ordinate part of the wave function must be antisymmetric with respect to these two particles. This means that the orbital angular momentum of their relative motion is at least 1 (p-state). The corresponding wave function contains an extra (as compared with the s-state wave function) power of the wave vector f†; hence the probability of such a triple collision is decreased by a factor $(fa)^2 \sim a^2(N/V)^{2/3}$ compared with the probability of a "head-on" collision of particles not obeying the Pauli principle. As a result the triple collisions contribute to the energy only in the terms containing the volume as $1/V^2 V^{2/3}$. In other words, all the terms of the energy expansion up to terms of the order of

$$\frac{a\hbar^2}{m} \frac{N^2}{V}\left[a\left(\frac{N}{V}\right)^{1/3}\right]^4$$

inclusive, can be expressed in terms of the characteristics of the double collisions only. However, these characteristics will include not only the s-scattering amplitude for slow collisions (as in (76.28)), but also its derivatives with respect to energy, and the amplitude of the p-scattering.

Finally it is necessary to make the following remark concerning the model of the non-perfect Fermi-gas we have considered. At the first sight one has the impression that the formulae obtained allow both signs of the scattering amplitude, i.e. both repulsion and attraction between the particles. However, the above results apply only to the case of repulsion (positive a). It turns out that attraction between the particles leads to instability of that state, which is the ground state in the case of repulsion. This instability is displayed in a tendency to form bound "pairs" of particles. As a result, a Bose type spectrum arises in such a gas, which becomes super fluid.‡

† See *Quantum Mechanics*, §33.
‡ We refer here to the original papers: L. N. Cooper, *Phys. Rev.*, **104**, 1189 (1956), J. Bardeen, L. N. Cooper, J. R. Schrieffer, *Phys. Rev.* **106**, 162 (1957); see also N. N. Bogoliubov, *Zh. éksp. teor. fiz.* **34**, No. 1, 1958.

CHAPTER VIII

PHASE EQUILIBRIUM

§77. The conditions for phase equilibrium

The (equilibrium) state of a uniform body is determined by specifying any two thermodynamic quantities, for instance the volume, V, and energy, E. However, there is no reason to assume that, for every pair of values of V and E, the thermal equilibrium will correspond to a uniform state of the body. It may happen that, for given volume and energy, the body is not uniform when in thermal equilibrium, but falls into two uniform parts in contact with each other, which are in different states.

Such states of a substance which can exist simultaneously in equilibrium with each other while in contact are called different *phases* of the substance.

Let us write down the condition for the equilibrium of two phases. First of all, as for any bodies in equilibrium, the temperatures T_1 and T_2 of the two phases must be equal:

$$T_1 = T_2.$$

In addition, we must have the pressures of the two phases equal:

$$P_1 = P_2,$$

since the two phases must exert equal and opposite forces on each other over their surface of contact.

Lastly we have the condition that the chemical potentials of the two phases must be equal:

$$\mu_1 = \mu_2$$

which is derived for the two phases just as it was derived in §25 for any two regions of a body in contact with each other. If the potentials are expressed as functions of pressure and temperature then, denoting the equal temperatures and pressures of the two phases by T and P, we obtain the equation

$$\mu_1(P, T) = \mu_2(P, T), \tag{77.1}$$

whence the pressure and temperature of phases in equilibrium can be expressed as functions of each other. Thus two phases cannot be in equilibrium at arbitrary temperature and pressure; on the contrary, when one of these quantities is given the other is completely determined.

If one plots the pressure and temperature along the co-ordinate axes then the points at which phase equilibrium is possible will lie on some curve (the phase equilibrium curve). The points on either side of this curve will represent uniform states of the body. As the state changes along a line cutting the equilibrium curve, a separation of the phases takes place (at the point of intersection of the curves) after which the body passes to the other phase. Note that, if the state of the body changes slowly it can sometimes remain uniform even when two phases should separate for total equilibrium. Such states, however, are metastable and, for example, bringing a body in such a state into contact with another phase is sufficient to bring about the immediate appearance of the separation and change of phase. Examples are supercooled vapours and superheated liquids.

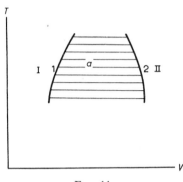

Fig. 11

If one represents the phase equilibrium by means of a diagram with temperature and volume (of a definite quantity of the substance) plotted along the co-ordinate axes, then states in which both phases are simultaneously present cover an area of the plane and not just one curve; this difference from the P, T diagram is related to the fact that the volume V, unlike the pressure, is not the same for the two phases. As a result we obtain a diagram of the type shown in Fig. 11. Points in regions I and II, outside the shaded area, represent uniform states of the first and second phases. The shaded area represents states in which the two phases exist in equilibrium with each other: at some point a phases I and II are in equilibrium, with their specific volumes determined by the abscissae of the points 1 and 2 situated on the horizontal straight line passing through the point a. It is easy to conclude, directly from the conservation of the quantity of the substance, that the quantities of the phases I and II are inversely proportional to the lengths of the lines $a1$ and $a2$. (This is known as *"the leverage rule"*.)

Like the conditions for the equilibrium of two phases, the equilibrium of three phases of the same substance is determined by the relations

$$P_1 = P_2 = P_3, \quad T_1 = T_2 = T_3, \quad \mu_1 = \mu_2 = \mu_3. \tag{77.2}$$

If again one denotes the common values of the pressure and temperature by P and T we obtain

$$\mu_1(P, T) = \mu_2(P, T) = \mu_3(P, T). \tag{77.2a}$$

These are two equations in two unknowns, P and T. Their solutions are definite pairs of values of P and T. States in which three phases exist at the same time (known as *triple points*) will be represented in the P, T diagram by isolated points, being the points of intersection of the equilibrium curves of each two of the three phases (Fig. 12, areas I, II, III are the areas of the three uniform phases). Equilibrium of more than three phases of the same substance is clearly impossible.

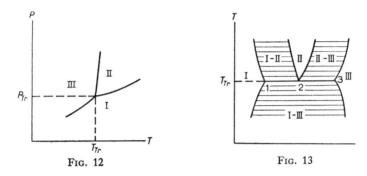

FIG. 12 FIG. 13

In the T, V diagram the neighbourhood of a triple point takes the form shown in Fig. 13 where the shaded areas are the areas of equilibrium of the phases taken in pairs. The specific volumes of the three phases in equilibrium at the triple point are determined by the abscissae of points 1, 2, 3.

The transition from one phase to another is accompanied by the emission or absorption of a certain amount of heat (known as the *latent heat of transition* or simply latent heat). According to the equilibrium conditions such a transition takes place at constant pressure and temperature. But the quantity of heat absorbed by the body is equal to the change in its heat function. Hence the latent heat per molecule is

$$q = w_2 - w_1, \tag{77.3}$$

where w_1 and w_2 are the heat functions per molecule of the two phases.

Since μ (for bodies consisting of one substance) is the thermodynamic potential for one molecule we may write $\mu = \epsilon - Ts + Pv$ (ϵ, s, v being the molecular energy, entropy, and volume). Hence the condition $\mu_1 = \mu_2$ gives:

$$(\epsilon_2 - \epsilon_1) - T(s_2 - s_1) + P(v_2 - v_1) = (w_2 - w_1) - T(s_2 - s_1) = 0,$$

where P and T are the pressure and temperature of the two phases, whence

$$q = T(s_2 - s_1). \tag{77.4}$$

Thus the latent heat is equal to the difference in entropy of the two phases multiplied by the temperature at which the transition takes place. The heat q is positive if heat is absorbed in a transition from the first phase to the second (and given out in the reverse transition). On the other hand q is negative when heat is given out in such a transition. Note that (77.4) follows immediately from $q = \int T \, ds$, the temperature T being constant. (This formula is applicable in this case since the transition is a reversible one, both phases remaining in equilibrium with each other during these transitions.)

Let the two curves in Fig. 14 represent the chemical potentials of the two phases as a function of temperature (at given pressure). The point of intersection of the two curves determines the temperature T_0 at which (for the given pressure) the two phases can be in equilibrium with each other. At

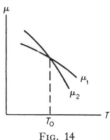

FIG. 14

all other temperatures either one phase or the other can exist. It is easy to see that at temperatures below T_0 the first phase exists (i.e. is stable) and at temperatures above T_0 the second. This follows from the fact that the stable state is the one with smaller μ (since the thermodynamic potential tends to a minimum for given P and T). On the other hand, at the point of intersection of the two curves the derivative $\partial\mu_1/\partial T$, is greater than $\partial\mu_2/\partial T$, i.e. the entropy of the first phase $s_1 = -\partial\mu_1/\partial T$ is smaller than the entropy of the second $s_2 = -\partial\mu_2/\partial T$. Hence the latent heat $q = T(s_2 - s_1)$ is positive. Thus we conclude that, if the body passes from one phase to the other as the temperature increases then heat is absorbed. This result could also have been obtained from Le Chatelier's principle.

PROBLEMS

1. Determine the relation between temperature and the saturated vapour pressure of a solid (considering the saturated vapour as a perfect gas; both gas and solid having constant specific heat).

SOLUTION: The chemical potential of the vapour is given by (43.4) and that of the solid by (62.6). (Since the pressure of the saturated vapour is comparatively small one can neglect PV for the solid and take Φ as equal to F). Equating the two expressions we obtain:

$$ P = \text{const } T^{(c_{p2}-c_1)/k} \, e^{(\epsilon_{01}-\epsilon_{02})/kT}, $$

where the suffix 1 refers to the solid and 2 to the vapour.

To the same approximation one can take the heat function of the solid to be equal to its energy; the latent heat (heat of sublimation) $q = w_2 - w_1$, is equal to,

$$ q = (c_{p2}-c_1)T + (\epsilon_{02}-\epsilon_{01}). $$

In particular, the latent heat at $T = 0$ is $q_0 = \epsilon_{02} - \epsilon_{01}$, so that one can write

$$ P = \text{const } T^{(c_{p2}-c_1)/k} \, e^{-q_0/kT}. $$

2. Find the rate of evaporation of a condensed body into a vacuum.

SOLUTION: The rate of evaporation into a vacuum is defined as the number of particles leaving unit surface area of the body in unit time. Consider a body in equilibrium with its saturated vapour. Then the number of particles leaving the surface is equal to the number of particles which fall on the surface in the same time and "adhere" to it, i.e. it is equal to

$$\frac{P_0}{\sqrt{(2\pi mkT)}}(1-R)$$

where $P_0 = P_0(T)$ is the saturated vapour pressure, and R is a mean "reflection coefficient" for the gas particles colliding with the body (see 39.2). If P_0 is not too large, then the number of particles leaving the surface of the body is independent of whether or not it is surrounded by vapour and thus the expression written above gives the required rate of evaporation into a vacuum.

§78. The Clausius-Clapeyron equation

Let us differentiate both sides of the equilibrium condition

$$\mu_1(P, T) = \mu_2(P, T)$$

with respect to the temperature, remembering, of course, that the pressure P is not an independent variable but a function of the temperature determined by this same equation. Hence we write:

$$\frac{\partial \mu_1}{\partial T} + \frac{\partial \mu_1}{\partial P}\frac{dP}{dT} = \frac{\partial \mu_2}{\partial T} + \frac{\partial \mu_2}{\partial P}\frac{dP}{dT}.$$

Making use of the identity $d\mu = -s\,dT + v\,dP$ (24.12) we hence obtain:

$$-s_1 + v_1\frac{dP}{dT} = -s_2 + v_2\frac{dP}{dT},$$

or

$$\frac{dP}{dT} = \frac{s_1 - s_2}{v_1 - v_2}, \tag{78.1}$$

where s_1, v_1, s_2, v_2 are the molecular entropies and volumes of the two phases.

In this formula the difference $s_1 - s_2$ is conveniently expressed in terms of the latent heat of the transition from one phase to the other. Substituting $q = T(s_2 - s_1)$ we obtain what is known as the *Clausius-Clapeyron equation*

$$\frac{dP}{dT} = \frac{q}{T(v_2 - v_1)}. \tag{78.2}$$

It determines the change in the pressure of two phases in equilibrium with a change in temperature, or in other words the change of pressure with temperature along the phase equilibrium curve. The same formula, written in the form

$$\frac{dT}{dP} = \frac{T(v_2 - v_1)}{q},$$

determines the variation of the temperature of the transition from one phase to another (the freezing and boiling points, for example) with pressure. Since the molecular volume of a gas is always larger than that of the liquid, and since heat is absorbed in a transition from liquid to vapour, the boiling point always rises as the pressure increases (dT/dP is positive). The freezing point rises or falls with increasing pressure according as the volume increases or decreases during melting.

All these consequences of (78.2) are in complete agreement with Le Chatelier's principle. Consider, for example, a liquid in equilibrium with its saturated vapour. If one increases the pressure, then the boiling point also rises and, as a result, part of the vapour will liquefy, thus in turn reducing the pressure, i.e. the system acts so as to oppose the effect disturbing its equilibrium.

Consider the special case of formula (78.2) when we are concerned with the equilibrium of a solid or a liquid with its vapour. Formula (78.2) determines, in this case, the variation of the saturated vapour pressure with temperature.

The volume of the gas is normally much larger than the volume of a condensed body containing the same number of particles. Hence in (78.2) we may neglect the volume v_1 in comparison with v_2 (we take the gas as the second phase), i.e. we take $dP/dT = q/Tv_2$. Considering the vapour as a perfect gas, we can express its volume in terms of its temperature and pressure in accordance with the Clapeyron formula $v_2 = kT/P$; we then obtain:

$$\frac{dP}{dT} = \frac{qP}{kT^2},$$

or

$$\frac{d \log P}{dT} = \frac{q}{kT^2}. \tag{78.3}$$

Note that in a temperature interval over which the latent heat may be considered constant, the saturated vapour pressure varies exponentially with temperature ($\sim e^{-q/kT}$).

PROBLEMS

1. Find the specific heat of a vapour along the equilibrium curve of a liquid and its saturated vapour (i.e. the specific heat for a process in which the liquid remains all the time in equilibrium with its saturated vapour). The vapour is assumed to be a perfect gas.

SOLUTION: The required specific heat h is equal to

$$h = T \, ds/dT$$

where ds/dT is the derivative taken along the equilibrium curve, i.e.

$$h = T\frac{ds}{dT} = T\left(\frac{\partial s}{\partial T}\right)_P + T\left(\frac{\partial s}{\partial P}\right)_T \frac{dP}{dT} = c_p - T\left(\frac{\partial v}{\partial T}\right)_P \frac{dP}{dT}.$$

Substituting for dP/dT from (78.3), and putting $v = kT/P$ we find:

$$h = c_p - \frac{q}{T}.$$

For low temperatures h is negative, i.e. if one extracts heat in such a way that the vapour always remains in equilibrium with the liquid, the temperature will rise.

2. Find the rate of change with temperature of the volume of a vapour for a process in which the vapour remains all the time in equilibrium with the liquid (i.e. along the equilibrium curve between the liquid and its vapour).

SOLUTION: We need to find the derivative dv/dT along the equilibrium curve:

$$\frac{dv}{dT} = \left(\frac{\partial v}{\partial T}\right)_P + \left(\frac{\partial v}{\partial P}\right)_T \frac{dP}{dT}.$$

Substituting (78.3) and putting $v = kT/P$, we find:

$$\frac{dv}{dT} = \frac{1}{P}\left(k - \frac{q}{T}\right).$$

At low temperatures $dv/dT < 0$, i.e. for the process under consideration the volume of the vapour decreases with increasing temperature.

§79. The critical point

The phase equilibrium curve (in the P, T plane) may terminate at some point (Fig. 15). Such a point is called *critical* and the corresponding temperature and pressure are called the *critical temperature* and *critical pressure*. At temperatures above T_c and pressures greater than P_c different phases do not exist, and the body is always homogeneous. One can say that at the critical point the difference between the two phases disappears.

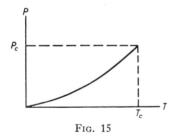

FIG. 15

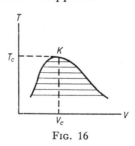

FIG. 16

In the equilibrium diagram with co-ordinates T, V the critical point appears as is shown in Fig. 16. As the temperature approaches the critical value the specific volumes of the two phases in equilibrium approach each other and coincide at the critical point (K in Fig. 16). The P, V diagram has a similar form.

When the critical point exists, a continuous transition between any two states of matter is possible, in which the separation into phases does not occur at any point—to do this the change of state must take place along some curve passing through the critical point and nowhere cutting the equilibrium curve. In this sense the very concept of different phases becomes a convention, when the critical point exists and it is not always possible to distinguish one from the other. Strictly speaking, one can speak of two phases only in the case when they exist at the same time touching each other, i.e. for points situated on the equilibrium curve.

It is clear that a critical point can exist only for phases between which the difference is of a purely quantitative nature. Such, for example, are liquid and gas which are distinguished from each other merely by a greater or smaller interaction between their molecules.

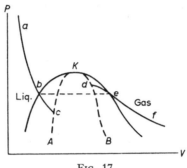

FIG. 17

Phases such as liquid and solid (crystalline) or different crystalline modifications of a substance are qualitatively different from one another since they differ in their internal symmetry (Chapter XIII deals with this in more detail). It is clear that about each symmetry property (element) we can only say that it exists or that it does not exist; it can appear or disappear only suddenly with a jump and not gradually. In each state the body will have either one symmetry or the other and hence one can always indicate to which of the two phases it belongs. Hence a critical point cannot exist for such phases and the equilibrium curve must either go off to infinity or end intersecting the equilibrium curves of other phases.

A normal phase transition point does not represent any special point in the mathematical sense as far as the thermodynamic quantities of the substance are concerned. In fact, every phase can also exist (at any rate as a metastable state) on the other side of the transition point; the thermodynamic inequalities at this point are not violated. At the transition point the chemical potentials of the two phases are equal: $\mu_1(P, T) = \mu_2(P, T)$ and this point is in no way different for either of the two functions.

Consider in the P, V plane some *isotherm* of the liquid and gas; i.e. the curve showing the relation between P and V in an isothermal expansion of the uniform body (*abc* and *def* in Fig. 17).

According to the thermodynamic inequality $(\partial P/\partial V)_T < 0$, P is a decreasing function of V. This slope of the isotherms must still continue some distance beyond their points of intersection with the equilibrium curve of the liquid and gas (points b and e); the sections bc and ed of the isotherms correspond to the metastable superheated liquid and supercooled vapour in which the thermodynamic inequalities are satisfied as before.†

If one takes into account the fact that the points b and e, corresponding to liquid and gas in equilibrium, have the same ordinate, then it is clear that the two isotherms cannot join each other continuously but there must be a break between them. The isotherms come to an end at the points (c and d) at which the thermodynamic inequality is violated, i.e. $(\partial P/\partial V)_T$ vanishes. Constructing the locus of the end points of the isotherms of the liquid and gas we obtain the curve (AKB in Fig. 17) on which the thermodynamic inequalities (for a homogeneous body) are violated; it bounds the region in which the body can never exist as a homogeneous one in any state. The areas between this curve and the phase equilibrium curve are areas in which the existence of superheated fluid or supercooled vapour is possible. Obviously the two curves must touch each other at the critical point as shown in Fig. 17.

As regards the points of the curve AKB itself, only one corresponds to an actually existing state of a homogeneous body—namely the critical point K, the only point at which this curve touches the region of homogeneous stable states. From what we have said above we must have for the critical state:

$$\left(\frac{\partial P}{\partial V}\right)_T = 0. \tag{79.1}$$

In the next section it will be shown that the equilibrium of a state with $(\partial P/\partial V)_T$ equal to zero requires the second derivative to vanish simultaneously:

$$\left(\frac{\partial^2 P}{\partial V^2}\right)_T = 0 \tag{79.2}$$

and that the third derivative should be negative:

$$\left(\frac{\partial^3 P}{\partial V^3}\right)_T < 0. \tag{79.3}$$

Eqs. (79.1–2) are two equations in two unknowns which can only be satisfied at an isolated point—the critical point of the substance.

From eq. (79.1) and formula (16.10) for the difference $C_p - C_v$ it follows that, at the critical point

$$C_p = \infty, \tag{79.4}$$

the specific heat at constant pressure becomes infinite. The specific heat C_v and the adiabatic compressibility remain finite; for the latter, at the critical

---

† To a completely equilibrium, isothermal change of state between points b and e there corresponds, of course, the horizontal line be along which the body is separated into two phases.

point, we have from (16.16) and (79.1):

$$\left(\frac{\partial P}{\partial V}\right)_S = -\frac{T}{C_v}\left(\frac{\partial P}{\partial T}\right)_V^2.$$

It is useful to note that condition (79.1) for the critical point can also be derived by the following simple argument. Near the critical point the specific volumes of liquid and vapour are close to each other. Denoting them by V and $V+\delta V$, we write the condition that the pressures of the two phases should be equal in the form

$$P(V, T) = P(V+\delta V, T). \tag{79.5}$$

Expanding the right-hand side of this equation in powers of δV and dividing by the small but finite quantity δV, we find:

$$\left(\frac{\partial P}{\partial V}\right)_T + \frac{\delta V}{2}\left(\frac{\partial^2 P}{\partial V^2}\right)_T + \dots = 0. \tag{79.6}$$

Hence we see that as δV tends to zero, i.e. at the critical point, $(\partial P/\partial V)_T$ must certainly vanish.

In connection with the discussion of metastable states of a liquid, we note the following interesting fact. The section of the isotherm corresponding to a superheated liquid (*bc* in Fig. 17) may be situated in part under the horizontal axis. In other words the superheated liquid may have negative pressure; such a liquid acts on the surface enclosing it with a force directed into the volume of the liquid. Thus the pressure is not necessarily a positive quantity and states of a body can actually exist, though only metastable ones, in which the pressure is negative. (We mentioned this above in §12).

Finally the following note must be added, about the statements made in this section concerning the critical point. The derivation of conditions (79.1–3) (which are, in particular, the basis of the further theory developed in §81) is based on the assumption that along the curve *AKB*, which includes the critical point itself, the thermodynamic quantities of the substance (as functions of the variables T and V) have no mathematical singularity, so that this curve is only determined by the vanishing of $(\partial P/\partial V)_T$†. But there are reasons to suspect that in actual fact the line bounding the region where the existence of a homogeneous body is impossible is a line of singular points of the thermodynamic quantities. As yet we have no idea of the nature of this singularity and it is not known whether it affects the essential results of the theory discussed here.‡

---

† As functions of the variables P and T the thermodynamic quantities have in this case a singularity connected with the vanishing of the Jacobian of the transformation of the variables $\partial(P, T)/\partial(V, T)$.

‡ The fact that at the critical point the derivatives $(\partial P/\partial V)_T$ and $(\partial^2 P/\partial V^2)_T$ vanish seems to have been established beyond doubt on the basis of experimental data about the behaviour of substances near this point, but as regards the finiteness of the third derivative $(\partial^3 P/\partial V^3)_T$, the truth of the statement is far less certain.

§80. The thermodynamic inequalities at the critical point

In deriving the thermodynamic inequalities in §21 we started from condition (21.1)

$$\delta E - T\delta S + P\delta V > 0 \tag{80.1}$$

which must be satisfied for any small deviation from equilibrium of any small part of the body. From this we obtained the inequality

$$\frac{\partial^2 E}{\partial S^2}\delta S^2 + 2\frac{\partial^2 E}{\partial S\partial V}\delta S\delta V + \frac{\partial^2 E}{\partial V^2}\delta V^2 > 0, \tag{80.2}$$

which is satisfied under the conditions

$$\frac{\partial^2 E}{\partial S^2} > 0, \tag{80.3}$$

$$\frac{\partial^2 E}{\partial S^2}\frac{\partial^2 E}{\partial V^2} - \left(\frac{\partial^2 E}{\partial S\partial V}\right)^2 > 0. \tag{80.4}$$

The first of these inequalities gives $C_v > 0$, and the second: $(\partial P/\partial V)_T < 0$.

To the case in which we are now interested, $(\partial P/\partial V)_T = 0$ corresponds a special case of the condition for an extremum, when (80.4) contains an equality sign

$$\frac{\partial^2 E}{\partial S^2}\frac{\partial^2 E}{\partial V^2} - \left(\frac{\partial^2 E}{\partial S\partial V}\right)^2 = 0. \tag{80.5}$$

The quadratic form (80.2) may now be zero as well as positive, depending on the values of δS and δV. Hence further consideration is necessary to decide whether the quantity $E - T_0 S + P_0 V$ is a minimum.

We must obviously examine just the case when (80.2) contains an equality sign.

$$\frac{\partial^2 E}{\partial S^2}\delta S^2 + 2\frac{\partial^2 E}{\partial S\partial V}\delta V\delta S + \frac{\partial^2 E}{\partial V^2}\delta V^2 = 0. \tag{80.6}$$

Taking (80.5) into account this equation may be written in the following way:

$$\frac{1}{\partial^2 E/\partial S^2}\left(\frac{\partial^2 E}{\partial S^2}\delta S + \frac{\partial^2 E}{\partial S\partial V}\delta V\right)^2 = \frac{1}{\partial^2 E/\partial S^2}\left[\delta\left(\frac{\partial E}{\partial S}\right)\right]^2 = 0.$$

Since $(\partial E/\partial S)_V = T$ it follows that $\delta T = 0$.

Thus eq. (80.6) means that we must consider the deviations from equilibrium at constant temperature.

At constant temperature our initial inequality takes the form

$$\delta F + P\delta V > 0. \tag{80.7}$$

Expanding the free energy as a series in powers of δV (at constant T) we obtain:

$$\delta F = \frac{\partial F}{\partial V}\delta V + \frac{1}{2}\frac{\partial^2 F}{\partial V^2}\delta V^2 + \frac{1}{3!}\frac{\partial^3 F}{\partial V^3}\delta V^3 + \frac{1}{4!}\frac{\partial^4 F}{\partial V^4}\delta V^4 + \dots$$

$$= -P\delta V - \frac{1}{2}\left(\frac{\partial P}{\partial V}\right)_T \delta V^2 - \frac{1}{3!}\left(\frac{\partial^2 P}{\partial V^2}\right)_T \delta V^3 - \frac{1}{4!}\left(\frac{\partial^3 P}{\partial V^3}\right)_T \delta V^4 \dots$$

Substituting this into 80.7 and making use of the fact that we have assumed $(\partial P/\partial V)_T = 0$, we find that:

$$\frac{1}{3!}\left(\frac{\partial^2 P}{\partial V^2}\right)_T \delta V^3 + \frac{1}{4!}\left(\frac{\partial^3 P}{\partial V^3}\right) \delta V^4 + \dots < 0.$$

For this inequality to hold for all δV, the third-order term must vanish and the fourth-order term must be negative

$$\left(\frac{\partial^2 P}{\partial V^2}\right)_T = 0 \qquad \left(\frac{\partial^3 P}{\partial V^3}\right)_T < 0. \tag{80.8}$$

Note that the case when (80.3) contains an equality sign, i.e.

$$\frac{\partial^2 E}{\partial S^2} = 0$$

(or, which comes to the same thing, $C_v = \infty$) is impossible since it would violate (80.4). The simultaneous vanishing of expressions (80.3) and (80.4) is also impossible. In fact the equilibrium conditions for $(\partial P/\partial V)_T = 0$ require, as we have just found, that the quantity $(\partial^2 P/\partial V^2)_T$ should vanish also; if we were to add another condition we would get three equations in two unknowns which, in general, have no common solution. Thus the specific heat C_v cannot become infinite.

§81. Properties of a substance near the critical point

Starting from the conditions

$$\left(\frac{\partial P}{\partial V}\right)_T = 0, \qquad \left(\frac{\partial^2 P}{\partial V^2}\right)_T = 0, \qquad \left(\frac{\partial^3 P}{\partial V^3}\right)_T < 0,$$

which are assumed to hold at the critical point, one can study the properties of a substance in states near the critical state. We must emphasise again that the reliability of the results of such an investigation remains uncertain until the nature of the singularities which thermodynamic quantities probably have at the critical point has been clarified.

We introduce the notation†

$$T-T_c = t, \qquad V-V_c = v. \qquad (81.1)$$

We shall consider the properties of substances for small t and v. We expand $(\partial P/\partial V)_T$ as a series in powers of t and v, restricting ourselves to the first terms of the expansion

$$-(\partial P/\partial V)_T = At+Bv^2. \qquad (81.2)$$

The term proportional to v does not appear, since the coefficient of v is the second derivative of the pressure with respect to the volume, which is equal to zero at the critical point; as regards the product term tv it is certainly smaller than the term At. The same applies to the term proportional to t^2. On the other hand we must retain Bv^2, for although both t and v are assumed to be small we can say nothing about their relative magnitude, so that the term Bv^2 is not necessarily smaller than At.

Since $(\partial^3 P/\partial V^3)_T$ must be negative at the critical point, the coefficient B must be positive:

$$B > 0 \qquad (81.3)$$

In addition, for all points representing stable states of the body near the critical point we must have

$$-(\partial P/\partial V)_T > 0.$$

Since all points with temperatures greater than T_c (i.e. $t > 0$) must correspond to stable states (for these the separation into phases never occurs) one can see from this that the coefficient A must be positive:

$$A > 0. \qquad (81.4)$$

Integrating (81.2) we obtain for the pressure near the critical point the expression

$$P = -Atv-(Bv^3/3)+f(t) \qquad (81.5)$$

where $f(t)$ is a function of t only, which is unimportant for the case we are considering.

Formula (81.5) determines the shape of the isotherms of a homogeneous substance near the critical point. For $t > 0$ (temperatures above the critical) the isotherm $P(v)$ is a monotonically decreasing function (curve 1 in Fig. 18). The isotherm corresponding to the critical temperature ($t = 0$) has a point of inflection at the critical point ($v = 0$) (curve 2). Finally, for temperatures below the critical ($t < 0$) the isotherms (curves 3 and 4) have a maximum and a minimum between which lies a region with $(\partial P/\partial v)_t > 0$ (represented

---

† v in this section must not be confused with the molecular volume which we use in other sections.

in Fig. 18 by the broken line) which does not correspond to any actually existing homogeneous states of the substance.†

As was already explained in §79, an equilibrium transition from liquid to gas corresponds to some horizontal line (*AD* on curve 4). *AB* is the isotherm of the superheated liquid, *DC* that of the supercooled vapour.

Let us find the abscissae of points *A* and *D*, i.e. the volumes v_1 and v_2

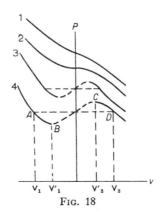

Fig. 18

of liquid and gas in equilibrium‡. We write down the condition for phase equilibrium $\mu_1 = \mu_2$ in the form

$$\int_1^2 d\mu = 0$$

where $\int_1$ means the integral along the transition curve from a state with one phase to a state with the other phase. If we integrate along the isotherm *ABCD*, then since for $T = \text{const}$ we have $d\mu = V\,dP = (V_c + v)\,dP$,

$$\int_1^2 d\mu = \int_1^2 v\,dP + V_c(P_2 - P_1) = 0,$$

but the pressures of the two phases in equilibrium are equal, $P_1 = P_2$, so that we finally obtain

$$\int_1^2 v\,dP = 0. \qquad (81.6)$$

---

† In actual fact one would expect that in a theory which properly takes into account the singularities of the thermodynamic quantities at the boundary of the metastable states the curve *BC* would not exist at all.

‡ "Volume" means, of course, in all cases, the volume of a definite quantity of the substance.

Expressing this integral in the form

$$\int_{v_1}^{v_2} v(\partial P/\partial v)_t \, dv = 0$$

and substituting (81.2) for $(\partial P/\partial v)_t$ we find that the integrand is an odd function of v. Hence it is clear that we must have

$$v_1 = -v_2. \tag{81.7}$$

Now making use of the condition that the pressures are equal and formula (81.5) we find:

$$Atv_1 + (Bv_1{}^3/3) = -Atv_1 - (Bv_1{}^3/3)$$

i.e.

$$At + (Bv_1{}^2/3) = 0,$$

and the same holds for v_2. Hence

$$v_1 = -v_2 = -\sqrt{(-3At/B)}. \tag{81.8}$$

Thus v_1 and v_2 are of equal absolute value and are proportional to the square root of $T_c - T$. In other words the phase equilibrium curve in the T, v diagram has a simple maximum at its critical point.

The volumes $v_1{}'$ and $v_2{}'$, corresponding to the boundary of the metastable areas (points B and C in isotherm 4 in Fig. 18), are easily determined. For these points we have

$$-(\partial P/\partial v)_t = At + Bv^2 = 0,$$

whence

$$v_1{}' = -v_2{}' = -\sqrt{(-At/B)}. \tag{81.9}$$

These volumes are also proportional to the square root of $T_c - T$ and are $\sqrt{3}$ times smaller than volumes v_1 and v_2 at the same temperature.

The latent heat (of evaporation) vanishes at the critical point. The law governing its disappearance is easily determined in the following manner. Since the temperature of the two phases in equilibrium is the same, and the difference in their volumes is small near the critical point, then for the latent heat we may write

$$q = T(S_2 - S_1) \simeq T_c(\partial S/\partial v)_t(v_2 - v_1).$$

Since the difference $v_2 - v_1$ is proportional to $\sqrt{(T_c - T)}$, the latent heat is proportional to the same root.

Finally we shall obtain the law of increase of the specific heat C_p near the critical point.

Substituting (81.5) into the formula

$$C_p - C_v = -T\frac{(\partial P/\partial t)_v{}^2}{(\partial P/\partial v)_t},$$

we find that

$$C_p \propto \frac{1}{At+Bv^2}.$$

For points situated on the equilibrium curve v is proportional to $\sqrt{t}$ and hence $C_p \sim 1/t$.

§82. The law of corresponding states

The interpolatory equation of Van der Waals

$$\left(P+\frac{N^2a}{V^2}\right)(V-Nb) = NkT$$

agrees qualitatively with the properties of the transition from liquid to vapour which have been described in previous sections. The isotherms given by this

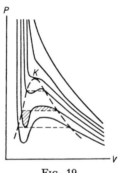

Fig. 19

equation are shown in Fig. 19. It is easy to see that they are similar to those in Fig. 18. To equilibrium transitions from liquid to gas there correspond also in this case horizontal lines whose position is determined by the equilibrium condition

$$\int_1^2 V\,dP = 0, \tag{82.1}$$

where the integral in this case is taken along the Van der Waals isotherm connecting the beginning and end points of the horizontal line. Geometrically this means that the shaded areas shown in Fig. 19 for one of the isotherms must be equal.

We can express the critical temperature, pressure, and volume in terms of the parameters a and b of the Van der Waals equation. To do this we write it in the form

$$P = \frac{NkT}{V-Nb} - \frac{N^2a}{V^2}.$$

and equate to zero the derivatives

$$\left(\frac{\partial P}{\partial V}\right)_T = -\frac{NkT}{(V-Nb)^2}+\frac{2N^2a}{V^3} = 0,$$

$$\left(\frac{\partial^2 P}{\partial V^2}\right)_T = \frac{2NkT}{(V-Nb)^3}-\frac{6N^2a}{V^4} = 0.$$

From these three equations we obtain

$$T_c = \frac{8}{27}\frac{a}{bk}, \qquad V_c = 3Nb, \qquad P_c = \frac{1}{27}\frac{a}{b^2}, \tag{82.2}$$

We now introduce, instead of T, P, V, the quantities

$$T' = \frac{T}{T_c}, \qquad P' = \frac{P}{P_c}, \qquad V = \frac{V}{V_c}. \tag{82.3}$$

These are called the reduced temperature, pressure, and volume. At the critical point they are all equal to unity.

If we substitute T', P', V', in the Van der Waals equation in place of T, P, V, we then obtain:

$$\left(P'+\frac{3}{V'^2}\right)(3V'-1) = 8T'. \tag{82.4}$$

This is known as the *reduced Van der Waals equation*. This equation involves only V', P' and T' and no other characteristics of the given substance. Hence eq. (82.4) is the equation of state for all substances to which Van der Waals' equation applies. States of two substances having equal T', P', V' are called *corresponding states* (the critical states of all substances are obviously corresponding states). It follows from 82.4 that if two bodies have two of the three quantities T', P', V' equal, then they must have the third equal as well, i.e. they are in corresponding states (*the law of corresponding states*).

The "reduced" isotherms $P' = P'(V')$ determined by eq. (82.4) are the same for all substances. Hence also the position of the straight lines defining the transition points from liquid to gas will be the same. Thus we can conclude that at equal reduced temperatures all substances must have (1) equal reduced saturated vapour pressures, (2) equal reduced specific volume for the saturated vapour, (3) equal reduced specific volume of the liquid in equilibrium with the saturated vapour.

The law of corresponding states can also be applied to the latent heat of the transition from a liquid to a gaseous state. The part of the "reduced latent heat of evaporation" must here be played by a dimensionless quantity, i.e. q/kT_c. Thus we can write†.

$$q/kT_c = f(T/T_c). \tag{82.5}$$

In conclusion we remark that the law of corresponding states is somewhat more general than Van der Waals' equation since it does not involve any specific form of the equation of state. However, even its applicability is in general very restricted.

---

† At temperatures appreciably below the critical the ratio q/kT_c is approximately equal to ten (q being the molecular latent heat of evaporation).

CHAPTER IX

SOLUTIONS

§83. Systems of different particles

So far, we have limited our discussion to bodies consisting of identical particles. We now turn to the examination of systems made up of different particles. They include every kind of mixture of several substances; if the mixture contains very much more of one substance than of the others, then it is called a *solution* of these other substances in the predominant one (the solvent).

The number of substances whose quantities can be chosen arbitrarily in a state of total equilibrium is usually called the number of independent components of the system. All thermodynamic quantities, in complete equilibrium, are completely determined if one gives, for example, the values of the temperature, pressure, and the number of particles of the independent components. The number of independent components need not be the same as the total number of substances in the system if a chemical reaction can take place between them; if such a system is in incomplete equilibrium, then, to determine its thermodynamic quantities, we need to know, in general, the quantities of all the substances of which it is made up.

The results of §24 are easily generalised for bodies made up of different particles. First of all, the thermodynamic quantities must be homogeneous linear functions of all the additive variables (the numbers of the different particles and the volume).

Further, in the thermodynamic identities (24.5), (24.7–9) we must now write the sum $\sum_i \mu_i \, dN_i$ in place of $\mu \, dN$, where N_i is the number of particles of type i and the quantities μ_i are called the chemical potentials of the corresponding substances. Similarly (24.6) and (24.10) must now be written with the suffix i labelling the chemical potential and number of particles. To find the chemical potential of any of the substances in the mixture, one must differentiate one of the quantities E, F, Φ, W with respect to the corresponding number of particles. In particular,

$$\mu_i = \left(\frac{\partial \Phi}{\partial N_i} \right)_{P\,T}. \tag{83.1}$$

The chemical potentials are expressed here as functions of the pressure, temperature, and *concentrations*, i.e. the ratios of the numbers of particles of the different substances. The latter can enter into μ_i only as ratios since, because Φ is a homogeneous function of first order in the N_i, the chemical potentials must be homogeneous functions of zero order in these variables.

From the fact that Φ is a homogeneous linear function of the N_i it follows from Euler's theorem that

$$\Phi = \sum_i N_i \frac{\partial \Phi}{\partial N_i} = \sum_i \mu_i N_i \tag{83.2}$$

which is a generalisation of the formula $\Phi = N\mu$.

For the potential Ω we now have

$$\Omega = F - \Sigma \mu_i N_i$$

whence we again obtain the formula $\Omega = -PV$. This ceases to apply only for a body in an external field, when the pressure varies from one part of the body to another.

The results of §25 can also be directly generalised; the equilibrium conditions require the chemical potential of every component to be constant throughout the system, as well as the temperature:

$$\mu_i = \text{const.} \tag{83.3}$$

Finally, the Gibbs distribution for systems composed of different particles takes the form

$$w_{nN_1 N_2 \ldots} = \exp\left\{ \frac{\Omega + \Sigma \mu_i N_i - E_{nN_1 N_2 \ldots}}{kT} \right\}, \tag{83.4}$$

which is the natural generalisation of (35.2).

§84. The phase rule

Now consider a system of many different substances which form a certain number (r) of adjacent phases (each phase, in general, containing all of the substances).

Let n be the number of independent components of the system. Then each phase is specified by its pressure, temperature and n chemical potentials. We know from §77 that the equilibrium conditions for phases consisting of identical particles are equality of temperature, pressure and chemical potential. It is obvious that in the general case of several components the equilibrium conditions between the phases will be that the temperature, pressure and each of the chemical potentials should be equal. Let the common temperature and pressure in all the phases be T and P; to distinguish the chemical potentials related to different phases and components we shall give them two suffices of which the upper (roman numerals) will denote the phase and the lower (arabic numerals) will denote the component. Then the phase equilibrium conditions may be written in the form:

$$\begin{aligned}
\mu_1{}^I &= \mu_1{}^{II} = \;.... \;= \mu_1{}^r, \\
\mu_2{}^I &= \mu_2{}^{II} = \;.... \;= \mu_2{}^r, \\
&\cdot\;\cdot\;\cdot\;\cdot\;\cdot\;\cdot\;\cdot\;\cdot\;\cdot\;\cdot\;\cdot\;\cdot\;\cdot \\
\mu_n{}^I &= \mu_n{}^{II} = \;.... \;= \mu_n{}^r.
\end{aligned} \right\} \qquad (84.1)$$

Each of these potentials is a function of $n+1$ independent variables: of P, T and the $n-1$ concentrations of the different components in the particular phase (in each phase there are n independent numbers of different particles between which there are $n-1$ independent ratios).

The conditions (84.1) represent a system of $n(r-1)$ equations. The number of unknowns in these equations is $2+r(n-1)$. For solutions of these equations to exist there must certainly not be more of them than the number of unknowns, i.e. $n(r-1) \leqslant 2+r(n-1)$, whence

$$r \leqslant n+2. \qquad (84.2)$$

In other words, in a system consisting of n independent components, not more than $n+2$ phases can exist in equilibrium. This is known as *Gibbs' phase rule*. We had a special case of this rule in §77: in the case of a single component, no more than three phases can exist simultaneously in contact with one another.

If r, the number of phases existing simultaneously, is less than $n+2$ then, obviously, in eqs. (84.1) $n+2-r$ variables may have arbitrary values. In other words one can arbitrarily change any $n+2-r$ variables without disturbing the equilibrium; in this case, of course, the remaining variables change in a completely determined manner. The number of variables which can be arbitrarily changed without disturbing the equilibrium is called the number of *thermodynamic degrees of freedom* of the system. If this number is denoted by the letter f then the phase rule may be written

$$f = n+2-r \qquad (84.3)$$

where f, of course, cannot be less than zero. If the number of phases is equal to its maximum possible value, $n+2$, then $f = 0$, i.e. in eqs. (84.1) all the variables are completely determined and none can be changed without disturbing the equilibrium or causing one of the phases to disappear.

§85. Weak solutions

We shall spend the next few sections (§§85–90) discussing the thermodynamic properties of weak solutions, i.e. solutions in which the numbers of molecules of the solutes are very much smaller than the number of molecules of the solvent. Consider, first of all, the case of a solution with a single solute. One can easily generalise to the case of a solution with many solutes.

Let N be the number of molecules of the solvent in the solution and n

the number of molecules of the solute. We call the ratio $n/N = c$ the concentration of the solution; according to the assumption made above $c \ll 1$.

Let us find an expression for the thermodynamic potential of the solution. Let $\Phi_0(P, T, N)$ be the thermodynamic potential of the pure solvent (with nothing dissolved in it). According to the formula $\Phi = N\mu$ (which is valid for pure substances) it can be written in the form $\Phi_0 = N\mu_0(P, T)$ where $\mu_0(P, T)$ is the chemical potential of the pure solvent. Now assume that a single molecule of the solute is introduced into the solvent. Then its thermodynamic potential will change. Since, however, this change will be quite insignificant, one can assume that it will take the form $\Phi_0 + \alpha(P, T, N)$ where α is some small function. If another molecule is now introduced then, since the interaction between the molecules is negligible, the thermodynamic potential of the solution will become $\Phi_0 + 2\alpha$. Continuing this process until all the n molecules are dissolved we shall find that the thermodynamic potential of the solution will be $\Phi_0 + n\alpha$. The mutual interaction of the molecules of the solute can still be neglected owing to the initial assumption that the solution is very weak.

However, in the expression $\Phi_0 + n\alpha$ obtained in this way, we have not properly taken account of the fact that all the n molecules of the solute are identical. In other words, this is the expression which would be obtained from (31.5) if, in the calculation of the partition function all the particles of the solute were considered to be different. As we know (cf. (31.7)) the partition function calculated in this way must actually be divided by $n!$†. This leads to the appearance in the free energy, and hence in the potential Φ, of an extra term $kT \log n!$. Thus,

$$\Phi = N\mu_0(P, T) + n\alpha(P, T, N) + kT \log n!.$$

Furthermore, since n itself is a very large number (although very small compared with N) one can write, in the last term, $\log n! = n \log (n/e)$. Then

$$\Phi = N\mu_0 + n\left(\alpha + kT \log\frac{n}{e}\right) = N\mu_0 + nkT \log\left(\frac{n}{e}e^{\alpha/kT}\right).$$

Now we make use of the fact that Φ must be a linear homogeneous function of n and N. For this to be true it is clearly necessary for the function under the logarithm to be of zero order in n and N. Hence $e^{\alpha/kT}$ must be inversely proportional to N, i.e. it must be of the form $f(P, T)/N$. Thus

$$\Phi = N\mu_0 + nkT \log\left[\frac{n}{eN}f(P, T)\right].$$

Introducing a new function of P and T: $\psi(P, T) = kT \log f(P, T)$ we finally

---

† We are neglecting quantum effects here. This is always permissible for a weak solution, just as in the case of a sufficiently thin gas.

obtain the expression for the thermodynamic potential of the solution:

$$\Phi = N\mu_0(P, T) + nkT \log \frac{n}{eN} + n\psi(P, T). \tag{85.1}$$

The assumption made at the beginning of this section about the addition of the term $n\alpha$ to the potential of the pure solvent amounts, in fact, just to an expansion in powers of n retaining only the first-order terms. The term in Φ of the next order in n is of the form $n^2 f_1(P, T, N)$ but, since Φ must be a homogeneous function of N and n, $f_1(P, T, N)$ must be inversely proportional to N, i.e. $f_1(P, T, N) = \beta(P, T)/2N$ where β is a function of P and T only. Thus, to second order, the thermodynamic potential of a weak solution has the form

$$\Phi = N\mu_0(P, T) + nkT \log \frac{n}{eN} + n\psi(P, T) + \frac{n^2}{2N}\beta(P, T). \tag{85.2}$$

For the case of a weak solution of several substances, the thermodynamic potential obviously has, instead of (85.1), the form:

$$\Phi = N\mu_0 + \sum_i n_i kT \log \frac{n_i}{eN} + \sum_i n_i \psi_i, \tag{85.3}$$

where n_i are the numbers of molecules of the solutes and $\psi_i(P, T)$ are different functions. Similarly (85.2) is generalised to become

$$\Phi = N\mu_0 + \sum_i n_i kT \log \frac{n_i}{eN} + \sum_i n_i \psi_i + \sum_{i,k} \frac{n_i n_k}{2N}\beta_{ik}. \tag{85.4}$$

From (85.1) the chemical potentials for the solvent (μ) and the solute (μ') in the solution are easily found. The first is

$$\mu = \frac{\partial \Phi}{\partial N} = \mu_0 - kT\frac{n}{N} = \mu_0 - kTc, \tag{85.5}$$

and the second is

$$\mu' = \frac{\partial \Phi}{\partial n} = kT \log \frac{n}{N} + \psi = kT \log c + \psi. \tag{85.6}$$

§86. Osmotic pressure

In this section and the ones following we shall study some of the properties of solutions. We assume, as before, that the solutions are weak and hence we shall use the formulae of the previous section.

Assume that two solutions of the same substance in the same solvent, but having different concentrations c_1 and c_2, are separated from each other by a partition through which molecules of the solvent can pass, but not those of the solute (a semi-permeable membrane). The pressure on the two sides of the partition will be different (the arguments of §12 for constant pressure do not apply here, owing to the presence of the semi-permeable membrane). The difference between these pressures is called the *osmotic pressure.*

The equilibrium conditions between the two solutions will require (in addition to equal temperatures) that the chemical potential of the solvent must be the same in both of them. The chemical potentials of the solute do not need to be equal since, owing to the semi-permeability of the membrane, the equilibrium takes place only with respect to the solvent.

Denoting the pressures of the two solutions by P_1 and P_2, and using (85.5), we obtain the equilibrium condition in the form:

$$\mu_0(P_1, T) - c_1 kT = \mu_0(P_2, T) - c_2 kT. \tag{86.1}$$

The pressure difference $P_2 - P_1 = \Delta P$ (i.e. the osmotic pressure) for weak solutions is comparatively small. Hence we may expand $\mu(P_2, T)$ in powers of ΔP and retain only the first two terms:

$$\mu_0(P_2, T) = \mu_0(P, T) + \Delta P \frac{\partial \mu_0}{\partial P}.$$

Substituting this into (86.1), we obtain:

$$\Delta P \frac{\partial \mu_0}{\partial P} = (c_2 - c_1) kT.$$

But $\partial \mu_0 / \partial P$ is simply the molecular volume of the pure solvent. Thus we get,

$$\Delta P = (c_2 - c) \frac{kT}{v}. \tag{86.2}$$

In particular, when there is pure solvent on one side of the membrane ($c_1 = 0$, $c_2 = c$), then the osmotic pressure becomes

$$\Delta P = \frac{ckT}{v} = \frac{nkT}{V} \tag{86.3}$$

where n is the number of molecules of the solute in a volume V of the solvent. (Owing to the weakness of the solution, V is almost exactly equal to the total volume of the solution.) Formula (86.3) is called *van t'Hoffs formula.* It should be noticed that it applies to weak solutions of any solute in any solvent and also that it is similar to the Clapeyron formula. Instead of the gas pressure we have osmotic pressure; instead of the volume of the gas we have the volume of the solution; and instead of the number of particles of the gas we have the number of molecules of the solute.

In conclusion, note that the generalisation of (86.2) and (86.3) to the case of several solutes presents no difficulty. Obviously the osmotic pressure in this case is equal to the sum of the osmotic pressures of each of the solutes, i.e. the pressure which would exist if only the one solute were present.

§87. **Phases of the solvent in contact**

Consider the equilibrium of two phases of the solvent in contact, each containing a certain quantity of the same solute. The equilibrium conditions (in addition to equality of pressure and temperature) will be the equality of the chemical potentials of the solvent and the solute in the two phases. We shall use the first here and write it in the form

$$\mu_0^I(P, T) - c_I kT = \mu_0^{II}(P, T) - c_{II} kT, \tag{87.1}$$

where c_I and c_{II} are the two concentrations, and μ_0^I and μ_0^{II} are the chemical potentials of the two phases of the pure solvent.

Note that the system we are considering, consisting of two components and existing in two phases, has two thermodynamic degrees of freedom. Hence only two of the four quantities P, T, c_I and c_{II} can be chosen at random; if, for example, we choose P or T and one of the concentrations, the other concentration will be completely determined.†

If neither phase of the solvent contained any solute, then the equilibrium condition would be

$$\mu_0^I(P_0, T_0) = \mu_0^{II}(P_0, T_0) \tag{87.2}$$

(the temperature and pressure of the two phases being denoted by T_0, P_0).

Thus, when the relation between temperature and pressure for phase equilibrium of the pure solvent is given by (87.2), the corresponding relation, after some of the solute has been dissolved in each phase, will be given by (87.1). For weak solutions these two curves lie very close together.

We now expand $\mu_0^I(P, T)$ and $\mu_0^{II}(P, T)$ in equation (87.1) in powers of $P - P_0 = \Delta P$ and $T - T_0 = \Delta T$ where P_0 and T_0 are the pressure and temperature of a point on the phase equilibrium curve of the pure solvent near the given point P, T on the phase equilibrium curve of the solution. Retaining only first order terms in ΔP and ΔT, and bearing (87.2) in mind, we obtain, from (87.1):

$$\frac{\partial \mu_0^I}{\partial T} \Delta T + \frac{\partial \mu_0^I}{\partial P} \Delta P - c_I kT = \frac{\partial \mu_0^{II}}{\partial T} \Delta T + \frac{\partial \mu_0^{II}}{\partial P} \Delta P - c_{II} kT.$$

But $\partial \mu_0^I / \partial T$ and $\partial \mu_0^I / \partial P$ are simply the entropy s_I and volume v_I of the first phase of the pure solvent (per molecule). Similarly $\partial \mu_0^{II} / \partial T$ and $\partial \mu_0^{II} / \partial P$ are the entropy s_{II} and volume v_{II} of the second phase of the pure solvent.

---

† One could, in principle, determine the relation between the concentrations c_I and c_{II} with the aid of the equilibrium condition governing the chemical potential of the solute in the two phases.

Substituting all these into our equation, we obtain:

$$-(s_I - s_{II})\Delta T + (v_I - v_{II})\Delta P = (c_I - c_{II})kT. \tag{87.3}$$

According to formula (77.4), we have: $(s_{II} - s_I)T = q$, where q is the latent heat of the transition from the first phase to the second. Hence (87.3) can also be rewritten in the form

$$\frac{q}{T}\Delta T + (v_I - v_{II})\Delta P = (c_I - c_{II})kT. \tag{87.4}$$

Consider now two special cases of this formula. First choose the point P_0, T_0 so that $P_0 = P$. Then ΔT will be the distance along the T axis between these two curves for the same ordinate. In other words, ΔT will be the change of the transition temperature between the two phases during the time of solution, i.e. the difference between the temperature T of this transition (at pressure P) when both phases are solutions, and the temperature T_0 of the transition (at the same pressure) for the pure solvent. Since $\Delta P = 0$ here, we obtain, from (87.4)

$$\Delta T = \frac{kT^2(c_I - c_{II})}{q}. \tag{87.5}$$

In the case where one of the phases is pure solvent, for instance $c_{II} = 0$, $c_I = c$, then

$$\Delta T = \frac{kT^2 c}{q}. \tag{87.6}$$

This formula determines, in particular, the change in the freezing point of the solution as compared with that of the pure solvent when the solute is not soluble in the solid phase; the two phases are, in this case, the liquid solution and the solid solvent. During the freezing, heat is released, i.e. q is negative. Hence also $\Delta T < 0$, i.e. if the pure solvent does freeze out, then the process of solution lowers the freezing point.

The relation (87.6) also determines the shift of the boiling point if the solute is not volatile; the two phases are in this case the liquid solution and the vapour of the solvent. ΔT is now the difference between the temperature at which the solvent boils out of the solution and the boiling point of the pure solvent. Since heat is absorbed in boiling, $q > 0$ and hence $\Delta T > 0$, i.e. the boiling point of the solution is higher than that of the solvent.

All these consequences of formula (87.6) are in entire agreement with Le Chatelier's principle. For instance, suppose that a liquid solution is in equilibrium with the solid solvent. If the concentration of the solution is raised, then, according to Le Chatelier's principle, the freezing point must be lowered enough for some solid solvent to go into solution and lower the concentration.

Similarly, if the concentration of a liquid solution in equilibrium with the vapour of the solvent is raised, the boiling point must rise sufficiently to allow part of the vapour to condense into the solution and lower the concentration.

Consider next another special case of formula (87.4), choosing the point P_0, T_0 so that $T = T_0$. ΔP will then be the separation of the two curves for the same abscissa, i.e. the difference between the equilibrium pressures of the two phases of the solution and the two phases of the pure solvent (at the same temperature). Now $\Delta T = 0$ and from (87.4) we get:

$$\Delta P = \frac{kT(c_{\mathrm{I}} - c_{\mathrm{II}})}{v_{\mathrm{I}} - v_{\mathrm{II}}}. \tag{87.7}$$

Note that the ratio

$$\frac{\Delta P}{\Delta T} = \frac{q}{T(v_{\mathrm{I}} - v_{\mathrm{II}})}$$

agrees with the Clapeyron-Clausius formula (applied to the pure solvent), as one would expect, owing to the comparative smallness of ΔP and ΔT.

Now apply formula (87.7) to the equilibrium between the liquid and gaseous phases. In this case the volume of one of the phases (the liquid) can be neglected in comparison with the volume of the other, and (87.7) becomes

$$\Delta P = \frac{kT(c_{\mathrm{I}} - c_{\mathrm{II}})}{v}. \tag{87.8}$$

where v is the molecular volume of the gaseous (1st) phase. Bearing in mind that $P_v = kT$ and replacing P, to the same accuracy, by P_0 (P_0 being the pressure of the saturated vapour over the pure solvent), this may be written in the form

$$\Delta P = P_0(c_{\mathrm{I}} - c_{\mathrm{II}}). \tag{87.9}$$

If the gaseous phase is the vapour of the pure solvent ($c_{\mathrm{I}} = 0$, $c_{\mathrm{II}} = c$), then (87.9) becomes

$$\frac{\Delta P}{P_0} = -c, \tag{87.10}$$

where c is the concentration of the solution. This formula determines the difference between the saturated vapour pressure of the solvent over the solution (P), and over the pure solvent (P_0). The relative drop in the saturated vapour pressure during the process of solution is equal to the concentration of the solution (Raoul's Law)†.

---

† Remember that c is the molecular concentration (the ratio of the numbers of molecules n/N).

§88. Equilibrium with respect to the solute

Next consider a system made up of two solutions of the same solute in two different solvents (for example in two non-miscible liquids) in contact with each other. We denote their concentrations by c_1 and c_2.

The equilibrium condition for this system is that the chemical potentials of the solute in both solutions should be equal. With the aid of (85.6) this condition may be written

$$kT \log c_1 + \psi_1(p, T) = kT \log c_2 + \psi_2(p, T).$$

The functions ψ_1 and ψ_2 are, of course, different for the two solvents. Hence we find

$$\frac{c_1}{c_2} = e^{(\psi_2 - \psi_1)kT}. \tag{88.1}$$

The right hand side of this equation is a function of P and T only. Thus the solute is distributed between the two solvents so that the ratio of the concentrations is (for given pressure and temperature) always a constant independent of the total quantities of the solute and the solvents (the *distribution law*). The same law also applies, obviously, to the solution of one solute in two adjacent phases of the same solvent.

Next consider the equilibrium between a gas (assumed perfect) and its solution in some condensed solvent. The equilibrium condition, i.e. the equality of the chemical potentials of the pure gas and the dissolved gas, may be expressed (using (42.6) and (85.6)) in the form:

$$kT \log c + \psi(P, T) = kT \log P + \chi(T).$$

From this we obtain

$$c = Pe^{(\chi - \psi)/kT}. \tag{88.2}$$

The function $\psi(P, T)$ specifies the properties of the liquid (or solid) solution. However, for small pressures, the properties of the liquid are almost independent of pressure. Hence we may ignore the dependence of $\psi(P, T)$ on pressure and assume that the coefficient of P in (88.2) is a constant, independent of pressure.

$$c = P. \text{ const.} \tag{88.3}$$

Thus when a gas dissolves, the concentration of the (weak) solution is proportional to the pressure of the gas (Henry's law)†.

---

† We are assuming that the gas molecules pass into solution unchanged. If, when they are dissolved, the molecules dissociate (for example when hydrogen H_2 is dissolved in certain metals) then the dependence of concentration on pressure is quite different. (See Problem 2 in §100.)

PROBLEM

1. Find the change of concentration with height for a solution in the field of gravity.

SOLUTION: We apply the equilibrium conditions (83.3) in the external field, writing it for the solute: $kT \log c + \psi(P, T) + mgz = \text{const}$, since the potential energy of the molecules of the solute is mgz (z being the height, m the mass of the molecule). We differentiate this equation with respect to height, remembering that the temperature is constant (this being one of the equilibrium conditions):

$$\frac{kT}{c}\frac{dc}{dz} + mg + \frac{\partial\psi}{\partial P}\frac{dP}{dz} = 0.$$

Since the volume of the solution is equal to $\partial\Phi/\partial P = N(\partial\mu_0/\partial P) + n(\partial\psi/\partial P)$ (substituting into (85.1)) we may call $\partial\psi/\partial P$ the volume v' per molecule of the solute. Hence

$$\frac{kT}{c}\frac{dc}{dz} + mg + v'\frac{dP}{dz} = 0.$$

To find out how P depends on z we use the equilibrium condition for the solvent† :

$$v\frac{dP}{dz} + mg = 0$$

where $v = \partial\mu_0/\partial P$ is the molecular volume, and M is the mass of a molecule of the solvent. Substituting for dP/dz in the previous condition, we have

$$\frac{kT}{c}\frac{dc}{dz} + mg - Mg\frac{v'}{v} = 0.$$

If the solution can be considered incompressible, i.e. if v and v' are constant, then we obtain from this:

$$c = c_0 e^{(-gz/kT)(m - v'M/v)}$$

(c_0 being the concentration at $z = 0$) i.e. the usual barometric formula corrected according to Archimedes Law.

§89. Evolution of heat and change of volume in the process of solution

The process of solution is accompanied by the evolution or the absorption of heat; we shall now proceed to calculate this heat effect. To begin with we shall determine the maximum work which can be performed as a result of the process of solution.

Assume that the process of solution takes place at constant pressure and temperature. In this case the maximum work is determined by the change in the thermodynamic potential. We shall calculate it for the process in which a small number δn of molecules of the solute are dissolved in a solution with concentration c. The change in the total thermodynamic potential of the whole system, $\delta\Phi$, is equal to the sum of the changes of potential for the solution and the pure solute. Since δn molecules of the solute were added to the

---

† The term involving the concentration ($-kT(dc/dz)$) is small and may be neglected. (In the condition for the solute it had c in the denominator and thus was not small.)

solution, the change in its thermodynamic potential is

$$\delta\Phi_{\text{sol}} = \frac{\partial\Phi_{\text{sol}}}{\partial n}\delta n = \mu'\delta n,$$

where μ' is the chemical potential of the solute in the solution. The change in the potential Φ'_0 of the pure solute is equal to

$$\delta\Phi_0' = -\frac{\partial\Phi_0'}{\partial n}\delta n = -\mu_0'\delta n,$$

since the number of molecules is decreased by δn (μ_0' is the chemical potential of the pure solute). Hence the total change in the thermodynamic potential in the process under consideration is equal to

$$\delta\Phi = \delta n(\mu' - \mu_0'). \tag{89.1}$$

We now substitute for μ' from (85.6):

$$\delta\Phi = -\delta n(\mu_0' - \psi - kT\log c)$$

or

$$\delta\Phi = -kT\delta n\log\frac{c_0(P, T)}{c}, \tag{89.2}$$

where the quantity

$$c_0(P, T) = e^{(\mu_0' - \psi)/kT} \tag{89.3}$$

is the solubility, i.e. the concentration of the saturated solution (the solution in equilibrium with the pure solute). This follows directly from the fact that Φ must be a minimum for equilibrium, i.e. we must have $\delta\Phi = 0$. (89.3) can also be obtained directly from the equilibrium condition between the solution and the pure solute, i.e. from the equality of the chemical potentials of the pure and dissolved solute.

It should be mentioned that c_0 can be identified with the concentration of the saturated solution only when c_0 is small, since all the formulae of the preceding sections apply only to small concentrations.

The expression we have obtained determines the required work: the quantity $|\delta\Phi|$ is the maximum work which can be done as a result of dissolving δn molecules; it is also the minimum work which must be performed to extract δn molecules of solute from a solution with concentration c.

It is now easy to calculate the heat δQ_P absorbed during a process of solution at constant pressure (if $\delta Q_P < 0$ then heat is released). The amount of heat absorbed during a process taking place at constant pressure is equal to the change in the heat function (§14). On the other hand, since

$$W = -T^2\left(\frac{\partial}{\partial T}\frac{\Phi}{T}\right)_P,$$

we have:†

$$\delta Q_P = -T^2 \left(\frac{\partial}{\partial T} \frac{\delta \Phi}{T} \right)_P. \tag{89.4}$$

Substituting into this formula from (89.2) we obtain the required quantity of heat:

$$\delta Q_P = kT^2 \delta n \frac{\partial \log c_0}{\partial T}. \tag{89.5}$$

Thus the thermal effect of the process of solution is connected with the relation between solubility and temperature. We see that ∂Q_P is directly proportional to δn; hence this formula can be applied to the process of solution of any finite quantity of the solute, (as long as the solution remains weak, of course). The quantity of heat absorbed when n molecules are dissolved is equal to

$$Q_P = kT^2 n \frac{\partial \log c_0}{\partial T}. \tag{89.6}$$

We can also find the change in volume during the process of solution, i.e. the difference between the volume of the solution and the sum of the volumes of the pure solute and the solvent in which it is dissolved. Let us calculate this change δV for the process of solution of δn molecules. The volume is the derivative of the thermodynamic potential with respect to the pressure. Hence the change in volume is equal to the derivative with respect to pressure of the change in the thermodynamic potential during the given process

$$\delta V = \frac{\partial}{\partial P} \delta \Phi. \tag{89.7}$$

Substituting for $\delta \Phi$ from (89.2), we find:

$$\delta V = -kT \delta n \frac{\partial}{\partial P} \log c_0. \tag{89.8}$$

To end this section, note that (89.6) is in accordance with Le Chatelier's principle. Assume, for example, that δQ_P is negative, i.e. heat is released during the process of solution. Consider the saturated solution; if it is cooled then, according to Le Chatelier's principle, the solubility must increase, so

---

† The corresponding formula for the quantity of heat absorbed during a process occurring at constant volume is

$$\delta Q_V = -T^2 \left(\frac{\partial}{\partial T} \frac{\delta F}{T} \right)_V \tag{89.4a}$$

$\left(\text{since in this case } \delta Q_V = \delta E \text{ and } E = -T^2 \left(\frac{\partial}{\partial T} \frac{F}{T} \right)_V \right).$

that more of the solute will dissolve. In this case heat will be released, i.e. as if the system were resisting the cooling which disturbed its equilibrium. The same follows from (89.6) since in this case is negative. Similar reasoning will show agreement between Le Chatelier's principle and (89.8).

PROBLEMS

1. Determine the maximum work which can be performed in the formation of a saturated solution.

SOLUTION: Before the process the thermodynamic potential of the pure solvent is $N\mu_0$ and that of the pure solute $n\mu_0'$. The potential of the whole system is $\Phi_1 = N\mu_0 + n\mu_0'$. After the process of solution the thermodynamic potential becomes $\Phi_2 = N\mu_0 + nkT \log(n/eN) + n\psi$. The maximum work

$$R_{\max} = \Phi_1 - \Phi_2 = -nkT \log\frac{n}{eN} + n(\mu_0' - \psi) = nkT \log\frac{ec_0}{c}.$$

(This quantity can also be obtained by integrating (89.2).) If a saturated solution is formed, i.e. $c = c_0$ and $n = Nc = Nc_0$, then

$$R_{\max} = nkT = Nc_0 kT.$$

2. Find the minimum work which must be performed in order to increase the concentration of a solution from c_1 to c_2 by removing some of the solvent.

SOLUTION: Before the removal of the solvent the thermodynamic potential of the solution is $\Phi_1 = N\mu_0 + Nc_1 kT \log(c_1/e) + Nc_1\psi$. (The number of molecules of the solute is Nc_1, where N is the initial number of molecules of the solvent.) To increase the concentration to c_2 one must remove $N[1 - (c_1/c_2)]$ molecules of the solvent. The sum of the thermodynamic potentials of the remaining solution and the removed solvent gives $\Phi_2 = N\mu_0 + Nc_1 kT \log (c_2/e) + Nc_1\psi$. The minimum work is

$$R_{\min} = \Phi_2 - \Phi_1 = Nc_1 kT \log(c_2/c_1).$$

§90. Mutual influence of solutes

Consider a weak solution of two different solutes in the same solvent. Let c_{01} and c_{02} be the solubilities (concentrations of the saturated solutions) of the two solutes dissolved separately†; the solubilities of the two solutes in each other's presence being: $c_{01}' = c_{01} + \delta c_{01}$ and $c_{02}' = c_{02} + \delta c_{02}$. Let us determine the relation between δc_{01} and δc_{02}.

To solve this problem we must, of course, take into account terms in the thermodynamic potential which involve simultaneously the concentrations of both solutes. Such terms occur in second order. To second order the thermodynamic potential of a solution of two solutes is, according to (85.4), given by

$$\Phi = N\mu_0 + n_1 kT \log\frac{n_1}{eN} + n_2 kT \log\frac{n_2}{eN} + n_1\psi_1 + n_2\psi_2 +$$

$$+ \frac{n_1^2}{N}\frac{\beta_{11}}{2} + \frac{n_2^2}{N}\frac{\beta_{22}}{2} + \frac{n_1 n_2}{N}\beta_{12}.$$

† It is assumed, of course, that the saturated solution is sufficiently weak for all our formulae to apply.

The chemical potentials of the two solutes are:

$$\left.\begin{aligned} \mu_1' &= \frac{\partial \Phi}{\partial n_1} = kT \log c_1 + \psi_1 + c_1\beta_{11} + c_2\beta_{12}, \\ \mu_2' &= \frac{\partial \Phi}{\partial n_2} = kT \log c_2 + \psi_2 + c_1\beta_{12} + c_2\beta_{22}. \end{aligned}\right\} \tag{90.1}$$

$(c_1 = n_1/N, c_2 = n_2/N)$. Let μ_{01}' and μ_{02}' be the chemical potentials of the pure solutes. The solubilities c_{01} and c_{02} are determined from the equilibrium condition between each pure solute and the same solute in solution, i.e.

$$\left.\begin{aligned} \mu_{01}' &= kT \log c_{01} + \psi_1 + c_1\beta_{11}, \\ \mu_{02}' &= kT \log c_{02} + \psi_2 + c_2\beta_{22}. \end{aligned}\right\} \tag{90.2}$$

The solubilities c_{01}' and c_{02}' are given by the equilibrium conditions

$$\left.\begin{aligned} \mu_{01}' &= kT \log c_{01}' + \psi_1 + c_1\beta_{11} + c_2\beta_{12}, \\ \mu_{02}' &= kT \log c_{02}' + \psi_2 + c_2\beta_{22} + c_1\beta_{12}. \end{aligned}\right\} \tag{90.3}$$

Subtracting (90.2) from (90.3) term by term and assuming that the changes in the solubilities are small ($\delta c_{01} \ll c_{01}$, $\delta c_{02} \ll c_{02}$), we obtain the approximation

$$kT\frac{\delta c_{01}}{c_{01}} = -c_{02}\beta_{12}, \qquad kT\frac{\delta c_{02}}{c_{02}} = -c_{01}\beta_{12},$$

since $\log c_{01}' - \log c_{01} \approx \delta c_{01}/c_{01}$ and similarly for δc_{02}. Hence we obtain:

$$\delta c_{01} = \delta c_{02} \tag{90.4}$$

i.e. the changes in the solubilities of the two solutes are equal.

Similarly, one can determine the change in the saturated vapour pressures of two solutes when they are simultaneously dissolved. Let P_1 and P_2 be the saturated vapour pressures of the two solutes with concentrations c_1 and c_2 when dissolved separately; let $P_1' = P_1 + \delta P_1$, $P_2' = P_2 + \delta P_2$ be the saturated vapour pressures of the same solutes when dissolved together (with the same concentrations). The chemical potentials of the vapours of the two solutes are $kT \log P_1 + \chi_1(T)$ and $kT \log P_2 + \chi_2(T)$. Hence the pressures P_1 and P_2 are determined by the relations

$$\left.\begin{aligned} kT \log P_1 + \chi_1(T) &= kT \log c_1 + \psi_1 + c_1\beta_{11}, \\ kT \log P_2 + \chi_2(T) &= kT \log c_2 + \psi_2 + c_2\beta_{22}, \end{aligned}\right\} \tag{90.5}$$

and P_1' and P_2' by the relations

$$\left.\begin{aligned} kT \log P_1' + \chi_1 &= kT \log c_1 + \psi_1 + c_1\beta_{11} + c_2\beta_{12}, \\ kT \log P_2' + \chi_2 &= kT \log c_2 + \psi_2 + c_2\beta_{22} + c_1\beta_{12}, \end{aligned}\right\} \tag{90.6}$$

Subtracting (90.5) from (90.6) and assuming that the changes are small, we find that:

$$kT\frac{\delta P_1}{P_1} = c_2\beta_{12}, \qquad kT\frac{\delta P_2}{P_2} = c_1\beta_{12},$$

whence

$$\frac{\delta P_1}{\delta P_2} = \frac{P_1 c_2}{P_2 c_1}. \qquad (90.7)$$

Thus the relative changes in the saturated vapour pressures $\delta P_1/P_1$ and $\delta P_2/P_2$ are inversely proportional to the corresponding concentrations, c_1 and c_2.

§91. Solutions of strong electrolytes

The method of expanding the thermodynamic functions in powers of the concentration, which was used in the preceding section, becomes completely inapplicable in the important case of solutions of strong electrolytes, i.e. of substances which in solution dissociate almost completely into ions. The slow decrease with distance of the Coulomb interaction between ions leads to the appearance of terms varying with a lower power of the concentration than the second (actually the power is 3/2).

It is easy to see that the problem of finding the thermodynamic functions of a dilute solution of a strong electrolyte reduces to the problem of an almost perfect ionised gas, which was considered in §74. To see this we start from the basic statistical eq. (31.5) for the determination of the free energy. We carry out the integration in the partition function in two stages. First we integrate over the co-ordinates and momenta of the particles of the solvent. Then the partition function takes the form

$$\int e^{-F(p,q)/kT}\, d\Gamma$$

where the integration extends now only over the phase space of the solute particles, and $F(p, q)$ is the free energy of the system consisting of the solvent, with the ions inserted, with the co-ordinates and momenta of the latter as given parameters. We know from electrodynamics that the free energy of a system of charges placed in a medium (for a given volume and temperature of the latter) is obtained from the energy of the charges in free space if we divide each product of charges by the dielectric permeability of the medium, ϵ†. The remainder of the calculation leading to the derivation of the final expression for the free energy of the solution is, therefore, the same as that carried out in §74.

Thus the required contribution to the free energy of the solution of a

---

† This statement implies that the distances between the ions are large compared to molecular dimensions. But we know from §74 that in the approximation considered here just such distances contribute.

strong electrolyte is given according to (74.12) by the expression

$$-\frac{2e^3}{3\epsilon^{3/2}}\left(\frac{\pi}{kTV}\right)^{1/2}(\Sigma_a n_a z_a^2)^{3/2}$$

where the summation extends over all types of ion in the solution, and the number of particles of type a is denoted by n_a, in line with the notation of the present chapter. This also represents the contribution to the thermodynamic potential, at given pressure and temperature. If we introduce the molar volume of the solvent $v(P, T)$ by $V \cong Nv$, we may write the thermodynamic potential of the solution in the form:

$$\Phi = N\mu_0 + \sum_a n_a kT \log\frac{n_a}{eN} + \sum_a n_a\psi_a - \frac{2e^3}{3\epsilon^{3/2}}\left(\frac{\pi}{NvkT}\right)^{1/2}(\Sigma_a n_a z_a^2)^{3/2}. \quad (91.1)$$

From this expression we can derive, by the usual rules, any thermodynamic properties of the solution of an electrolyte.

Thus if we want to calculate the osmotic pressure we may write for the chemical potential of the solvent:

$$\mu = \mu_0 - \frac{kT}{N}\sum_a n_a + \frac{e^3}{3\epsilon^{3/2}}\left(\frac{\pi}{vkT}\right)^{1/2}\left(\frac{\Sigma_a n_a z_a^2}{N}\right)^{3/2}. \quad (91.2)$$

Hence we find the osmotic pressure (at a boundary with pure solvent) by the same method as in §86:

$$\Delta P = \frac{kT}{V}\sum_a n_a - \frac{e^3}{3\epsilon^{3/2}}\left(\frac{\pi}{kT}\right)^{1/2}\left(\frac{\Sigma_a n_a z_a^2}{V}\right)^{3/2}. \quad (91.3)$$

The heat function of the solution is given by

$$W = -T^2\left(\frac{\partial}{\partial T}\frac{\Phi}{T}\right)_P$$

$$= Nw_0 - T^2\sum_a n_a\frac{\partial}{\partial T}\frac{\psi_a}{T} + \frac{2e^3}{3}\left(\frac{\pi}{kN}\right)^{1/2}(\Sigma_a n_a z_a^2)^{3/2}T^2\frac{\partial}{\partial T}\left(\frac{1}{\epsilon^{3/2}T^{3/2}v^{1/2}}\right). \quad (91.4)$$

From this we may find the so-called "heat of solution" Q, which is released if we add to the solution (at constant P and T) a very large quantity of solvent, so that the concentration tends to zero. The heat release in this process is given by the change in the heat function. The terms which are linear in the number of particles evidently do not contribute to the required difference, and we obtain from (91.4):

$$Q = \frac{2e^3}{3}\left(\frac{\pi}{kN}\right)^{1/2}(\Sigma_a n_a z_a^2)^{3/2}T^2\frac{\partial}{\partial T}\left(\frac{1}{\epsilon^{3/2}T^{3/2}v^{1/2}}\right). \quad (91.5)$$

The only condition for the applicability of the formulae obtained above is that the concentration be sufficiently small. Indeed the fact that the electrolyte is strong shows that the energy of attraction between unlike ions must always be less than kT. It follows, therefore, that at distances which are large compared to molecular dimensions the interaction energy must be small compared to kT, and hence the condition

$$n \ll (\epsilon kT/z^2 e^2)^3$$

(cf. eq. 74.2) is identical with the condition that the solution be dilute.

PROBLEM

Find the change in the solubility (assumed small) of a strong electrolyte caused by the addition of a certain quantity of a different electrolyte (neither of the ions of the latter being identical with those of the main electrolyte).

SOLUTION: The solubility (i.e. the concentration of a saturated solution) of a strong electrolyte is found from the equation

$$\mu_{\text{sol}}(P, T) = \sum_a \nu_a \mu_a = kT \sum_a \nu_a \log (n_a/N) + \sum_a \nu_a \psi_a -$$

$$- \frac{e^3}{N\epsilon^{3/2}} \left(\frac{\pi}{\nu kT} \right)^{1/2} (\sum_a \nu_a z_a^2)(\sum_b n_b z_b^2)^{1/2}. \tag{1}$$

Here μ_{sol} is the chemical potential of the pure solid electrolyte, and ν_a is the number of ions of type a in one molecule of electrolyte. If we add other ions to the solution the chemical potentials of the original ions will change because of the change of the sum $\sum n_b z_b^2$, which has to include all ions present in the solution. If we define the solubility c_0 by $n_a/N = \nu_a c_0$, we find its change by varying (1) at constant P and T:

$$\delta c_0 = \frac{\pi^{1/2} e^3 \delta(\sum_b n_b z_b^2)}{2\epsilon^{3/2} \nu^{1/2} (kT)^{3/2} N^2 \sum_a \nu_a}.$$

The sum inside the variation includes only the types of ion which have been added. We note that in the circumstances we have considered the solubility increases.

§92. Mixtures of perfect gases

The thermodynamic quantities (such as energy, entropy, etc.) are additive only provided that the interaction between different parts of the system can be neglected. Hence for a mixture of several substances, for instance a mixture of several liquids, the thermodynamic quantities will not be equal to the sum of the thermodynamic quantities of the separate components of the system.

An exception is the case of a mixture of perfect gases since, by definition, the interaction of their molecules can be neglected. For example, the entropy of such a mixture is equal to the sum of the entropies of each of the gases in the mixture when all the other gases are absent and it is allowed to occupy the whole volume of the mixture, its pressure then being its partial pressure in the mixture. The partial pressure P_i of the ith gas is expressed in terms of the pressure P of the whole mixture as follows:

$$P_i = \frac{N_i kT}{V} = \frac{N_i}{N} P \qquad (92.1)$$

where N is the total number of molecules in the mixture and N_i is the number of molecules of the ith gas. Hence, according to (42.7), the entropy of a mixture of two gases is equal to

$$S = N_1 k \log \frac{eV}{N_1} + N_2 k \log \frac{eV}{N_2} - N_1 f_1'(T) - N_2 f_2'(T), \qquad (92.2)$$

or, from (42.8),

$$S = -N_1 k \log P_1 - N_2 k \log P_2 - N_1 \chi_1'(T) - N_2 \chi_2'(T)$$

$$= -(N_1 + N_2)k \log P - N_1 k \log \frac{N_1}{N} - N_2 k \log \frac{N_2}{N} -$$

$$- N_1 \chi_1'(T) - N_2 \chi_2'(T). \qquad (92.3)$$

From (42.4) the free energy of the mixture is

$$F = -N_1 kT \log \frac{eV}{N_1} - N_2 kT \log \frac{eV}{N_2} + N_1 f_1(T) + N_2 f_2(T). \qquad (92.4)$$

Similarly, using (42.6) we find, for the potential Φ:

$$\Phi = N_1 kT \log P_1 + N_2 kT \log P_2 + N_1 \chi_1(T) + N_2 \chi_2(T)$$

$$= N_1(kT \log P + \chi_1) + N_2(kT \log P + \chi_2) +$$

$$+ N_1 kT \log \frac{N_1}{N} + N_2 kT \log \frac{N_2}{N}. \qquad (92.5)$$

From this it can be seen that the chemical potentials of the two gases in the mixture are equal to

$$\left. \begin{array}{l} \mu_1 = kT \log P_1 + \chi_1 = kT \log P + \chi_1 + kT \log \dfrac{N_1}{N}, \\[4mm] \mu_2 = kT \log P_2 + \chi_2 = kT \log P + \chi_2 + kT \log \dfrac{N_2}{N}, \end{array} \right\} \qquad (92.6)$$

i.e. each has a potential which is of the same form as that for a pure gas with pressure P_1 or P_2.

Note that the free energy of the mixture of gases (92.4) is of the form

$$F = F_1(N_1, V, T) + F_2(N_2, V, T)$$

where F_1 and F_2 are the free energies of the first and second gases as functions of the numbers of particles, volume and temperature; for the thermodynamic potential the corresponding relation does not hold: the potential Φ of the mixture has the form

$$\Phi = \Phi_1(N_1, P, T) + \Phi_2(N_2, P, T) + N_1 kT \log\frac{N_1}{N} + N_2 kT \log\frac{N_2}{N}.$$

Suppose that we have two different gases with N_1 and N_2 particles respectively, contained in vessels of volumes V_1 and V_2 with equal temperatures and pressures. The two vessels are then connected and the gases are mixed. The volume of the mixture will be $V_1 + V_2$ and the temperature and pressure will remain, of course, as before. However, the entropy changes in this case; before mixing, the total entropy of the two gases, equal to the sum of their entropies, was:

$$S_0 = N_1 k \log\frac{eV_1}{N_1} + N_2 k \log\frac{eV_2}{N_2} - N_1 f_1'(T) - N_2 f_2'(T).$$

After mixing, the entropy is, according to (92.2):

$$S = N_1 k \log\frac{e}{N_1}(V_1 + V_2) + N_2 k \log\frac{e}{N_2}(V_1 + V_2) - N_1 f_1' - N_2 f_2'.$$

The change in entropy is

$$\Delta S = S - S_0 = N_1 k \log\frac{V_1 + V_2}{V_1} + N_2 k \log\frac{V_1 + V_2}{V_2},$$

or, since for the same temperature and pressure the volume is inversely proportional to the number of particles:

$$\Delta S = N_1 k \log\frac{N}{N_1} + N_2 k \log\frac{N}{N_2}. \tag{92.7}$$

This quantity is positive, i.e. the entropy increases after mixing, as one would expect, owing to the obvious irreversibility of the process. The quantity ΔS is called the *entropy of mixing*.

If the two gases were identical, then after connecting the vessels the entropy would be:

$$S = (N_1 + N_2)k \log\frac{V_1 + V_2}{N_1 + N_2} - (N_1 + N_2)f'$$

and since

$$\frac{V_1 + V_2}{N_1 + N_2} = \frac{V_1}{N_1} = \frac{V_2}{N_2}$$

(owing to the equality of pressure and temperature), the change in entropy would be zero.

Thus we see that the difference between the molecules of the mixed gases is responsible for the change in entropy when mixing takes place. This corresponds to the fact that it is necessary to perform some work in order to separate the molecules of one gas from those of the other.

§93. Isotopic mixtures

Mixtures of different isotopes (in any state of aggregation) are a special kind of "solution". For simplicity we shall discuss below a mixture of two isotopes of the same element although the same results apply to mixtures of an arbitrary number of isotopes and also to complex substances (chemical compounds) whose different molecules contain different isotopes.

In classical mechanics the only difference between isotopes is the difference in their mass; the interaction laws are the same for atoms of different isotopes. This allows us to express the thermodynamic quantities of the mixture simply in terms of the thermodynamic quantities of the pure isotopes. The difference in the calculation of the partition function is reduced simply to dividing the phase volume element not by $N!$ as for a pure substance, but by the product $N_1! \, N_2!$ of the factorials of the numbers of particles of the components of the mixture. This leads to the appearance of additional terms in the free energy

$$N_1 kT \log \frac{N_1}{N} + N_2 kT \log \frac{N_2}{N}$$

(where $N = N_1 + N_2$), corresponding to the "entropy of mixing" which we discussed for mixtures of gases in §92.

The same terms also occur in the thermodynamic potential of the mixture, which can be expressed in the form:

$$\Phi = N_1 kT \log \frac{N_1}{N} + N_2 kT \log \frac{N_2}{N} + N_1 \mu_{01} + N_2 \mu_{02}. \tag{93.1}$$

Here μ_{01} and μ_{02} are the chemical potentials of each of the pure isotopes. They differ only by a constant multiple of the temperature:

$$\mu_{01} - \mu_{02} = -\frac{3}{2} kT \log \frac{m_1}{m_2}, \tag{93.2}$$

where m_1 and m_2 are the atomic masses of the two isotopes (this difference arises from the integration with respect to the atomic momenta in the partition function; in the case of gases (93.2) is simply the difference in the chemical constants multiplied by kT).

The difference (93.2) is the same for all phases of a given substance. Hence the phase equilibrium equation (the condition that the chemical potentials of the phases should be equal) is the same for the different isotopes. The position is as simple as this only provided that the substance can be described by classical statistics. In quantum theory, the differences between isotopes go considerably deeper, in connection with the differences in the vibrational and rotational levels of the molecules, their different nuclear spins, etc.

It is important to note, however, that even when the first correction terms in the thermodynamic quantities are taken into account (terms of order $\hbar^2$; see §33), the thermodynamic potential of the mixture can still be written in the form (93.1). These corrections are in the form of a sum, each of whose terms involves the mass of only one of the atoms (see formula (33.15) for the free energy). Hence all the terms of the sum can be arranged so that they are included in the chemical potentials μ_{01} and μ_{02}; as a result (92.1) still holds (but certainly not (93.2)).

We must call attention to the fact that the thermodynamic potential (93.1) is of exactly the same form as that for the case of two arbitrary gases (§92). Mixtures with this property are called perfect. Thus mixtures of isotopes are perfect up to second order in $\hbar^2$. In this respect mixtures of isotopes form a special case, since condensed mixtures of different substances can be perfect only to a very rough approximation.

Within the limits of applicability of (93.1), one can draw definite conclusions regarding the vapour pressures of two isotopes over a condensed mixture of them. The chemical potentials of the two components of this mixture are

$$\mu_1 = kT \log c_1 + \mu_{01}$$
$$\mu_2 = kT \log c_2 + \mu_{02}$$

(where $c_1 = N_1/N$, $c_2 = N_2/N$ are the concentrations of the isotopes). Equating these to the chemical potentials of the gaseous phases ($kT \log P_1 + \chi_1(T)$ and $kT \log P_2 + \chi_2(T)$), we obtain, for the partial vapour pressures

$$P_1 = P_{01}c_1, \qquad P_2 = P_{02}c_2 \qquad (93.3)$$

where P_{01} and P_{02} denote the vapour pressure of the pure isotopes (at the given temperature). Thus the partial vapour pressures of the two isotopes are proportional to their concentrations in the condensed mixture.

As far as the saturated vapour pressures of the pure isotopes are concerned, $P_{01} = P_{02}$ in the classical approximation, as we have already shown. But when quantum effects are taken into account they differ from each other. This difference cannot be calculated in general form for any substance. It can be done only for monatomic elements (the noble gases) with accuracy up to terms in $\hbar^2$ (K. HERZBERG, E. TELLER, 1938).

The correction to the thermodynamic potential of the liquid phase is determined by (33.15)†; referring it to one atom, we obtain the chemical

---

† We again make use of the fact that small additions to the different thermodynamic potentials, expressed in terms of corresponding variables, are equal to one another (§15).

potential

$$\mu = \mu_{cl} + \frac{\hbar^2}{24mkT}\overline{F^2},$$

where

$$\overline{F^2} = \overline{\left(\frac{\partial U}{\partial x}\right)^2} + \overline{\left(\frac{\partial U}{\partial y}\right)^2} + \overline{\left(\frac{\partial U}{\partial z}\right)^2}$$

is the mean square force exerted on one atom of the liquid by all the others. The chemical potential of the gas remains equal to its classical value, since one may neglect the interaction of the particles (atoms) of the gas. Equating the chemical potentials of the gas and the liquid, we find the correction to the classical value of the vapour pressure, and the difference between the vapour pressures of the two isotopes in which we are interested will be

$$P_{01} - P_{02} = P_0 \frac{\hbar^2 \overline{F^2}}{24(kT)^2}\left(\frac{1}{m_1} - \frac{1}{m_2}\right) \tag{93.4}$$

where P_0 is the common classical value of P_{01} and P_{02}. We see that the sign of this difference is determined by the difference of the reciprocals of the masses of the isotopic atoms, and that the vapour pressure of the lighter isotope is the greater.

§94. Vapour pressure of a concentrated solution

We shall now consider the equilibrium of a solution with its vapour which in general also contains both substances. The solution may be either weak or strong, i.e. the quantities of the two substances may be arbitrary (remember that the results obtained in §87 refer only to weak solutions).

Since the solution and vapour are in equilibrium with each other, the chemical potentials, μ_1 and μ_2 of the two components in the solution and in the vapour are equal to one another. If we denote the numbers of particles of the two substances in the solution by $N_1{}^s$ and $N_2{}^s$ then for the solution we may write identity (24.14) in the form

$$d\Omega = -N_1{}^s d\mu_1 - N_2{}^s d\mu_2 - S^s dT - P dV^s. \tag{94.1}$$

Here S^s and V^s are the entropy and volume of the solution; the temperature T and the pressure P are the same for the solution and the vapour.

We shall assume that the vapour over the solution is so rarefied that it may be regarded as a perfect gas; its pressure is small. For this reason, we neglect in (94.1) the terms proportional to P i.e. $P dV$ and $d\Omega$. Consider first all the derivatives at constant temperature. We then obtain from (94.1)

$$N_1{}^s d\mu_1 + N_2{}^s d\mu_2 = 0. \tag{94.2}$$

On the other hand, for the gaseous phase

$$\mu_1{}^g = kT \log P_1 + \chi_1(T)$$

$$\mu_2{}^g = kT \log P_2 + \chi_2(T)$$

where P_1 and P_2 are the partial pressures of the two components of the vapour. Differentiating these expressions (at $T = $ const) we find:

$$d\mu_1{}^g = kT \, d(\log P_1), \qquad d\mu_2{}^g = kT \, d(\log P_2).$$

Substituting this into (94.2) we obtain

$$N_1{}^s \, d(\log P_1) + N_2{}^s \, d(\log P_2) = 0. \tag{94.3}$$

Now we introduce the concentration ξ of the solution as the ratio of the number of particles of the first component to the total number of particles:

$$\xi = \frac{N_1{}^s}{N_1{}^s + N_2{}^s}$$

and similarly the concentration x of the vapour. The partial pressures P_1 and P_2 are equal to the product of the total vapour pressure P and the concentration of the corresponding components, i.e. $P_1 = xP$, $P_2 = (1-x)P_1$. Substituting all this into (94.3) and dividing the equation by the total number of particles in the solution, $N = N_1{}^s + N_2{}^s$, we find:

$$\xi \, d(\log Px) + (1-\xi) \, d[\log P(1-x)] = 0,$$

whence

$$d(\log P) = \frac{x - \xi}{x(1-x)} \, dx$$

or,

$$\xi = x - x(1-x) \frac{\partial(\log P)}{\partial x}. \tag{94.4}$$

This equation connects the concentrations of the solution and vapour with the dependence of the vapour pressure on its concentration.

Another useful relation can be obtained by examining the temperature dependence of these quantities. We write down the condition that the chemical potential of one of the components is the same in the solution and the vapour, the first component, for example:

$$\mu_1{}^g = \frac{\partial \Phi^s}{\partial N_1{}^s}.$$

Dividing both sides of the equation by T and remembering that the differentiation with respect to the number of particles is taken at constant temperature, we write:

$$\frac{\mu_1{}^g}{T} = \frac{\partial}{\partial N_1{}^s} \frac{\Phi^s}{T}.$$

We now take the total derivative with respect to temperature of both sides of the equation. It can be assumed, to sufficient accuracy, that the thermodynamic potential of the condensed phase (the solution) is independent of the pressure. Noting also that the partial derivative with respect to the temperature

$$\frac{\partial}{\partial T} \frac{\Phi}{T} = -\frac{1}{T^2}\left(\Phi - T\frac{\partial \Phi}{\partial T}\right) = -\frac{W}{T^2},$$

we obtain the following relation:

$$kT^2\frac{\partial(\log P_1)}{\partial T} = w_1{}^g - \frac{\partial W^s}{\partial N_1{}^s}. \tag{94.5}$$

Here $w_1{}^g$ is the molecular heat function of the vapour of the first substance, and the derivative $\partial W^s/\partial N_1{}^s$ determines the change in the heat function of the solution when one molecule of this substance is added to it. Hence the right-hand side of (94.5) represents the heat absorbed when one particle of the first substance goes from the liquid to the vapour.

In the absence of the second substance (94.5) becomes the usual Clapeyron-Clausius equation,

$$kT^2\frac{\partial(\log P_{10})}{\partial T} = w_1{}^g - w_2{}^l$$

where P_{10} is the vapour pressure of the pure first substance, $w_1{}^l$ its molecular heat function in the liquid state. Subtracting this equation term by term from (94.5) we finally obtain the following relation:

$$kT^2\frac{\partial}{\partial T}\log\frac{P_1}{P_{10}} = -q_1, \tag{94.6}$$

where $q_1 = \partial W^s/\partial N_1{}^s - w_1{}^l$ denotes the molecular "heat of solution", which is the quantity of heat absorbed when one molecule of the liquid first substance goes into solution. The same relation, obviously, can also be written down for the second substance.

§95. Thermodynamic inequalities for solutions

It was shown in §21 that a body can exist only in those states satisfying certain conditions known as thermodynamic inequalities. These conditions were, however, deduced for bodies consisting of identical particles. We shall now carry out a similar investigation for solutions, restricting ourselves to mixtures of two substances only.

For the equilibrium condition, in §21, we used, not that the entropy of the body as a whole should be a maximum, but an equivalent condition requiring that the minimum work necessary to change some small part of the body from its equilibrium state to a neighbouring state should be positive.

We shall now proceed in a similar manner. Consider a small part of the solution, the number of particles of the solvent and solute contained in it being N and n. At equilibrium, the temperature, pressure and concentration of this part are equal to their values in the remaining solution (which acts as the "external medium"). Let us determine the minimum work which must be performed for our selected part, containing N particles of the solvent, to acquire temperature, pressure, and number of particles of the solute differing by small (but finite) amounts δT, δP, and δn from their equilibrium values.

The minimum work would be done if the process were carried out reversibly. The work done by the external source is equal to the change in the energy of the system, i.e.

$$\delta R_{\min} = \delta E + \delta E_0$$

(quantities without a suffix refer to the small part and those with a suffix to the remaining system). We may replace δE_0 by several terms, from the thermodynamic identity,

$$\delta R_{\min} = \delta E + T_0\,\delta S_0 - P_0\,\delta V_0 + \mu_0'\,\delta n_0,$$

where μ_0' is the chemical potential of the solute in the medium; the number of particles of the solvent remains unchanged in this process and hence we need not write down a similar term for the solvent.† It follows from the reversibility of the process that $\delta S_0 = -\delta S$ and by considering the total volume and the quantity of the solute in the solution we see that $\delta V = -\delta V_0$, $\delta n = -\delta n_0$. Substituting for these quantities, we find the required expression for the minimum work:

$$\delta R_{\min} = \delta E - T_0\,\delta S + P_0\,\delta V - \mu_0'\,\delta n. \tag{95.1}$$

Thus for our equilibrium condition we require that for any small part of the solution the inequality

$$\delta E - T_0\,\delta S + P_0\,\delta V - \mu_0'\,\delta n > 0 \tag{95.2}$$

should be satisfied. In future, as in §21, we shall omit the suffix zero in the

---

† The thermodynamic identity for the medium (at constant N) is

$$dE_0 = T_0\,dS_0 - P_0\,dV_0 + \mu_0'\,dn_0.$$

Since T_0, P_0, μ_0' may be considered as constant for the medium, then the integration of this identity will yield the same relation between finite changes of the quantities.

μ_0' must not be confused with the chemical potential of the pure solute.

coefficients of the variations of quantities from their equilibrium values; we shall always take the values of these coefficients to be the equilibrium values.

We may expand δE in powers of δV, δS, and δn (regarding E as a function of V, S, and n). Up to terms of second order

$$\delta E = \frac{\partial E}{\partial S}\delta S + \frac{\partial E}{\partial V}\delta V + \frac{\partial E}{\partial n}\delta n + \frac{1}{2}\left[\frac{\partial^2 E}{\partial S^2}\delta S^2 + \frac{\partial^2 E}{\partial V^2}\delta V^2 + \right.$$
$$\left. +\frac{\partial^2 E}{\partial n^2}\delta n^2 + 2\frac{\partial^2 E}{\partial S\,\partial V}\delta S\,\delta V + 2\frac{\partial^2 E}{\partial S\,\partial n}\delta S\,\delta n + 2\frac{\partial^2 E}{\partial V\,\partial n}\delta V\,\delta n\right].$$

But

$$\frac{\partial E}{\partial V} = -P, \qquad \frac{\partial E}{\partial S} = T, \qquad \frac{\partial E}{\partial n} = \mu'.$$

Thus, when we substitute into (95.2), the first-order terms cancel and we obtain

$$2\delta R_{\min} = \frac{\partial^2 E}{\partial S^2}\delta S^2 + \frac{\partial^2 E}{\partial V^2}\delta V^2 + \frac{\partial^2 E}{\partial n^2}\delta n^2 + 2\frac{\partial^2 E}{\partial S\,\partial V}\delta S\,\delta V +$$
$$+2\frac{\partial^2 E}{\partial S\,\partial n}\delta S\,\delta n + 2\frac{\partial^2 E}{\partial V\,\partial n}\delta V\,\delta n > 0 \tag{95.3}$$

It is well known from the theory of quadratic forms that, for a form in three variables (in this case δS, δV, and δn) to be positive definite, its coefficients must satisfy three conditions which are, for (95.3):

$$\begin{vmatrix} \dfrac{\partial^2 E}{\partial V^2} & \dfrac{\partial^2 E}{\partial V\,\partial S} & \dfrac{\partial^2 E}{\partial V\,\partial n} \\[2mm] \dfrac{\partial^2 E}{\partial S\,\partial V} & \dfrac{\partial^2 E}{\partial S^2} & \dfrac{\partial^2 E}{\partial S\,\partial n} \\[2mm] \dfrac{\partial^2 E}{\partial n\,\partial V} & \dfrac{\partial^2 E}{\partial n\,\partial S} & \dfrac{\partial^2 E}{\partial n^2} \end{vmatrix} > 0,$$

$$\begin{vmatrix} \dfrac{\partial^2 E}{\partial V^2} & \dfrac{\partial^2 E}{\partial V\,\partial S} \\[2mm] \dfrac{\partial^2 E}{\partial S\,\partial V} & \dfrac{\partial^2 E}{\partial S^2} \end{vmatrix} > 0, \qquad \frac{\partial^2 E}{\partial S^2} > 0. \tag{95.4}$$

Substituting in these conditions the values of the derivatives of E with respect to V, S, and n, one can express the conditions in the form:

$$
\begin{vmatrix}
\dfrac{\partial P}{\partial V} & \dfrac{\partial P}{\partial S} & \dfrac{\partial P}{\partial n} \\[2mm]
\dfrac{\partial T}{\partial V} & \dfrac{\partial T}{\partial S} & \dfrac{\partial T}{\partial n} \\[2mm]
\dfrac{\partial \mu'}{\partial V} & \dfrac{\partial \mu'}{\partial S} & \dfrac{\partial \mu'}{\partial n}
\end{vmatrix} < 0,
\qquad
\begin{vmatrix}
\dfrac{\partial P}{\partial V} & \dfrac{\partial P}{\partial S} \\[2mm]
\dfrac{\partial T}{\partial V} & \dfrac{\partial T}{\partial S}
\end{vmatrix} < 0,
\qquad
\dfrac{\partial T}{\partial S} > 0.
$$

Each derivative is taken with the other two of the variables V, S, n constant. These determinants are the Jacobians

$$
\frac{\partial(P, T, \mu')}{\partial(V, S, n)} < 0,
\qquad
\left(\frac{\partial(P, T)}{\partial(V, S)}\right)_n < 0,
\qquad
\left(\frac{\partial T}{\partial S}\right)_{V,n} > 0. \qquad (95.5)
$$

The second and third of these conditions give us the inequalities $(\partial P / \partial V)_{T,n} < 0$ and $C_v > 0$ which we already know. The first condition may be transformed in the following manner:

$$
\frac{\partial(P, T, \mu')}{\partial(V, S, n)} = \frac{\dfrac{\partial(P, T, \mu')}{\partial(P, T, n)}}{\dfrac{\partial(V, S, n)}{\partial(P, T, n)}} = \frac{\left(\dfrac{\partial \mu'}{\partial n}\right)_{P,T}}{\left(\dfrac{\partial(V, S)}{\partial(P, T)}\right)_n} < 0.
$$

Since, according to the second condition in (95.5), the denominator of this is negative, it follows that:

$$
\left(\frac{\partial \mu'}{\partial n}\right)_{P,T} > 0. \qquad (95.6)
$$

Introducing the concentration $c = n/N$ instead of n we find (since N is constant)

$$
\left(\frac{\partial \mu'}{\partial c}\right)_{P,T} > 0. \qquad (95.7)
$$

Thus, for solutions, inequality (95.7) must be satisfied, as well as the inequalities $(\partial P / \partial V)_{T,c} < 0$ and $C_v > 0$.

Note that, for weak solutions $\partial \mu' / \partial c = kT/c$ so that inequality (95.7) is always satisfied.

The case when

$$
\left(\frac{\partial \mu'}{\partial c}\right)P, T = 0. \qquad (95.8)
$$

requires special examination. Such a state is called a critical point of the solution; for other aspects of this concept see the next section.

Eq. (95.8) corresponds to the vanishing of the first of the determinants (95.4) (the third order determinant). In this case the quadratic form (95.3) may vanish (for certain values of δS, δV, δn), and to find out under what conditions the inequality (95.2) is satisfied, it is necessary to investigate the higher order terms in the expansion (cf. §80).

The quadratic form (95.3) can be identically rewritten in the form

$$2\delta R_{\min} = \delta S\, \delta\left(\frac{\partial E}{\partial S}\right)_{V,n} + \delta V\, \delta\left(\frac{\partial E}{\partial V}\right)_{S,n} + \delta n\, \delta\left(\frac{\partial E}{\partial n}\right)_{S,V}$$

$$= \delta S\, \delta T - \delta V\, \delta P + \delta n\, \delta\mu'. \tag{95.9}$$

For $(\partial\mu'/\partial n)_{P,T} = 0$ we have

$$\delta\mu' = \frac{\partial\mu'}{\partial T}\delta T + \frac{\partial\mu'}{\partial P}\delta P;$$

hence, if δT and δP vanish, then $\delta\mu'$ also vanishes and with it the whole expression (95.9)†. Thus in order to investigate the vanishing of the quadratic form, it is sufficient to consider deviations from equilibrium occurring at constant T and P.

However, for such deviations, the inequality (95.2) may be expressed in the form

$$\delta\Phi - \mu'\, \delta n > 0.$$

Expanding $\delta\Phi$ in powers of δ_n at constant P and T, and remembering that $\partial\Phi/\partial n = \mu'$, we find:

$$\frac{1}{2}\frac{\partial\mu'}{\partial n}\delta n^2 + \frac{1}{6}\frac{\partial^2\mu'}{\partial n^2}\delta n^3 + \frac{1}{24}\frac{\partial^3\mu'}{\partial n^3}\delta n^4 + \ldots > 0$$

(all the derivatives being taken at constant P and T). If $\partial\mu'/\partial n = 0$, this inequality can be satisfied for all δn only if, at the same time, the coefficient of δn^3 vanishes and the coefficient of δn^4 is positive.

Thus, at the critical point, together with eq. (95.8) we must also have:

$$\left(\frac{\partial^2\mu'}{\partial c^2}\right)_{P,T} = 0. \tag{95.10}$$

$$\left(\frac{\partial^3\mu'}{\partial c^3}\right)_{P,T} > 0. \tag{95.11}$$

Eqs. (95.8) and (95.10) determine some line in the co-ordinate system P, T, c (called a *critical line*).

We must emphasise, however, that all our conclusions about critical points in a solution are subject to the reservation made in §79 with regard to

---

† The case of the second and third of the expressions (95.4) vanishing cannot arise, since then the other conditions would also be broken (See the end of §80).

the critical point of a pure substance: they are based on the assumption that the thermodynamic quantities are nonsingular (as functions of c, V, T); in view of the lack of justification for this assumption we cannot be certain that the results we have obtained are correct.

§96. Equilibrium curves

The state of a body made up of identical particles is determined by the values of any two quantities such as P and T.

To determine the state of a two-component system (a binary mixture) the values of three quantities must be given, for example P, T and the concentration. The concentration of a mixture, in this section and the ones following, will be defined as the ratio of the quantity of one of the substances in the mixture to the total quantity of the two substances; we shall denote it by the letter x (obviously x can take values from 0 to 1). The state of a binary mixture may be represented by a point in the three-dimensional co-ordinate system, along whose axes are plotted the values of these three quantities (just as the state of a system consisting of identical particles was represented by a point in the P, T plane).

According to the phase rule, a two-component system can consist of not more than four adjacent phases. Moreover, such a system has two degrees of freedom with two phases, one with three phases, and none with four phases. Hence states in which two phases are in equilibrium may be represented by the points lying on a surface in the three-dimensional space, states with three phases in equilibrium (triple points) by the points of a line (called a *line of triple points* or three-phase line) and states with four phases in equilibrium by isolated points.

Remember (§77) that in the case of a single-component system states with two phases in equilibrium are represented by a curve in the P, T diagram; each point of this curve determines the temperature and pressure of the two phases (which must be identical according to the equilibrium condition). Points on either side of the curve represent homogeneous states of the body. If, however, the axes represent volume and temperature, then phase equilibrium is represented by a curve, the points within which represent states in which there occurs a separation into two phases, represented by the intersections of the line $T = \text{const}$ with the curve.

A similar state of affairs also holds for mixtures. If the co-ordinate axes measure P, T, and the chemical potential of one of the components (i.e. quantities having the same value in the adjacent phases) then the equilibrium of two phases will be represented by a surface, each point of which determines P, T, and μ for the two phases in equilibrium. In the case of three phases the points representing their equilibrium (the triple points) will lie on the curves of intersection of the equilibrium surfaces of each pair of phases.

However, P, T, and μ are not convenient for our purposes and we shall use P, T, and x as independent variables in future. In terms of these variables, the equilibrium of two phases is represented by a surface whose points of intersection with the straight line $P =$ const, $T =$ const, represent the states of the two adjacent phases for the given P and T (i.e. determine their concentrations which, naturally, may be different for the two phases). The points lying on the straight line between the two intersection points represent states in which the homogeneous body is unstable and in which, therefore, the separation into the two phases (represented by the points of intersection) takes place. Since the surface represents the equilibrium of two phases with each other, then clearly it must be such that any straight line parallel to the x-axis intersects it in an even number of points.

We shall, below, be using two dimensional diagrams in which the co-ordinate axes will represent P and x or T and x; in these co-ordinates one can draw the curves of intersection of the equilibrium surface with planes of constant temperature or pressure. Such curves are called *equilibrium curves*.

Consider the points of an equilibrium curve at which the concentration of the two phases becomes the same. There are two cases of this: (1) when at such a point all the other properties of the two phases become identical; (2) when two separate phases continue to exist at such a point. In the first case the point is called *critical* and in the second case *a point of equal concentration*.

Near a critical point the equilibrium curve has the form shown in Fig. 20, or the analogous form when the critical point K is a minimum (x is measured along the abscissal axis, and P or T along the ordinate axis; the curve is then the intersection of the equilibrium surface with planes of constant temperature or pressure respectively).

Points within this curve (in the shaded part) represent those states in which the separation into two phases takes place; the concentrations in these phases are determined by the points of intersection of the curve with the corresponding horizontal straight line. At the point K the two phases coincide; that they are the same phase at this point can be seen from the fact that one can perform a continuous transition along any path outside the shaded area without any separation into two phases taking place.

As can be seen from Fig. 20 near the critical point there are states for which the two phases can be in equilibrium with arbitrarily close values of the concentration, x and $x+\mathrm{d}x$. For such phases the equilibrium condition takes the form

$$\mu(P, T, x) = \mu(P, T, x+\mathrm{d}x)$$

where μ is the chemical potential of one of the components of the mixture. Hence we see (cf. eqs. 79.5–6) that at the critical point the condition

$$\left(\frac{\partial\mu}{\partial x}\right)_{P,T} = 0 \tag{96.1}$$

must be satisfied.

This condition is identical with (95.8); hence the two definitions of the critical point (here and in §95) are equivalent. Note that, in (96.1), μ may be taken as the chemical potential of either of the two components of the mixture. However, the two conditions obtained by taking each of the two potentials in (96.1) are really equivalent, as can easily be seen if we note that each of the chemical potentials is the derivative of Φ with respect to the corresponding number of particles and that Φ is a homogeneous linear function of the two numbers of particles.

The critical points, obviously, lie on some line on the equilibrium surface (as was noted in §95).

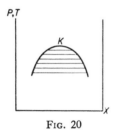

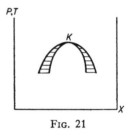

Fig. 20   Fig. 21

Near a point of equal concentration the equilibrium curves will have the form shown in Fig. 21 (or a corresponding form when the point of equal concentration is a minimum). The two curves touch at the maximum (or minimum) point. The region between the two curves is the region of separation into phases. At the point K the concentrations of the two phases in equilibrium with one another become the same but nevertheless the phases continue to exist separately. In fact one can go from one of the two points coinciding at K to the other only by crossing the region of phase separation. Like the critical points, points of equal concentration lie on some line of the equilibrium surface.

Now let us consider the properties of equilibrium curves for small concentrations (i.e. when there is much more of one substance than of another; x being near to zero or unity).

In §87 it was shown that for small concentrations (weak solutions) the difference between the phase equilibrium temperatures of a solution and the pure solvent (at the same pressure) is proportional to the difference of concentration of the two phases. The same applies to the difference in pressure for the same temperature. Moreover in §88 it was shown (again for small concentrations) that the ratio of the concentrations in the two phases depends on P and T only, and hence in the region near $\alpha = 0$ this ratio may be considered constant.

It immediately follows, from these considerations, that, for small concentrations, the equilibrium curves have the form shown in Fig. 22, i.e. they consist of two straight lines intersecting on the co-ordinate axis (the two lines may similarly be directed upwards). The region between the two straight lines is that of phase separation. The regions below and above the curves are regions representing one phase or the other by itself.

At the beginning of this section it was already mentioned that a system with two components may consist of three adjacent phases. Near a triple point the equilibrium curves look as shown in Fig. 23. All three phases have the same temperature and pressure at equilibrium. Hence the points A, B, C which determine their concentrations lie on a straight line parallel to the x-axis. The point A which determines the concentration of the first phase at the triple point is the point of intersection of the equilibrium curves,

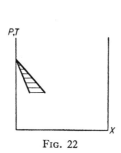

Fig. 22

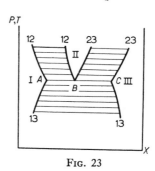

Fig. 23

12 and 13, of the first phase with the second, and the first phase with the third. Similarly points B and C are the intersections of the equilibrium curves 12 and 23, (point B) and of the curves, 23 and 13, (point C). All the points A, B, C are, of course, intersections of the plane $P = \text{const}$ or $T = \text{const}$ with three lines of the equilibrium surface. Of these lines, we shall call the one which corresponds to point B the line of triple points, or the three-phase line. The regions I, II, and III represent states with a single phase: the first, second, and third respectively. The region between the two curves 13 below the straight line ABC is the region of separation into the first and third phases, and the regions between the two curves 12 and between the two curves 23 (above ABC) are similarly regions of separation into the first and second phases and the second and third phases. Region II must obviously lie entirely above ABC (or entirely below ABC). At the points A, B, and C the curves 12, 13 and 23 intersect at some angle, in general, and do not form a continuous line. Curves 12, 13, and 23 do not, of course, necessarily have the directions shown in Fig. 23. All that is necessary is that the curves 12 and 23 and the curve 13 should lie on opposite sides of the straight line ABC.

If one projects one of these special lines of the equilibrium surface on to the P, T plane, then such a projection will divide the plane into two parts. In the case of a critical line the points corresponding to two separate phases and the points corresponding to the separation into these two phases will be projected on to one part of the plane and points representing homogeneous states in which no separation occurs into two phases on to the other part. In Fig. 24 the dotted line represents the projection of the critical line on to the P, T plane. The letters a, b represent the two phases. The symbol a-b denotes states of the two phases separately and states in which these two phases are in equilibrium. The symbol ab denotes the single phase into which both a and b merge above the critical points.

Similarly, the projection of a three-phase line also divides the P, T plane into two parts. Fig. 25 shows which points are projected into these parts. The symbol a-b-c denotes the region into which are projected points representing the single phases a, b, and c, and states in which separation into phases a and b, and b and c occurs.

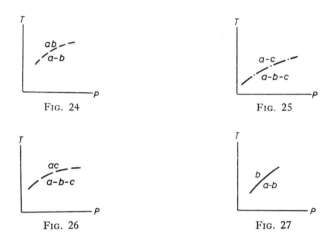

FIG. 24   FIG. 25

FIG. 26   FIG. 27

Fig. 26 shows such a projection for a line of points of equal concentration and Fig. 27 for a phase equilibrium line of a pure substance (i.e. points where $x = 0$ or 1); the latter obviously already lies in the P, T plane. The letter b in Fig. 27 indicates that on to this part of the plane are projected points corresponding to states of phase b only. We shall give a meaning to the order of the letters in the symbols a-b, a-b-c, the letter b denoting a phase with higher concentration than a and c denoting a phase with higher concentration than b.†

Note that the four types of special point of the equilibrium curves (triple point, point of equal concentration, critical point, and pure component point) represent four possible types of maximum (or minimum) for these curves.

If any of these phases has always (i.e. independently of P and T) the same composition then the equilibrium curves near the points we have considered become somewhat simpler. Examples of such phases are chemical compounds of the two components or phases of pure substances, i.e. phases which always have $x = 0$ (or $x = 1$).

---

† To avoid misunderstanding we must emphasise that the notation a-b-c in the case of a line of equal concentrations (in contrast with the three-phase line) is, in a sense, conventional; the letters a and c refer in this case to states which are not, strictly speaking, two different phases, since they never exist simultaneously in contact.

Consider the form of the equilibrium curves in the presence of a phase of constant composition near the endpoint of the line corresponding to this phase. It is clear that such a point must be a maximum or a minimum of the equilibrium curves and thus belong to one of the types of point we have studied in this section.

If the phase of constant composition is a phase of a pure substance with concentration $x = 0$, then the line corresponding to it coincides with the P or T axis and can end in a point of the type shown in Fig. 28. In this diagram the form of the equilibrium curve near such a point is shown; one of the straight lines of Fig. 22 coincides with the axis.

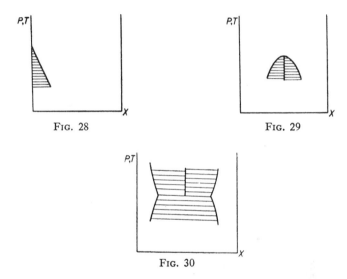

FIG. 28   FIG. 29

FIG. 30

If one of the phases is a chemical compound of definite composition, then near a point of equal concentration the equilibrium curve will look as shown in Fig. 29, i.e. the interior region of Fig. 21 becomes a vertical straight line. The shaded area on each side is an area of separation into two phases, one of which will be the chemical compound whose composition is determined by the straight line. At the maximum point the curve (like that in Fig. 21) has no kink.

Similarly, near a triple point the equilibrium curve takes the form shown in Fig. 30. The phase which is the chemical compound is represented by the vertical line to which the area II in Fig. 23 is reduced.

§97. Examples of state diagrams

In this section we shall list the basic types of equilibrium curve; in contrast to the preceding section we shall now examine them not only near the special points, but as a whole. These curves (also called *state diagrams*) can have a large variety of forms but in the majority of cases they belong to one of the types we shall study below or are a combination of several of them. In all these diagrams the shaded areas represent areas of phase separation and the unshaded areas represent homogeneous states. The points of intersection of horizontal lines with the curves bounding the phase separation areas determine the composition of the phases in equilibrium (for the given P and T). The relative quantities of the two phases are given by the same "leverage rule" as was mentioned in §77.

For the sake of explicitness we shall refer below to T, x diagrams; similar diagrams are possible for the co-ordinates P and x. The concentration x is measured along the abscissae and varies from 0 to 1.

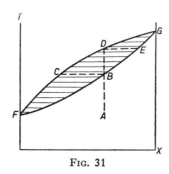

Fig. 31

1. There are two phases; each may have any concentration (i.e. the two components mix in arbitrary proportions in both phases). In the simplest case, when the curves have no maxima or minima (except the pure substance points) the state diagram is as shown in Fig. 31 (called "cigar shaped").

For example, one of the phases may be liquid (the region below the cigar), and the other, vapour (the region above the cigar); in this case the upper curve of the cigar is called the condensation curve and the lower one the boiling point curve.

If a liquid mixture of definite composition is heated, then, at a temperature determined by the intersection of the vertical straight line AD (corresponding to the given concentration) with the lower curve of the cigar (the point B), the liquid will begin to boil. The vapour, which then boils off, has a composition determined by the point C, i.e. it has lower concentration than the liquid. The concentration of the remaining liquid will obviously rise, and so also will its boiling point. With further heating the point representing the state of the liquid phase will move up the lower curve and the point representing the escaping vapour will move up the upper curve. The temperature at which the boiling concludes will depend on how the process takes place. If the boiling takes place in a closed vessel so that the vapour remains continuously in contact with the liquid, then the liquid will have completely boiled out at the temperature at which the vapour has a concentration equal to the initial concentration of the liquid (point D). Thus in this case the boiling begins and ends at temperatures determined by the intersections of the vertical line AD with the lower and upper curves of the cigar. If the vapour is continuously removed (boiling in an open vessel) then at every instant the fresh vapour alone is in equilibrium with the liquid. It is obvious that in this case the boiling will stop at the point G, the boiling point of the pure substance, at which the composition of the liquid and gas is the same. The condensation of vapour into liquid takes place in a similar way.

An exactly similar situation arises when the two phases are liquid (the region above the cigar) and solid (the region below the cigar).

Fig. 32

2. Both components mix in the two phases in arbitrary proportions (as in the previous case) but there is a point of equal concentration. The state diagram then has the form shown in Fig. 32 (or similarly with a minimum). At the point of equal concentration, both curves have a maximum or a minimum and touch each other.

The transition from one phase to the other takes place just as was described in the previous case, the only difference being that the process may terminate (if one of the phases is constantly removed, as in boiling in an open vessel, for instance) not only at a pure substance point but also at the point of equal concentration. Should the composition correspond to this particular point the whole transition takes place at the same temperature.

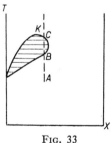

Fig. 33

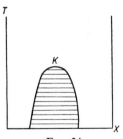

Fig. 34

3. There are two phases (liquid and gas) in which the two components are arbitrarily mixed and there is a critical point. The state diagram is as shown in Fig. 33 (K being the critical point). The region to the right of the curve corresponds to liquid states and that to the left corresponds to gaseous ones. It should be remembered, however, that when a critical point exists the liquid and gaseous phases can, strictly speaking, be distinguished only when the two are simultaneously in equilibrium.

A diagram of this type leads to the following unusual phenomenon. If a liquid, whose composition is represented by the line AC (passing to the right of K), is heated in a closed vessel then, after boiling has begun (at the point B), further heating will gradually increase the quantity of vapour, but after a certain time it begins to decrease again until the vapour disappears altogether at the point C (this is called *retrograde condensation*).

4. Two liquids are mixed but not in arbitrary proportions. The state diagram is shown in Fig. 34. At temperatures above that of the critical point K, the components mix in arbitrary proportions. Below this temperature the components do not mix in the proportions represented by points within the shaded region, but in this region phase separation occurs into two liquid mixtures, whose concentrations are determined by the intersections of the corresponding horizontal line with the equilibrium curve. Similar diagrams are possible in which the point K is a minimum or in which there are two critical points: an upper and a lower one, so that the region of separation into two phases (two solutions) is bounded by a closed curve.

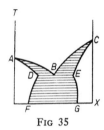

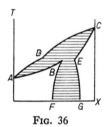

FIG 35   FIG. 36

5. In the liquid (or gaseous) state the two components mix arbitrarily, while in the solid (or liquid) state they do not mix in arbitrary proportions (limited miscibility). In this case there exists a triple point. Depending on whether the temperature of the triple point is lower than the temperatures of phase equilibrium of the pure components (points A and C), or between them,† the state diagram takes the form shown in Fig. 35 or 36 respectively. For example, suppose that the phase with unlimited miscibility is the liquid one, and that with limited miscibility the solid. The region above the curve ABC (Fig. 35) or ADC (Fig. 36) is the region of liquid states; the regions to the sides of ADF and CEG (Fig. 35) or ABF and CEG (Fig. 36) are regions of homogeneous solid phases (solid solutions). At the triple point (whose temperature is determined by the straight line DBE) one liquid and two solid solutions (with different concentrations) are in equilibrium. Point B in Fig. 35 is called the *eutectic point*. A liquid mixture whose concentration corresponds to this point freezes entirely with this same concentration (while for different concentrations a solid freezes out whose concentration differs from that of the liquid). The regions ADB and CBE (Fig. 35) or ADB and CDE (Fig. 36) are regions of separation into the liquid and one of the solid phases. The regions $DEGF$ (Fig. 35) and $BEGF$ (Fig. 36) are regions of separation into the two solid phases.

---

† Obviously it cannot be higher, since we have assumed that the components can be arbitrarily mixed in the higher phase.

If, in the case of a diagram of the type shown in Fig. 35, the two components do not mix at all in the solid state, then the state diagram becomes as shown in Fig. 37. In the shaded regions above the line ABC the mixed liquid phase is in equilibrium with one of the pure solid phases, and below ABC the solid phases of the two pure substances are in equilibrium with each other. As the temperature of the liquid mixture falls, one or other of the pure substances will freeze out, according as the concentration of the liquid lies to the right or to the left of the eutectic point. As the temperature falls still further the composition of the liquid changes along the curve DB or EB and the liquid freezes completely at the eutectic point B.

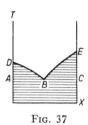

Fig. 37

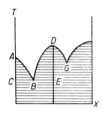

Fig. 38

6. In the liquid state the two components mix in arbitrary proportions, while in the solid state they do not mix at all, but form a chemical compound of definite composition. The state diagram is shown in Fig. 38. The straight line DE determines the composition of the chemical compound. There are two triple points, B and G, at each of which the liquid phase, the solid chemical compound, and the solid phase of one pure component, are in equilibrium. Between the points B and G there is a point of equal concentration, D (cf. Fig. 29). It is easy to see where, and into which phases, separation takes place: in the region DBG into the liquid phase and the solid chemical compound; below the straight line CE into the chemical compound and one of the solid pure substances, etc. The freezing of the liquid will terminate at one of the two eutectic points B and G according as the concentration of the liquid lies to the right or to the left of the straight line DE.

7. In the liquid state the two components mix in arbitrary proportions, while in the solid state they do not mix at all but form a chemical compound which, however, decomposes at some temperatures before melting takes place. The straight line which determines the composition of the compound cannot end at a point of equal concentration, as before, since it does not reach the melting point. Hence it can end at a triple point of the type shown in Fig. 30 in §96 (point A in Fig. 39). In Fig. 39, representing the state diagram for this case, it is easy to see into which phases the separation takes place at different points of the shaded region.

8. The two components do not mix at all in the solid state, and not in arbitrary proportions in the liquid state. In this case there are two triple points: one at which the liquid state is in equilibrium with the two solid

pure substances (point B in Fig. 40) and one at which one of these pure substances is in equilibrium with two mixed liquid phases of different concentrations (point D). The unshaded areas above ABC and above DE represent liquid states with different concentrations; the shaded region above CD is the region of separation into the two liquid phases; the region DEF is the region of separation into the liquid and one of the solid substances, etc.

FIG. 39   FIG. 40

§98. The intersection of the special lines of the equilibrium surface

The four types of line which we considered in §96 (critical, three-phase, equal concentration and pure substance) all lie on the same surface (the equilibrium surface). Hence, in general, they intersect one another. We now examine some of the properties of the points of intersection of these lines.

It can be shown that two critical lines cannot intersect. Nor can two lines of equal concentration. We shall not give a proof of these assertions here.

We shall now list (again without proof) the properties of the remaining points of intersection. These properties all follow almost at once from the general properties of the equilibrium curves, which we discussed in §96. In the diagrams we shall show the projections of the intersecting lines on the P, T plane (see §96). Their shape is, of course, chosen quite arbitrarily. A dotted line always indicates a critical line, a solid line indicates a pure substance line, a dashed line indicates a line of equal concentration and a line made up of dashes and dots indicates a three-phase line. The letters mean the same as in Figs. 24–27 of §96.

At the intersection of a critical line with a pure substance line (Fig. 41a) both lines come to an end. A critical line and a three-phase line also both end at their intersection (Fig. 41b). At the intersection of a pure substance line with a line of equal concentration only the latter comes to an end (Fig. 41c). In this case the two curves touch at the point of intersection. The same takes place at the intersection of a line of equal concentration with a critical line (Fig. 41d) or with a three-phase line (Fig. 41e). In each of these cases, at the intersection point, the line of equal concentration ends, and the two curves touch.

The intersection of three-phase lines (Fig. 41f) is a quadruple point, i.e. a point at which four phases are in equilibrium with one another. At the point of intersection four three-phase lines meet, corresponding to equilibrium between each three out of the four phases.

Lastly, the intersection of a pure substance line with a three-phase line (Fig. 41g) must, obviously, be the simultaneous intersection of the three-phase line with each of the three-phase equilibrium lines of the pure substance (corresponding to equilibrium between each two of the three phases of the pure substance).

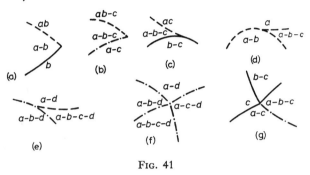

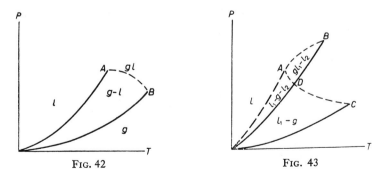

FIG. 41

§99. Liquid and gas

We shall now consider, in greater detail, the equilibrium of liquid and gaseous phases consisting of two components.

For sufficiently high temperatures (when kT is large compared with the mean interaction energy of the molecules) all substances mix in arbitrary proportions. Since a substance at such a temperature is a gas, we may say that in the gaseous phase all substances have unlimited miscibility. In the liquid state, however, some substances mix in arbitrary proportions while others do not (liquids of limited miscibility).

FIG. 42

FIG. 43

In the former case, when the two components mix freely in both phases, the state diagrams have no triple points since the system cannot consist of more than two phases (all the liquid states are in one phase and the same is true of the gaseous states). Consider the projection of the special lines of the equilibrium surface on to the P, T plane. We have two phase equilibrium lines for pure substances. One of these lines itself lies in the P, T plane, and the other in a parallel plane, so that its projection is exactly the same as the line itself. Each of these lines ends at some point which is the critical point for the phases of the corresponding pure substance. At these points the

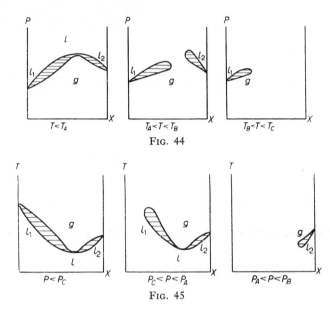

FIG. 44

FIG. 45

critical line begins and ends. Thus the projection of all these lines onto the P, T plane looks as in Fig. 42 (the notation is the same as in §§96, 98). The letter g denotes gas and the letter l denotes liquid; they have the same significance as the letters a, b, c in the diagrams of §§96, 98; on to the regions g and l are projected gaseous and liquid states; on to the region g–l are projected both, together with states in which the separation into liquid and gas takes place; above the critical line, the difference between gas and liquid disappears.

If there is also a line of equal concentration, its projection on the P, T plane has the form shown in Fig. 43. The projection of the line of equal concentration lies above the line going from the origin to B (as in Fig. 43) or below OC, but not between them. The only points of intersection of the different lines are A, B, C. The point D does not correspond to the actual intersection of the pure substance line with the critical line and exists only in the projection. The letters l_1, l_2 refer to liquid phases with different concentrations. Above the line of equal concentration only one liquid phase exists.†

---

† Not being concerned with the solid phases we draw for simplicity the lines on all the P, T diagrams as if they started at the origin and solidification did not occur.

All these properties of the projections of the special lines on the P, T plane become obvious if we consider state diagrams corresponding to sections of the equilibrium surface by planes of different temperature (or pressure).

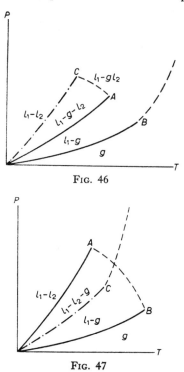

Fig. 46

Fig. 47

Thus, sections corresponding to pressures up to that of point B, and pressures between those of points A and B, in Fig. 42, give state diagrams like those of Figs. 31 and 33 respectively. In Fig. 44 are shown sections for a series of temperatures in Fig. 43 (T_A, T_B, T_C being the temperatures corresponding to the points A, B, C): the region of separation into two phases "breaks up" at the point of equal concentration, and as a result two critical points appear; then gradually, as they shrink to points on the ordinate axis, first one and then the other of these shaded areas disappear. In Fig. 45 are shown sections for a series of pressures in the same case.

If the two components have a limited miscibility in the liquid state, then there exists a three-phase line. This line will end at some point at which it meets a critical line which begins there. In Figs. 46 and 47 are shown the two basically different types of diagram (their projections on the P, T plane) which may occur in this case. They differ in that the projection of the three-phase line passes above both pure substance lines in Fig. 46 and between them in Fig. 47 (it cannot pass below both since for gaseous states the two components mix in arbitrary proportions). In each case there are two critical lines, one of which goes off in the direction of increasing pressure.

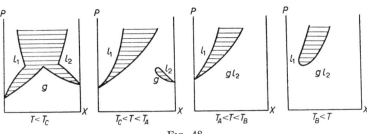

Fig. 48

In Fig. 48 and Fig. 49 are shown a series of sections by P, x planes and T, x planes for the case represented by Fig. 46.

In conclusion, we must stress that the examples of P, T diagrams we have considered in this section are only the most typical ones for equilibrium between liquid and gaseous phases, but by no means exhaust all the variants which are possible in principle.

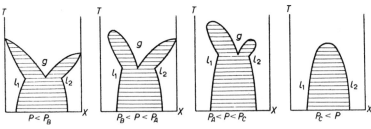

Fig. 49

CHAPTER X

CHEMICAL REACTIONS

§100. Conditions for chemical equilibrium

Chemical reactions occurring in mixtures of reacting substances lead, in the end, to the establishment of a state of equilibrium in which the quantity of each substance taking part in the reaction remains constant. This case of thermodynamic equilibrium is called *chemical* equilibrium. Every chemical reaction proceeds, in general, in both directions; before equilibrium is set up, one of the directions of the reaction predominates, while at equilibrium the two opposite reactions take place at speeds such that the total number of particles of each of the reagents remains constant. The subject of thermodynamics, as applied to a chemical reaction, is the study of the chemical equilibrium only, and not of the reaction leading to it.

It is essential to note that the state of chemical equilibrium does not depend upon the way (under what conditions) the reaction occurred;† it depends only on the condition of the mixture of the reagents in the actual state of chemical equilibrium. Hence, to deduce conditions for chemical equilibrium, one can make any assumptions at all as to the way the reaction took place.

Chemical reactions are expressed in terms of symbolic equations which we shall write in general form:

$$\sum_i \nu_i A_i = 0, \tag{100.1}$$

where A_i are the chemical symbols of the reagents and the coefficients ν_i are positive or negative integers. For example, for the reaction $2H_2 + O_2 = 2H_2O$, or $2H_2 + O_2 - 2H_2O = 0$ the coefficients are $\nu_{H_2} = 2$, $\nu_{O_2} = 1$, $\nu_{H_2O} = -2$.

Let us assume that the reaction takes place at constant temperature and pressure. In such a process the thermodynamic potential of the system tends to a minimum. Hence, at equilibrium, the potential Φ must have its smallest possible value (for the given P and T). We shall denote by N_1, N_2, ... the numbers of particles of the different substances taking part in the reaction. Then one of the necessary conditions for Φ to be a minimum can be expressed as the vanishing of the total derivative of Φ (for the given P and T). With respect to one of the N_i, say N_1,

$$\frac{\partial \Phi}{\partial N_1} + \frac{\partial \Phi}{\partial N_2}\frac{dN_2}{dN_1} + \frac{\partial \Phi}{\partial N_3}\frac{dN_3}{dN_1} + \ldots = 0.$$

† In particular, it is independent of whether the reaction occurred under catalysis or not.

315

The changes in the numbers N_i during the reaction are related to one another by means of the equation of the reaction; it is clear that, if N_1 changes by ν_1 then each of the other numbers N_i will change by ν_i. In other words, one can write $dN_i = \nu_i/\nu_1\, dN_1$, or $dN_i/dN_1 = \nu_i/\nu_1$. Hence the previous equation may be written as

$$\sum_i \frac{\partial \Phi}{\partial N_i}\frac{\nu_i}{\nu_1} = 0.$$

Finally, putting $\partial \Phi/\partial N_i = \mu_i$ and cancelling out ν_1 we obtain:

$$\sum_i \nu_i \mu_i = 0. \tag{100.2}$$

This is the required equation for chemical equilibrium. To write it down, therefore, we must replace the symbols A_i in the equation of the chemical reaction by the corresponding chemical potentials μ_i. When several different reactions are possible in the mixture, the equilibrium conditions will be a system of several equations of the type (100.2). Each of these equations is constructed from the equation of the corresponding reaction in the way indicated above.

Note that (100.2) retains its form also when the reagents are distributed in the form of solutions of the reacting substances in two (different) adjacent phases. This follows from the fact that at equilibrium the chemical potential of each substance is the same in both phases, owing to the phase equilibrium condition.

§101. The law of mass action

We now apply the general equation for chemical equilibrium, obtained in the previous section, to reactions taking place in a gaseous substance, assuming that the gas can be considered perfect.

The chemical potential of each of the gases in the mixture is (see §92)

$$\mu_i = kT \log P_i + \chi_i(T), \tag{101.1}$$

where P_i is the partial pressure of the ith gas in the mixture; $P_i = c_i P$. In this case P is the total pressure of the mixture, and $c_i = N_i/N$ is the concentration of the given gas, which we define as the ratio of the number N_i of molecules of this gas to the total number $N = \sum_i N_i$ of molecules in the mixture.

The condition for chemical equilibrium for reactions occurring in the gaseous mixture can now easily be written down. Substituting (101.1) into (100.2), we find:

$$\sum_i \nu_i \mu_i = kT \sum_i \nu_i \log P_{0i} + \sum_i \nu_i \chi_i = 0,$$

where P_{0i} are the partial pressures of the gases in the state of chemical equilibrium, or

$$\sum_i \nu_i \log P_{0i} = -\frac{1}{kT} \sum_i \nu_i \chi_i.$$

Introducing the notation

$$K_p(T) = e^{-(\Sigma \nu_i \chi_i)/kT}, \tag{101.2}$$

we obtain from this:

$$\prod_i P_{0i}^{\nu_i} = K_p(T). \tag{101.3}$$

We may replace P_{0i} by Pc_{0i}, where the c_{0i} are the concentrations of the gases in the chemical equilibrium state; we then get:

$$\prod_i c_{0i}^{\nu_i} = P^{-\Sigma \nu_i} K_p(T) \equiv K_c(P, T). \tag{101.4}$$

The right-hand side of eq. (101.3) or (101.4) is a function of temperature and pressure only, and is independent of the initial quantities of the reacting gases; this quantity is usually called the *chemical equilibrium constant*.

The fact that, in the equilibrium state, the product $\prod_i c_{0i}^{\nu_i}$ or $\prod_i P_{0i}^{\nu_i}$ is constant (for given P and T) is called the *law of mass action*.

The pressure dependence of the equilibrium constant for a gas reaction is completely determined by the factor $P^{-\Sigma \nu_i}$ on the right-hand side of eq. (101.4) (when the quantities of the reacting substances are expressed in terms of their partial pressures, the equilibrium constant is independent of pressure). However, its dependence on temperature requires some further assumptions as to the properties of the gases.

Thus, if the gases have constant specific heats, then comparison of (101.1) with the formula (43.4) for the thermodynamic potential of such a gas shows that the function $\chi_i(T)$ has the form

$$\chi_i(T) = \epsilon_{0i} - c_{pi}T \log kT - kT\zeta_i, \tag{101.5}$$

where c_{pi} is the specific heat, and ζ_i the chemical constant of the gas. Substituting this into (101.2), we obtain the following formula for the equilibrium constant:

$$K_p(T) = e^{\Sigma \nu_i \zeta_i} [(kT)^{(\Sigma c_{pi} \nu_i)/k}] e^{-(\Sigma \nu_i \epsilon_{0i})/kT}. \tag{101.6}$$

Its temperature dependence is essentially exponential.

The law of mass action is also valid for reactions between solutions, if we consider the solutions to be weak. The chemical potential of each of the solutes has the form

$$\mu = kT \log c_i + \psi_i(P, T) \tag{101.7}$$

(we obtain this by differentiating the thermodynamic potential (85.3) with respect to n_i). The concentration c_i is defined in this case as the ratio of the number of particles of the given solute to the number of particles of the solvent $(c_i = n_i/N)$. Substituting (101.7) into the equilibrium condition (100.2), we obtain, in the same way:

$$\prod_i c_{0i}{}^{\nu_i} = K(P, T) \tag{101.8}$$

where the equilibrium constant

$$K(P, T) = e^{-(\Sigma \nu_i \psi_i)/kT} \tag{101.9}$$

The difference between this and the gas reaction is that in this case the pressure dependence of the equilibrium constant remains indeterminate.

If not only gases and solutions, but also substances in pure condensed phases (i.e. not mixed with any other substance), such as solids, take part in the reaction, then the equilibrium condition again leads to the law of mass action. In this case, however, since the chemical potentials of the pure phases depend only on the pressure and temperature, the left-hand side of this equation describing this law will not contain factors referring to the pure phases, i.e. the product of the concentrations of the gases (or solutions) must be written as if the solids were not present. The latter only affect the dependence of the equilibrium constant on the temperature and pressure.

If only solids and gases take part in the reaction then, since the gas pressure is comparatively small, one can assume the chemical potentials of the solids to be independent of pressure, and the relation between the equilibrium constant and the pressure remains the same as in (101.4). In this case, however, ever, the sum $\Sigma \nu_i$ in the exponent must mean the sum of the coefficients in the reaction equation of the gaseous substances only.

Lastly, the law of mass action is also valid for reactions in weak solutions in which the solvents take part, as well as the solutes. Indeed, when we substitute the chemical potential of the solvent into the chemical equilibrium condition, the small terms involving the concentrations may be neglected and it will reduce to a quantity depending on temperature and pressure only. Hence we again obtain the equation of the law of mass action, and its left-hand side will again involve only the concentrations of the reacting solutes, but not that of the solvent.

PROBLEMS

1. Find the equilibrium constant for the dissociation of a diatomic gas at high temperature; the molecules of the gas consisting of identical atoms, with no spin or orbital angular momentum in the ground state.

SOLUTION: We are dealing, in this case, with a reaction of the type $A_2 = 2A$. The specific heats of the gases A_2 and A are $c_{pA_2} = 9/2k$, $c_{pA} = 5/2k$ and their chemical constants (see (45.4), (46.4), (46.8)) are

$$\zeta_A = \log\left[g_A\left(\frac{m}{2\pi\hbar^2}\right)^{3/2} \right], \qquad \zeta_{A2} = \log\left[\frac{I}{\hbar^6 \omega}\left(\frac{m}{\pi}\right)^{3/2} \right],$$

where m is the mass of the atom A (the mass of the molecule A_2 being $2m$), g_A is the statistical weight of the ground state of the atom A (at sufficiently high temperatures $g_A = (2S+1) \times (2L+1)$, where S, L are the spin and orbital angular momenta of the atom). Substituting into (101.6) we obtain:

$$K_p(T) = \frac{8I}{g_A^2 \omega} \left(\frac{\pi}{m}\right)^{3/2} \frac{1}{\sqrt{(kT)}} e^{\epsilon_0/kT},$$

where $\epsilon_0 = 2\epsilon_{0A} - \epsilon_{0A_2}$ is the energy of dissociation of one molecule.

2. Determine the relation between the concentration of hydrogen dissolving in a metal in the form of H atoms and the pressure of the H_2 gas over the metal.

SOLUTION: Treating the process as the chemical reaction $H_2 = 2H$ we write the equilibrium condition in the form $\mu_{H_2} = 2\mu_H$; μ_{H_2} can be written as the chemical potential of an ideal gas: $\mu_{H_2} = kT \log P + \chi(T)$, and μ_H as the chemical potential of a solute in a solvent: $\mu_H = kT \log c + \psi$. Bearing in mind that ψ is almost independent of the pressure (cf. §88), we obtain

$$c = \text{const} \sqrt{P}.$$

§102. Heat of reaction

A chemical reaction is accompanied by the absorption or the evolution of heat. In the first case we talk of an endothermic, and in the second of an exothermic reaction. It is clear that if a reaction is exothermic then the inverse one will be endothermic, and *vice versa*.

The thermal effect of a reaction depends on the conditions in which the reaction takes place. Hence, for example, we must distinguish between the thermal effects of a reaction occurring at constant volume and at constant pressure. (This difference, however, is usually not large.)

As in the calculation of the heat of solution (§89) we shall first of all determine the maximum work which may be produced as a result of the chemical reaction.

We shall call a reaction between one set of molecules described by the equation of the reaction an "elementary reaction", and we shall calculate the changes in the thermodynamic potential of the mixture of the reacting substances after a certain small number, δn, of elementary reactions have taken place; we assume that the reaction takes place at constant temperature and pressure. We have:

$$\delta\Phi = \sum_i \frac{\partial\Phi}{\partial N_i} \delta N_i = \sum_i \mu_i \delta N_i.$$

Hhe change in the number of molecules of the ith substance, after δn elementary reactions will be obviously, $\delta N_i = -\nu_i \delta n$. Thus,

$$\delta\Phi = -\delta n \sum_i \nu_i \mu_i. \tag{102.1}$$

At equilibrium $\delta\Phi/\delta n$ vanishes, as it should.

The quantity (102.1) is the general expression for the minimum work which must be expended to carry out δn elementary reactions. It is also the maximum work which can be obtained as a result of the same number of reactions taking place in the opposite direction.

Assume, first, that the reaction is one between gases. Using the expression (101.1) for μ_i, we obtain:

$$\delta\Phi = -\delta n(kT \sum_i \nu_i \log P_i + \sum_i \nu_i \chi_i),$$

or, introducing the equilibrium constant:

$$\delta\Phi = kT\delta n[- \sum_i \nu_i \log P_i + \log K_p(T)]$$

$$= kT\delta n[- \sum_i \nu_i c_i + \log K_c(P, T)]. \tag{102.2}$$

For reactions in solutions we find, similarly, with the aid of (101.7):

$$\delta\Phi = -\delta n(kT \sum_i \nu_i \log c_i + \sum_i \nu_i \psi_i),$$

or, introducing the equilibrium constant $K(P, T)$:

$$\delta\Phi = kT\delta n[- \sum_i \nu_i \log c_i + \log K(P, T)]. \tag{102.3}$$

The sign of the quantity $\delta\Phi$ determines the direction in which the reaction takes place; since Φ tends to a minimum, then for $\delta\Phi < 0$ the reaction goes in the forward direction (i.e. from "left to right" in the equation of the chemical reaction) and if $\delta\Phi > 0$ then in the given mixture the reaction takes place in the opposite direction. Note, however, that the direction of the reaction can also be derived directly from the law of mass action. We construct the product $\prod_i P_i^{\nu_i}$ for the given mixture and compare it with the value of the equilibrium constant for this reaction; if, for example, it should happen that $\prod_i P_i^{\nu_i} > K_p$ then the reaction will proceed in the forward direction, so that the partial pressures of the initial substances (which are those with positive ν_i in the reaction equation) decrease and the pressures of the reaction products (for which $\nu_i < 0$) increase.

We can also determine the quantity of heat absorbed (or evolved, depending on the sign obtained), again for δn elementary reactions. According to (89.4) this heat, δQ_p, for a reaction taking place at constant temperature and pressure, is

$$\delta Q_p = -T^2 \left(\frac{\partial}{\partial T} \frac{\delta\Phi}{T}\right)_P.$$

For a reaction between gases we have, substituting from (102.2):

$$\delta Q_p = -kT^2\delta n \frac{\partial[\log K_p(T)]}{\partial T}. \tag{102.4}$$

Similarly, for solutions:

$$\delta Q_p = -kT^2\delta n \frac{\partial[\log K(P, T)]}{\partial T}. \tag{102.5}$$

Note that δQ_p is simply proportional to δn and is independent of the values of the concentrations at any given moment; hence these formulae can also be applied when δn is large.

If $Q_p > 0$ (i.e. the reaction is endothermic) then $\partial(\log K)/\partial T < 0$, i.e. the equilibrium constant decreases as the temperature increases. Conversely, for an exothermic reaction ($Q_p < 0$) the equilibrium constant increases with temperature. On the other hand an increase in the equilibrium constant means that the chemical equilibrium shifts towards the reproduction of the initial substances (the reaction takes place "from right to left") so that the product $\prod_i c_{0i}^{\nu_i}$, will increase. Conversely a decrease in the equilibrium constant means that the equilibrium will shift towards the production of reaction products. In other words, one can formulate the following rule: heating shifts the equilibrium in the direction in which the process takes place endothermically, while cooling shifts it in the direction in which it takes place exothermically. This rule is in complete agreement with Le Chatelier's principle.

In the case of a reaction between gases, the thermal effects of the reaction taking place at constant volume (and temperature) are also of interest. This quantity δQ_v is connected quite simply with the heat δQ_p. The former is equal to the change in the energy of the system, while the latter is equal to the change in the heat function. Since $E = W - PV$, it is clear that

$$\delta Q_v = \delta Q_p - \delta(PV).$$

But according to the Clapeyron equation, $PV = NkT$ (where $N = \sum_i N_i$ is the total number of molecules in the gas), so that:

$$\delta(PV) = kT \sum_i \delta N_i = -kT\delta n \sum \nu_i$$

Thus

$$\delta Q_v = \delta Q_p + kT\delta n \sum_i \nu_i. \tag{102.6}$$

Lastly, we shall also determine the change in the volume of a mixture of reacting substances as a result of a reaction taking place at constant pressure (and temperature). For gases this is trivial, since the volume of an ideal gas for given P and T is immediately determined by the number of its molecules, with the aid of the Clapeyron equation. Hence it is clear that

$$\delta V = \frac{kT}{P} \delta N = -\frac{kT}{P} \delta n \sum_i \nu_i. \tag{102.7}$$

In particular, reactions in which the total number of particles remains constant ($\sum \nu_i = 0$) take place with no change in volume.

For reactions in weak solutions we use the formula $\delta V = (\partial/\partial P)\delta\Phi$ and, substituting into (102.3), we obtain:

$$\delta V = kT\delta n \frac{\partial \log K(P, T)}{\partial P} \tag{102.8}$$

(for the case of gases, if we substitute $K = K_p(T)P^{-\Sigma \nu_i}$, this formula obviously becomes (102.7)).

Thus the change in volume during a reaction is related to the way in which the equilibrium constant depends on the pressure. By means of similar arguments to those we used when discussing temperature dependence, it is easy to see that an increase in pressure assists reactions taking place with decreasing volume and that a decrease in pressure assists reactions tending to increase the volume, again in complete agreement with Le Chatelier's principle.

§103. Ionisation equilibrium

At sufficiently high temperatures collisions between gas particles may be accompanied by ionisation. The existence of this *"thermal ionisation"* leads to the setting up of thermal equilibrium when definite proportions of the total number of gas particles are in different stages of ionisation. Consider the thermal ionisation of a monatomic gas; this case is the one of greatest interest, since at the thermal ionisation temperature the chemical bonds are usually completely dissociated.

From the thermodynamic point of view, ionisation equilibrium is a special case of chemical equilibrium, corresponding to several "ionisation reactions" taking place simultaneously, which may be expressed in the form

$$A_0 = A_1 + e^-, \qquad A_1 = A_2 + e^-, ..., \qquad (103.1)$$

where the symbol A_0 denotes a neutral atom, A_1, A_2, ... etc. denote singly, doubly ... etc. ionised atoms, and e^- denotes an electron. When applied to these reactions, the law of mass action leads to the set of equations

$$\frac{c_{n-1}}{c_n c} = P K_p^{(n)}(T) \qquad (n = 1, 2, ...), \qquad (103.2)$$

where c_0 is the concentration of neutral atoms, c_1, c_2, ... are the concentrations of ions of different orders and c is the concentration of electrons (each of these concentrations being defined as the ratio of the number of particles of the given kind to the total number of particles, including electrons). To these equations must be added the one ensuring electrical neutrality:

$$c = c_1 + 2c_2 + 3c_3 + ... \qquad (103.3)$$

The system of eqs. (103.2, 3) determines the concentrations of the different ions at ionisation equilibrium.

The equilibrium constant $K_p^{(n)}$ can also be easily calculated. All the gases taking part in the "reactions" (the gases of neutral atoms, ions, and electrons) are monatomic and have constant specific heats $c_p = 5k/2$, and chemical constants

$$\zeta = \log \left[g \left(\frac{m}{2\pi \hbar^2} \right)^{3/2} \right],$$

where m is the mass of a particle of the given gas and g is the statistical weight of its ground state; for electrons $g = 2$, while for the atoms and ions $g = (2L+1)(2S+1)$ (L, S, being the orbital angular momentum and spin of the atom or ion)†. Substituting these values into (101.6), we obtain the following expression for the required equilibrium constants:

$$K_p^{(n)}(T) = \frac{g_{n-1}}{2g_n}\left(\frac{2\pi}{m}\right)^{3/2}\frac{\hbar^3}{(kT)^{5/2}}e^{I_n/kT}. \tag{103.4}$$

Here m is the mass of an electron and $I_n = \epsilon_{0,n} - \epsilon_{0,n-1}$ is the energy of the nth ionisation (the nth ionisation potential of the atom).

The degree of ionisation of the gas (of given order n) becomes of order unity when, as the temperature increases, the decreasing equilibrium constant $K_c^{(n)} = PK_p^{(n)}$ becomes of order unity. It is very important to note that in spite of the exponential temperature dependence of the equilibrium constant, this does not occur at $kT \sim I_{\text{ion}}$ but at considerably lower temperatures. The reason for this is the smallness of the coefficient of the exponential factor: the quantity

$$\frac{P}{kT}\left(\frac{\hbar^2}{mkT}\right)^{3/2} = \frac{N}{V}\left(\frac{\hbar^2}{mkT}\right)^{3/2},$$

is in general very small. For $kT \sim I$ it is of the same order as the ratio of the atomic volume V/N per atom in the gas.

Thus the gas will already be considerably ionised at temperatures which are small compared with the ionisation energy. At the same time, the number of excited atoms in the gas will still be very small, since the excitation energy of the atom is, in general, of the same order of magnitude as the ionisation energy.

When kT becomes comparable with the ionisation energy the gas is almost completely ionised. At temperatures of the order of magnitude of the binding energy of the last electron in the atom, the gas may be considered to consist only of electrons and bare nuclei.

The binding energy, I_1, of the first electron is usually considerably smaller than the following energies I_n; hence there exists a range of temperatures over which the gas may be considered to consist of neutral atoms and singly charged ions only. Introducing the "degree of ionisation" α of the gas as the ratio of the number of ionised atoms to the total number of atoms we have:

$$c = c_1 = \frac{\alpha}{1+\alpha}, \qquad c_0 = \frac{1-\alpha}{1+\alpha},$$

---

† For reasons given below it can be assumed that, even in a considerably ionised gas, all the atoms and ions are in their ground state.

If the ground state of the atoms (or ions) possesses a fine structure, then we assume that kT is large compared with the intervals of this fine structure.

and eq. (103.2) gives:

$$\frac{1-\alpha^2}{\alpha^2} = PK_p^{(1)},$$

whence

$$\alpha = \frac{1}{\sqrt{(1+PK_p^{(1)})}}, \tag{103.5}$$

which completely determines the dependence of the degree of ionisation on the temperature and pressure (over the temperature range in question).

CHAPTER XI

THE PROPERTIES OF MATTER AT VERY HIGH TEMPERATURES AND DENSITIES

§104. Equilibrium with respect to pair production

Consider the properties of matter at extremely high temperatures, when kT becomes comparable to the rest energy of the electron, mc^2 (m being the mass of the electron and c the velocity of light),† At such temperatures, collisions of particles may be accompanied by the production of electron pairs (electrons and positrons), and consequently the number of particles is no longer a given quantity but will depend on the thermal equilibrium conditions.

Pair production (or annihilation) may be considered, from the thermodynamic point of view, as the "chemical reaction"

$$e^+ + e^- = \gamma$$

where the symbols e^+ and e^- denote a positron or an electron, and the symbol γ denotes one or several photons. The chemical potential of the photon gas is zero (§60) and hence the equilibrium conditions relating to pair production will be of the form

$$\mu^- + \mu^+ = 0, \tag{104.1}$$

where μ^- and μ^+ are the chemical potentials of the electron and positron gases. We must emphasise that μ in this case means the relativistic expression for the chemical potential, which includes the rest energy of the particles (cf. §27) with which the process of pair production is fundamentally connected.

As will be seen from the formulae obtained below, already at temperatures $kT \sim mc^2$ the number of electron pairs created (per unit volume) is very large compared with the density of atomic electrons. Hence we may, to sufficient accuracy, regard the numbers of electrons and positrons as equal. In this case $\mu^- = \mu^+$, and the condition (104.1) gives:

$$\mu^- = \mu^+ = 0,$$

i.e. at equilibrium the chemical potentials of the electrons and positrons must vanish.

The electrons and positrons obey Fermi statistics. Hence their numbers

---

† The energy $mc^2 = 0.51 . 10^6$ eV so that the temperature $mc^2/k = 6.10^9$ degrees.

may be obtained by integrating the distribution (55.3) with

$$N^+ = N^- = \frac{V}{\pi^2 \hbar^3} \int_0^\infty \frac{p^2 \, dp}{e^{\epsilon/kT} + 1} \tag{104.2}$$

where ϵ is defined by the relativistic expression $\epsilon = c\sqrt{(p^2 + m^2 c^2)}$.

For $kT \ll mc^2$ this number is exponentially small ($\sim e^{-mc^2/kT}$) but in the opposite case, $kT \gg mc^2$ we may put $\epsilon = cp$, and (104.2) gives

$$N^+ = N^- = \frac{V}{\pi^2} \left(\frac{kT}{\hbar c} \right)^3 \int_0^\infty \frac{x^2 \, dx}{e^x + 1}.$$

This integral can be expressed in terms of the ζ-function of argument 3 (see footnote on page 164), and we obtain:†

$$N^+ = N^- = \frac{3\zeta(3)}{2\pi^2} \left(\frac{kT}{\hbar c} \right)^3 = 0 \cdot 183 \left(\frac{kT}{\hbar c} \right)^3. \tag{104.3}$$

In the same way we can find the energy of the positron and electron gases:

$$E^+ = E^- = \frac{VkT}{\pi^2} \left(\frac{kT}{\hbar c} \right)^3 \int_0^\infty \frac{x^2 \, dx}{e^x + 1}.$$

The integral in this is equal to $7\pi^4/120$, so that we obtain:

$$E^+ = E^- = \frac{7\pi^2}{120} \frac{(kT)^4}{(\hbar c)^3} V. \tag{104.4}$$

This quantity is equal to 7/8 of the energy of black-body radiation in the same volume.

PROBLEM

Determine the equilibrium density of electrons and positrons for $kT \ll mc^2$.

SOLUTION: Making use of expression (46.1a) for the chemical potential (to which we must add mc^2), we obtain:

$$n^+ = n^- = 4 \left(\frac{mkT}{2\pi\hbar^2} \right)^3 e^{-2mc^2/kT},$$

where $n = N^-/V$, $n^+ = N^+/V$ are the densities of the electrons and positrons. If n_0 is the initial density of electrons (in the absence of pair creation), then $n^- = n^+ + n_0$ and we obtain:

$$n^+ = n^- - n^0 = -\frac{n_0}{2} + \left[\frac{n_0^2}{4} + \frac{1}{2} \left(\frac{mkT}{\pi\hbar^2} \right)^3 e^{-2mc^2/kT} \right]^{1/2}.$$

---

† For $kT \sim mc^2$ the volume allotted to a single created particle is of the order of $(\hbar/mc)^3$ i.e. the cube of the Compton wavelength. This volume is very small compared with the atomic dimensions (for example with the cube of the Bohr radius $(\hbar^2/me^2)^3$).

§105. The equation of state for very dense matter

In addition to the properties of matter at extremely high temperatures, an interesting problem is the study of matter at very high density. Let us examine qualitatively the changes in behaviour as the density increases.

At the end of §56 a peculiar property of the degenerate Fermi gas was noted: its "perfectness" increases as the density rises. Hence, for a sufficiently compressed substance, the effect of the interaction of its atomic electrons with the nuclei becomes insignificant and the substance may be regarded as a degenerate perfect Fermi electron gas. (We assume the temperature of the substance not to be too high.)† According to (56.9) this occurs when the inequality

$$n_e \gg \left(\frac{m_e e^2}{\hbar^2} \right)^3 Z^2,$$

is satisfied, where n_e is the number density of the electrons, m_e the mass of the electron and Z some average atomic number of the substance. We hence obtain the following inequality for the total density of the substance.‡

$$\rho \gg \left(\frac{m_e e^2}{\hbar^2} \right)^3 m' Z^2 \sim 20 Z^2 \text{g/cm}^3, \tag{105.1}$$

where m' is the mass per electron in the substance, so that $\rho = m' n_e$∥. The thermodynamic quantities of the substance are given, in the region under consideration, by the formulae obtained in §56. In particular, for the pressure we have:

$$P = \frac{(3\pi^2)^{2/3}}{5} \frac{\hbar^2}{m_e} \left(\frac{\rho}{m'} \right)^{5/3}. \tag{105.2}$$

The condition (105.1) gives the following numerical inequality for the pressure:

$$P \gg 5 \cdot 10^8 Z^{10/3} \text{ atm.}$$

In the above formulae, the electron gas was assumed to be non-relativistic. This requires the limiting Fermi momentum p_0 to be small compared with mc (see §56), which leads to the numerical inequalities

$$\rho \ll 2 \cdot 10^6 \text{ g/cm}^3, \qquad P \ll 10^{17} \text{ atm.}$$

When the density and pressure of the gas become comparable with the

---

† As far as the "nuclear gas" is concerned, owing to the large mass of the nuclei, it may be far from degenerate, but its contribution, for example to the pressure of the substance, is in any case quite insignificant compared with the pressure of the electron gas.

‡ In all the numerical calculations in this section it is assumed that for each electron the substance possesses a mass, m', equal to twice the proton mass.

∥ The degeneracy temperature, corresponding to the substance having a density $\rho \sim 20 Z^2$ g/cm³ is of the order of $10^6 Z^{4/3}$ degrees.

values quoted, the electron gas becomes relativistic and when they satisfy the opposite inequalities, it becomes extreme relativistic. In the latter case the equation of state for the substance is given by (58.4) according to which

$$P = \frac{(3\pi^2)^{1/3}}{4}\hbar c\left(\frac{\rho}{m'}\right)^{4/3}. \tag{105.3}$$

A further increase in the density leads to states in which nuclear reactions consisting of the capture of electrons by the nucleus (with the simultaneous emission of a neutrino) become thermodynamically favourable. As a result of such a reaction, the charge of the nucleus decreases (while its mass remains the same) which leads, in general, to a decrease in the binding energy of the nucleus, i.e. to a decrease in its mass defect. The energetic disadvantage of such a process is easily compensated, at sufficiently high densities, by the decrease in the energy of the degenerate electron gas due to the decrease in the number of its electrons.

It is not difficult to write down the thermodynamic conditions governing the "chemical equilibrium" of the nuclear reaction just described, which may be expressed by the symbolic equation

$$A_Z + e^- = A_{Z-1} + \nu,$$

where A_Z denotes a nucleus of mass A and charge Z; e^- denotes an electron and ν a neutrino. The neutrinos are not retained by the substance and leave the body; this process must lead to a continual cooling of the body. Hence there is no point in examining the thermal equilibrium in such conditions unless we assume the temperature to be zero. The chemical potential of the neutrino then does not occur in the equilibrium equation. The chemical potential of the nucleus is mainly determined by its intrinsic energy which we shall denote by $-\epsilon_{A,Z}$ (the positive quantity $\epsilon_{A,Z}$ is usually called the binding energy). Lastly, we shall denote by $\mu_e(n_e)$ the chemical potential of the electron gas as a function of the number density of the particles in it. The chemical equilibrium condition then takes the form $-\epsilon_{A,Z} + \mu_e(n_e) = -\epsilon_{A,Z-1}$ or, introducing the notation $\epsilon_{A,Z} - \epsilon_{A,Z-1} = \Delta$:

$$\mu_e(n_e) = \Delta.$$

Using the formula (58.2) for the chemical potential of an extreme relativistic degenerate gas, we obtain:

$$n_e = \frac{\Delta^3}{3\pi^2(c\hbar)^3}. \tag{105.4}$$

Thus the equilibrium condition leads to a constant value of the electron density. This means that if the density of the substance gradually increases, the above nuclear reaction will start when the electron density reaches the value (105.4). As the substance is further compressed, more and more nuclei will capture an electron so that the total number of electrons will diminish, but their density will remain constant. Besides the electronic density, the pressure of the substance will also remain constant. As before, it will be principally determined by the pressure of the electron gas; substitution of (105.4) into (105.3) gives:

$$P = \frac{\Delta^4}{12\pi^2(\hbar c)^3}. \tag{105.5}$$

The process will continue in this way until each of the nuclei has captured an electron.

For still higher densities and pressures there will occur further capture of electrons by the nuclei, accompanied by further decreases in the nuclear charge. As a result, the nuclei containing too many neutrons will become unstable and they will disintegrate. For densities $\rho \sim 3 \cdot 10^{11}$ g/cm^3 (and pressures $P \sim 10^{24}$ atm) the number of neutrons begins to exceed the number of electrons and already at $\rho \sim 10^{12}$ g/cm^3 their pressure also begins to predominate. At this point begins the region in which the substance may be essentially regarded as a degenerate Fermi neutron gas with a small admixture of electrons and various nuclei, whose concentrations are determined by the equilibrium conditions for the corresponding nuclear reactions. The equation of state for the substance in this region is:

$$P = \frac{(3\pi^2)^{2/3}}{5} \frac{\hbar^2}{m_n^{8/3}} \rho^{5/3}, \tag{105.6}$$

where m_n is the mass of a neutron.

Finally, for densities $\rho \gg 6 \cdot 10^{15}$ g/cm^3 the degenerate neutron gas becomes an extreme relativistic one and the equation of state will be given by the formula†

$$P = \frac{(3\pi^2)^{1/3}}{4} \hbar c \left(\frac{\rho}{m_n} \right)^{4/3}. \tag{105.7}$$

In this gas, however, a certain number of protons and electrons will always be present which appear as a result of the neutron disintegration

$$n = p + e^- + \nu.$$

Although this reaction leads to an increase in the total number of particles, nevertheless, it may be thermodynamically favourable, owing to the decrease in the limiting energy of the Fermi distribution of the neutrons (it must be remembered that each kind of particle—neutron, proton, and electron fills its own series of states). A quantitative calculation can easily be carried out with the help of the chemical equilibrium condition for this reaction,

---

† It should be borne in mind that for densities of the order of magnitude of the density of nuclear matter the specific nuclear interaction forces become of prime importance. In this range of the density formulae (105.6) and (105.7) can have only a qualitative meaning.

which gives:

$$\mu_n(n_n) = \mu_e(n_e) + \mu_p(n_p),$$

where μ_n, μ_p and μ_e are the chemical potentials of the neutrons, protons, and electrons as functions of the number densities of the corresponding particles. But the numbers of protons and electrons are obviously equal ($n_p = n_e$) and the chemical potential of an extreme relativistic degenerate gas is proportional to $n^{1/3}$ and is independent of the mass of the particles (see (58.2)). Hence the stated condition gives $n_n^{1/3} = 2n_p^{1/3}$, whence

$$\frac{n_p}{n_n} = \frac{1}{8},$$

i.e. the number of protons (and electrons) will be eight times as small as the number of neutrons. The total pressure of the substance, as is easily verified, is almost unaffected by this (formula (102.7) is multiplied by 0·96).

§106. The equilibrium of bodies of large mass

Consider a body of very large mass, whose parts are kept together by gravitational attraction. Actually, we meet bodies of large mass in the form of stars, continuously emitting energy, and by no means in a state of thermal equilibrium. However, the study of bodies of large mass in equilibrium is of considerable theoretical interest. In this case, we shall neglect the effect of temperature on the equation of state, i.e. we shall consider a body at absolute zero (a "cold" body). Since under real conditions the temperature of the external surface is considerably lower than the internal temperature, the study of a body with a non-zero constant temperature is, in any case, of no physical significance.

Let us further assume that the body does not rotate; then it will have a spherical shape in equilibrium, and the density distribution in it will have central symmetry.

The equilibrium distribution of density (and the other thermodynamic quantities) in the body will be determined by the following equations. The Newtonian gravitational potential ϕ satisfies the differential equation

$$\Delta\phi = 4\pi G\rho,$$

where ρ is the density of the substance and G Newton's gravitational constant; in the centrally symmetric case, we have:

$$\frac{1}{r^2}\frac{d}{dr}\left(r^2\frac{d\phi}{dr}\right) = 4\pi G\rho. \tag{106.1}$$

For thermal equilibrium condition (25.2) must also be satisfied; in the gravitational field the potential energy of a particle of mass m' is $m'\phi$, so that we have:

$$\mu + m'\phi = \text{const} \tag{106.2}$$

where m' is the mass of a particle of the body and μ is the chemical potential of the substance in the absence of a field (we have omitted the suffix zero, for brevity). By expressing ϕ in terms of μ from (106.2) and substituting into (106.1), we can write the latter in the form:

$$\frac{1}{r^2}\frac{d}{dr}\left(r^2\frac{d\mu}{dr}\right) = -4\pi m'G\rho. \tag{106.3}$$

As the mass of the gravitating body increases, so, naturally, does its average density (this assertion will be substantiated by further calculations below). Hence, for sufficiently large total mass M of the body, we can, according to the last section, consider the substance of the body as a degenerate Fermi gas of electrons, first non-relativistic and then, for still greater mass, relativistic.

The chemical potential of a non-relativistic degenerate electron gas is related to the density ρ by the equation

$$\mu = \frac{(3\pi^2)^{2/3}}{2}\frac{\hbar^2}{m_e m'^{2/3}}\rho^{2/3} \tag{106.4}$$

(formula (56.3), with $\rho = m'N/V$; m' being the mass per electron and m_e the mass of the electron). Expressing ρ in this case in terms of μ, and substituting into (106.3), we obtain the following equation:†

$$\frac{1}{r^2}\frac{d}{dr}\left(r^2\frac{d\mu}{dr}\right) = -\lambda\mu^{3/2}, \qquad \lambda = \frac{2^{7/2}m_e^{3/2}m'^2G}{3\pi\hbar^3}. \tag{106.5}$$

Physically significant solutions of this equation must have no singularities at the origin: $\mu \to \text{const}$ as $r \to 0$. This requirement automatically leads to

---

† It is easy to see that for an electrically neutral gas, consisting of electrons and atomic nuclei, the equilibrium condition may be written in the form (106.2) with μ the chemical potential of the electrons, and m' the mass per electron. In fact, the derivation of this equilibrium condition (§25) is connected with the transfer of an infinitely small quantity of the substance from one place to another. But in a gas consisting of charged particles of both signs, such a transfer must be envisaged as the transfer of a certain quantity of neutral substance (i.e. electrons and nuclei together). The separation of charges of opposite sign is, thermodynamically, very unfavourable, owing to the large electric fields which then occur. Hence we obtain the equilibrium condition in the form:

$$\mu_{\text{nucl}} + Z\mu_{\text{el}} + (m_{\text{nucl}} + Zm_{\text{el}})\phi = 0$$

(for each nucleus there are Z electrons). Owing to the very large mass of the nuclei (compared with the mass of the electrons) their chemical potential is very small compared with μ_{el}. Neglecting μ_{nucl} and dividing the equation by Z, we get:

$$\mu_{\text{el}} + m'\phi = 0.$$

If we assume that the atomic weight of the nuclei is approximately twice their atomic number, one can take m' to be equal to twice the mass of a proton ($m' = 2m_p$).

the condition on the first derivative:

$$\frac{d\mu}{dr} = 0 \quad \text{for} \quad r = 0. \tag{106.6}$$

From (106.5) it follows directly, after integration with respect to r, that

$$\frac{d\mu}{dr} = -\frac{\lambda}{r^2} \int_0^r r^2 \mu^{3/2} \, dr.$$

One can already obtain some important results by applying simple dimensional considerations to (106.5). The solution of eq. (106.5) contains only two independent parameters, the constant λ and the radius R of the body, for instance, whose value determines the solution uniquely. From these two quantities, only one with the dimensions of a length can be constructed (the radius R itself) and one with the dimensions of energy: $1/\lambda^2 R^4$ (the constant λ has dimensions cm^{-2} . erg$^{-1/2}$). Hence it is clear that the function $\mu(r)$ must have the form

$$\mu(r) = \frac{1}{\lambda^2 R^4} f\left(\frac{r}{R}\right) \tag{106.7}$$

where f is some function of the dimensionless ratio r/R. Since the density ρ is proportional to $\mu^{3/2}$, the density distribution must take the form:

$$\rho(r) = \frac{\text{const}}{R^6} F\left(\frac{r}{R}\right).$$

Thus there exists a similarity law for the dependence of the density distribution on the size of the sphere, and at corresponding points the density changes inversely as R^6. In particular, the mean density of the sphere must be inversely proportional to R^6.

$$\bar{\rho} \propto \frac{1}{R^6}.$$

The total mass of the body, M, is hence inversely proportional to the cube of the radius:

$$M \propto \frac{1}{R^3}.$$

These two relations may also be written in the form

$$R \propto M^{-1/3}, \quad \rho \propto M^2. \tag{106.8}$$

Thus the dimensions of the sphere in equilibrium are inversely proportional to the cube root of its total mass, and the mean density is proportional to the square of the total mass. The latter confirms the assumption made above that the density of a gravitating body increases with its mass.

The fact that a gravitating sphere of non-relativistic degenerate Fermi gas can be in equilibrium with any value of its total mass M could have been foreseen from the following qualitative considerations. The total kinetic energy of the particles of such a gas is proportional to $N(N/V)^{2/3}$ (see (56.6)), or, which comes to the same thing, to $m^{5/3}/R^2$, while the gravitational energy of the gas as a whole is negative and proportional to M^2/R. The sum of two expressions of these types may have a minimum (as a function of R) for any M, and at the minimum point $R \propto M^{-1/3}$.

Substituting (106.7) into (106.5) and introducing the dimensionless variable $\xi = r/R$, we find that the function $f(\xi)$ satisfies the equation

$$\frac{1}{\xi^2} \frac{d}{d\xi} \left(\xi^2 \frac{df}{d\xi} \right) = -f^{3/2} \tag{106.9}$$

with boundary conditions $f'(0) = 0$, $f(1) = 0$. This equation cannot be solved analytically and must be integrated numerically. In particular, the following values are found in this way:

$$f(0) = 178 \cdot 2, \qquad f'(1) = -132 \cdot 4.$$

With the help of these numerical values it is easy to determine the value of the constant MR^3. Multiplying (106.1) by $r^2 \, dr$ and integrating from 0 to R, we get:

$$GM = R^2 \frac{d\phi}{dr} \bigg|_{r=R} = -\frac{R^2}{m'} \frac{d\mu}{dr} \bigg|_{r=R} = -\frac{f'(1)}{m'\lambda^2 R^3}$$

whence:†

$$MR^3 = 91 \cdot 9 \frac{\hbar^6}{G^3 m_e^3 m^{15}}. \tag{106.10}$$

Finally, the ratio of the central density $\rho(0)$ to the mean density $\bar{\rho} = 3M/4\pi R^2$ is easily found to be:

$$\frac{\rho(0)}{\bar{\rho}} = -\frac{f^{3/2}(0)}{3f'(1)} = 5 \cdot 99. \tag{106.11}$$

Fig. 50 (curve 1) shows the graph of the ratio $\rho(r)/\rho(0)$ as a function of r/R. We now turn to an examination of the equilibrium of a sphere consisting

---

† In the last section we saw that the substance may be regarded as a non-relativistic electron gas at densities $\rho \gg 20Z^2$ g/cm³. If one requires that this condition should be satisfied by the mean density of the sphere under consideration, then we obtain the condition for its mass:

$$M \gg 5 \cdot 10^{-3} Z \odot$$

where $\odot = 1 \cdot 99 \cdot 10^{33}$ gm is the mass of the sun, and m' is taken to be twice the mass of the proton. The radii corresponding to these masses are below $5 \cdot 10^1 Z^{-1/3}$ km.

Note for future reference that for $m' = 2m_p$

$$MR^3 = 1 \cdot 40 \cdot 10^{60} \text{g/cm}^3$$

of degenerate extreme relativistic electron gas. The total kinetic energy of such a gas is proportional to $N(N/V)^{1/3}$ (see (58.3)) or, alternatively, $M^{4/3}/R$; the gravitational energy is proportional to M^2/R. Thus both these quantities depend on R in the same way, and their sum will also have the form const $\times R^{-1}$. It follows from this that the body will be unable to exist in equilibrium: if the constant is positive it will tend to expand (until the gas becomes non-relativistic); if the constant is negative then the decrease in the total energy will correspond to R tending to zero, i.e. the body will

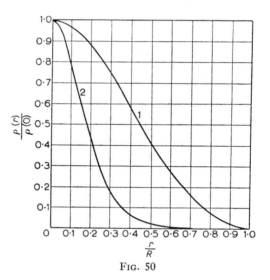

Fig. 50

contract indefinitely. Only for the special case, when the constant equals zero, can the body be in equilibrium, which will be neutral equilibrium with R taking arbitrary values.

This qualitative reasoning is, of course, confirmed by exact quantitative analysis. The chemical potential of the relativistic gas under consideration is related to its density (see (58.2)) by the relation

$$\mu = (3\pi^2)^{1/3}\hbar c\left(\frac{\rho}{m'}\right)^{1/3}. \tag{106.12}$$

We now obtain, in place of (106.5):

$$\frac{1}{r^2}\frac{d}{dr}\left(r^2\frac{d\mu}{dr}\right) = -\lambda\mu^3, \qquad \lambda = \frac{4Gm'^2}{3\pi c^3\hbar^3}. \tag{106.13}$$

Bearing in mind that λ now has the dimensions $erg^{-2}cm^{-2}$, we find that $\mu(r)$ must have the form

$$\mu(r) = \frac{1}{R\sqrt{\lambda}}f\left(\frac{r}{R}\right) \tag{106.14}$$

and the density distribution

$$\bar{\rho}(r) = \frac{\text{const}}{R^3} F\left(\frac{r}{R}\right).$$

Thus the mean density now will be inversely proportional to R^3, and the total mass $M \propto R^3\bar{\rho}$ turns out to be independent of the size

$$\rho \propto \frac{1}{R^3}, \qquad M = \text{const} \equiv M_0. \qquad (106.15)$$

M_0 is the only value of the mass for which equilibrium is possible; for $M > M_0$ the body will tend to contract while for $M < M_0$ it will expand.

For an exact calculation of the "critical mass" M_0, it is necessary to integrate numerically the equations

$$\frac{1}{\xi^2}\frac{d}{d\xi}\left(\xi^2\frac{df}{d\xi}\right) = -f^3, \qquad f'(0) = 0, \ f(1) = 0, \qquad (106.16)$$

which are satisfied by the function $f(\xi)$ in 106.14). We now obtain:

$$f(0) = 6\cdot897, \quad f'(1) = -2\cdot018.$$

For the total mass we find:

$$GM_0 = R^2\frac{d\phi}{dr}\bigg|_{r=R} = -\frac{f'(1)}{m'\sqrt{\lambda}},$$

whence

$$M_0 = \frac{3\cdot1}{m'^2}\left(\frac{\hbar c}{G}\right)^{3/2}. \qquad (106.17)$$

Putting m' equal to twice the mass of the proton we find that $M_0 = 1\cdot45\,\odot$. Lastly, the ratio of the central density to the mean density

$$\frac{\rho(0)}{\bar{\rho}} = -\frac{f^3(0)}{3f'(1)} = 54\cdot2.$$

Curve 2 of Fig. 50 gives $\rho(r)/\rho(0)$ as a function of r/R in the extreme relativistic case.

The results obtained for the relation between the mass and the radius of a "cold" spherical body in equilibrium can be shown on a single curve giving the function $M = M(R)$ over the entire range of values of R. For large R (and correspondingly low densities of the body) the electron gas may be considered as non-relativistic and the function $M(R)$ is proportional to R^{-3}. For sufficiently small R the density is large enough for the extreme relativistic case to occur, and the function $M(R)$ is almost constant and equal to M_0 (strictly speaking $M(R) \to M_0$ as $R \to 0$). Fig. 51 shows the curve

$M = M(R)$ calculated for $m' = 2m_p$.† Attention must be paid to the fact that the limiting value $1{\cdot}45 \odot$ is reached very gradually. This is connected with the fact that the density falls off rapidly away from the centre of the body; hence the gas may already be in an extreme relativistic state near the centre, while, at the same time it may be non-relativistic over a considerable region of the body. Note also that the beginning of the curve (very small R) has no real physical significance. Indeed, for sufficiently small radii, the density becomes so large that nuclear reactions begin to take place (see §105). The pressure will then increase with the density more slowly than $\rho^{4/3}$ and equilibrium is impossible for such an equation of state.‡

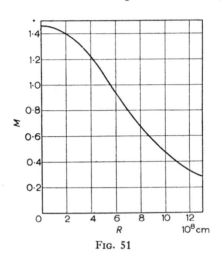

FIG. 51

Finally, this curve also becomes meaningless for too large R (and small M). As was already pointed out, (see footnote on page 333), the equation of state we were using ceases to apply in this region. In this connection, it should be pointed out that there exists an upper limit to the possible size of a "cold" body. On the curve in Fig. 51, large dimensions of the body correspond to small mass and density. But for sufficiently small densities the substance will be in its usual "atomic" state and, at the temperatures in which we are interested, it will be solid. The dimensions of a body constructed of such a substance will obviously decrease with a further decrease

---

† The intermediate portion of the curve is constructed by integrating equation (106.3) numerically, using the exact equation of state for the degenerate gas, i.e. using a chemical potential related to the density by

$$\rho = \frac{m'}{3\pi^2 \hbar^3} p_0^3 = \frac{m'}{3\pi^2 \hbar^3} \left(\frac{\mu^2}{c^2} - m_e^2 c^2 \right)^{3/2},$$

where p_0 is the limiting Fermi momentum.

‡ If the chemical potential is proportional to some power of the density, $\mu \propto \rho^n$ (and correspondingly $P \propto \rho^{n+1}$) then the intrinsic energy of the body is proportional to $V\rho^{n+1}$ or alternatively M^{n+1}/R^{3n}, while the gravitational energy, as before, is proportional to M^2/R. It can easily be seen that, for $n < \frac{4}{3}$, although the sum of two such terms has an extremum, it will be a maximum and not a minimum.

in its mass, and not increase as shown in Fig. 51. The real curve $R = R(M)$ must thus have a maximum for some value of M.

The order of magnitude of the maximum value of the radius is easily determined, when we note that it must correspond to the density at which the interaction between the electrons and the nuclei becomes important, i.e. for

$$\rho \sim \left(\frac{m_e e^2}{\hbar^2} \right)^3 m' Z^2$$

(see (105.1)). Combining this relation with eq. (106.10) we obtain:

$$R_{\max} \sim \frac{\hbar^2}{G^{1/2} e m_e m' Z^{1/3}} \sim 10^5 \frac{m_p}{m' Z^{1/3}} \text{km.} \tag{106.18}$$

§107. The energy of a gravitating body

The gravitational potential energy of a body is given, as is well known, by the integral

$$E_{gr} = \tfrac{1}{2} \int \rho\phi \, dV, \tag{107.1}$$

taken over the total volume of the body. It will be more convenient, however, for us to start from another expression for this quantity, which can be obtained in the following way. Imagine the body to be gradually "built up" from matter "brought" from infinity. Let $M(r)$ be the mass of the substance contained in a sphere of radius r. We assume that mass $M(r)$, for some definite r, has already been "brought" from infinity. Then the work necessary to "add" an additional mass $dM(r)$ will be equal to the potential energy of this mass (distributed as a spherical layer of radius r and thickness dr) in the field of the mass $M(r)$, i.e.

$$-\frac{GM(r)\,dM(r)}{r}.$$

Hence the total gravitational energy of a sphere of radius R will be

$$E_{gr} = -G \int \frac{M(r)\,dM(r)}{r}. \tag{107.2}$$

After differentiating the equilibrium condition (107.2) we obtain

$$v\frac{dP}{dr} + m'\frac{d\phi}{dr} = 0$$

(the differentiation must be carried out at constant temperature and

$(\partial\mu/\partial P)_T = v$ is the volume per particle). The derivative $-d\phi/dr$ is the attractive force per unit mass at a distance r from the centre; it is equal to $-GM(r)/r^2$. Introducing also the density $\rho = m'/v$, we obtain:

$$\frac{1}{\rho}\frac{dP}{dr} = -\frac{GM(r)}{r^2}. \tag{107.3}$$

From this equation, we substitute into (107.2) $-GM(r)/r = (r/\rho)(dP/dr)$, while we write $dM(r)$ in the form $\rho(r) . 4\pi r^2\, dr$:

$$E_{gr} = 4\pi \int\limits_0^R r^3\frac{dP}{dr}\,dr,$$

and we integrate by parts (bearing in mind that at the surface of the body $P(R) = 0$ and that $r^3 P \to 0$ as $r \to 0$):

$$E_{gr} = -12\pi \int\limits_0^R Pr^2\, dr$$

or, finally,

$$E_{gr} = -3 \int P\, dV. \tag{107.4}$$

Thus the gravitational energy of a body in equilibrium can be related to the volume integral of the pressure.

We apply this formula to bodies of degenerate Fermi gas, which we studied in the last section. We do this for the general case, assuming the chemical potential of the body to be proportional to some power of the density:

$$\mu = k\rho^n. \tag{107.5}$$

Bearing in mind that $d\mu = v dP = m'/\rho\, dP$, we find that the pressure

$$P = \frac{n}{n+1}\frac{K}{m'}\rho^{n+1}. \tag{107.6}$$

In the equilibrium condition $(\mu/m') + \phi = $ const, the constant on the right hand side of the equation is simply the potential at the boundary of the body where μ vanishes; this potential is equal to $-GM/R$ ($M = M(R)$, the total mass of the body), so that one can write:

$$\phi = -\frac{\mu}{m'} - \frac{GM}{R}.$$

Substituting this expression into the integral (107.1) which determines the gravitational energy, and using (107.5–6), we find:

$$E_{gr} = -\frac{1}{2m'}\int \mu\rho\, dV - \frac{GM}{2R}\int \rho\, dV$$

$$= -\frac{K}{2m'}\int \rho^{n+1}\, dV - \frac{GM^2}{2R} = -\frac{n+1}{2n}\int P\, dV - \frac{GM^2}{2R}.$$

Finally, expressing the integral on the right hand side of the equation in terms of E_{gr} by means of (107.4), we obtain:

$$E_{gr} = \frac{n+1}{6n}E_{gr} - \frac{GM^2}{2R},$$

whence

$$E_{gr} = -\frac{3n}{5n-1}\frac{GM^2}{R}. \tag{107.7}$$

Thus the gravitational energy of the body can be expressed simply in terms of its total mass and radius.

One can obtain a similar expression for the intrinsic thermal energy of the body, E. The internal energy per particle is equal to $\mu - P_v$ (for zero temperature and entropy); hence the energy per unit volume is

$$\frac{1}{v}(\mu - Pv) = \frac{\rho\mu}{m'} - P,$$

or, substituting from (107.5) and (107.6):

$$\frac{K}{m'}\frac{\rho^{n+1}}{n+1} = \frac{P}{n}.$$

Hence the intrinsic energy of the whole body is

$$E = \frac{1}{n}\int P\, dV = -\frac{1}{3n}E_{gr} = \frac{1}{5n-1}\frac{GM^2}{R}. \tag{107.8}$$

Finally, the total energy of the body

$$E_{tot} = E + E_{gr} = -\frac{3n-1}{5n-1}\frac{GM^2}{R}. \tag{107.9}$$

For a non-relativistic degenerate gas we have $n = 2/3$, so that†

$$E_{gr} = -\frac{6}{7}\frac{GM^2}{R}, \qquad E = \frac{3}{7}\frac{GM^2}{R}, \qquad E_{tot} = -\frac{3}{7}\frac{GM^2}{R}. \tag{107.10}$$

---

† Note that, in this case $2E = -E_{gr}$ in agreement with the virial theorem, of mechanics, applied to a system of particles interacting according to Newton's Law. (See *Mechanics*, §10, Moscow, 1958.)

In the extreme relativistic case we have $n = 1/3$, so that

$$E_{\text{gr}} = -E = -\frac{3}{2}\frac{GM^2}{R}, \qquad E_{\text{tot}} = 0. \qquad (107.11)$$

The total energy vanishes in this case, in agreement with the qualitative reasoning in the preceding section about the equilibrium of such a body.

§108. The equilibrium of a "neutron sphere"

For a body of large mass, there exist two possible alternative types of equilibrium states. One of these corresponds to the electron-nuclear state of the substance as was assumed in the quantitative work in §106. The other corresponds to the "neutronic" state of the substance in which almost all the electrons have been captured by protons and the substance may be regarded as a neutron gas. When the mass of the body becomes sufficiently large, the second possibility inevitably becomes more favourable, thermodynamically, than the first. Although the transformation of nuclei and free electrons into free neutrons involves the expenditure of a considerable amount of energy, nevertheless for sufficiently large values of the total mass of the body, this energy will be more than compensated by the gravitational energy released due to the decreased size and increased density of the body (see below).

First of all we shall consider under what conditions the neutronic state of a body can correspond to any type of thermodynamic equilibrium at all (even metastable). For this purpose we start from the equilibrium condition

$$\mu + m_n \phi = \text{const},$$

where μ is the chemical potential (thermodynamic potential per neutron), m_n is the mass of a neutron, and ϕ is the gravitational potential.

Since the pressure must vanish at the surface of the body, it is clear that there will be an external layer in which the pressure and density of the substance will be small, and it will consequently be in the electron-nuclear state. Although the thickness of such an "envelope" may be comparable to the radius of the inner dense neutronic "core", nevertheless its mass may be considered small compared with the mass of the "core" because of the considerably lower density of this layer.[†]

Let us compare the values of $\mu + m_n \phi$ at two points: in the dense core near its boundary, and near the external boundary of the envelope. The gravitational potential of these points may be taken as $-GM/R$ and $-GM/R'$, where R and R' are the radii of the core and the envelope and M is the mass of the nucleus which, in our approximation, is the same as the total mass of the body. The chemical potential in both cases is determined

---

† Obviously there is no sharp boundary between the "core" and the "envelope" and there is continuous transition between them.

essentially by the internal energy (binding energy) of the corresponding particles, which is large compared with their thermal energy. Hence the difference between the two chemical potentials may be taken simply as the difference between the rest energy, per unit atomic weight, of a neutral atom (i.e. a nucleus with Z electrons) and the rest energy of a neutron. We shall denote this quantity by Δ†. Thus, equating the values of $\mu + m_n \phi$ at the two points, we obtain:

$$m_n MG \left(\frac{1}{R} - \frac{1}{R'} \right) = \Delta.$$

It can be seen from this that whatever the radius R', the mass and radius of the neutronic core must in any case satisfy the inequality

$$\frac{m_n MG}{R} > \Delta. \tag{108.1}$$

On the other hand, using the results of §106 for a spherical body consisting of degenerate (non-relativistic) neutron gas, we find that M and R are connected by the relation

$$MR^3 = 91 \cdot 9 \frac{\hbar^6}{G^3 m_n^8} = 7 \cdot 2 \cdot 10^{51} \text{g/cm}^3 \tag{108.2}$$

((106.10) with m_e and m' replaced by m_n). Hence, expressing M in terms of R and substituting into (108.1), we obtain an inequality for M. Numerically it gives

$$M > \sim 0 \cdot 2 \odot.$$

For example, taking the value of Δ for oxygen, we get $M > 0 \cdot 17 \odot$, for iron $M > 0 \cdot 18 \odot$. These masses correspond to values of the radius $R < 26$ km.

The inequality we have obtained determines the lower limit of the mass below which the neutronic state of the body cannot be stable at all. However, it does not ensure the complete stability of the state which may turn out to be metastable. To determine the limit of metastability, we must compare the total energies of bodies in the two states: neutronic and electron-nuclear. On the one hand the transformation of the whole mass M from the electron-nuclear state to the neutronic state requires the expenditure of energy

$$\frac{M}{m_n} \Delta$$

to compensate for the binding energy of the nuclei. On the other hand energy will be released owing to the compression of the body; according to

---

† Δ/c^2 is simply the difference between the so-called "packing fractions" of the nucleus and neutron multiplied by the nuclear unit of mass.

(107.10) this gain in energy will be equal to

$$\frac{3GM^2}{7}\left(\frac{1}{R_\mathrm{n}}-\frac{1}{R_\mathrm{e}}\right),$$

where R_n is the radius of the body in the neutronic state, determined by (108.2) and R_e is the radius of the body in the electron-nuclear state determined by (106.10). Since $R_\mathrm{e} \gg R_\mathrm{n}$, we may neglect the quantity $1/R_\mathrm{e}$ and we obtain the following condition which ensures the complete stability of the neutronic state of the body (we omit the suffix in R_n):

$$\frac{3GMm_\mathrm{n}}{7R} > \Delta. \tag{108.3}$$

Comparing this with (108.1) and using (108.2), we see that the lower limit for the mass determined by (108.3) is $(7/3)^{3/4} = 1 \cdot 89$ times higher than that we obtained in (108.2). Numerically, the limit of metastability for the neutronic state thus occurs for a mass

$$M \simeq \tfrac{1}{3}\odot$$

(and radius $R \simeq 22$ km).†

We now turn to the upper limit on the value of the mass for a "neutronic" body to be in equilibrium. If we were to apply the results of §106 (equation (106.17), with m_n instead of m'), we would get a value $6\odot$ for this limit. In actual fact, however, these results are inapplicable to this case for the following reason. In a relativistic neutron gas the kinetic energy of the particles is of the same order of magnitude as the rest energy (or even larger).‡ Owing to this, the use of the Newtonian theory of gravitation becomes unjustified, and the calculations must be carried out on the basis of the general theory of relativity. Then, as we shall see below, the extreme relativistic case is never achieved; hence the calculations must be carried out using the exact equation of state for a degenerate Fermi gas (the parametric equation obtained in problem 3 in §58).

The calculations are carried out by numerically integrating the equations for a centrally symmetric statistical gravitational field, and lead to the following results.‖

The limiting value for the mass of a neutronic sphere in equilibrium is only $M_\mathrm{max} = 0 \cdot 76\odot$, and this value is already reached at a finite radius (equal to $R_\mathrm{min} = 9 \cdot 42$ km); in Fig. 52 is shown the graph of the relation

---

† The mean density of the body is then equal to $1 \cdot 4 \cdot 10^{13}$ g/cm³ so that the neutronic gas may truly be considered non-relativistic, and the use of the formulae we have applied is justified.

‡ In the relativistic electron gas the kinetic energy of the particles is comparable with the rest energy of the electrons, but is still small compared with the rest energy of the nuclei, which constitute the major part of the mass of the substance.

‖ For the details of the calculation, reference should be made to the original paper J. R. OPPENHEIMER and G. VOLKOFF, *Phys. Rev.* **55**, 374, 1939.

obtained between the mass M and radius R. Stable neutronic spheres of larger mass or smaller radius cannot exist.†

The question arises of the behaviour of a body with mass greater than M_{max}. It is clear from the start that such a body must tend to contract indefinitely. The explanation of the nature and course of such a contraction requires the study of the non-stationary solutions of the gravitational equations. Such a study has been carried out only for the simplest case of the

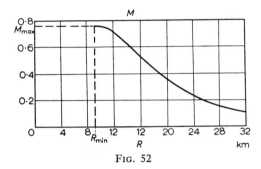

Fig. 52

equation of state $P = 0$, i.e. for a sphere consisting of a very thin substance; it probably gives also a correct indication of the nature of the process for the general case of an exact equation of state. Referring readers to the original paper‡ for the details, we restrict ourselves here to some very general indications.

From the point of view of a distant observer (the reference system is Galilean at infinity) the sphere contracts so that its radius tends asymptotically to a value equal to its gravitational radius ($2M_{gr}G/c^2$); the rate of contraction tends to zero in a corresponding manner. From the point of view of a "local" observer the substance "collapses" with a velocity approaching that of light, and it reaches the centre in a finite proper time.

The question still remains of the quantitative effects of the non-zero pressure of the substance on the contraction process, and, in particular, of the minimum value of the mass of the sphere for which the process becomes possible at all.

---

† The mass M is taken to mean the product $M = Nm_n$, where N is the number of neutrons in the sphere. It should be borne in mind that it does not coincide with the gravitational mass of the body which determines its gravitational field; owing to the "gravitational mass defect," $M_{gr} < M$ always. For $M = M_{max}$ the gravitational mass $M_{gr} = 0.72\odot$.

The point at the end of the curve of Fig. 52, $R = R_{min}$ is in fact a maximum of the curve $M = M(R)$ obtained by integrating the gravitational equations. The curve extends beyond the maximum to a somewhat smaller radius, and at this point of the curve M decreases with R. This part of the curve, however, does not correspond to stable equilibrium for the sphere.

‡ J. R. Oppenheimer and H. Snyder, *Phys. Rev.* **56**, 455, 1939.

CHAPTER XII

FLUCTUATIONS

§109. The Gaussian distribution

It has already been emphasised several times that the physical quantities which describe a macroscopic body in equilibrium are practically always equal to their mean values with very great accuracy. However, small as they are, deviations from these mean values do occur, (the quantities fluctuate, as one says), and the question arises of finding the probability distribution for such fluctuations.

Consider some closed system, and let x be some physical quantity characterising the system as a whole or some part of it (in the first case it must not be a quantity which remains strictly constant for a closed system, like its energy). It will be convenient to assume that the mean value $\bar{x}$ has been subtracted from x, so that we put $\bar{x}=0$ everywhere below.

The arguments of §7 showed that if one formally regards the entropy of the system as a function of the exact values of the energies of the subsystems then the function $e^{S/k}$ will give the probability distribution for these energies (see (7.17)). It is easy to see, however, that in this derivation no specific properties of the energy were used. Hence exactly similar arguments will lead to the result that the probability for the quantity x to have a value between x and $x+dx$ is proportional to $e^{S(x)/k}$, $S(x)$ being the entropy, considered formally as a function of the exact value of x. Denoting the probability by $w(x)\,dx$, we have:

$$w(x)\,dx = \text{const}.\,e^{S(x)/k}\,dx. \tag{109.1}$$

Before discussing the further deductions which can be drawn from this formula we consider the limits of its applicability. The entire reasoning which led to formula (109.1), implicitly requires that the quantity x should behave classically.† Thus we must find the condition which ensures that quantum effects may be neglected.

There is a well-known relation in quantum mechanics between the quantum uncertainties in the energy and in some quantity x, which is, in the quasi-classical case:

$$\Delta E\,\Delta x \sim \hbar\dot{x},$$

where $\dot{x}$ is the classical rate of change of the quantity x.‡

---

† This does not mean, of course, that the entire system must be classical. Quantities other than x, which belong to it, can be of a quantum nature.
‡ See *Quantum Mechanics*, §14, equation (14.11).

Let τ be a time characterising the rate of change of the quantity when it has some non-equilibrium value†; then $\dot{x} \sim x/\tau$ so that

$$\Delta E \, \Delta x \sim \hbar x/\tau.$$

It is clear that one can speak of a definite value of the quantity x only when its quantum uncertainty is small: $\Delta x \ll x$ whence:

$$\Delta E \gg \hbar/\tau.$$

Thus the quantum uncertainty in the energy must be large compared with $\hbar/\tau$ and the entropy of the system will then have uncertainty

$$\Delta S \gg \frac{\hbar}{\tau T}.$$

For (109.1) to have any real meaning it is obviously necessary that the uncertainty in the entropy should be small compared with k: $\Delta S \ll k$, whence

$$kT \gg \frac{\hbar}{\tau}, \qquad \tau \gg \frac{\hbar}{kT}. \tag{109.2}$$

This is the required condition. For too low temperatures, or too rapid a change in the quantity x (too small τ) the fluctuations cannot be considered thermodynamically, and the purely quantum fluctuations become important.

We now return to (109.1). The entropy S has a maximum at $x = \bar{x} = 0$. Hence

$$\frac{\partial S}{\partial x}\bigg|_{x=0} = 0, \qquad \frac{\partial^2 S}{\partial x^2}\bigg|_{x=0} < 0.$$

The quantity x is very small for fluctuations. Expanding $S(x)$ in powers of x and restricting ourselves to second order terms, we obtain:

$$S(x) = S(0) - \frac{\beta}{2}x^2$$

where β is a positive constant. Substituting into (109.1) we obtain the probability distribution in the following form:

$$w(x) \, dx = A e^{-\beta x^2/2k} \, dx.$$

The normalising constant A is given by the condition

$$A \int\limits_{-\infty}^{+\infty} e^{-\beta x^2/2k} \, dx = 1.$$

---

† The time τ is not necessarily the relaxation time for reaching equilibrium with respect to the quantity x, but can be smaller than it, if the quantity x tends to $\bar{x}$ while at the same time undergoing oscillations. For example, if we talk of changes in the pressure in a small part of a body (with linear dimensions $\sim a$), then τ will be of the order of magnitude of the period of a sound oscillation with wavelength $\lambda \sim a$, i.e. $\tau \sim a/c$ where c is the velocity of sound.

Although we have used here the expression for $w(x)$ valid for small x, the integration may be extended to all values of x from $-\infty$ to $+\infty$ owing to the rapid convergence of the integral. Carrying out the integration, we obtain $A = \sqrt{(\beta/2\pi k)}$.

Thus the probability distribution for different values of the fluctuation x is given by the formula

$$w(x)\,dx = \sqrt{\left(\frac{\beta}{2\pi k}\right)}\, e^{-\beta/2kx^2}\,dx. \tag{109.3}$$

A distribution of this type is called a *Gaussian distribution*; it has a maximum at $x = 0$ and falls off rapidly as $|x|$ increases, being symmetrical about $x = 0$.

The mean square of the fluctuation is

$$\overline{x^2} = \sqrt{\left(\frac{\beta}{2\pi k}\right)} \int\limits_{-\infty}^{+\infty} x^2 e^{-\beta/2kx^2}\,dx = \frac{k}{\beta}.$$

In this way $\overline{x^2} = k/\beta$ and we may write the distribution in the form

$$w(x)\,dx = \frac{1}{\sqrt{(2\pi\overline{x^2})}}\, \exp(-x^2/2\overline{x^2}). \tag{109.4}$$

As one would expect, the smaller $\overline{x^2}$, the sharper is the maximum of $w(x)$.

Knowing the mean square $\overline{x^2}$, one can find the corresponding quantity for any function $\phi(x)$. We have, since x is small:

$$\Delta\phi = \frac{d\phi}{dx}\bigg|_{x=0} x,$$

whence

$$\overline{\Delta\phi^2} = \left(\frac{d\phi}{dx}\right)^2_{x=0} \overline{x^2}. \tag{109.5}$$

§110. The Gaussian distribution for several quantities

In the last section, we studied the probability of deviations of a single thermodynamic quantity from its mean value, without considering the values of other quantities, i.e. assuming their values to be arbitrary.† Similarly, one can determine the probability of simultaneous deviations of a series of thermodynamic quantities from their mean values; we shall denote these deviations by $x_1, x_2, ..., x_n$.

We introduce the entropy $S(x_1, ..., x_n)$ as a function of all these quantities

---

† This means that the function $S(x)$ which we have used in §109 is the largest possible value which the entropy can assume for a given, non-equilibrium value of x.

$x_1, x_2, ..., x_n$ and for the probability distribution we have (analogously to (109.1)) the expression

$$w\, dx_1\, dx_2 ... dx_n = \text{const}\, e^{S/k}\, dx_1\, dx_2 ... dx_n. \tag{110.1}$$

We expand S in powers of x_i; up to second order the difference $S-S_0$ will be given as the negative definite quadratic form

$$S-S_0 = -\tfrac{1}{2} \sum_{i,k=1}^{n} \beta_{ik} x_i x_k. \tag{110.2}$$

Obviously $\beta_{ik} = \beta_{ki}$. In future we shall drop the summation sign, and always understand summation to be implied in the case of a repeated suffix (over all values from 1 to n). In this way, we write:

$$(S-S_0) = -\tfrac{1}{2}\beta_{ik} x_i x_k. \tag{110.3}$$

Substituting this into (110.1) we obtain, for the desired probability distribution, the expression:

$$w = A \exp\left(-\frac{1}{2k}\beta_{ik} x_i x_k\right)$$

The constant A is determined from the normalisation condition

$$A \int\limits_{-\infty}^{+\infty} ... \int\limits_{-\infty}^{+\infty} \exp\left(-\frac{1}{2k}\beta_{ik} x_i x_k\right) dx_1 ... dx_n = 1.$$

Here, for the same reasons as in §109, the integration with respect to each x_i can be taken from $-\infty$ to $+\infty$. To evaluate this integral, we proceed in the following manner. We carry out, on the quantities $x_1, x_2, ..., x_n$, the linear transformation

$$x_i = a_{ik}' x_k, \tag{110.3a}$$

which transforms the quadratic form $\beta_{ik} x_i x_k$ into the sum of squares of the x_i'. In order to satisfy

$$\frac{1}{k}\beta_{ik} x_i x_k = x_i'^2$$

or, as it may also be written,

$$\frac{1}{k}\beta_{ik} x_i x_k = x_i' x_k' \delta_{ik}$$

(where δ_{ik} is equal to zero when $i \neq k$ and to unity when $i = k$), the coefficients a_{ik} of the transformation must satisfy the conditions

$$\beta_{ik} a_{il} a_{im} = k\delta_{lm}.$$

The determinant constructed from the sums $a_{il} b_{lk}$ is equal, as is well known, to the product of the determinants $|a_{ik}|$ and $|b_{ik}|$ and similarly for a larger number of determinants. Since the determinant $|\delta_{ik}| = 1$, then, from relation (110.4) it follows that

$$\beta a^2 = k^n, \tag{110.4}$$

where β and a denote the determinants $|\beta_{ik}|$ and $|a_{ik}|$.

Carrying out the transformation in the normalisation integral, we obtain

$$Aa \int\limits_{-\infty}^{+\infty} \ldots \int\limits_{-\infty}^{+\infty} e^{-\frac{1}{2}x_i'^2}\, dx_1' \ldots dx_n' = 1,$$

since the Jacobian $\partial(x_1 \ldots x_n)/\partial(x_1' \ldots x_n') = a$. This integral now separates into the product of n integrals. Evaluating these, and taking (110.4) into account, we obtain:

$$A = (2\pi k)^{-n/2}\sqrt{\beta}.$$

In this way, we find that the final Gaussian distribution for several quantities takes the form

$$w = \frac{\sqrt{\beta}}{(2\pi k)^{n/2}} \exp\left(-\frac{1}{2k}\beta_{ik}x_i x_k\right) \tag{110.5}$$

We introduce the quantities

$$X_i = -\frac{\partial S}{\partial x_i} = \beta_{ik}x_k \tag{110.6}$$

and calculate the mean values of the products $x_i X_k$:

$$\overline{x_i X_k} = \frac{\sqrt{\beta}}{(2\pi k)^{n/2}} \int \ldots \int x_i \beta_{kl} \exp\left(-\frac{1}{2k}\beta_{ik}x_i x_k\right) dx_1 \ldots dx_n.$$

To evaluate this integral, assume for the moment that the mean values $\bar{x}_i$ are not zero, but are equal to some finite x_{i0}. Then in (110.5) we must write $x_i - x_{i0}$ in place of x_i, and from the definition of mean values we obtain:

$$\bar{x}_i = \frac{\sqrt{\beta}}{(2\pi k)^{n/2}} \int \ldots \int x_i \exp\left[-\frac{1}{2k}\beta_{ik}(x_i-x_{i0})(x_k-x_{k0})\right] dx_1 \ldots dx_n = x_{i0}.$$

Differentiating this equation with respect to x_{k0} and then assuming once more that all the $x_{10} \ldots, x_{n0}$ are equal to zero, we obtain δ_{ik} on the right hand side, and on the left we obtain just the required integral.

Thus we obtain:

$$\overline{x_i X_k} = k\delta_{ik}. \tag{110.7}$$

Substituting from (110.6) (and changing the notation of the suffices for the sake of convenience) we get:

$$\overline{\beta_{ml}x_l x_k} = k\delta_{mk}.$$

Multiplying both sides of this equation by β_{im}^{-1} (i.e. by the elements of the inverse matrix to β_{im}) and summing with respect to the suffix m

$$\beta_{im}^{-1}\overline{\beta_{ml}x_l x_k} = k\beta_{im}^{-1}\delta_{mk} = k\beta_{ik}^{-1}$$

But, by definition of the inverse matrix $\beta_{im}^{-1}\beta_{ml} = \delta_{il}$ so that we obtain† :

$$\overline{x_i x_k} = k\beta_{ik}^{-1}. \tag{110.8}$$

Finally, let us also determine $\overline{X_i X_k}$. According to (110.6) and (110.7), we have $\overline{X_i X_k} = \overline{\beta_{il}x_l X_k} = k\beta_{il}\delta_{ik}$, whence:

$$\overline{X_i X_k} = k\beta_{ik}. \tag{110.9}$$

It is also easy to determine the mean square fluctuation of any function $f(x_1 \ldots x_n)$ of the quantities $x_1, x_2, \ldots, x_n$. Provided that the deviations from the mean are small, $\Delta f = (\partial f/\partial x_i)x_i$. Here the $\partial f/\partial x_i$ are taken to be the values of the derivatives for $x_1 = 0, \ldots, x_n = 0$. Hence

$$\overline{(\Delta f)^2} = \frac{\partial f}{\partial x_i}\frac{\partial f}{\partial x_k}\overline{x_i x_k}$$

or, substituting into (110.8):

$$\overline{(\Delta f)^2} = k\frac{\partial f}{\partial x_i}\frac{\partial f}{\partial x_k}\beta_{ik}^{-1}. \tag{110.10}$$

If the fluctuations of two of the x_i (x_1 and x_2, say) are statistically independent, then the mean value $\overline{x_1 x_2}$ is equal to the product of their mean values $\overline{x_1}$ and $\overline{x_2}$, and since each of the latter is equal to zero then the product $\overline{x_1 x_2}$ also vanishes. According to (110.8) it follows that $\beta_{12}^{-1} = 0$. It can easily be seen that, for the Gaussian distribution the reverse theorem is also true: if $\overline{x_1 x_2} = 0$ (i.e. $\beta_{12}^{-1} = 0$) then the fluctuations in the quantities x_1 and x_2 are statistically independent.

Indeed the probability distribution w_{12} for the quantities x_1 and x_2 is obtained by integrating the distribution (110.5) with respect to all the other x_i; and one obtains an expression of the type:

$$w_{12} = \text{const}.\exp\left\{-\frac{\beta_{11}'}{2k}x_1^2 - \frac{\beta_{21}'}{k}x_1 x_2 - \frac{\beta_{22}'}{2k}x_2^2\right\}$$

(where the coefficients β_{ik}' in general differ from the corresponding components β_{ik}). Applying (110.8) to this distribution, we find that $\overline{x_1 x_2} = k\beta_{12}'^{-1}$. If $\overline{x_1 x_2} = 0$, then $\beta_{12}'^{-1} = 0$. But for a second-order matrix, the

---

† The quantity $x_i x_k/(\overline{x_i^2}\,\overline{x_k^2})^{\frac12}$ is called the *correlation* of the two quantities x_i and x_k.

vanishing of the component $\beta_{12}'^{-1}$ the inverse matrix implies the vanishing of the component β_{12}' of the original matrix†. As a result w_{12} splits into the product of two independent Gaussian distributions for the quantities x_1 and x_2, which means that they are statistically independent.

§111. Fluctuations of the basic thermodynamic quantities

We proceed to calculate the mean square fluctuations of the basic thermodynamic quantities relating to some selected small part of a body. This small part must, of course, still contain a sufficiently large number of particles. However, at very low temperatures this condition may be weaker than condition (109.2) which ensures the absence of quantum fluctuations; in this case the minimum permissible size of the part of the body will be determined by the latter condition‡. To avoid misunderstanding we must emphasise that the question of the importance of the quantum fluctuation bears no relation to the question of the influence of quantum effects on the thermodynamic properties (the equation of state) of the substance. The fluctuations may be purely classical while at the same time the equation of state may be determined by the quantum-mechanical formulae.

For quantities such as energy, volume, etc., which have purely mechanical meanings as well as thermodynamic ones, the concept of fluctuations is self-evident. It needs, however, further explanation in the case of quantities such as entropy and temperature, whose definitions essentially depend on our considering the body over a finite interval of time. Let, for example, $S(E, V)$ be the equilibrium entropy of the body as a function of its (mean) energy and volume. By a fluctuation in the entropy, we understand a change in the function $S(E, V)$, which we formally regard as a function of the exact (fluctuating) values of the energy and volume.

As we have seen in the preceding sections, the probability w of a fluctuation is proportional to $e^{S_t/k}$, where S_t is the total entropy of the closed system, i.e. of the body as a whole. An alternative form of this formula is

$$w \propto e^{\Delta S_t/k},$$

where ΔS_t is the change of entropy in the fluctuation. According to (20.8) we have: $\Delta S_t = -R_{\min}/T_0$ where $R_{\min}$ is the minimum work required to carry out reversibly the given change in the thermodynamic quantities of the given small part of the body (with respect to which all other parts act as

---

† For a second order matrix we have:

$$\beta_{12}^{-1} = \frac{\beta_{12}}{\beta_{12}{}^2 - \beta_{11}\beta_{22}}.$$

‡ Thus for fluctuations of the pressure, the condition $\tau \gg \hbar/kT$ with $\tau \sim a/c$ (see footnote on page 345) gives

$$a \gg \hbar c/kT.$$

a "medium"). In this way,

$$w \propto e^{-R_{\min}/kT_0} \tag{111.1}$$

We substitute for $R_{\min}$ the expression

$$R_{\min} = \Delta E - T_0 \Delta S + P_0 \Delta V,$$

where ΔE, ΔS, ΔV are the changes in the energy, entropy and volume of the given small part of the body as a result of the fluctuation and T_0 and P_0 are the temperature and pressure of the "medium", i.e. the (mean) equilibrium values of the temperature and pressure of the body. In future we shall omit the suffix zero in all quantities acting as coefficients of fluctuations; they are always taken to have their equilibrium values. Thus we have:

$$w \propto e^{-(\Delta E - T\Delta S + P\Delta V)/kT}. \tag{111.2}$$

Note that in this form the formulae can be applied to any fluctuations, small as well as considerable ones (by considerable we mean here fluctuations when, for example, ΔE is comparable with the energy of the small part of the body itself, but is, of course, still small compared with the energy of the whole body). When applied to a fluctuation which is small (as is usually the case) (111.2) gives the following result.

Expanding ΔE as a series, we obtain (cf. §21):

$$\Delta E - T\Delta S + P\Delta V = \frac{1}{2}\left[\frac{\partial^2 E}{\partial S^2}(\Delta S)^2 + 2\frac{\partial^2 E}{\partial S\,\partial V}\Delta S\,\Delta V + \frac{\partial^2 E}{\partial V^2}(\Delta V)^2\right].$$

It can easily be seen that this expression may be written in the form

$$\frac{1}{2}\left[\Delta S\,\Delta\left(\frac{\partial E}{\partial S}\right)_V + \Delta V\,\Delta\left(\frac{\partial E}{\partial V}\right)_S\right] = \frac{1}{2}(\Delta S\,\Delta T - \Delta P\,\Delta V).$$

Thus we obtain the probability (111.2) of a fluctuation in the form

$$w \propto e^{(\Delta P\,\Delta V - \Delta T\,\Delta S)/2kT}. \tag{111.3}$$

From this general formula, the fluctuations of the different thermodynamic quantities can be found. First choose V and T as independent variables. Then

$$\Delta S = \left(\frac{\partial S}{\partial T}\right)_V \Delta T + \left(\frac{\partial S}{\partial V}\right)_T \Delta V, \qquad \Delta P = \left(\frac{\partial P}{\partial T}\right)_V \Delta T + \left(\frac{\partial P}{\partial V}\right)_T \Delta V.$$

The first of these equations may be written in the form

$$\Delta S = \frac{C_v}{T}\Delta T + \left(\frac{\partial P}{\partial T}\right)_V \Delta V$$

(see eq. 16.3). Substituting these expressions into the exponent of (111.3) we find that the terms in $\Delta V \Delta T$ cancel and we are left with:

$$w \propto \exp\left\{-\frac{C_v}{2kT^2}(\Delta T)^2 + \frac{1}{2kT}\left(\frac{\partial P}{\partial V}\right)_T (\Delta V)^2\right\}. \tag{111.4}$$

This expression splits into two factors, each depending on ΔT or ΔV only. In other words, the fluctuations of the temperature and volume are statistically independent, and hence:

$$\overline{\Delta T \Delta V} = 0. \tag{111.5}$$

Comparing each of the two factors in (110.4) in turn with the general form (109.4) of the Gaussian distribution, we find the following expression for the mean square fluctuations of the temperature and volume:

$$\overline{(\Delta T)^2} = \frac{kT^2}{C_v}, \tag{111.6}$$

$$\overline{(\Delta V)^2} = -kT\left(\frac{\partial V}{\partial P}\right)_T. \tag{111.7}$$

The fact that these quantities are positive is ensured by the thermodynamic inequalities $C_v > 0$ and $(\partial P/\partial V)_T < 0$.

Now choose P and S as independent variables in (111.3). Then

$$\Delta V = \left(\frac{\partial V}{\partial P}\right)_S \Delta P + \left(\frac{\partial V}{\partial S}\right)_P \Delta S,$$

$$\Delta T = \left(\frac{\partial T}{\partial S}\right)_P \Delta S + \left(\frac{\partial T}{\partial P}\right)_S \Delta P.$$

But according to the relation $dw = TdS + VdP$ we have:

$$\left(\frac{\partial V}{\partial S}\right) = \frac{\partial^2 W}{\partial P \partial S} = \left(\frac{\partial T}{\partial P}\right)_S,$$

and therefore

$$\Delta V = \left(\frac{\partial V}{\partial P}\right)_S \Delta P + \left(\frac{\partial T}{\partial P}\right)_S \Delta S.$$

According to the formula $C_p = T(\partial S/\partial T)_P$ we have:

$$\Delta T = \frac{T}{C_p}\Delta S + \left(\frac{\partial T}{\partial P}\right)_S \Delta P.$$

Substituting ΔV and ΔT into (111.3), we find:

$$w \propto \exp\left\{\frac{1}{2kT}\left(\frac{\partial V}{\partial P}\right)_S (\Delta P)^2 - \frac{1}{2kC_p}(\Delta S)^2\right\}. \tag{111.8}$$

As in (111.4) this expression splits into two factors depending respectively on ΔP and ΔS. In other words, the fluctuations of the entropy and the pressure are statistically independent,† and hence

$$\overline{\Delta S \Delta P} = 0.$$

For the mean square fluctuations of the entropy and pressure, we find:

$$\overline{(\Delta S)^2} = kC_p \tag{111.10}$$

$$\overline{(\Delta P)^2} = -kT\left(\frac{\partial P}{\partial V}\right)_S. \tag{111.11}$$

From the formulae we have obtained, it is seen that the mean square fluctuations of the additive thermodynamic quantities (volume and entropy) are proportional to the size (volume) of the part of the body to which they refer. Correspondingly, the root mean square fluctuation of these quantities is proportional to the square root of the volume, and the relative fluctuation is inversely proportional to this root; this is in complete agreement with the general assertion made in §2 (eq. 2.5). But for quantities such as temperature and pressure, the root mean square fluctuations are themselves inversely proportional to the square root of the volume.

The relation (111.7) determines the fluctuation of the volume of some part of the body containing a definite number N of particles. Dividing both sides of the equation by N^2 we find the fluctuation of the volume per particle

$$\overline{\left(\Delta \frac{V}{N}\right)^2} = -\frac{kT}{N^2}\left(\frac{\partial V}{\partial P}\right)_T. \tag{111.12}$$

This fluctuation must, obviously, be independent of whether we consider fluctuations at constant volume or for a constant number of particles. Hence from (111.12) one can determine the fluctuation of the number of particles in a given volume of the body. In this case, we must write

$$\Delta \frac{V}{N} = V \Delta \frac{1}{N} = -\frac{V}{N^2}\Delta N.$$

Substituting this into (111.12) we find:

$$\overline{(\Delta N)^2} = -\frac{kTN^2}{V^2}\left(\frac{\partial V}{\partial P}\right)_T. \tag{111.13}$$

For some calculations it is more convenient to express this formula in a

---

† The statistical independence of the pairs of quantities T, V and S, P is immediately obvious from the following reasoning. If one chooses the quantities x_i (in the equations of §110) to be $x_i = \Delta S$, $x_2 = \Delta V$, then the corresponding X_i will be (see §22): $X_1 = \Delta T/T$, $X_2 = -\Delta P/T$. But $\overline{x_i X_k} = 0$ for $i \neq k$ (according to the general relation (110.7)) whence (111.5) and (111.9) follow.

different way. Noting that the derivative $(\partial V/\partial P)_T$ is understood to be taken at constant N, we write:

$$-\frac{N^2}{V^2}\left(\frac{\partial V}{\partial P}\right)_{T,N} = N\left(\frac{\partial}{\partial P}\frac{N}{V}\right)_{T,N}.$$

But, from considerations of similarity, the number of particles N, as a function of P, T, V must be of the form $N = Vf(P, T)$. In other words, N/V is a function of P and T only and hence it is immaterial whether one differentiates N/V at constant N or V, so that we may write:

$$N\left(\frac{\partial}{\partial P}\frac{N}{V}\right)_{T,N} = N\left(\frac{\partial}{\partial P}\frac{N}{V}\right)_{T,V} = \frac{N}{V}\left(\frac{\partial N}{\partial P}\right)_{T,V}$$

$$= \left(\frac{\partial N}{\partial P}\right)_{T,V}\left(\frac{\partial P}{\partial \mu}\right)_{T,V} = \left(\frac{\partial N}{\partial \mu}\right)_{T,V}$$

(we have used the relation $N/V = (\partial P/\partial \mu)_{T,V}$ which follows from the thermodynamic identity (24.14) $d\Omega = -V\,dP = -S\,dT - N\,d\mu$). In this way we obtain the following formula for the fluctuation of the number of particles.†

$$\overline{(\Delta N)^2} = kT\left(\frac{\partial N}{\partial \mu}\right)_{T,V}. \tag{111.14}$$

Besides the thermodynamic quantities, the body is described also by the momentum **P** of its macroscopic motion with respect to the medium. In the equilibrium state there is no macroscopic motion, i.e. **P** $= 0$. As a

---

† This can easily be obtained directly from the Gibbs distribution. According to the definition of mean value, we have:

$$\bar{N} = e^{\Omega/kT} \sum_N Ne^{\mu N/kT} \sum_n e^{-E_{nN}/kT}.$$

Differentiating this expression with respect to μ (at constant V and T) we obtain:

$$\frac{\partial \bar{N}}{\partial \mu} = \frac{1}{kT}e^{\Omega/kT} \sum_N \left(N^2 + N\frac{\partial \Omega}{\partial \mu}\right)e^{\mu N/kT} \sum_n e^{-E_{nN}/kT}$$

$$= \frac{1}{kT}\left(\overline{N^2} + \bar{N}\frac{\partial \Omega}{\partial \mu}\right).$$

But $\partial \Omega/\partial \mu = -\bar{N}$, so that

$$\frac{\partial \bar{N}}{\partial \mu} = \frac{1}{kT}(\overline{N^2} - \bar{N}^2) = \frac{1}{kT}\overline{(\Delta N)^2},$$

from which we obtain (111.14).

Starting from the Gibbs distribution, one could also obtain expressions for the fluctuations of other thermodynamic quantities.

result of the fluctuations, however, motion may occur; let us find the probability of such a fluctuation. The minimum work $R_{\min}$ is in this case equal
simply to the kinetic energy of the body:

$$R_{\min} = \frac{P^2}{2M} = \frac{Mv^2}{2},$$

where M is the mass, and $\mathbf{v} = \mathbf{P}/M$ is the velocity of the macroscopic motion.
In this way we have, for the desired probability:

$$w \propto e^{-Mv^2/2kT}. \tag{111.15}$$

Note that the fluctuations of the velocity are statistically independent of
the fluctuations of the other thermodynamic quantities. The mean square
fluctuation of each of the cartesian components of the velocity is equal to

$$\overline{(\Delta v_x)^2} = \frac{kT}{M}, \tag{111.16}$$

it is inversely proportional to the mass of the body.

From the formulae we have obtained, one can see that the mean square
fluctuations of quantities such as the energy, volume, pressure or velocity
vanish at absolute zero (with the first power of the temperature). This is a
general property of all thermodynamic quantities which also have a purely
mechanical significance, but does not apply, in general, to such thermodynamic quantities as the temperature and entropy.

Formula (111.6) for the fluctuation of the temperature can also be considered from another point of view. As we know, the concept of temperature
may also be introduced with the aid of the Gibbs distribution. In this case
the temperature is considered as a parameter which determines this distribution. When applied to an isolated body, the Gibbs distribution completely
describes its statistical properties, except that it gives very small, but nevertheless non-zero fluctuations of the total energy of the body, which cannot
exist in reality (see page 80). Conversely, if one assumes the energy to be
a given quantity, then one cannot ascribe a completely definite temperature
to the body and one must assume that the latter undergoes fluctuations
determined by (111.6), in which C_v is the specific heat of the body as a whole.
This quantity evidently determines the accuracy with which the temperature
of an isolated body can be specified.

PROBLEMS

1. Find the mean square fluctuation of the energy (using V and T as independent
variables).

SOLUTION: We have:

$$\Delta E = \left(\frac{\partial E}{\partial V}\right)_T \Delta V + \left(\frac{\partial E}{\partial T}\right)_V \Delta T = \left[T\left(\frac{\partial P}{\partial T}\right)_V - P\right]\Delta V + C_v \Delta T.$$

Squaring and taking the mean we obtain:

$$\overline{(\Delta E)^2} = -\left[T\left(\frac{\partial P}{\partial T}\right)_V - P\right]^2 kT\left(\frac{\partial V}{\partial P}\right)_T + C_v kT^2.$$

2.　Find $\overline{\Delta W^2}$ (using the variables P and S).

SOLUTION:

$$\overline{(\Delta W)^2} = -kTV^2\left(\frac{\partial P}{\partial V}\right)_S + kT^2 C_p.$$

3.　Find $\overline{\Delta T \Delta P}$ (using the variables V and T).

SOLUTION:

$$\overline{\Delta T \Delta P} = -kTV^2\left(\frac{\partial P}{\partial V}\right)_S + kT^2 C_p.$$

4.　Find $\overline{\Delta V \Delta P}$ (using the variables V and T).

SOLUTION:

$$\overline{\Delta V \Delta P} = \frac{kT^2}{C_v}\left(\frac{\partial P}{\partial T}\right)_V.$$

5.　Find $\overline{\Delta S \Delta V}$ (using the variables V and T).

SOLUTION:

$$\overline{\Delta S \Delta V} = \left(\frac{\partial V}{\partial T}\right)_P kT.$$

6.　Find $\overline{\Delta S \Delta T}$ (using the variables V and T).

SOLUTION:

$$\overline{\Delta S \Delta T} = kT.$$

7.　Find the mean square fluctuational deviation of a vertically suspended mathematical pendulum.

SOLUTION: Let l be the length of the pendulum, m its mass, ϕ the angle of deviation from the vertical. The work $R_{\min}$ in this case is simply the mechanical work done against gravity during the deviation of the pendulum; for small ϕ $R_{\min} = 1/2mg \cdot l\phi^2$. Hence

$$\overline{\phi^2} = \frac{kT}{mgl}.$$

8.　Find the mean square fluctuational displacement of the points of a stretched string.

SOLUTION: Let l be the length of the string, F the tension. Consider a point at a distance x from one of the ends of the string and let y be its transverse displacement. To determine $\overline{y^2}$, we must consider the equilibrium shape of the string for the given displacement y of the point x; this consists of two straight lines leading from the fixed points of the string to the point x, y. The work done in such a deformation of the string is equal to

$$R_{\min} = F(\sqrt{x^2+y^2}-x) + F[\sqrt{(l-x)^2+y^2}-(l-x)] \cong \frac{Fy^2}{2}\left(\frac{1}{x}+\frac{1}{l-x}\right).$$

Hence we find for the mean square:

$$\overline{y^2} = \frac{kT}{Fl}x(l-x).$$

9. Find the mean value of the product of the fluctuational displacements of two different points of the string.

SOLUTION: Let y_1, y_2 be the transverse displacements of points situated at distances x_1, x_2 from one of the ends of the string (and $x_2 > x_1$). The equilibrium shape for the given y_1 and y_2 is made up of three straight lines and the work,

$$R_{min} = \frac{F}{2}\left(y_1^2\frac{x_2}{x_1(x_2-x_1)} + y_2^2\frac{l-x_1}{(l-x_2)(x_2-x_1)} - 2y_1y_2\frac{1}{(x_2-x_1)} \right).$$

From (101.8) we find

$$\overline{y_1y_2} = \frac{kT}{Fl}x_1(l-x_2).$$

§112. Fluctuations in a perfect gas

The mean square fluctuation of the number of particles of a perfect gas in a given (comparatively small) part of the volume of the gas will be found by substituting $V = NkT/P$ into (111.13). This gives the following simple result.

$$\overline{(\Delta N)^2} = N. \tag{112.1}$$

The relative fluctuation of the number of particles is hence equal simply to the inverse square root of the average number of particles:

$$\frac{\sqrt{[\overline{(\Delta N)^2}]}}{N} = \frac{1}{\sqrt{N}}.$$

To calculate the fluctuations of the number of particles in a perfect Bose or Fermi gas, we must use (111.14), substituting into it the expression (55.5) for N as a function of μ, T, and V obtained by integrating the appropriate distribution function. We shall not write out here the rather cumbersome expressions obtained in this way. Note only the following fact. We have seen that for a Bose gas at temperatures $T < T_0$ (see §59) the pressure is independent of the volume; in other words its compressibility becomes infinite. According to (111.13) it would follow from this that the fluctuations of the number of particles also become infinite. This means that in calculating the fluctuations in a Bose gas at low temperatures, one cannot neglect the interaction of its particles, however small this may be; taking into account the interaction which must exist in any real gas leads to finite fluctuations.

Let us further consider the fluctuations in the distribution of particles amongst the various quantum states. We again introduce the quantum states of the particles (including also their different states of translational motion) and let n_k be their occupation numbers.

Consider the set of n_k particles which are in the kth quantum state. Owing to the complete statistical independence of this system of particles from the other particles of the gas (cf. §37) we can apply (111.14) to it.

$$\overline{(\Delta n_k)^2} = kT\frac{\partial \bar{n}_k}{\partial \mu}. \tag{112.2}$$

Applying this to the Fermi gas we must put

$$\bar{n}_k = \frac{1}{e^{(\varepsilon_k - \mu)/kT} + 1}.$$

After differentiation, we find:

$$\overline{(\Delta n_k)^2} = \frac{e^{(\varepsilon_k - \mu)/kT}}{(e^{(\varepsilon_k - \mu)/kT} + 1)^2} = \bar{n}_k(1 - \bar{n}_k). \tag{112.3}$$

In a similar way, for the Bose gas, we find:

$$\overline{(\Delta n_k)^2} = \frac{e^{(\varepsilon_k - \mu)/kT}}{(e^{(\varepsilon_k - \mu)/kT} - 1)^2} = \bar{n}_k(1 + \bar{n}_k). \tag{112.4}$$

For the Boltzmann gas, putting $\bar{n}_k = e^{(\mu - \varepsilon_k)/kT}$ we obtain, naturally, the result

$$\overline{(\Delta n_k)^2} = \bar{n}_k, \tag{112.5}$$

to which (112.3) and (112.4) tend for $\bar{n}_k \ll 1$.

We may now sum (112.3) or (112.4) over a group of G_j adjacent states containing, altogether, $N_j = \Sigma n_k$ particles. Owing to the above-mentioned statistical independence of the fluctuations of different n_k, we obtain:

$$\overline{(\Delta N_j)^2} = G_j \bar{n}_j(1 \mp \bar{n}_j) = \bar{N}_j\left(1 \mp \frac{\bar{N}_j}{G_j}\right), \tag{112.6}$$

where $\bar{n}_j$ is the common value of the adjacent $\bar{n}_k$, and $\bar{N}_j = \bar{n}_j G_j$.

The formulae we have obtained can be applied in particular to black body radiation (equilibrium Bose gas of photons), for which one must put $\mu = 0$ in (112.4). Consider the set of quantum states of the photons (in a volume V) with neighbouring frequencies in the small interval $\Delta\omega_j$; the number of such states is equal to

$$G_j = \frac{V\omega_j^2 \Delta\omega_j}{\pi^2 c^3}$$

(see (60.34)). The total energy of the quanta in this frequency range is $E_{\Delta\omega_j} = N_j \hbar\omega_j$. Multiplying (112.6) by $(\hbar\omega_j)^2$, and omitting the suffix j, we obtain the following expression for the fluctuation of the energy $E_{\Delta\omega}$

of the black-body radiation in the given frequency range $\Delta\omega$ (first derived by A. ENISTEIN, 1909).

$$\overline{(\Delta E_{\Delta\omega})^2} = \hbar\omega \cdot E_{\Delta\omega} + \frac{\pi^2 c^3 (E_{\Delta\omega})^2}{V\omega^2 \Delta\omega}. \tag{112.7}$$

PROBLEM

1. Determine $\overline{(\Delta N)^2}$ for an electron gas at temperatures well below the degeneracy temperature.

SOLUTION: In calculating $(\partial N/\partial\mu)_{T,V}$ one can use the expression (56.3) for μ at absolute zero. A simple calculation gives:

$$\overline{(\Delta N)^2} = \frac{3^{1/3} mkT}{\pi^{4/3}\hbar^2} \left(\frac{N}{V}\right)^{1/3} V.$$

§113. Poisson's Formula

Knowing the mean square fluctuation of the number of particles in a given volume of the gas (112.1), we can write down the corresponding Gaussian probability distribution for fluctuations of this number:

$$w(N)\,dN = \frac{1}{\sqrt{(2\pi\bar{N})}} \exp\left\{\frac{(N-\bar{N})^2}{2\bar{N}}\right\} dN. \tag{113.1}$$

This formula, however, only applies for small fluctuations. The difference $N-\bar{N}$ must be small, compared with the number $\bar{N}$ itself.

If the selected volume of the gas, V, is sufficiently small, then the number of particles in it is not large and it is interesting to consider also large fluctuations when $N-\bar{N}$ becomes comparable with $\bar{N}$. Note that there is no sense in applying this problem except to a Boltzmann gas, since for Fermi and Bose gases the probability of such a fluctuation is negligible except for such small volumes that the quantum fluctuations become predominant.

The solution to this problem is obtained most simply by the following method. Let V_0 and N_0 be the total volume of the gas and the total number of particles in it and let V be a part of the volume small compared with V_0. Owing to the homogeneity of the gas it is obvious that the probability that one particular particle is in the volume V is simply equal to the ratio V/V_0 and the probability that N particular particles are simultaneously in it is $(V/V_0)^N$. Similarly, the probability that a particle is not in V is equal to $(V_0-V)/V_0$, and the same probability for N_0-N particles at the same time is $[(V_0-V)/V_0]^{N_0-N}$. Hence the probability w_N that altogether some N molecules are in the volume V will be given by

$$w_N = \frac{N_0!}{N!(N_0-N)!} \left(\frac{V}{V_0}\right)^N \left(1-\frac{V}{V_0}\right)^{N_0-N}, \tag{113.2}$$

where we have introduced a factor giving the number of possible ways of choosing N out of N_0 particles.

In the case in which we are interested, $V \ll V_0$ and the number N, although it can differ considerably from its mean value $\bar{N}$ is still small compared with the total number of particles N_0. Thus we can put $N_0! \cong (N_0-N)! N_0{}^N$, and neglect N in the exponent of the bracket so that we obtain

$$w_N = \frac{1}{N!}\left(\frac{N_0 V}{V_0}\right)^N\left(1-\frac{V}{V_0}\right)^N.$$

But $N_0 V/V_0$ is simply the mean value $\bar{N}$ of the number of particles in the volume V. Thus we have:

$$w_N = \frac{\bar{N}^N}{N!}\left(1-\frac{\bar{N}}{N_0}\right)^{N_0}.$$

Finally, bearing in mind the well-known result

$$\lim_{n \to \infty}\left(1-\frac{x}{n}\right)^n = e^{-x},$$

we replace $(1-\bar{N}/N_0)^{N_0}$ where N_0 is large, by $e^{-\bar{N}}$ and finally obtain the required distribution in the form:†

$$w_N = \frac{\bar{N}^N e^{-\bar{N}}}{N!}. \tag{113.3}$$

This is known as *Poisson's formula*. It is easily seen that it satisfies the normalisation condition

$$\sum_{N=0}^{\infty} w_N = 1.$$

Let us calculate the mean square fluctuation of the number of particles. We write

$$\overline{N^2} = \sum_{N=0}^{\infty} N^2 w_N = e^{-\bar{N}} \sum_{N=1}^{\infty} \frac{\bar{N}^N N}{(N-1)!}$$

$$= e^{-\bar{N}} \sum_{N=2}^{\infty} \frac{\bar{N}^N}{(N-2)!} + e^{-\bar{N}} \sum_{N=1}^{\infty} \frac{\bar{N}^N}{(N-1)!}$$

$$= \bar{N}^2 + \bar{N}.$$

† For small fluctuations ($|N-\bar{N}| \ll \bar{N}$, $\bar{N}$ large) this transforms, naturally, into (113.1). This is easily seen by using Stirling's asymptotic formula for the factorial of a large number N

$$N! = \sqrt{(2\pi N)}.N^N e^{-N}$$

and expanding $\log w_N$ in powers of $N-\bar{N}$.

From this we find, for the required fluctuation, the previous value

$$\overline{(\Delta N)^2} = \overline{N^2} - \bar{N}^2 = \bar{N}. \tag{113.4}$$

Thus the mean square fluctuation of the number of particles is equal to $\bar{N}$, not only for large, but for all values of $\bar{N}$.

Note that (113.3) can be obtained directly from the Gibbs distribution. According to the latter, the distribution of N particles of the gas simultaneously over the various quantum states is given by the expression

$$\exp\left\{\frac{\Omega + \mu N - \Sigma\, \epsilon_k}{kT}\right\}$$

where $\Sigma\, \epsilon_k$ is the sum of the energies of the different particles. To obtain the required probability w_N, one must sum this expression over all the states of the particles "allotted" to the given volume V. Performing the summation over the states of each particle separately, we must simultaneously divide the result by $N!$ (see §41) so that we obtain:

$$w_N = \frac{e^{\Omega/kT}}{N!} (\, \Sigma_k\, e^{(\mu - \epsilon_k)/kT})^N.$$

But the sum in this expression is simply the mean number of particles in the volume under consideration:

$$\Sigma_k\, e^{(\mu - \epsilon_k)/kT} = \bar{N}.$$

Hence we find:

$$w_N = \text{const}\, \frac{\bar{N}^N}{N!}$$

after which, from the normalisation condition, we find that the constant is equal to $e^{-\bar{N}}$, bringing us once more to (113.3).†

§114. Fluctuations in solutions

The fluctuations of thermodynamic quantities in solutions can be calculated by the same method as the one used in §111 for fluctuations of bodies consisting of identical particles. The corresponding calculations will be greatly simplified if we take the following considerations into account beforehand.

We consider a small part of the solution containing a given number N of molecules of the solvent and let us set ourselves the task of calculating the mean fluctuation of the number n of molecules of the solute, or, what is the same thing, the fluctuation of the concentration $c = n/N$. We must

---

† i.e. $\Omega = -PV = -\bar{N}kT$ according to Clapeyron's equation.

consider, for this purpose, the most complete equilibrium of the solution possible for a given, non-equilibrium, value of n (cf. footnote on page 346). The fact that the concentration is given does not affect the setting up of equilibrium between the small part and the rest of the solution with respect to the exchange of energy between them or with respect to a change in their volume. The first requires (see §9) that the temperature should remain constant throughout the solution and the second that the same should be true of the pressure (§12). Hence, to calculate the mean square $\overline{(\Delta c)^2}$ it is sufficient to study fluctuations of the concentration which take place at constant temperature and pressure.

This fact itself already means that the fluctuations of the concentration, on the one hand, and of the temperature and pressure on the other, are statistically independent; that is†,

$$\overline{\Delta T \Delta c} = 0, \quad \overline{\Delta c \Delta P} = 0. \tag{114.1}$$

The minimum work necessary for n to change by Δn at constant pressure and temperature is, according to (100.1),

$$R_{\min} = \Delta\Phi - \mu' \Delta n,$$

where μ' is the chemical potential of the solute. Expanding $\Delta\Phi$ in powers of Δn, we have:

$$\Delta\Phi \cong \left(\frac{\partial\Phi}{\partial n}\right)_{P,T} \Delta n + \left(\frac{\partial^2\Phi}{\partial n^2}\right)_{P,T} \frac{(\Delta n)^2}{2}$$

$$= \mu' \Delta n + \left(\frac{\partial\mu'}{\partial n}\right)_{P,T} \frac{(\Delta n)^2}{2},$$

so that

$$R_{\min} = \frac{1}{2}\left(\frac{\partial\mu'}{\partial n}\right)_{P,T} (\Delta n)^2.$$

Substituting this expression into the general formula (111.1) and comparing it with the formula for the Gaussian distribution (109.4), we obtain, for the required mean square fluctuation of the number n:

$$\overline{(\Delta n)^2} = \frac{kT}{\left(\dfrac{\partial\mu'}{\partial n}\right)_{P,T}}, \tag{114.2}$$

---

† This can be shown more rigorously by the method indicated in the footnote on page 296. With the aid of the thermodynamic identity $dE = T\,dS - P\,dV + \mu'\,dn$ (N constant) we can rewrite (94.1) in the form

$$dR_{\min} = (T - T_0)\,dS - (P - P_0)\,dV + (\mu' - \mu_0')\,dn.$$

Hence one can see that if one chooses the following quantities for the x_i: $x_1 = \Delta S_1$, $x_2 = \Delta V$, $x_3 = \Delta n$, then the corresponding X_i will be: $X_1 = \Delta T/T$, $X_2 = -\Delta P/T$, $X_3 = \Delta\mu'/T$, Formula (114.1) then follows from $\overline{x_3 X_1} = 0$, $\overline{x_3 X_2} = 0$.

or, dividing by N^2, the mean square fluctuation of the concentration

$$\overline{(\Delta c)^2} = \frac{kT}{N\left(\dfrac{\partial \mu'}{\partial c}\right)_{P,T}}. \tag{114.3}$$

This is, as it should be (cf. page 353), inversely proportional to the quantity N of the solvent in the given small part of the solution.

For weak solutions, $\partial \mu'/\partial n = kT/n$ and (114.3) gives:

$$\overline{(\Delta n)^2} = n. \tag{114.4}$$

Note that this is (as we should expect) completely analogous to formula (112.1) for fluctuations of the number of particles of an ideal gas.

§115. Correlation of fluctuations

The assertion that the particles of a homogeneous isotropic body (liquid or gas) are equally likely to be at any position in space, applies to each separate particle on condition that all the other particles can have arbitrary positions. This assertion, certainly, does not contradict the fact that, owing to their interaction, there must exist some correlation between the relative positions of the different particles. This means that if we consider, say, two particles at the same time, then for a given position of one particle, different positions of the other will not be equally probable.

To simplify further expressions, we shall restrict ourselves to monatomic substances in which the position of each particle is completely determined by its three co-ordinates.

Let us denote by $n\,dV$ the number of particles situated (at a given moment of time) in the volume element dV. Since dV is infinitesimal, no more than one particle can be in it; the probability of two particles being in it simultaneously is an infinitesimal quantity of higher order. Hence the average number of particles $\bar{n}\,dV$ is also the probability that a particle is in the element dV.

Consider the mean value

$$\overline{(n_1 - \bar{n}_1)(n_2 - \bar{n}_2)} = \overline{n_1 n_2} - (\bar{n})^2 \tag{115.1}$$

where n_1, n_2 are the values of the number density of particles $n(\mathbf{r})$ at two different points, and $\bar{n}$ denotes the mean density which is the same at all points, owing to the homogeneity of the body ($\bar{n}_1 = \bar{n}_2 = \bar{n}$). If there were no correlation between the positions of the different particles, then we would have $\overline{n_1 n_2} = \overline{n_1}\,\overline{n_2} = (\bar{n})^2$, and the mean value (115.1) would vanish. Thus this quantity can serve as a measure of the correlation.

Let $n_{12}\,dV_2$ denote the probability that there is a particle in the volume element dV_2 given that there is one in the volume element dV_1; n_{12} is a function of the absolute value $r = |\mathbf{r}_2 - \mathbf{r}_1|$, the distance between the two volume elements.

Since, as was already noted, the number $n\, dV$ is 0 or 1, it is obvious that the mean value

$$\overline{n_1\, dV_1 . n_2\, dV_2} = \bar{n}_1\, dV_1 . n_{12}\, dV_2$$

or

$$\overline{n_1 n_2} = n_{12} \bar{n}.$$

In this relation, which holds for $\mathbf{r}_1 \neq \mathbf{r}_2$, one cannot, however, go to the limit $\mathbf{r}_2 \to \mathbf{r}_1$, since the derivation does not take account of the fact that if the points 1 and 2 coincide, then the particle in dV is also in dV_2. It can easily be seen that the relation which takes this into account is

$$\overline{n_1 n_2} = \bar{n} n_{12} + \bar{n}\delta(\mathbf{r}_2 - \mathbf{r}_1). \tag{115.2}$$

For, on multiplying (115.2) by $dV_1\, dV_2$, and integrating over a small volume ΔV, the term $\bar{n} n_{12}$ will give a second-order term (proportional to $(\Delta V)^2$) and the term with the δ-function will give ΔV, i.e. a first order quantity. Hence we obtain:

$$\overline{\left(\int_{\Delta V} n\, dV\right)^2} = \bar{n}\Delta V$$

as we should, bearing in mind that to first order there can only be 0 or 1 particle in the small volume.

Substituting (115.2) into (115.1), we find:

$$\overline{(n_1 - \bar{n}_1)(n_2 - \bar{n}_2)} = \bar{n}\,\delta(\mathbf{r}_2 - \mathbf{r}_1) + \bar{n}\nu(r) \tag{115.3}$$

where we have introduced the function

$$\nu(r) = n_{12} - \bar{n}, \tag{115.4}$$

which we shall call the "*correlation function*". It is clear that there can be no correlation when the distance r is infinite, i.e.

$$\nu(\infty) = 0. \tag{115.5}$$

We isolate some finite volume, V, of the body and after multiplying equation (115.3) by $dV_1\, dV_2$ we integrate with respect to dV_1 and dV_2. Bearing in mind that

$$\int (n_1 - \bar{n}_1)\, dV_1 = \int (n_2 - \bar{n}_2)\, dV_2 = N - \bar{N} \equiv \Delta N,$$

where N is the total number of particles in the volume V (so that $\bar{n}V = N$), we find:

$$\int\int \nu(r)\,dV_1 dV_2 = \frac{\overline{(\Delta N)^2}}{\bar{n}} - V.$$

Transforming from integration with respect to dV_1 and dV_2 to integration with respect to, say, dV_1 and the relative co-ordinates $\mathbf{r} = \mathbf{r}_2 - \mathbf{r}_1$ (we shall denote the product of its differentials by dV), and bearing in mind that ν depends upon r only, we finally obtain the following expression for the integral of the correlation function:

$$\int \nu\,dV = \frac{\overline{(\Delta N)^2}}{N} - 1. \tag{115.6}$$

Thus the integral of the correlation function over some volume is connected with the mean square fluctuation of the total number of particles in this volume. Using the thermodynamic formula (111.3) for the latter, this integral may be expressed in terms of thermodynamic quantities:

$$\int \nu\,dV = -\frac{kTN}{V^2}\left(\frac{\partial V}{\partial P}\right)_T - 1. \tag{115.7}$$

For the ordinary (classical) perfect gas, we obtain

$$\int \nu\,dV = 0,$$

as we should. It is clear that, in an ideal gas considered from the point of view of classical mechanics, there is no correlation whatsoever, since the particles of an ideal gas are assumed not to interact with one another.

On the other hand, for a liquid (at temperatures not near the critical point) the first term in (115.7) is small compared with unity, owing to the small compressibility of the liquid. In this case one can write

$$\int \nu\,dV \cong -1.$$

This value of the integral of the correlation function corresponds to the impenetrability of the particles of the liquid, which are considered as tightly packed hard spheres.

We next multiply (115.3) on both sides by $e^{-i\mathbf{f}.\mathbf{r}} = e^{-i\mathbf{f}.(\mathbf{r}_2-\mathbf{r}_1)}$ and again integrate it with respect to dV_1 and dV_2. We obtain:

$$\int\int \overline{(n_1-\bar{n})(n_2-\bar{n})}e^{i\mathbf{f}.(\mathbf{r}_1-\mathbf{r}_2)}\,dV_1 dV_2 = \bar{N} + \bar{N}\int \nu e^{-i\mathbf{f}.\mathbf{r}}\,dV$$

or, finally

$$\left| \int (n-\bar{n})e^{-i\mathbf{f.r}} \, dV \right|^2 = \bar{n}V(1+ \int \nu e^{-i\mathbf{f.r}} \, dV).$$ (115.8)

This relation determines the Fourier components of the correlation function in terms of the mean squares of the Fourier components of the density.

§116. Fluctuations at the critical point

At the critical point the compressibility of a substance $(\partial V/\partial P)_T$ and its specific heat C_p become infinite (§79). At the same time the expressions (111.7) and (111.10) for the fluctuations of the volume (i.e. density) and entropy formally become infinite; the fluctuations of the temperature and pressure, however, remain finite. This means that at the critical point the fluctuations of density and entropy become anomalously large and to calculate them it becomes necessary to extend the expansion of R_{min} in (111.1) beyond the terms of second order, which vanish in this case.† We shall examine in detail, here, fluctuations of the density near the critical point. (This question was first studied by ORNSTEIN and ZERNIKE, 1917).

Since the fluctuations of the density and temperature are statistically independent, we may assume the temperature to be constant when we consider fluctuations of the density. By definition the volume of the body as a whole is also constant. In these conditions the minimum work R_{min} is equal to the change ΔF_t in the total free energy of the body during the fluctuations, so that the probability of the latter can be written in the form:

$$w \propto e^{-\Delta F_t/kT}.$$ (116 1)

We may write the total free energy of the body as the integral

$$F_t = \int F \, dV,$$

taken over the total volume of the body, where F denotes the free energy per unit volume. Let $\bar{F}$ be the mean value of F, constant throughout the body. As a result of the fluctuation, F becomes, together with the density, a quantity which changes from point to point of the body and

$$\Delta F_t = \int (F-\bar{F}) \, dV.$$ (116.2)

We denote the number density of particles by n (its mean value being $\bar{n}$) and expand $F-\bar{F}$ in powers of $n-\bar{n}$ at constant temperature.

The first term in the expansion is proportional to $n-\bar{n}$, and vanishes on integration over the volume, owing to the constant total number of particles

---

† The same applies to fluctuations of the concentration in solutions; at points on the critical line $(\partial\mu'/\partial c)_{P,T} = 0$ (§95), and (114.3) becomes infinite.

in the body: $\int n \, dV = \int \bar{n} \, dV$. The second-order terms are of the form: $a/2 \, (n - \bar{n})^2$, where the positive coefficient a vanishes at the critical point and is small near to it.† The coefficient of the third-order term is also small near the critical point (at the critical point $\partial^2 P / \partial n^2$ vanishes, as well as $\partial P / \partial n$) so that one ought to take the fourth-order terms into account. In actual fact, however, the expansion of $F - \bar{F}$ involves larger terms of a different kind.

The point is that we have so far considered thermodynamic quantities of homogeneous bodies. But for an inhomogeneous body the expansion of F may contain not only the different powers of the density itself, but also its spatial derivatives of various orders. Since the body is isotropic, the first derivatives can only enter into the expansion of the density as the scalar combination $(\nabla n)^2$, and the second as the combination Δn (where Δ is the Laplacian operator). The integral of the term of the form const . Δn over the volume transforms into an integral over the surface of the body, representing an irrelevant surface effect, while the integral of the term $n \, \Delta n$ transforms into the integral of $(\nabla n)^2$. Thus quite generally we can assume

$$F - \bar{F} = \frac{a}{2}(n - \bar{n})^2 + \frac{b}{2}(\nabla n)^2, \qquad (116.3)$$

where b is a positive constant (for $b < 0$ the free energy could not have a minimum corresponding to $n = $ const); this constant need by no means vanish at the critical point and hence is not small near it.

Calculations of the mean fluctuation of the density in small regions of the body are of comparatively little interest; owing to the presence of terms involving the derivatives of the density in (116.3), these fluctuations will depend not only on the volume, but on the shape of the region.‡ The study of fluctuations of the Fourier components of the density near the critical point is of much greater interest.

If we expand $n - \bar{n}$ as a Fourier series in the volume V of the body, it takes the form

$$n - \bar{n} = \sum_{\mathbf{f}} n_{\mathbf{f}} e^{i\mathbf{f}\cdot\mathbf{r}}, \qquad (116.4)$$

---

† The derivative $(\partial F / \partial n)_T$ is the chemical potential. Therefore the second derivative:

$$a = \left(\frac{\partial^2 F}{\partial n^2} \right)_T = \left(\frac{\partial \mu}{\partial n} \right)_T = \frac{1}{n} \left(\frac{\partial P}{\partial n} \right)_T .$$

‡ At the critical point itself $a = 0$ and only the second term of (116.3) remains. If the density fluctuates in a region with linear dimensions $\sim l$, then $F - \bar{F} \sim b[(n - \bar{n})/b]^2$ and $\Delta F_l \sim b(n - \bar{n})^2 l$. The mean square fluctuation of the density will therefore be inversely proportional to l:

$$\overline{(\Delta n)^2} \propto \frac{1}{l},$$

i.e. inversely proportional to the cube root of the volume of the region (whereas away from the critical point the mean square fluctuation of the density decreases in inverse proportion to the volume).

where the components of the vector **f** take positive and negative values, and the coefficients

$$n_{\mathbf{f}} = \frac{1}{V} \int (n - \bar{n}) e^{-i\mathbf{f}.\mathbf{r}} \, dV$$

are connected by the relation

$$n_{-\mathbf{f}} = n^*{}_{\mathbf{f}}$$

which follows from the reality of $n - \bar{n}$. Substituting (116.4) into (116.3) and integrating over the volume we get:

$$\Delta F_t = \frac{V}{2} \sum_{\mathbf{f}} (a + bf^2) |n_{\mathbf{f}}|^2. \tag{116.5}$$

Each of the terms of this sum involves only one of the $n_{\mathbf{f}}$: hence the fluctuations of the different $n_{\mathbf{f}}$ are statistically independent. Every square $|n_{\mathbf{f}}|^2$ enters twice into the sum (116.5) (from $\pm\mathbf{f}$) so that the probability distribution is given by the expression

$$w \propto \exp\left\{-\frac{V}{kT}(a + bf^2)|n_{\mathbf{f}}|^2\right\}.$$

Bearing in mind that $|n_{\mathbf{f}}|^2$ is the sum of the squares of two independent quantities ($n_{\mathbf{f}}$ is complex), we obtain from this the required mean square fluctuation:

$$\overline{|n_{\mathbf{f}}|^2} = \frac{kT}{V(a + bf^2)}. \tag{116.6}$$

It must be emphasised that this formula only applies for values of the wave vector **f** which are not too large: for large **f** we can no longer restrict ourselves, in the expansion (116.3), to terms containing only the lower spatial derivatives of the co-ordinates.

The result we have obtained makes it possible to calculate the correlation function $\nu(r)$ near the critical point. According to the general formula (115.8) we have:

$$\int \nu e^{-i\mathbf{f}.\mathbf{r}} \, dV = \frac{V}{\bar{n}}\overline{|n\mathbf{f}|^2} - 1 = \frac{kT}{\bar{n}(a + bf^2)} - 1.$$

The first term on the right-hand side is, in general, large compared with unity, provided that both a and f are assumed small. Hence we may write:

$$\int \nu e^{-i\mathbf{f}.\mathbf{r}} \, dV = \frac{kT}{\bar{n}(a + bf^2)}. \tag{116.7}$$

From this, by means of an inverse Fourier transformation, we find†

$$v(r) = \frac{kT}{4\pi\bar{n}b}\frac{1}{r}e^{-(a/b)^{\frac{1}{2}}r} \tag{116.8}$$

The coefficient of r in the exponent is small, since a is small. At the critical point itself $a = 0$, so that the exponentially decreasing factor entirely disappears:

$$v'(r) = \frac{kT}{4\pi\bar{n}b}\frac{1}{r}. \tag{116.9}$$

Thus, near the critical point the correlation between the positions of different particles of the substance decreases slowly with the distance, i.e. becomes much stronger than under normal conditions, when it almost disappears already at distances of the order of magnitude of the intermolecular distance.

The whole theory of fluctuations near the critical point, which we have discussed in this section, must be subject to the same reservations as those mentioned in §79. As in that case the proofs we have given assume the absence of any essential singularities in the thermodynamic quantities near the critical point, and hence one cannot be certain that the results obtained in this way are correct.

§117. Correlation of fluctuations in a perfect gas

As we mentioned in §115, in a classical perfect gas there is no correlation between the positions of the various particles. In quantum mechanics, however, such correlation exists, owing to the fact that identical particles of a perfect gas "interact" with one another indirectly, as a result of the principle of symmetry of the wave function (the question of correlation in a Fermi gas was first studied by V. Fursov in 1937, and in a Bose gas by A. Galanin in 1940).

---

† If

$$\int \phi e^{-i\mathbf{f}.\mathbf{r}}\,dV = \frac{4\pi}{\chi^2+f^2}, \tag{1}$$

then the function ϕ is equal to

$$\phi = \frac{e^{-\chi r}}{r}. \tag{2}$$

This can most easily be seen by noting that the function (2) satisfies the differential equation

$$\Delta\phi-\chi^2\phi = -4\pi\,\delta(\mathbf{r}).$$

Multiplying this equation on both sides by $e^{-i\mathbf{f}.\mathbf{r}}$ and integrating over the total volume ($e^{-i\mathbf{f}.\mathbf{r}}\Delta\phi$ being integrated twice by parts) we obtain (1).

To simplify the following formulae, we shall initially disregard the possibility that the particles possess spin; taking the spin into account makes no fundamental difference to the results we obtain.

The problem of calculating the correlation function for a Fermi gas can be solved most simply by the method of the second quantisation. Using this method,[†] we introduce the set of normalised wave functions

$$\psi_{\mathbf{p}} = \frac{1}{\sqrt{V}} e^{(i/\hbar)\mathbf{p}.\mathbf{r}}, \tag{117.1}$$

describing the state of a particle of the gas moving freely in the volume. In the case of a finite volume V, the momentum $\mathbf{p}$ runs through an infinite series of discrete values, whose separation is, however, very small for large V.

We introduce, also, the operators $\hat{A}_{\mathbf{p}}$ and $\hat{A}_{\mathbf{p}}^{+}$ which respectively decrease and increase by unity the numbers $n_{\mathbf{p}}$ of particles in the various quantum states $\psi_{\mathbf{p}}$, and also the operators

$$\hat{\Phi}(\mathbf{r}) = \sum_{\mathbf{p}} \psi_{\mathbf{p}}(\mathbf{r})\hat{A}_{\mathbf{p}}, \qquad \hat{\Phi}^{+}(\mathbf{r}) = \sum_{\mathbf{p}} \psi_{\mathbf{p}}^{*}(\mathbf{r})\hat{A}_{\mathbf{p}}^{+}$$

which respectively "annihilate" and "create" one particle of the system at the point $\mathbf{r}$. As is well known, $\hat{\Phi}^{+}(\mathbf{r})\hat{\Phi}(\mathbf{r})\,dV$ is the operator of the number of particles whose co-ordinates lie in the range $dx\,dy\,dz = dV$[‡].

Hence $\hat{\Phi}^{+}\hat{\Phi}$ can be regarded as an operator $\hat{n}$ which, in the second quantisation method, represents the density of the spatial distribution of the particles of the gas:

$$\hat{n} = \hat{\Phi}^{+}(\mathbf{r})\hat{\Phi}(\mathbf{r}) = \sum_{\mathbf{p}} \sum_{\mathbf{p}'} \hat{A}_{\mathbf{p}}^{+}\hat{A}_{\mathbf{p}'}\psi_{\mathbf{p}}^{*}\psi_{\mathbf{p}'}. \tag{117.2}$$

The summations with respect to $\mathbf{p}$ and $\mathbf{p}'$ are carried out in this case over all their possible values. It can easily be seen that the "diagonal" terms of the sum $(\mathbf{p} = \mathbf{p}')$ give just the mean density. Indeed, since the operator $\hat{A}_{\mathbf{p}}^{+}\hat{A}_{\mathbf{p}}$ is simply the number of particles $n_{\mathbf{p}}$ in the given quantum state with momentum $\mathbf{p}$ and since, according to (117.1), we have $|\psi_{\mathbf{p}}|^2 = 1/V$, these terms equal

$$\sum_{\mathbf{p}} \hat{A}_{\mathbf{p}}\hat{A}_{\mathbf{p}}^{+}|\psi_{\mathbf{p}}|^2 = \frac{1}{V}\sum_{\mathbf{p}} n_{\mathbf{p}} = \frac{N}{V} = \bar{n},$$

where N is the total number of particles in the volume V.

Hence we can write:

$$\hat{n} - \bar{n} = \sum_{\mathbf{p}} \sum_{\mathbf{p}'}{}' \hat{A}_{\mathbf{p}}\hat{A}_{\mathbf{p}'}^{+}\psi_{\mathbf{p}}^{*}\psi_{\mathbf{p}'}, \tag{117.3}$$

where the accent on the summation sign means that we must omit terms with

---

† See *Quantum Mechanics*, §§62, 63.
‡ See *Quantum Mechanics*, page 220. Since we disregard the spin of the particles, in place of $d\xi$ we write here the volume element dV.

$\mathbf{p}' - \mathbf{p}$. With the aid of this expression, it is not difficult to calculate the mean value in which we are interested:

$$\overline{(n_1 - \bar{n})(n_2 - \bar{n})}.$$

The calculation of the mean value is done in two stages. First of all, we must carry out the quantum averaging, i.e. averaging with respect to the quantum states of the particles. This, as is well known, reduces to taking the appropriate diagonal matrix element of the given quantity. Multiplying two of the operators (117.3) referring to two different points $\mathbf{r}_1$ and $\mathbf{r}_2$ we obtain a sum of terms containing all the different products of the operators $\hat{A}_\mathbf{p}$, $\hat{A}_\mathbf{p}^+$ taken four at a time. But out of all these products the only ones with a diagonal matrix element are those which contain two pairs of the operators $\hat{A}_\mathbf{p}$, $\hat{A}_\mathbf{p}^+$ with the same suffix, i.e. the terms:

$$\sum_\mathbf{p} \sum_{\mathbf{p}'} {}' \hat{A}_{\mathbf{p}'}^+ \hat{A}_{\mathbf{p}} \hat{A}_\mathbf{p}^+ \hat{A}_\mathbf{p} \psi_{\mathbf{p}'}^*(\mathbf{r}_1)\psi_{\mathbf{p}'}(\mathbf{r}_1)\psi_\mathbf{p}^*(\mathbf{r}_2)\psi_\mathbf{p}(\mathbf{r}_2). \tag{117.4}$$

These terms represent diagonal matrices, seeing that

$$\hat{A}_{\mathbf{p}'}\hat{A}_{\mathbf{p}'}^+ = 1 \mp n_{\mathbf{p}'}, \qquad \hat{A}_\mathbf{p}^+\hat{A}_\mathbf{p} = n_\mathbf{p}.$$

(here and below the upper sign applies in the case of Fermi statistics and the lower one in that of Bose statistics). Substituting also for the functions $\psi_\mathbf{p}$ from (117.6), we obtain

$$\frac{1}{V^2} \sum_\mathbf{p} \sum_{\mathbf{p}'} {}' (1 \mp n_{\mathbf{p}'})n_\mathbf{p} e^{(i/\hbar)(\mathbf{p} - \mathbf{p}')(\mathbf{r}_2 - \mathbf{r}_1)}.$$

This expression must now be averaged in the statistical sense, i.e. averaged over the equilibrium distribution of the particles over the different quantum states. Since the particles in the various quantum states behave quite independently, the average of the numbers $n_\mathbf{p}$ and $n_{\mathbf{p}'}$ can be carried out independently, i.e.

$$\overline{(1 \mp n_{\mathbf{p}'})n_\mathbf{p}} = (1 \mp \bar{n}_{\mathbf{p}'})\bar{n}_\mathbf{p}.$$

The mean value $\bar{n}_\mathbf{p}$ is determined by the Fermi or Bose distribution function.

In this way, we obtain the following expression for the mean value in which we are interested:

$$\overline{(n_1 - \bar{n})(n_2 - \bar{n})} = \frac{1}{V^2} \sum_\mathbf{p} \sum_{\mathbf{p}'} {}' (1 \mp \bar{n}_{\mathbf{p}'})\bar{n}_\mathbf{p} e^{(i/\hbar)(\mathbf{p} - \mathbf{p}')(\mathbf{r}_2 - \mathbf{r}_1)}. \tag{117.5}$$

Bearing in mind that if the volume V is not too small the momentum $\mathbf{p}$ takes an almost continuous series of values, one can change this expression from a summation to an integration, multiplying it for that purpose by

$$\frac{V\,d^3p}{(2\pi\hbar)^3} \frac{V\,d^3p'}{(2\pi\hbar)^3}.$$

The integral of (117.5) splits into two parts, of which the first is†

$$\frac{1}{(2\pi\hbar)^6} \int \int \bar{n}_\mathbf{p} e^{(i/\hbar)(\mathbf{p}-\mathbf{p}')(\mathbf{r}_2-\mathbf{r}_1)} \, d^3p' d^3p$$

$$= \frac{1}{(2\pi\hbar)^3} \int e^{(i/\hbar)\mathbf{p}(\mathbf{r}_2-\mathbf{r}_1)} \bar{n}_\mathbf{p} \delta(\mathbf{r}_2-\mathbf{r}_1) \, d^3p$$

$$= \frac{1}{(2\pi\hbar)^3} \delta(\mathbf{r}_2-\mathbf{r}_1) \int \bar{n}_\mathbf{p} \, d^3p = \bar{n}\,\delta(\mathbf{r}_2-\mathbf{r}_1).$$

This is simply the first term in (115.3). Hence, for the correlation function (the second term in (115.3)) we obtain the following expression:

$$\nu(r) = \mp \frac{1}{\bar{n}(2\pi\hbar)^6} \int \int e^{(i/\hbar)(\mathbf{p}-\mathbf{p}')\mathbf{r}} \bar{n}_\mathbf{p} \bar{n}_{\mathbf{p}'} \, d^3p\,d^3p'$$

$$= \mp \frac{1}{\bar{n}(2\pi\hbar)^6} \left| \int e^{(i/\hbar)\mathbf{p}\cdot\mathbf{r}} \bar{n}_\mathbf{p} \, d^3p \right|^2. \tag{117.6}$$

If we take the spin of the particles into account from the start, (117.2), the formula for the operator for the numerical space density of the particles, must be written in the form

$$\hat{n} = \sum_\sigma \sum_\mathbf{p} \sum_{\mathbf{p}'} \hat{A}^+_{\mathbf{p}\sigma} \hat{A}_{\mathbf{p}'\sigma} \psi_{\mathbf{p}\sigma}{}^* \psi_{\mathbf{p}'\sigma}.$$

(σ being the projection of the spin). In the same way the expression (117.4) must also be summed with respect to the spin variable σ. As a result, the right-hand sides of (117.5) and (117.6) are multiplied by $g = 2s+1$, $\bar{n}_\mathbf{p}$ being the mean number of particles in the quantum state with a definite value of σ, i.e.

$$\bar{n}_\mathbf{p} = \frac{1}{e^{(\epsilon-\mu)/kT} \pm 1}. \tag{117.7}$$

In this way we finally obtain the following expression for the correlation function:

$$\nu(r) = \mp \frac{g}{\bar{n}(2\pi\hbar)^6} \left| \int \frac{e^{(i/\hbar)\mathbf{p}\cdot\mathbf{r}} \, d^3p}{e^{(\epsilon-\mu)/kT} \pm 1} \right|^2. \tag{117.8}$$

If we integrate with respect to the direction of the momentum, we find:

$$\nu(r) = \mp \frac{g}{4\pi^4 \bar{n} \hbar^4 r^2} \left| \int_0^\infty \frac{\sin(pr/\hbar) \cdot p \, dp}{e^{(\epsilon-\mu)/kT} \pm 1} \right|^2. \tag{117.9}$$

---

† We use the well-known result

$$\int e^{i\mathbf{k}\cdot\mathbf{r}} \, d^3k = (2\pi)^3 \delta(\mathbf{r}).$$

Expressions for the mean squares of the Fourier components of the fluctuation of the density are also easily obtained by substituting for $\nu(r)$ from (117.8) in the general formula (115.8) and integrating with respect to the co-ordinates:

$$\overline{|\int (n-\bar{n})e^{-i\mathbf{f}\mathbf{r}}\,dV|^2} = \frac{gV}{(2\pi\hbar)^3} \int \bar{n}_{\mathbf{p}}(1\mp\bar{n}_{\mathbf{p}+\hbar\mathbf{f}})\,d^3p. \tag{117.10}$$

From (117.8) we see, first of all, that for a Fermi gas $\nu(r) < 0$ and for a Bose gas $\nu(r) > 0$. In other words, for a Bose gas, the existence of a particle at some point makes it more probable that another particle will be situated near this point, i.e. the particles exhibit a peculiar mutual "attraction". For a Fermi gas the particles exhibit a similar "repulsion", (cf. page 159).

If we go to the classical limit ($\hbar \to 0$) then the correlation function vanishes, in agreement with what was said at the beginning of this section (as $\hbar \to 0$ the frequency of the oscillating factor $e^{(i/\hbar)\mathbf{p}\cdot\mathbf{r}}$ in the integrand in (117.8) increases indefinitely and the integral tends to zero).

As $r \to 0$ the function $\nu(r)$ tends to a finite limit. Since

$$\frac{g}{(2\pi\hbar)^3} \int \bar{n}_{\mathbf{p}}\,d^3p = \bar{n},$$

it can be seen from (117.8) that

$$\nu(0) = \mp\frac{\bar{n}}{g} \tag{117.11}$$

Let us apply the results we have obtained to a degenerate Fermi gas at absolute zero. In this case the distribution function $\bar{n}_{\mathbf{p}} = 1$ for $p < p_0$ and $\bar{n}_{\mathbf{p}} = 0$ for $p > p_0$, where $p_0 = \hbar\,(6\pi^2\,\bar{n}/g)^{1/3}$ is the limiting momentum for the Fermi distribution. Hence we have, from (117.9):

$$\nu(r) = -\frac{g}{4\bar{n}(\pi\hbar)^4 r^2} \left| \int_0^{p_0} p \sin\frac{pr}{\hbar}\,dp \right|^2.$$

Consider only distances which are not too small, i.e. assume that $p_0r/\hbar \gg 1$. We evaluate the integral accordingly, retaining only the term with the smallest power of $1/r$ and we obtain:

$$\nu(r) = \frac{3\hbar}{2\pi^2 p_0 r^4} \cos^2\frac{p_0 r}{\hbar}. \tag{117.12}$$

If we average out the rapidly changing squared cosine we find:

$$\nu(r) = \frac{3\hbar}{4\pi^2 p_0 r^4}. \tag{117.13}$$

Thus, the correlation function decreases as the inverse fourth power of the distance.

PROBLEMS

1. Find the mean squares of the Fourier components (with small wave vectors) of the fluctuation of the density of a Fermi gas at absolute zero.

SOLUTION: The integrand in (117.10) is non-zero (and is equal to unity) only at points for which $\bar{n}_{\mathbf{p}} = 1$, $\bar{n}_{\mathbf{p}+\hbar\mathbf{f}} = 0$, i.e. at points inside a sphere of radius p_0 centred at the origin, and at the same time outside a sphere of the same radius centres at the point $\hbar\mathbf{f}$. Calculating the volume of this region for $\hbar\mathbf{f} \ll p_0$ we obtain:

$$\left| \int (n-\bar{n})e^{-i\mathbf{f}.\mathbf{r}}\,\mathrm{d}V \right|^2 = \frac{g\pi\hbar f p_0^2}{(2\pi\hbar)^3}V = \frac{3\hbar f}{4p_0}N.$$

2. Determine the correlation function for a Fermi gas at temperatures much smaller than the degeneracy temperature.

SOLUTION: In the integral in (119.9) we put $\mu \simeq \epsilon_0 = p_0^2/2m$ and transform it as follows:

$$I = \int_0^\infty \frac{p\sin(pr/\hbar)\,.\,\mathrm{d}p}{e^{(\epsilon-\epsilon_0)/kT}+1} = -\hbar\frac{\partial}{\partial r}\int_0^\infty \frac{\cos(pr/\hbar)\,\mathrm{d}p}{e^{(\epsilon-\epsilon_0)/kT}+1}$$

$$= \hbar^2\frac{\partial}{\partial r}\int_0^\infty \frac{\sin(pr/\hbar)}{r}\,\mathrm{d}\left(\frac{1}{e^{(\epsilon-\epsilon_0)/kT}+1}\right)$$

Introducing the variable $x = p_0(p-p_0)/mkT$, and taking into account the fact that T is small and that the integrand decreases rapidly as $|x|$ increases, we may write

$$I = \hbar^2\frac{\partial}{\partial r}\int_{-\infty}^{+\infty}\sin\left(\frac{p_0 r}{\hbar}+\lambda xr\right)\mathrm{d}\left(\frac{1}{e^x+1}\right)$$

$$= \hbar^2\frac{\partial}{\partial r}\left\{\frac{\sin(p_0 r/\hbar)}{r}\int_{-\infty}^{+\infty}e^{i\lambda xr}\,\mathrm{d}\left(\frac{1}{e^x+1}\right)\right\}$$

(where $\lambda = mkT/\hbar p_0$). The integral thus obtained, with the substitution $(e^x+1)^{-1} = u$, leads to Euler's B-integral, and as a result we have:

$$I = \hbar^2\frac{\partial}{\partial r}\left\{\frac{\pi\lambda}{\mathrm{sh}(\pi\lambda r)}\sin\frac{p_0 r}{\hbar}\right\}$$

For distances $r \gg \hbar p_0$, averaging out the rapidly changing squared cosine, we finally obtain:

$$\nu(r) = -\frac{3(mkT)^2}{4p_0^3\hbar r^2}\,\mathrm{sh}^{-2}\frac{\pi mkTr}{\hbar p_0}$$

As $T \to 0$ this formula tends to (117.13).

§118. Correlation of fluctuations in time

Now consider some physical quantity which describes a body (or part of it) in a state of thermodynamic equilibrium. In time this quantity undergoes small changes, fluctuating about its mean value. Let $x(t)$ again denote the difference between the actual value of this quantity and its mean value (so that $\bar{x} = 0$).

Between the values of $x(t)$ at different times there exists some correlation; this means that the value of x at some time t affects the probabilities of different values at time $t+\tau$. Just as for the spatial correlation studied in the preceding sections, one can specify the time correlation by the mean values of the product, $x(t)x(t+\tau)$. The averaging is meant here in the usual statistical sense of the word, i.e. averaging over the probabilities of all values which the quantity can take at the given time t and the time $t+\tau$. As was pointed out in §1, such statistical averaging is equivalent to time averaging: in this case over values of the time t for a given value of τ.

The quantity obtained in this way is (since the state is a stationary one) a function of τ only. We denote it by $\phi(\tau)$:

$$\phi(\tau) = \overline{x(t)x(t+\tau)}. \tag{118.1}$$

As τ increases indefinitely, the correlation, obviously, must vanish, and thus the function $\phi(\tau)$ tends to zero.

We define the Fourier transform of the quantity $x(t)$ by[†]

$$x_\omega = \frac{1}{2\pi} \int\limits_{-\infty}^{\infty} x(t)e^{i\omega t} \, dt, \tag{118.2}$$

and the inverse relation

$$x(t) = \int\limits_{-\infty}^{\infty} x_\omega e^{-i\omega t} \, d\omega. \tag{118.3}$$

Inserting the last relation in

$$\phi(t'-t) = \overline{x(t)x(t')}$$

we obtain

$$\phi(t'-t) = \int\limits_{-\infty}^{\infty}\!\!\int \overline{x_\omega x_{\omega'}}e^{i(\omega t+\omega' t')} \, d\omega d\omega'.$$

The integral on the right-hand side will be a function of the difference $\tau = t'-t$ only if the integrand contains a δ-function of $\omega+\omega'$. This requires that

$$\overline{x_\omega x_{\omega'}} = (x^2)_\omega \delta(\omega+\omega'). \tag{118.4}$$

[†] The integral as written is actually divergent, since $x(t)$ does not tend to zero as $|t| \to \infty$. This fact is, however, of no significance for the formal development given below, which serves to calculate the evidently finite mean squares.

We are indebted to S. M. RYTOV who has pointed out to us the advantage of defining the Fourier transform in this manner, compared to the method used in the Russian edition of the book.

This relation has to be regarded as a definition of the quantity which has been denoted here symbolically by $(x^2)_\omega$. Although the x_ω are complex, the quantity $(x^2)_\omega$ is evidently real. (It is sufficient to remark that the left-hand side of (118.4) differs from zero only when $\omega' = -\omega$, and the change to complex conjugate quantities means changing the sign of ω, i.e. the interchange if ω and ω').

Inserting (118.4) in $\phi(\tau)$ and carrying out the integration over $d\omega'$, we find

$$\phi(\tau) = \int_{-\infty}^{\infty} (x^2)_\omega e^{-i\omega\tau} \, d\omega. \tag{118.5}$$

In particular, $\phi(0)$ is just the mean square of the fluctuating quantity itself,

$$\overline{x^2} = \int_{-\infty}^{\infty} (x^2)_\omega \, d\omega. \tag{118.6}$$

We see that the "spectral density" of the mean square fluctuations is just the quantity $(x^2)_\omega$ (or $2(x^2)_\omega$ if the integral is taken only over positive values of ω). These quantities are also, according to (118.5), the Fourier transform of the correlation function. Conversely,

$$(x^2)_\omega = \frac{1}{2\pi} \int_{-\infty}^{\infty} \phi(\tau) e^{i\omega\tau} \, d\tau. \tag{118.7}$$

By treating the quantity x as a function of time, we have implicitly assumed it to behave classically. All the above formulae can, however, easily be re-written so as to apply to quantum-mechanical quantities. For this purpose one has to consider, instead of the quantity x, its quantum-mechanical operator $\hat{x}(t)$, and its Fourier transform

$$\hat{x}_\omega = \frac{1}{2\pi} \int_{-\infty}^{\infty} \hat{x}(t) e^{i\omega t} \, dt. \tag{118.8}$$

The operators $\hat{x}(t)$ and $\hat{x}(t')$ for different instants of time do not, in general, commute, and the correlation function must now be defined as

$$\phi(t'-t) = \tfrac{1}{2}\overline{[\hat{x}(t)\hat{x}(t')+\hat{x}(t')\hat{x}(t)]}, \tag{118.9}$$

where the bar denotes averaging by means of the exact quantum-mechanical probabilities.† The quantity $(x^2)_\omega$ is introduced by

$$\tfrac{1}{2}(\hat{x}_\omega \hat{x}_{\omega'} + \hat{x}_{\omega'} \hat{x}_\omega) = (x^2)_\omega \delta(\omega + \omega'), \tag{118.10}$$

using these definitions the relations (118.5–7) retain their form.

We shall assume the quantity x to be such that by giving it a definite value (appreciably different from its mean fluctuation) one could characterise a certain state of incomplete equilibrium. In other words, the relaxation time for establishing the incomplete equilibrium corresponding to a specified value of x is assumed to be much less than the relaxation time for the quantity x itself. This condition is satisfied by a very wide class of quantities of physical interest. The fluctuations of such quantities will be called *thermodynamic* fluctuations. In the rest of this section and in §§119–121 we shall consider fluctuations of this type, and we shall, in addition, assume the quantities x to be classical.‡

We shall assume also for the rest of this section that in the process of reaching complete equilibrium, no other deviations from complete equilibrium occur in the system, which would require new quantities for their specification; in other words, at every moment of time the state of the body is completely determined by the value of x (for the more general case see §121).

Let the quantity $x(t)$ have, at some moment t, a value which is large compared with the mean fluctuation (i.e. compared with $(\overline{x^2})^{1/2}$). Then one can assert that immediately after this moment the body will tend to return to the equilibrium state, and thus x will decrease. Then, owing to the assumptions made above, its rate of change $\dot{x}$ will be at any time completely determined by the value of x itself at that same time: $\dot{x} = \dot{x}(x)$. If x is still comparatively small, (small compared with the range of its possible values), then one can expand $\dot{x}(x)$ in powers of x; retaining only the linear term:

$$\frac{dx}{dt} = -\lambda x \tag{118.11}$$

where λ is a positive constant.

Next, we introduce the quantity $\xi_x(\tau)$, defining it as the mean value of the quantity $x(t)$ at time $t + \tau$, given that at a previous time t it had the given value x; such a mean value will, in general, be non-zero. The correlation function $\phi(\tau)$ can obviously be written, using $\xi_x(\tau)$, in the form

$$\phi(\tau) = \overline{x \xi_x(\tau)} \tag{118.12}$$

where the averaging is carried out only over the probabilities of different values of x at the initial time t.

---

† Here again, one must remember that, according to the basic principles of statistics, the result of the averaging process is the same whether we just take the average mechanically over the exact wave function of a stationary state of the system, or use the Gibbs distribution. The only difference is that the required quantity is in the first case expressed as a function of the energy of the body, and in the second case as a function of its temperature.

‡ The final results for the thermodynamic fluctuations of quantum quantities differ from the classical ones only by simple changes in the form of the equations, which will be indicated in §124 (cf. (124.21)).

For ξ_x large compared with the mean fluctuation, it also follows from (118.11) that

$$\frac{d\xi_x(\tau)}{d\tau} = -\lambda\xi_x(\tau).$$ (118.13)

We must assume that this relation is also valid for arbitrarily small $\xi_x(\tau)$.

Integrating (118.13) and bearing in mind that, by definition, $\xi_x(0) = x$, we find:

$$\xi_x(\tau) = xe^{-\lambda\tau},$$

and finally, substituting in (118.12), we obtain a formula determining the time correlation function:

$$\phi(\tau) = \overline{x^2}e^{-\lambda\tau},$$

We must remember, however, that in this form this formula applies only for $\tau > 0$, since in the above proof (eq. 118.13) it was implicitly assumed that the moment $t+\tau$ occurs after t. On the other hand, we have identically

$$\phi(\tau) = \overline{x(t)x(t+\tau)} = \overline{x(t-\tau)x(t)} = \phi(-\tau),$$

since this transformation amounts simply to a change of the variable with respect to which the average is taken (t becomes $t-\tau$). In other words, $\phi(\tau)$ is an even function of τ.

Hence we can write, finally,

$$\phi(\tau) = \overline{x^2}e^{-\lambda|\tau|},$$ (118.14)

which applies for both positive and negative τ. This function possesses two different derivatives at $\tau = 0$. This arises as a result of our consideration of time intervals large compared with the time taken to set up the incomplete equilibrium (equilibrium for the given value of x). An examination of shorter time intervals, which is impossible within the framework of thermodynamic theory, would obviously lead to the result that $d\phi/d\tau = 0$ at $\tau = 0$, as it should be for any even function of τ.

A simple integration gives the following expression for the Fourier components of the function $\phi(\tau)$ introduced in (118.5–7)

$$(x^2)_\omega = \frac{1}{2\pi} \int\limits_{-\infty}^{+\infty} \phi(\tau)e^{i\omega\tau}\,d\tau = \frac{\lambda}{\pi(\omega^2+\lambda^2)}\overline{x^2} = \frac{\lambda k}{\pi\beta(\omega^2+\lambda^2)}.$$ (118.15)

The results we have obtained may also be expressed in another way, which is more convenient for practical applications.

The relation $\dot{x} = -\lambda x$ for the quantity x itself (and not for its mean value ξ_x) is true only, as was already pointed out, for values large compared with the mean fluctuation of x. For arbitrary x, we write $\dot{x}$ in the form

$$\dot{x} = -\lambda x + y, \tag{118.16}$$

which defines a new quantity $y(t)$.

The order of magnitude of the range over which y oscillates does not, of course, change with time, but when x is large (in the sense indicated above) it represents a comparatively small quantity which may be neglected in (118.16).

Multiplying (118.16) by $e^{i\omega t}$ and integrating with respect to t from 0 to T (the term $\dot{x}e^{i\omega t}$ being integrated by parts) we obtain:

$$x_\omega = \frac{y_\omega}{\lambda - i\omega}.$$

Now making use of (118.4) and (118.15), we obtain:

$$(y^2)_\omega = \frac{\lambda}{\pi}\overline{x^2}. \tag{118.17}$$

Note the interesting fact that this quantity is independent of the frequency.

The quantity (118.17) is, at the same time, the Fourier component of the mean value $\overline{y(t)y(t+\tau)}$ (just as $(x^2)_\omega$ is the Fourier component of the mean value $\overline{x(t)x(t+\tau)}$). But a function whose Fourier components are independent of frequency is proportional to the δ-function; i.e. as is easily seen,

$$\overline{y(t)y(t+\tau)} = 2\lambda\overline{x^2}\delta(\tau). \tag{118.18}$$

The fact that this expression vanishes for $\tau \neq 0$ means that values of $y(t)$ at different times show no correlation. Actually, of course, this assertion is only an approximation. It means only that values of $y(t)$ are correlated over intervals of time of the order of that required to establish the incomplete equilibrium (equilibrium for given x) which, in the theory discussed here is considered negligibly small. Note, in connection with this, that all the formulae obtained in this section for the Fourier components of the various quantities apply only for frequencies small compared with the reciprocal of the relaxation time for the incomplete equilibrium.

§119. The symmetry of the kinetic coefficients

Consider a closed system, not in statistical equilibrium, so that a set of thermodynamic quantities $x_1, x_2, \ldots, x_n$, which describe the system as a whole, or its separate parts, take non-equilibrium values (in the former case they must not be quantities such as energy and volume which are strictly constant for a closed system). As in §110, it will be convenient for us to assume that the equilibrium values of these quantities have already been subtracted, so that $x_1, x_2, \ldots, x_n$ directly describe the extent to which the system deviates from equilibrium.

The quantities $x_1, \ldots, x_n$ will change with time. We shall assume that this set of quantities is such that they completely determine the process of establishing equilibrium and that no other deviations from complete equilibrium occur in this process (cf. the last section). Then the rate of change $\dot{x}_i$ of the quantity x_i in each non-equilibrium state, is a function of the values of $x_1, \ldots, x_n$ in this state:

$$\dot{x}_i = \dot{x}_i(x_1, \ldots x_n). \tag{119.1}$$

We assume that the system is in a state comparatively near equilibrium; this means that the quantities x_i may be considered small. Then, after expanding the $\dot{x}_i$ in powers of $x_1, \ldots, x_n$ we can restrict ourselves to the first-order terms, i.e. express the $\dot{x}_i$ as linear combinations of the form

$$\dot{x}_i = - \sum_{k=1}^{n} \lambda_{ik} x_k,$$

with λ_{ik} some constant coefficients. Zero-order terms cannot occur in this expansion, since at equilibrium (i.e. for $x_1 = 0$, $x_2 = 0$, ...) all the rates of change $\dot{x}_i$ must also vanish. We shall, below, as in §110, omit the summation sign. Thus†

$$\dot{x}_i = -\lambda_{ik} x_k. \tag{119.2}$$

We introduce next the derivatives

$$X_i = -\frac{\partial S}{\partial x_i} \tag{119.3}$$

of the entropy S of the system. In the equilibrium state the entropy is a maximum, so that

$$X_1 = 0, \qquad X_2 = 0, \ldots, \qquad X_n = 0, \tag{119.4}$$

and for small x_i we can write, again restricting ourselves to first-order terms:

$$X_i = \beta_{ik} x_k, \tag{119.5}$$

(see (110.6)). It was already stated that

$$\beta_{ik} = \beta_{ki} \tag{119.6}$$

If one expresses the quantities x_i in terms of the X_i by means of (119.5),

---

† In practical applications, one comes across cases when the total equilibrium depends on some external parameters (volume, external field, etc.) which themselves change slowly with time: the equilibrium (mean) values of the quantities considered change with them. If this change is sufficiently slow, then we can still use all the relations we would otherwise use, the only difference being that the mean values $\bar{x}_i$ can no longer be considered to be zero, all the time; denoting them by $x_i^{(0)}$ we must replace (119.2), for example, by

$$\dot{x}_i = -\lambda_{ik}(x_i - x_i^{(0)}). \tag{119.2a}$$

and substitutes those in (119.2), then the rates of change $\dot{x}_i$ will also be expressed as linear combinations of the X_i, i.e. we get equations of the form

$$\dot{x}_i = -\gamma_{ik}X_k. \tag{119.7}$$

We shall call the quantities γ_{ik} *kinetic coefficients*. We shall now prove that these coefficients† are symmetric in the suffices i and k, i.e.

$$\gamma_{ik} = \gamma_{ki}. \tag{119.8}$$

This important result was first discovered by L. ONSAGER (1931).

To prove this, assume that the quantities x_i are not equal to their mean values, owing to the fact that the system undergoes fluctuations. Let us take the values of any one of the quantities x_i at time t, and the value of another x_k at time $t+\tau$, and average the product $x_i(t)x_k(t+\tau)$ with respect to the time t (for given positive τ). The mechanical equations of motion of the particles of the body (in the absence of an external magnetic field) are symmetric with respect to a change in the sign of the time. Hence it is quite immaterial whether one averages the quantity x_i at a later moment and x_i at an earlier one or *vice versa*. Hence the mean values of the products $x_i(t)x_k(t+\tau)$ and $x_i(t+\tau)x_k(t)$ must be equal:

$$\overline{x_i(t)x_k(t+\tau)} = \overline{x_i(t+\tau)x_k(t)}. \tag{119.9}$$

Differentiating this equation with respect to τ, and then setting $\tau = 0$, we obtain:

$$\overline{x_i\dot{x}_k} = \overline{\dot{x}_i x_k}. \tag{119.10}$$

To avoid misunderstanding, we must make the following remark about this proof. By changing the notation for the variable t, with respect to which we took the average, to $t-\tau$, we would obtain the equation:

$$\overline{x_i(t)x_k(t+\tau)} = \overline{x_i(t-\tau)x_k(t)},$$

which may be written in the form

$$\phi_{ki}(\tau) = \phi_{ik}(-\tau), \tag{119.11}$$

where we have introduced the notation

$$\phi_{ik}(\tau) = \overline{x_i(t+\tau)x_k(t)}. \tag{119.12}$$

At first glance it might seem that, by differentiating (119.11) with respect to τ and putting $\tau = 0$, one could get $\phi_{ik}(0) = 0$. In fact, however, as was shown in §118, in the approximation we are using the functions $\phi_{ik}(\tau)$ (like $\phi(\tau)$ in §118) have two different derivatives at the point $\tau = 0$; for $\tau \to +0$ and $\tau \to -0$.

---

† But not the coefficients λ_{ik} in (119.2).

We now substitute in (119.10) for $\dot{x}_i$ from (119.7):

$$\overline{x_i \gamma_{kl} X_l} = \overline{\gamma_{il} X_i x_k}.$$

But according to (110.7) we have $\overline{x_i X_l} = k\delta_{il}$ and therefore

$$\gamma_{kl}\delta_{il} = \gamma_{ki} = \gamma_{il}\delta_{ik} = \gamma_{ik};$$

which proves (119.8).

Two remarks must be made, however, regarding this relation. Its proof depends fundamentally on the symmetry of the equations of mechanics with regard to time. The formulation of this symmetry, however, becomes somewhat different for the case of fluctuations in a uniformly rotating body and for the case of bodies in an external magnetic field. In these cases, the symmetry with regard to a change in sign of the time holds only provided there is a simultaneous change of sign of the angular velocity $\boldsymbol{\Omega}$ or of the magnetic field $\mathbf{H}$. Hence the kinetic coefficients, which in this case depend on $\boldsymbol{\Omega}$ or $\mathbf{H}$ as parameters, will satisfy the following relations

$$\begin{aligned} \gamma_{ik}(\boldsymbol{\Omega}) &= \gamma_{ki}(-\boldsymbol{\Omega}) \\ \gamma_{ik}(\mathbf{H}) &= \gamma_{ki}(-\mathbf{H}) \end{aligned} \tag{119.13}$$

The proof of (119.8) contains also the implicit assumption that the quantities x_i themselves are such that they remain constant under a change in sign of the time. However, if these quantities are proportional to the velocities of some macroscopic motion, then they themselves will also change their sign with that of the time. It is easy to see that if any two of the quantities, x_i and x_k, both change sign then (119.10) will still hold, and hence also $\gamma_{ik} = \gamma_{ki}$, but if one of the quantities x_i, x_k changes sign and the other remains constant, then we shall have $\overline{x_i \dot{x}_k} = -\overline{\dot{x}_i x_k}$, and the corresponding kinetic coefficients will satisfy the relation

$$\gamma_{ik} = -\gamma_{ki}. \tag{119.14}$$

It follows, from (119.7) and (119.8) that the rates of change can be expressed as the derivatives

$$\dot{x}_i = -\frac{\partial f}{\partial X_i} \tag{119.15}$$

of some *"generating function"* f which is the quadratic form in the quantities X_i constructed from the coefficients γ_{ik}.

$$f = \tfrac{1}{2}\gamma_{ik}X_i X_k. \tag{119.16}$$

This function is important since it directly determines the time derivative of the entropy S. We have:

$$\dot{S} = \frac{\partial S}{\partial x_i}\dot{x}_i = -X_i\dot{x}_i = X_i\frac{\partial f}{\partial X_i}$$

and since f is a quadratic form in the X_i, EULER's theorem gives:

$$\dot{S} = 2f. \tag{119.17}$$

As the system approaches equilibrium, the entropy S must increase, tending to a maximum. Thus the quadratic form f must be positive definite. This puts certain conditions on the coefficients γ_{ik}.

In exactly the same way as (119.8) was proved, we can prove that if the time derivatives of the quantities X_i are expressed as linear combinations of the x_i:

$$\dot{X}_i = -\zeta_{ik} x_k, \tag{119.18}$$

then the coefficients ζ_{ik} are symmetric:

$$\zeta_{ik} = \zeta_{ki}. \tag{119.19}$$

Thus the $\dot{X}_i$ can be expressed as the derivatives

$$\dot{X}_i = -\frac{\partial f}{\partial x_i} \tag{119.20}$$

of the quadratic form

$$f = \tfrac{1}{2}\zeta_{ik} x_i x_k. \tag{119.21}$$

Using (119.5) and (118.6), we have:

$$\mathrm{d}S = \frac{\partial S}{\partial x_k}\mathrm{d}x_k = -X_k\,\mathrm{d}x_k = -\beta_{ki}x_i\,\mathrm{d}x_k = -x_i\,\mathrm{d}(\beta_{ik}x_k) = -x_i\,\mathrm{d}X_i,$$

whence we see that:

$$-\frac{\partial S}{\partial X_i} = x_i \tag{119.22}$$

where the entropy is now assumed to be expressed as a function of the quantities X_i. Hence the derivative $\dot{S}$ can also be written as

$$\dot{S} = \frac{\partial S}{\partial x_i}\dot{X}_i = -x_i\dot{X}_i = x_i\frac{\partial f}{\partial x_i} = 2f$$

with f as in (119.21). Comparing this with (119.17) we see that the two functions f, (119.16) and (119.21), are the same quantity, but expressed in terms of different variables.

For a system consisting of a body in an external medium, one can transform (119.17), using the fact that the change in the entropy of a closed system during a deviation from equilibrium is equal to $-R_{\min}/T_0$, where $R_{\min}$ is the minimum work necessary to transfer the system from its equilibrium state to the given state (see eq. 20.8)† By using also $R_{\min} = \Delta E - T_0 \Delta S + P_0 \Delta V$ (where E, S, V refer to the body, and T_0, P_0 are the temperature and pressure of the medium), we obtain:

$$\dot{E} = T_0 \dot{S} + P_0 \dot{V} = -2fT_0. \tag{119.23}$$

In particular, if the deviation from equilibrium occurs at constant temperature and pressure (equal to T_0 and P_0), then

$$\dot{\Phi} = -2fT, \tag{119.24}$$

and for constant temperature and volume,

$$\dot{F} = -2fT. \tag{119.25}$$

§120. The dissipative function

Macroscopic motion of a body surrounded by an external medium is accompanied by irreversible frictional effects, which eventually cause the motion to terminate. The kinetic energy of the body is then transformed into heat or, as we say, is dissipated.

A purely mechanical consideration of such motion is clearly impossible. Since the energy of the macroscopic motion is transformed into the energy of the thermal motion of the molecules of the body and the medium, such an investigation would require us to set up the equations of motion for all these particles. Hence the question of the possibility of establishing equations of motion in the medium which involve only the "macroscopic" co-ordinates of the bodies, is a statistical one.

This problem, however, cannot be solved in general form. Since the internal motion of the atoms of the body depends not only on the motion of the body at the given time, but also on the previous history of this motion, there will enter into the equations not only the macroscopic co-ordinates $Q_1, Q_2, \ldots, Q_s$ of the body, and their first and second time derivatives, but also all their higher derivatives (to be more precise, some integral operator in the co-ordinates). There exists no Lagrangian function for the macroscopic motion of the system in this case, and the equations of motion will be of quite different kinds in the various cases.

The nature of the equations of motion can be established in general terms for the case in which we can assume that the co-ordinates Q_i and velocities $\dot{Q}_i$ completely determine the state of the system at the given time, and that we can neglect the higher derivatives (a more accurate criterion of

---

† Owing to this relation between the change of entropy and $R_{\min}$, the definition of the quantity X_i can also be written as

$$X_i = \frac{1}{T_0} \frac{\partial R_{\min}}{\partial x_i} \tag{119.3a}$$

which is sometimes more convenient than the definition (119.3) (cf. (22.7)).

smallness must be established in each actual case). We shall also assume that the velocities $\dot{Q}_i$ are small enough for their higher powers to be neglected. Lastly, we shall assume that the motion consists of small oscillations about some equilibrium positions, which is the case with which we are usually concerned in this connection. We may choose the co-ordinates Q_i for convenience in such a way that $Q_i = 0$ for the equilibrium position. Then the kinetic energy of the system, $K(\dot{Q}_i)$, will be a quadratic function of the velocities $\dot{Q}_i$ independent of the co-ordinates Q_i themselves, while the potential energy $U(Q_i)$ due to the action of the external forces, will be a quadratic function of the co-ordinates Q_i.

We introduce the generalised momenta P_i, defining them as usual by

$$P_i = \frac{\partial K(\dot{Q}_i)}{\partial \dot{Q}_i}. \tag{120.1}$$

These equations determine the momenta as linear combinations of the velocities. With their aid we can express the velocities in terms of the momenta and, substituting into the kinetic energy, we obtain the latter as a quadratic function of the momenta, satisfying the equations

$$\dot{Q}_i = \frac{\partial K(P_i)}{\partial P_i}. \tag{120.2}$$

If we completely neglect the dissipative processes, then the equations of motion will be the usual mechanical equations, according to which the time derivatives of the momenta are equal to the corresponding generalised forces $-\partial U/\partial Q_i$:

$$\dot{P}_i = -\frac{\partial U}{\partial Q_i}. \tag{120.3}$$

Note, first of all, that eqs. (120.2–3) formally agree with the principle of symmetry of the kinetic coefficients, established in §119, if we interpret the quantities $x_1, x_2, \ldots, x_{2s}$ introduced there as the co-ordinates Q_i and momenta P_i. Indeed, the minimum work necessary to bring the bodies from a state of rest in their equilibrium positions to positions Q_i with momenta P_i is $R_{\min} = K(P_i) + U(Q_i)$. Hence the quantities $X_1, X_2, \ldots, X_{2s}$ will be interpreted as the derivatives (see footnote on page 348):

$$X_{Q_i} = \frac{1}{T}\frac{\partial R_{\min}}{\partial Q_i} = \frac{1}{T}\frac{\partial U}{\partial Q_i},$$

$$X_{P_i} = \frac{1}{T}\frac{\partial R_{\min}}{\partial P_i} = \frac{1}{T}\frac{\partial K}{\partial P_i},$$

while eq. (120.2–3) will correspond to (119.7) and

$$\gamma_{Q_i P_i} = -T = -\gamma_{P_i Q}$$

according to (119.14) (we are dealing with a case when one of the quantities (Q_i) remains constant, and the other, (P_i), changes sign, under a change in sign of the time).

Following the general relation (119.7), we can now write down the equations of motion, taking the dissipative processes into account by adding to the right-hand sides of (120.2–3) some further linear combinations of the quantities X_{P_i}, X_{Q_i} such that the required symmetry of the kinetic coefficients is satisfied. It is easy to see, however, that eqs. (120.2) must be left unaltered; these equations are simply a consequence of the definition of the momenta (120.1), which has no connection with the presence or absence of dissipative processes. Hence it follows that only linear combinations of the quantities X_{P_i} (i.e. the derivatives $\partial K/\partial P_i$) can be added to eq. (120.3) since otherwise the symmetry of the kinetic coefficients will be disturbed.

Thus we obtain a set of equations of the form

$$\dot{P}_i = -\frac{\partial U}{\partial Q_i} - \sum_{k=1}^{s} \gamma_{ik} \frac{\partial K}{\partial P_k},$$

where the constant coefficients γ_{ik} are connected by the relations

$$\gamma_{ik} = \gamma_{ki}. \tag{120.4}$$

Replacing $\partial K/\partial P_k$ by $\dot{Q}_k$, we write, finally:

$$\dot{P}_i = -\frac{\partial U}{\partial Q_i} - \sum_{k=1}^{s} \gamma_{ik}\dot{Q}_k. \tag{120.5}$$

This is the required set of equations of motion. We see that the presence of the dissipative processes leads, in our approximation, to the appearance of additional "frictional forces", depending linearly on the velocities of the motion. Because of (120.4) these forces can be expressed as the derivatives, with respect to the corresponding velocities, of the quadratic form

$$f = \tfrac{1}{2} \sum_{i,k} \gamma_{ik}\dot{Q}_i\dot{Q}_k, \tag{120.6}$$

which is called the *dissipative function*. Then

$$\dot{P}_i = -\frac{\partial U}{\partial Q_i} - \frac{\partial f}{\partial Q_i}. \tag{120.7}$$

Introducing the Lagrangian function $L = K - U$, these equations of motion can be written in the form

$$\frac{d}{dt}\frac{\partial L}{\partial \dot{Q}_i} - \frac{\partial L}{\partial Q_i} = -\frac{\partial f}{\partial \dot{Q}_i}, \tag{120.8}$$

which differ from the usual form of LAGRANGE'S equations by the derivative
of the dissipative function on the right-hand side.

The presence of friction leads to a decrease in the total mechanical energy
$(K+U)$ of the moving bodies. According to the general results of §119,
the rate of this decrease is determined by the dissipative function. In view
of the differences of notation between this section and §119, we shall show
this once more. We have:

$$\frac{d}{dt}(K+U) = \sum_{i=1}^{s}\left(\frac{\partial K}{\partial p_i}\dot{P}_i + \frac{\partial U}{\partial Q_i}\dot{Q}_i\right) = \sum_{i}\dot{Q}_i\left(\dot{P}_i + \frac{\partial U}{\partial Q_i}\right)$$

or, substituting from (120.7), and bearing in mind that the dissipative function is quadratic:

$$\frac{d}{dt}(K+U) = -\sum_{i}\dot{Q}_i\frac{\partial f}{\partial \dot{Q}_i} = -2f, \tag{120.9}$$

as we should expect.

In the case when an external magnetic field is present the equations of
motion still take the form (120.5), the only difference being that (120.4) must
be replaced by

$$\gamma_{ik}(\mathbf{H}) = \gamma_{ki}(-\mathbf{H}).$$

Because of this, however, there can exist no dissipative function whose
derivatives define a frictional force; hence the equations of motion cannot be
written in the form (120.7).

§121. Correlation in time of the fluctuations of several quantities

The results obtained in §118 for the time correlation function of one
fluctuating quantity can be generalised to the fluctuations of several thermodynamic quantities $x_1, x_2, \ldots, x_n$, simultaneously deviating from their
equilibrium values.

We introduce the correlation functions ϕ_{ik} in a similar way to the definition
(118.1):

$$\phi_{ik}(\tau) = \overline{x_i(t+\tau)x_k(t)}. \tag{121.1}$$

They identically satisfy the relations

$$\phi_{ik}(\tau) = \phi_{ki}(-\tau) \tag{121.2}$$

(see (119.11)).

In place of (117.7) we now have

$$(x_i x_k)_\omega = \frac{1}{2\pi}\int_{-\infty}^{\infty}\phi_{ik}e^{i\omega\tau}\,d\tau \tag{121.3}$$

where the quantity $(x_i x_k)_\omega$ is defined by

$$\overline{x_{i\omega} x_{k\omega'}} = (x_i x_k)_\omega \delta(\omega + \omega'). \tag{121.4}$$

Consider the mean value of $x_i(t) X_k(t+\tau)$. Substituting $X_k = \beta_{kl} x_l$, we obtain

$$\overline{x_i(t) X_k(t+\tau)} = \beta_{kl} \phi_{li}(\tau).$$

On the other hand, introducing the mean values $\Xi_k(\tau)$ of the quantities X_k, and the mean values $\xi_x(\tau)$ of the quantities x_k, at time $t+\tau$, for given values of $x_1, x_2 \dots$ at time t, we can write (cf. (118.12)).

$$\overline{x_i(t) X_k(t+\tau)} = \overline{x_i \Xi_k(\tau)}.$$

We differentiate this equation on both sides with respect to τ, and substitute for the derivatives $d\Xi_k/d\tau$ the expressions

$$\dot{\Xi}_k = -\zeta_{kl} \xi_l$$

with the same coefficients as in (119.18). Bearing in mind that $\overline{x_i \xi_l(\tau)} = \phi_{li}(\tau)$, we obtain the set of equations

$$\beta_{kl} \frac{d\phi_{li}}{d\tau} = -\zeta_{kl} \phi_{li} \qquad (\tau > 0), \tag{121.5}$$

which determine the relation between ϕ_{ik} and τ; it must be borne in mind, however, that the equations in this form only apply for $\tau > 0$ (cf. §118).

To calculate the Fourier components of the function ϕ_{ik}, we multiply eq. (121.5) on both sides by $e^{i\omega\tau}$ and integrate with respect to τ from 0 to ∞. Integrating by parts, and remembering that $\phi_{ik}(\infty) = 0$, we find:

$$-\beta_{kl} \phi_{li}(0) - i\omega \beta_{kl} \int_0^\infty \phi_{li}(\tau) e^{i\omega\tau} \, d\tau = -\zeta_{kl} \int_0^\infty \phi_{li}(\tau) e^{i\omega\tau} \, d\tau.$$

But according to (110.8)

$$\phi_{li}(0) = \overline{x_i x_l} = k\beta_{il}^{-1},$$

so that

$$(\zeta_{kl} - i\omega\beta_{kl}) \int_0^\infty \phi_{li}(\tau) e^{i\omega\tau} \, d\tau = k\delta_{ki}.$$

Hence we see:

$$\int_0^\infty \phi_{li} e^{i\omega\tau} \, d\tau = k(\zeta - i\omega\beta)_{li}^{-1}$$

where $(\zeta-i\omega\beta)_{li}^{-1}$ is a component of the inverse matrix to $(\zeta-i\omega\beta)_{li}$. Replacing τ by $-\tau$, ω by $-\omega$, and using the relation (121.2), we obtain:

$$\int_{-\infty}^{0} \phi_{li}(\tau)e^{-i\omega\tau}\,d\tau = k(\zeta+i\omega\beta)_{li}^{-1}.$$

Finally, combining these two equations and using (121.3) we obtain the formula

$$2\pi(x_ix_k)_\omega = k(\zeta-i\omega\beta)_{ki}^{-1}+k(\zeta+i\omega\beta)_{ik}^{-1}, \qquad (121.6)$$

which is a generalisation of (118.15)†

The quantities β_{li} always form a symmetric matrix. In the absence of a magnetic field, ζ_{li} are also symmetric and thus so is the matrix $\zeta_{li}\pm i\omega\beta_{li}$ and its inverse.‡

As at the end of §118, the results we have obtained can be expressed in another form introducing new quantities Y_i according to

$$\dot{X}_i = -\zeta_{ik}x_k+Y_i; \qquad (121.7)$$

these quantities can be neglected when the x_k become larger than their mean fluctuations. Just as in §118, we obtain, after an elementary calculation, the following result:

$$(Y_iY_k)_\omega = \frac{k}{2\pi}(\zeta_{ik}+\zeta_{ki}). \qquad (121.8)$$

These quantities again appear to be independent of ω.

Analogously, for the quantities y_i, defined by

$$\dot{x}_i = -\gamma_{ik}X_k+y_i, \qquad (121.9)$$

we have:

$$(y_iy_k)_\omega = \frac{k}{2\pi}(\gamma_{ik}+\gamma_{ki}). \qquad (121.10)$$

---

† If there is only one quantity x, then we have:

$$2\pi(x^2)_\omega = \frac{k}{\zeta-i\omega\beta}+\frac{k}{\zeta+i\omega\beta} = \frac{2k\zeta}{\zeta^2+\omega^2\beta^2}.$$

From the definition of the quantities λ, β, ζ we have, in this case, simply

$$X = \beta x, \qquad \dot{X} = -\zeta x, \qquad \dot{x} = -\lambda x;$$

hence $\zeta = \lambda\beta$ and we again get (118.15).

‡ If one of the quantities x_i, x changes sign under time reversal then the matrix (121.6) should be antisymmetric. This is actually so, since in this case $\zeta_{il} = -\zeta_{li}$ (cf. eq. 119.14) and $\beta_{li} = 0$. The latter follows from the fact that β_{li} is the coefficient of the product x_ix_l in the quadratic form giving the change in the entropy due to a departure from equilibrium. Since the entropy is invariant with respect to time reversal and the product x_ix_l changes sign on replacing t by $-t$, the entropy cannot depend on this term, i.e. $\beta_{li} = 0$.

This formula is immediately obvious without further calculation, if one notices that the quantities x_i and X_i are symmetrically related; just as X_i are the derivatives of the entropy with respect to x_i, the quantities x_i are, conversely, derivatives of the entropy with respect to the X_i.

We note also the formula

$$\overline{y_i(t)y_k(t+\tau)} = k(\gamma_{ik}+\gamma_{ki})\delta(\tau) \tag{121.10a}$$

which corresponds to (121.10) in the same way as (118.18) corresponds to (118·17).

For practical applications, (121.8) and (121.10) have the advantage that they involve the matrix elements ζ_{ik} and γ_{ik}, and not the inverse matrix elements.

As an example of the applications of the formulae we have obtained, consider the fluctuations of a one-dimensional oscillator. In other words, consider a body at rest in its equilibrium position ($Q = 0$) but which is able to oscillate along the macroscopic co-ordinate Q. Owing to these fluctuations, the co-ordinate Q will in actual fact undergo deviations from the value $Q = 0$. The mean square of this deviation is easily calculated in the following way.

We write the potential energy of the oscillator in the form

$$U = \frac{m\omega_0^2}{2}Q^2,$$

where m is its "mass" (i.e. the coefficient of proportionality between the generalised momentum P and the velocity $\dot{Q}$: $P = m\dot{Q}$) and ω_0 is the frequency of its free oscillations in the absence of friction). Then the mean square fluctuation (cf. problem 7, §111) will be

$$\overline{Q^2} = \frac{kT}{m\omega_0^2}. \tag{121.11}$$

The calculation of the "Fourier components" of the fluctuation of the co-ordinate is, however, of greater interest. Let us calculate them for the general case when the vibrations of the oscillator are accompanied by friction. The equations of motion of an oscillator with friction are:

$$\dot{Q} = \frac{P}{m} \tag{121.12}$$

$$\dot{P} = -m\omega_0^2 Q - \gamma\frac{P}{m}, \tag{121.13}$$

where $-\gamma P/m = -\gamma\dot{Q}$ is the "frictional force". As was explained in the last section, if Q and P are interpreted as the quantities x_1 and x_2, then the corresponding X_1 and X_2 will be: $m\omega_0^2Q/T$ and P/mT. Eqs (121.12, 13) then act as the relations $\dot{x}_i = -\gamma_{ik}X_k$, so that

$$\gamma_{11} = 0, \qquad \gamma_{12} = -\gamma_{21} = -T, \qquad \gamma_{22} = \gamma T.$$

To apply these equations to the fluctuations, we rewrite (121.13) in the form

$$\dot{P} = -m\omega_0^2 Q - \gamma \frac{P}{m} + y. \tag{121.14}$$

Eq. (121.12), which is the equation defining the momentum, is to be left unchanged. According to (121.10), we immediately obtain:

$$(y^2)_\omega = \frac{k}{\pi}\gamma_{22} = \frac{\gamma k T}{\pi}.$$

Finally, to obtain from this the required $(Q^2)_\omega$ we substitute $P = m\dot{Q}$ into (121.14)†:

$$m\ddot{Q} + \gamma\dot{Q} + m\omega_0^2 Q = y. \tag{121.15}$$

Multiplying this equation by $e^{i\omega t}$, and integrating with respect to the time, we obtain:

$$(-m\omega^2 - i\omega\gamma + m\omega_0^2)Q_\omega = y_\omega$$

whence, finally:

$$(Q^2)_\omega = \frac{\gamma k T}{\pi[m^2(\omega^2 - \omega_0^2) + \omega^2\gamma^2]}. \tag{121.16}$$

§122. Generalised susceptibility

It is impossible to obtain a general formula for the spectral distribution of non-thermodynamic fluctuations similar to formulae of the type (118.15) for the thermodynamic fluctuations. However, in a number of cases it proves possible to connect the properties of non-thermodynamic fluctuations with the effects on the body of certain external influences. This may apply to classical quantities as well as to those of a quantum character.

The physical quantities in this category have the property that for each of them there exists an external influence which is described by the occurrence of a perturbing operator of the form

$$\hat{V} = -\hat{x}f(t) \tag{122.1}$$

in the Hamiltonian of the body, where $\hat{x}$ is the quantum-mechanical operator corresponding to the given physical quantity, and the "perturbing force" f is a given function of the time‡.

The quantum-mechanical average $\bar{x}$ does not vanish in the presence of such a perturbation (whereas in the equilibrium state in the absence of the

---

† Considering (121.15) as the "equation of motion" of the fluctuating oscillator, the quantity y is sometimes called the "random force" acting on the oscillator.

‡ As an example we may choose for f an external electric field, and for x the electric dipole moment which the body acquires in the field.

perturbation $\bar{x} = 0$) and can be expressed as $\hat{\alpha}f$, where $\hat{\alpha}$ is a linear integral operator, whose effect on a function $f(t)$ is given by an equation of the form

$$\bar{x}(t) = \int_0^\infty K(\tau) f(t-\tau) \, d\tau \tag{122.2}$$

where K is a function of time which depends on the properties of the medium. The values of $\bar{x}$ at a certain instant t can, of course, depend only on the values of the "force" f during the preceding (but not the subsequent) instants of time; the form of (122.2) has been chosen so as to satisfy this requirement.

Any time-dependent perturbation can, by means of a Fourier transformation, be reduced to a set of monochromatic components, whose time dependence is given by a factor $e^{-i\omega t}$. For such a perturbation the relation between $\bar{x}$ and f takes the form

$$\bar{x} = \alpha(\omega)f, \tag{122.3}$$

where the function $\alpha(\omega)$ is defined as

$$\alpha(\omega) = \int_0^\infty K(\tau) e^{i\omega\tau} \, d\tau. \tag{122.4}$$

Given $\alpha(\omega)$, the behaviour of the body under the particular kind of disturbance is completely determined.† We shall call α the *generalised susceptibility*.‡ It will play a fundamental part in the theory to be presented, since it can be used to express the fluctuations in the quantity x.

The function $\alpha(\omega)$ is, in general, complex. We shall denote its real and imaginary parts by α' and α'':

$$\alpha = \alpha' + i\alpha''. \tag{122.5}$$

From the definition (122.4) we see immediately that

$$\alpha(-\omega) = \alpha^*(\omega). \tag{122.6}$$

By resolving this relation into its real and imaginary parts we obtain

$$\alpha'(-\omega) = \alpha'(\omega), \qquad \alpha''(-\omega) = -\alpha''(\omega), \tag{122.7}$$

i.e. $\alpha'(\omega)$ is an even, and $\alpha''(\omega)$ an odd function of the frequency. At $\omega = 0$ the function $\alpha''(\omega)$ changes sign, passing through zero (or, in some cases, through infinity).

---

† In the example of the preceding footnote α represents the electric polarisability of the body.

‡ We prefer to use the quantity α defined in this manner to the commonly used quantity $Z(\omega) = -1/i\omega\alpha$, which is called the generalised impedance, and which occurs as the coefficient in the relation $f = Z\dot{x}$.

It should be stressed that the property (122.6) expresses simply the fact that the operator relation $\bar{x} = \hat{\alpha}f$ must lead to real $\bar{x}$ for any real f. If the function $f(t)$ is given by the real expression

$$f = \tfrac{1}{2}(f_0 e^{-i\omega t} + f_0{}^* e^{i\omega t}), \tag{122.8}$$

then by applying the operation $\hat{\alpha}$ to each of the two terms we find

$$\bar{x} = \tfrac{1}{2}[\alpha(\omega)f_0 e^{-i\omega t} + \alpha(-\omega)f_0{}^* e^{i\omega t}]; \tag{122.9}$$

the condition for this to be real is the same as (122.6).

In the limit $\omega \to \infty$ the function $\alpha(\omega)$ tends to a finite real limit α_∞. For the sake of definiteness we shall assume below that this limit is zero: a non-zero limit requires only some slight and obvious changes in the form of some of the equations derived below.

The change of state of the body under the influence of the "force" f is accompanied by the absorption (dissipation) of energy; the source of this energy is the external disturbance, and after its absorption by the body it is converted into heat (dissipated) within the body. This dissipation may also be expressed in terms of the quantity α. For this purpose we use the fact that the time derivative of the mean energy of the body equals the mean value of the partial derivative with respect to time of the Hamiltonian of the body (cf. §11):

$$\frac{dE}{dt} = \frac{\partial \bar{H}}{\partial t}.$$

Since in the Hamiltonian $\hat{H}$ only the perturbation $\hat{V}$ can depend on time, we have

$$\frac{dE}{dt} = -\bar{x}\frac{df}{dt}. \tag{122.10}$$

This relation will play an important part in the applications of the theory presented below. If we have a definite expression for the energy change in a particular process we may, by comparing it with (122.10), establish what quantity plays the part of the "force" f for the variable x with which we are concerned.

The average energy dissipation (per second) Q can be obtained from (122.10) by inserting for $\bar{x}$ from (122.9) and averaging over the period of the external disturbance. The terms containing a factor $e^{\pm 2i\omega t}$ then cancel, and we find

$$Q = \frac{i\omega}{4}(\alpha^* - \alpha)|f_0|^2 = \frac{\omega}{2}\alpha''|f_0|^2. \tag{122.11}$$

We see from this that the imaginary part of the susceptibility determines the energy dissipation. Since every real process is always accompanied by some energy absorption ($Q > 0$), we reach the important conclusion that at all positive frequencies α'' is non-zero and positive.

It proves possible to get some very general relations for the function $\alpha(\omega)$ by using the mathematical techniques of the theory of functions of a complex variable. For this purpose we shall regard ω as a complex variable ($\omega = \omega' + i\omega''$) and we shall investigate the properties of the function $\alpha(\omega)$ in the upper half-plane of this variable. From the definition (122.4) and from the fact that $K(\tau)$ is finite for all positive τ, it follows that $\alpha(\omega)$ is a single-valued function in the whole of the upper half-plane, and there does not become infinite anywhere, i.e. has no singular points. Indeed, if $\omega'' > 0$, the integrand of (122.4) contains an exponentially decreasing factor $e^{-\tau\omega''}$, and since the function $K(\tau)$ is finite throughout the region of integration, the integral must converge. The function $\alpha(\omega)$ also has no singularities on the real axis, ($\omega'' = 0$), except, possibly, at the origin.†

It is useful to point out that the absence of singularities of the function $\alpha(\omega)$ in the upper half-plane represents, from the physical point of view, a consequence of the principle of casuality. The latter has been used in carrying the integration in (122.2) only over times which are earlier than the given time t, and this is the reason why the range of integration in (122.4) is from 0 to ∞ (rather than from $-\infty$ to $+\infty$).

From the definition (122.4) it is further obvious that

$$\alpha(-\omega^*) = \alpha^*(\omega). \tag{122.12}$$

This is a generalisation of the relation (122.6) which holds for real values of ω. In particular for purely imaginary values of ω we have $\alpha(i\omega'') = \alpha^*(i\omega'')$, so that we may conclude that on the imaginary axis the function $\alpha(\omega)$ is real.

We shall prove the following theorem. The function $\alpha(\omega)$ is not real at any finite point of the upper half-plane, except on the imaginary axis; on the latter $\alpha(\omega)$ decreases monotonically from some positive value $\alpha_0 > 0$ at $\omega = i0$ to 0 at $\omega = i\infty$. From this it will follow in particular that $\alpha(\omega)$ has no zeros in the upper half-plane.

To prove this‡, we use a well-known theorem of complex analysis according to which the integral

$$\frac{1}{2\pi i} \int_C \frac{d\alpha(\omega)}{d\omega} \frac{d\omega}{\alpha(\omega) - a} \tag{122.13}$$

taken around a closed contour C, equals the difference between the number of zeros and the number of poles of the function $\alpha(\omega) - a$ in the region bounded by the contour C. We let a be real, and take for C the contour consisting

---

† In the lower half-plane the definition (122.4) is inapplicable, since the integral diverges. Thus in the lower half-plane the function $\alpha(\omega)$ can be defined only as the analytic continuation of the expression (122.4) from the upper half-plane. In this region the function may, in general, have singularities.

‡ The proof given here is due to N. N. MEIMAN.

of the real axis and an infinite semicircle in the upper half-plane (Fig. 53.) Assume first that a as finite. Since in the upper half-plane the function $\alpha(\omega)$, and hence also $\alpha(\omega) - a$ has no poles, the integral gives simply the number of zeros of the difference $\alpha - a$, i.e. the number of points at which α takes the real value a.

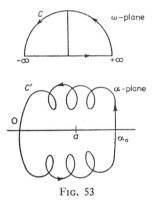

Fig. 53

To evaluate the integral, we write it in the form:

$$\frac{1}{2\pi i} \int_{C'} \frac{d\alpha}{\alpha - a},$$

where the integration extends over the contour C' in the plane of the complex variable α which is the image of the contour C in the ω plane. The whole of the infinite semi-circle is mapped on the point $\alpha = 0$, and the origin into another real point α_0. The positive and negative parts of the real ω-axis are mapped in the α plane on some very complicated curves (in general self-intersecting) which lie entirely in the upper or lower half-plane, respectively. It is essential that these curves will not cross the real axis anywhere (except at $\alpha = 0$ and $\alpha = \alpha_0$), since α does not become real for any finite real value of ω, except $\omega = 0$. In view of this property of the contour C' the total variation of the argument of the complex number $\alpha - a$ in passing around the contour is 2π if the point a lies between 0 and α_0 (as shown in Fig. 53), and zero if a lies outside this interval. This conclusion is not affected by the existence of any number of loops in the contour. Hence the expression (122.13) equals unity when $0 < a < \alpha_0$, and zero for any other value of a.

We thus conclude that the function $\alpha(\omega)$ takes in the upper ω half-plane just once any real value a lying in the stated interval (and never takes any real value outside that interval). From this we may conclude first of all that on the imaginary axis, where the function $\alpha(\omega)$ is real, it cannot have a maximum or minimum, otherwise it would have to take certain values at least twice. Therefore the function $\alpha(\omega)$ varies monotonically along the imaginary axis on which it takes once any value between α_0 and 0, and takes these values nowhere else.

If $\alpha_0 = \infty$, (i.e. $\alpha(\omega)$ has a pole at the point $\omega = 0$) the proof changes only in that the part of the contour C along the real axis has to by-pass the origin by an infinitesimal semi-circle in the upper half-plane. The change of the contour C' in Fig. 53 can then be represented as the result of moving α_0 away to infinity.

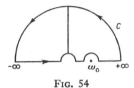

FIG. 54

Now we shall derive a formula which connects the real and imaginary part of the function $\alpha(\omega)$ with each other. For this purpose we choose any real value ω_0, and then integrate the expression $\alpha/(\omega - \omega_0)$ along the contour shown in Fig. 54. This contour extends along the whole real axis, avoiding the point $\omega = \omega_0 > 0$ (and also the point $\omega = 0$ if this is a pole of the function $\alpha(\omega)$). The contour is closed by an infinite semicircle. At infinity $\alpha \to 0$ and therefore the function $\alpha/(\omega - \omega_0)$ tends to zero faster than $1/\omega$. Hence the integral

$$\int_C \frac{\alpha}{\omega - \omega_0} \, d\omega$$

converges; as $\alpha(\omega)$ has no singularities in the upper half-plane, and the point $\omega = \omega_0$ is excluded, the function is analytic in the whole interior of the contour C, and the integral vanishes.

The integral over the infinite semi-circle vanishes by itself. We avoid the point ω_0 by means of an infinitesimal semi-circle (letting its radius ρ tend to zero). This is passed in a clockwise direction and thus gives to the integral a contribution $-i\pi\alpha(\omega_0)$. If α_0 is finite, there is no need to avoid the origin, and the integration over the real axis gives, therefore:

$$\lim_{\rho \to 0} \left\{ \int_{-\infty}^{\omega_0 - \rho} \frac{\alpha}{\omega - \omega_0} \, d\omega + \int_{\omega_0 + \rho}^{\infty} \frac{\alpha}{\omega - \omega_0} \, d\omega \right\} - i\pi\alpha(\omega_0) = 0$$

The first term is the principal part of the integral from $-\infty$ to ∞. Indicating the principal part as usual by a stroke through the integral sign, we have

$$i\pi\alpha(\omega_0) = \fint_{-\infty}^{+\infty} \frac{\alpha}{\omega - \omega_0} \, d\omega. \tag{122.14}$$

The integration variable ω here takes only real values. We change the symbol for the integration variable to ξ and denote the given real value

ω_0 now by ω; we also write the function $\alpha(\omega)$ of the real variable ω in the form $\alpha = \alpha' + i\alpha''$. Separating the real and imaginary parts in (122.14) we find finally the following two relations:

$$\alpha'(\omega) = \frac{1}{\pi} \int\limits_{-\infty}^{+\infty} \frac{\alpha''(\xi)}{\xi - \omega} \, d\xi \tag{122.15}$$

$$\alpha''(\omega) = -\frac{1}{\pi} \int\limits_{-\infty}^{+\infty} \frac{\alpha'(\xi)}{\xi - \omega} \, d\xi. \tag{122.16}$$

They were first derived by H. A. KRAMERS and R. DE L. KRONIG (1927). We stress that the only property of the function $\alpha(\omega)$ which has been used in the derivation of these relations is the absence of singularities in the upper half-plane.† It may therefore be said that the Kramers-Kronig relations, (as well as the indicated properties of the function $\alpha(\omega)$) are direct consequences of the physical principle of causality.

Remembering that $\alpha''(\xi)$ is an odd function we may also write (122.15) in the form

$$\alpha'(\omega) = \frac{1}{\pi} \int\limits_{0}^{\infty} \frac{\alpha''(\xi)}{\xi - \omega} \, d\xi + \frac{1}{\pi} \int\limits_{0}^{\infty} \frac{\alpha''(\xi)}{\xi + \omega} \, d\xi,$$

or

$$\alpha'(\omega) = \frac{2}{\pi} \int\limits_{0}^{\infty} \frac{\xi \alpha''(\xi)}{\xi^2 - \omega^2} \, d\xi. \tag{122.17}$$

If the function $\alpha(\omega)$ has a pole at $\omega = 0$, near which $\alpha = iA/\omega$, the semicircle avoiding this pole gives in the integral an additional real term $-A/\omega_0$, which has to be added to the left-hand side of eq. (122.14). A similar term therefore appears also in (122.16):

$$\alpha''(\omega) = -\frac{1}{\pi} \int\limits_{-\infty}^{\infty} \frac{\alpha'(\xi)}{\xi - \omega} + \frac{A}{\omega}, \tag{122.18}$$

However, the relation (122.15) or (122.17) remains unchanged.

We also derive a relation which expresses the values of $\alpha(\omega)$ on the upper imaginary half-axis in terms of the values of $\alpha''(\omega)$ on the real axis. For

---

† The assumption that $\alpha \to 0$ for $\omega \to \infty$ is not essential: if the limit α_∞ were different from zero one should simply have to consider in place of α the difference $\alpha - \alpha_\infty$ with corresponding obvious changes in (122.15–16).

this purpose consider the integral

$$\int \frac{\omega\alpha(\omega)}{\omega^2+\omega_0^2}\,d\omega$$

taken over a contour which consists of the real axis and an infinite semi-circle in the upper half-plane (ω_0 is a real number). This integral is calculated by means of the residue of the integrand at the pole $\omega = i\omega_0$. On the other hand the integral over the infinite semi-circle vanishes, so that we find:

$$\int_{-\infty}^{\infty} \frac{\omega\alpha(\omega)}{\omega^2+\omega_0^2}\,d\omega = i\pi\alpha(i\omega_0).$$

On the left-hand side the real part vanishes because the integrand is an odd function of the integration variable. Changing the notation again from ω_0 to ω and from ω to ξ, we have finally

$$\alpha(i\omega) = \frac{2}{\pi}\int_0^{\infty} \frac{\xi\alpha''(\xi)}{\omega^2+\xi^2}\,d\xi. \tag{122.19}$$

If we integrate both sides of this relation with respect to $d\omega$ we obtain

$$\int_0^{\infty} \alpha(i\omega)\,d\omega = \int_0^{\infty} \alpha''(\omega)\,d\omega. \tag{122.20}$$

§123. Non-thermodynamic fluctuations of one quantity

Let the body to which the quantity x refers be in some definite stationary state (say the nth). The average (118.10) is then calculated as the corresponding diagonal matrix element:

$$\tfrac{1}{2}(\hat{x}_\omega\hat{x}_{\omega'}+\hat{x}_{\omega'}\hat{x}_\omega) = \tfrac{1}{2}\sum_m [(x_\omega)_{nm}(x_{\omega'})_{mn}+(x_{\omega'})_{nm}(x_\omega)_{mn}] \tag{123.1}$$

where the summation extends over the whole spectrum of energy levels. (The two terms in the square brackets are not identical since the operator $\hat{x}$ is complex).

The time dependence of the operator $\hat{x}(t)$ means that in the calculation of its matrix elements one must use time-dependent wave functions. Hence

$$(x_\omega)_{nm} = \frac{1}{2\pi}\int_{-\infty}^{+\infty} x_{nm}e^{i(\omega_{nm}+\omega)t}\,dt = x_{nm}\delta(\omega_{nm}+\omega) \tag{123.2}$$

where x_{nm} is the usual time-independent matrix element of the operator $\hat{x}$, expressed as a function of the co-ordinates of the particles in the body, and $\omega_{nm} = (E_n - E_m)/\hbar$ is the frequency of the transition between the states n and m.

In this way:

$$\tfrac{1}{2}(\hat{x}_\omega \hat{x}_{\omega'} + \hat{x}_{\omega'} \hat{x}_\omega) = \tfrac{1}{2} \sum_m |x_{nm}|^2 [\delta(\omega_{nm} + \omega)\delta(\omega_{mn} + \omega') + \delta(\omega_{nm} + \omega')\delta(\omega_{mn} + \omega)]$$

(we have here used the fact that x is real and therefore $x_{nm} = x_{mn}^*$). The product of δ-functions in the square brackets can obviously be written in the form:

$$\delta(\omega_{nm} + \omega)\delta(\omega + \omega') + \delta(\omega_{mn} + \omega)\,\delta(\omega + \omega')$$

Comparing this with (118.10), we find the following expression for $(x^2)_\omega$:

$$(x^2)_\omega = \tfrac{1}{2} \sum_m |x_{nm}|^2 [\delta(\omega + \omega_{nm}) + \delta(\omega + \omega_{mn})]. \tag{123.3}$$

We can make the following comment on the form in which this expression is written. Although the energy levels of a macroscopic body are, strictly speaking, discrete, they are so closely spaced that they form practically a continuous spectrum. The eq. (123.3) may be written without δ-functions, if it is averaged over small frequency intervals (but still large enough to contain many levels). If $\Gamma(E)$ is the number of levels of the body with energies less than E, then

$$(x^2)_\omega = \frac{\hbar}{2}|x_{nm}|^2 \left(\frac{d\Gamma}{dE_m} + \frac{d\Gamma}{dE_m'} \right)$$

where $E_m = E_n + \hbar\omega$, $E_m' = E_n - \hbar\omega$.

Assume now that there is a periodic perturbation with frequency ω acting on the body, which has the operator

$$\hat{V} = -f\hat{x} = -\tfrac{1}{2}(f_0 e^{-i\omega t} + f_0^* e^{i\omega t})\hat{x} \tag{123.4}$$

Under the influence of this perturbation the system will make transitions, and the probability of the transition $n \to m$ (per unit time) is given by the equation†

$$w_{nm} = \frac{\pi |f_0|^2}{2\hbar^2} |x_{mn}|^2 \{\delta(\omega + \omega_{mn}) + \delta(\omega + \omega_{nm})\}. \tag{123.5}$$

The two terms in this expression come from the two terms in (123.4) respectively. In each transition the system absorbs (or emits) a quantum $\hbar\omega_{nm}$. The sum

$$Q = \sum_m \omega_{nm}\hbar\omega_{mn}$$

† Cf. *Quantum Mechanics*, §42.

gives the mean energy absorbed by the body per unit time. Inserting in (123.5) we find

$$Q = \frac{\pi}{2\hbar}|f_0|^2 \sum_m |x_{nm}|^2\{\delta(\omega+\omega_{mn})+\delta(\omega+\omega_{nm})\}\omega_{nm}$$

or, if we remember that the δ-functions vanish unless the argument vanishes:

$$Q = \frac{\pi}{2\hbar}\omega|f_0|^2 \sum_m |x_{nm}|^2\{\delta(\omega+\omega_{nm})-\delta(\omega+\omega_{mn})\}. \tag{123.6}$$

By comparing (123.6) with (122.11) we find:

$$\alpha''(\omega) = \frac{\pi}{\hbar} \sum_m |x_{nm}|^2\{\delta(\omega+\omega_{nm})-\delta(\omega+\omega_{mn})\}. \tag{123.7}$$

The two quantities $(x^2)_\omega$ and $\alpha''(\omega)$ which we have now determined are connected with each other by a simple relation. This appears, however, only after these quantities have been expressed as functions of the temperature of the body. To carry this out we form the average by means of the Gibbs distribution. (Cf. footnote on p. 80). This gives

$$(x^2)_\omega = \tfrac{1}{2} \sum_n \sum_m e^{(F-E_n)/kT}\{\delta(\omega+\omega_{nm})+\delta(\omega+\omega_{mn})\},$$

where E_n are the energy levels, and F the free energy of the body. Since the summation now extends over both suffixes n and m, we may change them to different symbols. We open the curly bracket and interchange m and n in the second term. We then find:

$$(x^2)_\omega = \tfrac{1}{2} \sum_n \sum_m (e^{(F-E_n)/kT}+e^{(F-E_m)/kT})|x_{nm}|^2\delta(\omega+\omega_{nm}) =$$

$$= \tfrac{1}{2} \sum_n \sum_m e^{(F-E_n)/kT}(1+e^{\hbar\omega_{nm}/kT})|x_{nm}|^2\delta(\omega+\omega_{nm}),$$

or, because of the presence of the δ-function in the summand,

$$(x^2)_\omega = \tfrac{1}{2}(1+e^{-\hbar\omega/kT}) \sum_n \sum_m e^{(F-E_n)/kT}|x_{nm}|^2\delta(\omega+\omega_{nm}).$$

In an exactly similar way we find that

$$\alpha''(\omega) = \frac{\pi}{\hbar}(1-e^{-\hbar\omega/kT}) \sum_n \sum_m e^{(F-E_n)/kT}|x_{nm}|^2\delta(\omega+\omega_{nm}).$$

By comparing the last two expressions we see that

$$(x^2)_\omega = \frac{\hbar\alpha''}{2\pi}\coth\frac{\hbar\omega}{2kT} = \frac{\hbar\alpha''}{\pi}\left\{\frac{1}{2}+\frac{1}{e^{\hbar\omega/kT}-1}\right\} \tag{123.8}$$

The complete mean square of the fluctuating quantity is then given by the integral

$$\overline{x^2} = \frac{\hbar}{\pi} \int_0^\infty \alpha''(\omega) \coth\frac{\hbar\omega}{2kT} \, d\omega. \tag{123.9}$$

These important relations (found by H. B. CALLEN and T. A. WELTON, 1951) connect the fluctuations of physical quantities with the dissipative properties of the system when external disturbances act on it. We note that the factor in curly brackets in (123.8) represents formally the energy (in units of $\hbar\omega$) of an oscillator of frequency ω at temperature T; the term $\frac{1}{2}$ is the zero-point energy.

The results which we have obtained may be presented in a different form if one regards, in a purely formal sense, the spontaneous fluctuations of the quantity x as the result of the action of fictitious "random forces" f. It is then convenient to write our equations in terms of "Fourier components" x_ω and f_ω as if x were an ordinary quantity and not an operator. The relation between them is given by

$$x_\omega = \alpha(\omega) f_\omega \tag{123.10}$$

and then the mean square fluctuations can be written in the form:

$$\overline{x_\omega x_{\omega'}} = \alpha(\omega)\alpha(\omega')\overline{f_\omega f_{\omega'}} = (\overline{x^2})_\omega \delta(\omega+\omega') = |\alpha|^2 (\overline{f^2})_\omega \delta(\omega+\omega').$$

For the spectral density of the mean square of the random forces we find therefore from (123.8)

$$(\overline{f^2})_\omega = \frac{\hbar\alpha''}{2\pi|\alpha|^2} \coth\frac{\hbar\omega}{2kT}. \tag{123.11}$$

This treatment of the fluctuations may have definite advantages in particular applications.

At temperatures for which $kT \gg \hbar\omega$ we have $\coth(\hbar\omega/2kT) \cong (2kT/\hbar\omega)$ and (123.8) takes the form:

$$(\overline{x^2})_\omega = \frac{kT}{\pi\omega} \alpha''(\omega). \tag{123.12}$$

Here the quantum constant has disappeared, in accordance with the fact that in these conditions the fluctuations are classical.

If the inequality $kT \gg \hbar\omega$ holds for all relevant frequencies (frequencies for which $\alpha'(\omega)$ is appreciably different from zero) one can make the transition to the classical case also in the integral formula (123.9)

$$\overline{x^2} = \frac{2kT}{\pi} \int_0^\infty \frac{\alpha''(\omega)}{\omega} \, d\omega.$$

But according to (122.17) this integral can be expressed in terms of the static value $\alpha'(0) = \alpha(0)$, so that

$$\overline{x^2} = kT\alpha(0).$$

But $\alpha(0) = 1/\beta T$ (see eq. (124.19), below). Thus we come back to the familiar result (109.4). This is not surprising, since this latter result depended only on x being a classical quantity but did not assume the fluctuations to be thermodynamic.

PROBLEM

1.   Derive the relation (122.17) by a direct quantum-mechanical calculation of the average value $\bar{x}$ in the perturbed system.

SOLUTION: Let $\Psi_n^{(0)}$ be the eigenfunctions of the unperturbed system. By the general method† we look for eigenfunctions of the perturbed system to first order in the form:

$$\Psi_n = \Psi_n^{(0)} + \sum_m a_{mn}\Psi_m^{(0)}$$

where the coefficients a_{mn} satisfy the equations

$$i\hbar\frac{da_{mn}}{dt} = V_{mn}e^{i\omega_{mn}t} = -\tfrac{1}{2}x_{mn}e^{i\omega_{mn}t}(f_0 e^{-i\omega t} + f_0^* e^{i\omega t}).$$

Hence

$$a_{mn} = \frac{1}{2\hbar}x_{mn}e^{i\omega_{mn}t}\left(\frac{f_0 e^{-i\omega t}}{\omega_{mn}-\omega} + \frac{f_0^* e^{i\omega t}}{\omega_{mn}+\omega}\right)$$

We assume here that $|\omega|$ does not coincide with any of the frequencies ω_{mn}. With this function Ψ_n we now calculate the average value of x as the corresponding diagonal matrix element of the operator $\hat{x}$; to the same order of approximation:

$$\bar{x} = \int \Psi_n^* \hat{x}\Psi_n \, dq = \sum_m (a_{mn}x_{nm}e^{i\omega_{nm}t} + a_{mn}^* x_{mn}e^{i\omega_{mn}t})$$

$$= \frac{1}{2\hbar}\sum_m\left[\frac{x_{mn}x_{nm}}{\omega_{mn}-\omega} + \frac{x_{mn}x_{nm}}{\omega_{mn}+\omega}\right](f_0 e^{-i\omega t} + f_0^* e^{i\omega t})$$

$$= \frac{1}{2\hbar}\sum_m\frac{\omega_{mn}|x_{mn}|^2}{\omega_{mn}^2-\omega^2}(f_0 e^{-i\omega t} + f_0^* e^{i\omega t}).$$

Comparing this expression with the definition (122.3), we see that

$$\alpha'(\omega) = \frac{2}{\hbar}\sum_m\frac{\omega_{mn}|x_{nm}|^2}{\omega_{mn}^2-\omega^2} \tag{1}$$

(the imaginary part of α drops out from this calculation, of course, since we have assumed that $|\omega| \neq \omega_{mn}$). Inserting (1) in (123.7) and (122.17) one easily verifies that the latter is indeed, satisfied identically. (One must remember that in the integration over positive ξ only one of the δ-functions in $\alpha''(\xi)$ may be non-zero.)

---

† See *Quantum Mechanics*, §40.

§124. Non-thermodynamic fluctuations of several quantities

The above results can easily be generalised for the case when one is concerned simultaneously with several fluctuating quantities x_i. We shall give the derivation for this case without repeating the details of calculations which are completely analogous with those of the preceding sections.

Let x_i and x_k be any two of the physical quantities under consideration. Introduce the quantum-mechanical average of the symmetrised operator product

$$\overline{\tfrac{1}{2}(\hat{x}_{i\omega}\hat{x}_{k\omega'}+\hat{x}_{k\omega'}\hat{x}_{i\omega})} = (x_i x_k)_\omega \delta(\omega+\omega') \tag{124.1}$$

which generalises (123.1). By proceeding as in the derivation of (123.3) we arrive at the following result:

$$(x_i x_k)_\omega = \tfrac{1}{2} \sum_m \{(x_i)_{nm}(x_k)_{mn} \delta(\omega+\omega_{nm})+(x_k)_{nm}(x_i)_{mn} \delta(\omega+\omega_{mn})\}. \tag{124.2}$$

The external perturbation acting on the body will be taken in the form†

$$\hat{V} = -f_i \hat{x}_i = -\tfrac{1}{2}\{f_{0i}e^{-i\omega t}+f^*_{0i}e^{i\omega t}\}\hat{x}_i. \tag{124.3}$$

A calculation like the derivation of (123.6) gives for the energy absorbed by the body per unit time:

$$Q = \frac{\pi}{2\hbar}\omega \sum_n f_{0i}f^*_{0k}[(x_i)_{mn}(x_k)_{nm} \,\delta(\omega+\omega_{nm})-(x_i)_{nm}(x_k)_{mn} \,\delta(\omega+\omega_{mn})] \tag{124.4}$$

The definition (122.9) is generalised as follows:

$$\overline{x_i} = \tfrac{1}{2}(\alpha_{ik}f_{0k}e^{-i\omega t}+\alpha^*_{ik}f_{0k}e^{i\omega t}), \tag{124.5}$$

or

$$\overline{x_i} = \alpha_{ik}f_k \tag{124.6}$$

if all quantities are expressed in complex form ($\sim e^{-i\omega t}$). The rate of change of the energy is expressed in terms of the external disturbance by

$$\dot{E} = -\overline{x}_i\dot{f}_i. \tag{124.7}$$

The last formula, like (122.10) usually serves in particular applications of the theory to establish the correspondence between x_i and f_i.

Inserting (124.7) in (124.5), and averaging over the period of the external disturbance, we find in place of (122.11) the following expression for the energy dissipation

$$Q = \frac{i\omega}{4}(\alpha^*_{ik}-\alpha_{ki})f_{0i}f^*_{0k}. \tag{124.8}$$

---

† Remember that a summation is always implied over repeated suffixes i, k.

Comparison with (124.4) gives

$$\alpha^{*}{}_{ik}-\alpha_{ki} = -\frac{2\pi i}{\hbar}\sum_{m}[(x_{i})_{mn}(x_{k})_{nm}\,\delta(\omega+\omega_{nm})-(x_{i})_{nm}(x_{k})_{mn}\,\delta(\omega+\omega_{mn})].$$
(124.9)

If we average this expression and (124.2) over the Gibbs distribution, as was done in the previous section, we obtain the following result as a generalisation of (123.8):

$$(x_{i}x_{k})_{\omega} = \frac{i\hbar}{4\pi}(\alpha^{*}{}_{ik}-\alpha_{ki})\coth\frac{\hbar\omega}{2kT}$$
(124.10)

In the same way as in eqs. (123.10–11), we may express also eq. (124.10) in terms of "random forces", which would produce equivalent results to the spontaneous fluctuations of the quantities x_{i}. For this purpose we write

$$x_{i\omega} = \alpha_{ik}f_{k\omega}; \qquad f_{i\omega} = \alpha_{ik}^{-1}x_{k\omega}$$
(124.11)

and further

$$(f_{i}f_{k})_{\omega} = \alpha_{il}^{-1}\alpha_{km}^{-1}(x_{l}x_{m})_{\omega}.$$

Inserting here from (124.10), we find

$$(f_{i}f_{k})_{\omega} = \frac{i\hbar}{4\pi}(\alpha_{ik}^{-1}-\alpha^{*}{}_{ki}^{-1})\coth\frac{\hbar\omega}{2kT}$$
(124.12)

The relations which we have obtained make it possible to draw definite conclusions about the symmetry properties of the quantities α_{ik}[†]. We assume, to start with, that the quantities x_{i}, x_{k} are such that they remain unchanged under time reversal; the corresponding operators $\hat{x}_{i}$, $\hat{x}_{k}$ are then purely real. In addition we shall assume that the body has no "magnetic structure" and is not subject to the action of an external magnetic field; then the wave functions of its stationary states are also real.[‡] Therefore the matrix elements of the quantities x are real, and because of the Hermitian nature of the matrix we have then $x_{nm}=x^{*}{}_{mn}=x_{mn}$. Thus $\alpha^{*}{}_{ik}-\alpha_{ki}=\alpha^{*}{}_{ki}-\alpha_{ik}$ or $\alpha_{ik}+\alpha^{*}{}_{ik}=\alpha_{ki}+\alpha^{*}{}_{ki}$, in other words, we conclude that the real part of α_{ik} is symmetric.

But the real and imaginary parts α_{ik}', α_{ik}'' of each of the quantities α_{ik} are related to each other by linear integral equations, the relations of KRAMERS and KRONIG. Therefore the symmetry of α_{ik}' requires also the symmetry

---

[†] The results which follow are due to H. B. CALLEN, M. L. BARASH, J. L. JACKSON and R. F. GREEN (1952).

[‡] The exact energy levels of a system of interacting particles can be degenerate only with respect to the direction of the total angular momentum of the system. This source of degeneracy can be excluded if we assume the body enclosed in a container with rigid walls. Then the energy levels of the body will be non-degenerate and then the corresponding exact wave functions may be taken as real.

of α_{ik}'' and thus of the whole α_{ik}. We therefore find the final answer

$$\alpha_{ik} = \alpha_{ki}. \tag{124.13}$$

The form of the relation (124.13) changes somewhat if the body is in a uniform external magnetic field **H**. The wave functions of a system in a magnetic field are not real, but have the property

$$\psi^*(\mathbf{H}) = \psi(-\mathbf{H}).$$

Similarly we have for the matrix elements of the quantity x

$$x_{nm}(\mathbf{H}) = x_{mn}(-\mathbf{H})$$

and the expression on the right of (124.9) remains unchanged only if besides interchanging the suffixes i, k we also reverse the field **H**. We therefore find the relation

$$\alpha^*_{ik}(\mathbf{H}) - \alpha_{ki}(\mathbf{H}) = \alpha^*_{ki}(-\mathbf{H}) - \alpha_{ik}(-\mathbf{H}).$$

One further relation is provided by the Kramers-Kronig relation (122.14) which establishes a connection of the form

$$\alpha_{ki} = i\hat{f}(\alpha_{ki})$$

where $\hat{f}$ is a certain real linear operator. Adding to this relation its Hermitian conjugate $\alpha^*_{ik} = -i\hat{f}(\alpha^*_{ik})$, we find

$$\alpha^*_{ik} + \alpha_{ki} = -i\hat{f}(\alpha^*_{ik} - \alpha_{ki})$$

(all the α_{ik} are here, of course, taken for the same value of **H**). From this we see that if the difference $\alpha^*_{ik} - \alpha_{ki}$ possesses some kind of symmetry, the same will apply to the sum $\alpha^*_{ik} + \alpha_{ki}$, and hence to the coefficients α_{ik} themselves. Thus

$$\alpha_{ik}(\mathbf{H}) = \alpha_{ki}(-\mathbf{H}). \tag{124.14}$$

Finally, let us assume that amongst the quantities x there are some which change sign under time reversal. The quantum-mechanical operator belonging to such a quantity is purely imaginary, and therefore $x_{nm} = x^*_{mn} = -x_{mn}$. If both quantities x_i, x_k are of this kind, then the whole derivation and the result (124.13) remains unchanged. If, however, only one of the two quantities changes sign under time reversal, then we see that with an interchange of the suffixes i, k the right-hand side of (124.9) changes sign. In place of (124.13) we therefore find now

$$\alpha_{ik} = -\alpha_{ki}. \tag{124.15}$$

Similarly we have in a magnetic field, instead of (124.14):

$$\alpha_{ik}(\mathbf{H}) = -\alpha_{ki}(-\mathbf{H}). \tag{124.16}$$

All these relations may, of course, also be derived from (124.10) as a consequence of the time symmetry of the fluctuations. In the Fourier components the time reversal appears as a change of ω to $-\omega$ (if the quantity x itself remains unchanged by time reversal). In the expressions (124.1) (which in fact are different from zero only if $\omega' = -\omega$) this amount to interchanging ω and ω' and this means the same thing as interchanging the suffices i, k. Hence the time symmetry of the fluctuations means that

$$(x_i x_k)_\omega = (x_k x_i)_\omega,$$

i.e. the left (and hence also the right) of eq. (124.10) is symmetrical with respect to i, k and we arrive once again at the relation (124.13). This derivation of the symmetry properties of the coefficients α_{ik} is analogous to the usual derivation of the symmetry principle of the kinetic coefficients of ONSAGER (§119). We shall see later that eqs. (124.13–16) may be regarded as a generalisation of that principle.

We shall now show how the general theory presented above is related to the theory of thermodynamic fluctuations. Quantities whose fluctuations may be regarded as thermodynamic are characterised by the fact that they obey equations of the type

$$\dot{x}_i = -\gamma_{ik} X_k$$

for the behaviour of a closed system which is not in equilibrium. If the system is not closed, but subject to external forces, we must add on the right-hand side of this equation a further term, which we shall denote by y_i:

$$\dot{x}_i = -\gamma_{ik} X_k + y_i. \tag{124.17}$$

It is easy to express y_i in terms of the quantities f_i which characterise the given perturbation†.

For this purpose we assume that the forces acting on the body are static, i.e. the f_i are constant. This disturbance will lead to a "displacement" of the equilibrium state in which the mean values of X_i will not vanish. These mean values may be expressed in terms of f_i in the following way: The energy of the body under the influence of the constant perturbation is $E = E_0 - f_i \bar{x}_i$, where E_0 is the energy in the absence of the perturbation. The thermodynamic identity for this is

$$dE = T\,dS + \frac{\partial E}{\partial f_i}\,df_i.$$

But according to the general formula (11.4) we have:

$$\left(\frac{\partial E}{\partial f_i}\right)_S = \frac{\overline{\partial H}}{\partial f_i} = \frac{\overline{\partial V}}{\partial f_i} = -\bar{x}_i$$

---

† It should be pointed out that eq. (124.17) may also be given a different meaning: the quantities y_i (or f_i) may be regarded not as the result of some external perturbation on a system, which is far from equilibrium, but as "random forces" whose introduction in the equation makes the latter applicable to the fluctuating changes in x_i in a closed system. This treatment corresponds to the presentation of the basic formula in the form (124.12).

so that

$$dE = d(E_0 - f_i \bar{x}_i) = T\,dS - \bar{x}_i\,df_i$$

or

$$dE_0 = T\,dS + f_i\,d\bar{x}_i.$$

Hence we find the equilibrium values

$$X_i = -\left(\frac{\partial S}{\partial \bar{x}_i}\right)_{E_0} = \frac{f_i}{T}.$$

On the other hand, for the equilibrium state the right-hand side of (124.17) must vanish. We see therefore, that these equations can, with the use of the quantities f_i, be written in the form:

$$\dot{x}_i = -\gamma_{ik}\left(X_k - \frac{f_k}{T}\right). \qquad (124.18)$$

We can now relate the coefficients α_{ik}, which occurred in the general theory presented above, with the kinetic coefficients γ_{ik}. To do so we insert in (124.18) for x_i from (124.5), and represent X_i as a linear combination

$$X_i = \beta_{ik} x_k.$$

Separating in (124.18) the terms which contain $e^{-i\omega t}$ and those which contain $e^{i\omega t}$, we find

$$i\omega \alpha_{im} f_{0m} = \gamma_{ik}\beta_{kl}\alpha_{lm}f_{0m} - \frac{1}{T}\gamma_{im}f_{0m}$$

and from this we find, because the f_{0m} are arbitrary, the following relations between the coefficients:

$$i\omega \alpha_{im} - \gamma_{ik}\beta_{kl}\alpha_{lm} = -\frac{1}{T}\gamma_{im}$$

or

$$\alpha_{ik} = \frac{1}{T}(\beta_{ik} - i\omega\gamma_{ik}^{-1})^{-1} \qquad (124.19)$$

where the exponent -1 indicates the inverse matrix. This is the required connection.

Since the coefficients β_{ik} are, by definition, symmetric in their suffices, the symmetry of the α_{ik} also ensures the symmetry of γ_{ik}, i.e. the general principle of the symmetry of the kinetic coefficients.

Inserting (124.19) in (124.12) we find

$$(f_i f_k)_\omega = \frac{\hbar\omega T}{4\pi}(\gamma_{ik}^{-1} + \gamma_{ki}^{-1})\coth\frac{\hbar\omega}{2kT}$$

or, for the quantities $y_i = -\gamma_{ik} f_k / T$:

$$(y_i y_k)_\omega = \frac{\hbar\omega}{4\pi T}(\gamma_{ik}+\gamma_{ki})\coth\frac{\hbar\omega}{2kT}. \qquad (124.20)$$

This relation differs from (121.10), which applies to the fluctuations of a classical quantity x_i by a factor

$$\frac{\hbar\omega}{2kT}\coth\frac{\hbar\omega}{2kT} \qquad (124.21)$$

In the classical limit, $\hbar\omega \ll kT$, this factor tends to unity, so that (124.20) and (121.10) become identical.

CHAPTER XIII

THE SYMMETRY OF MACROSCOPIC BODIES

§125. Symmetry of the configuration of the particles in a body

In this chapter we shall study the different symmetry properties which macroscopic bodies can possess. We shall begin by studying the commonest of the symmetry properties, the symmetry of the configuration of the particles in the body.

The moving atoms and molecules do not occupy strictly determined positions in the body, and to give a rigorous statistical description of their configuration one must introduce the "density function" $\rho(x, y, z)$ which determines the probabilities of different positions of the particles; ρdV is the probability for particles to be in the volume element dV. The symmetry properties of the particle configuration are determined by the co-ordinate transformations (translations, rotations, reflections) which leave the function $\rho(x, y, z)$ invariant. The set of all such *symmetry transformations* of a given body form its *symmetry group*.

If the body is made up of different atoms then ρ must be separately determined for each type of atom. This fact, however, is of no importance, since for a real body all these functions will have actually identical symmetry. One could also use the function defined as the total electronic density created by the atoms at each point.

The most symmetrical bodies are *isotropic bodies*, whose properties are the same in all directions; these include gases and liquids (and amorphous solids). It is obvious that for every particle of such a body all positions in space must be equally probable, i.e. we must have $\rho = \text{const}$.[†] Indeed, if certain positions of the particles were more probable than others, then the properties of the body in different directions (for example directions passing through a maximum of the probability and directions not passing through one) would differ.

Conversely, in *anisotropic crystalline* solids the density function is by no means constant. In this case it becomes a triply periodic function (with periods equal to those of the crystal lattice) and has sharp maxima at points corresponding to the lattice points. As well as translational symmetry, the lattice also has symmetry with respect to various rotations and reflections. Lattice points which can be interchanged by some symmetry transformation

---

[†] We must emphasise, however, that the condition $\rho = \text{const}$ is by no means sufficient to ensure the isotropy of a body. The body may have a constant density function and at the same time be anisotropic due to some of its other properties (see §123).

are called *equivalent*. The types of crystal symmetry will be considered in §§124–129.

The possibility of the actual existence of bodies whose density function depends not on all three, but only on one or two of the co-ordinates, is a question of considerable theoretical interest (it was discussed by R. E. PEIERLS 1934, and L. LANDAU, 1937). A body with $\rho = \rho(x)$ could be envisaged as consisting of equally spaced parallel planes (perpendicular to the x-axis) in each of which, however, the atoms are placed at random. For $\rho = \rho(x, y)$ the atoms would be randomly distributed along straight lines parallel to the z-axis, while these straight lines themselves would be regularly spaced relative to one another.

To investigate this problem, consider the displacements which small regions of the body undergo as a result of fluctuations. It is clear that if such displacements increase indefinitely as the size of the body increases, then this will result in a spreading out of the function ρ, i.e. the assumption we have made is contradicted. In other words, only those distributions ρ can exist for which the mean fluctuational displacement remains finite however large the body.

Let us check, first of all, that this condition is satisfied for the usual crystals. Let $\mathbf{u}(x, y, z)$ denote the displacement vector of a small element with co-ordinates (x, y, z) and let us express $\mathbf{u}$ as the Fourier series

$$\mathbf{u} = \sum_{\mathbf{f}} \mathbf{u}_{\mathbf{f}} e^{i\mathbf{f}.\mathbf{r}}; \tag{125.1}$$

this series will contain only terms with not too large wave vectors ($f \gtrsim 1/d$, where d is the linear dimension of the displaced region.) Consider fluctuations of $\mathbf{u}$ at constant temperature; their probabilities are given by formulae (116.1–2).

To calculate ΔF_t we must expand $F - \bar{F}$ in powers of the displacements. This expansion will contain only the derivatives of $\mathbf{u}(x, y, z)$ and not the function itself (cf. §116), since $F - \bar{F}$ must vanish for $\mathbf{u} = \text{const}$, which corresponds to a simple displacement of the body as a whole. As regards the various derivatives of $\mathbf{u}$ with respect to the co-ordinates, it is obvious, first of all, that no linear terms in them can occur; otherwise F could not have a minimum at $\mathbf{u} = 0$. Furthermore, owing to the smallness of the wave vectors in the expansion of the free energy, we can restrict ourselves to terms which are quadratic in the first derivatives of $\mathbf{u}$, neglecting terms involving higher derivatives. As a result we find that ΔF_T takes the form

$$\Delta F_t = V \sum_{\mathbf{f}} |\mathbf{u}_{\mathbf{f}}|^2 \phi(f_x, f_y, f_z),$$

where $\phi(f_x, f_y, f_z)$ is a quadratic function of the components of the vector $\mathbf{f}$.

It follows from this that the mean square of the fluctuation $\mathbf{u}_{\mathbf{f}}$ will be

$$\overline{|\mathbf{u}_{\mathbf{f}}|^2} \sim \frac{kT}{V} \frac{1}{\phi(f_x, f_y, f_z)},$$

and for the mean square of the total displacement we obtain

$$\overline{u^2} = \sum_{\mathbf{f}} \overline{|u_{\mathbf{f}}|^2} \sim kT \iiint \frac{\mathrm{d}f_x\,\mathrm{d}f_y\,\mathrm{d}f_z}{\phi(f_x,f_y,f_z)} \tag{125.2}$$

(The summation over $\mathbf{f}$ is replaced in the usual way by multiplication by $V\,\mathrm{d}f_x\,\mathrm{d}f_y\,\mathrm{d}f_z$ and integration.). This integral converges at the lower limit $(\mathbf{f} \to 0)$ linearly in f. Thus the mean square fluctuational displacement is, as it should be, a finite quantity independent of the size of the body.

Consider next a body with density function $\rho = \rho(x)$. Since $\rho = \mathrm{const}$ along the y and z axes of such a body, no displacement parallel to these axes can spread out the density function and hence we can ignore such displacements. Thus we consider only the displacement u_x. Furthermore, it can easily be seen that the derivatives $\partial u_x/\partial y$, $\partial u_x/\partial z$ cannot enter into the expansion of the free energy. For if one rotates the body as a whole about the y or z axes, then these derivatives will change, but the free energy must obviously remain the same. Thus in the expansion of $F - \bar{F}$, we must consider the following quadratic terms:

$$\left(\frac{\partial u_x}{\partial x}\right)^2, \quad \frac{\partial u_x}{\partial x}\left(\frac{\partial^2 u_x}{\partial y^2}+\frac{\partial^2 u_x}{\partial z^2}\right), \quad \left(\frac{\partial^2 u_x}{\partial y^2}+\frac{\partial^2 u_x}{\partial z^2}\right)^2$$

(the derivatives with respect to y and z must appear as symmetrical combinations, owing to the complete symmetry in the y, z plane). Substituting into (125.1), they give, respectively, terms of the form

$$|u_{x\mathbf{f}}|^2 f_x^2, \quad |u_{x\mathbf{f}}|^2(f_y^2+f_z^2)f_x, \quad |u_{x\mathbf{f}}|^2(f_y^2+f_z^2)^2.$$

Although the last two expressions contain higher powers of the components of the wave vector than the first term, they may still be of the same order of magnitude, since nothing is known beforehand about the relative magnitudes of f_x, f_y, f_z.

Thus the change in the free energy will take the form

$$\Delta F_T = V \sum_{\mathbf{f}} |u_{\mathbf{f}x}|^2 \phi(f_x, f_y^2+f_z^2), \tag{125.3}$$

where ϕ is a quadratic function of the two variables f_x and $f_y^2+f_z^2$. We now have in place of (122.2):

$$\overline{u_x^2} \sim kT \iiint \frac{\mathrm{d}f_x\,\mathrm{d}f_y\,\mathrm{d}f_z}{\phi(f_x,f_y^2+f_z^2)}. \tag{125.4}$$

But this integral, as can easily be seen, diverges logarithmically as $\mathbf{f} \to 0$.

The divergence of the mean fluctuation of the displacement u_x means that a point corresponding to a definite value of $\rho(x)$ can be displaced through very large distances. In other words, the density $\rho(x)$ will be "spread out" over the whole body, so that no function $\rho = \rho(x)$ (except the trivial one $\rho = \mathrm{const}$), is possible.

Similar reasoning for the case of a body with $\rho = \rho(x, y)$ leads to the following expression for the mean squares of the displacements

$$\overline{u_x{}^2}, \overline{u_y{}^2} \sim kT \int \int \int \frac{\mathrm{d}f_x\,\mathrm{d}f_y\,\mathrm{d}f_z}{\phi(f_x,f_y,f_z{}^2)}. \tag{125.5}$$

This integral converges, as is easily seen, so that the fluctuations remain finite. Thus a body with such a density function could exist, in principle; it is not known, however, whether any such body actually exists in nature.

§126. Symmetry with respect to the orientation of molecules

We have already noted that the condition $\rho = $ const is a necessary but not a sufficient condition for a body to be isotropic. This is clear from the following example. Imagine a body consisting of non-spherical molecules such that all positions in space of a molecule as a whole (of its centre of gravity) are equally probable, but the axes of the molecules are mostly oriented in one direction. It is clear that such a body will be anisotropic, although $\rho = $ const for each of the atoms composing the molecule.

The symmetry property which we are discussing is obviously a correlation between the positions of different atoms. Let $\rho_{12}\,\mathrm{d}V_2$ be the probability that atom number 2 is in the volume element $\mathrm{d}V_2$, for a given position of atom number 1 (in this case we usually have to deal with atoms of different kinds); ρ_{12} is a function of the radius vector $\mathbf{r}_{12}$ between the two atoms, and the symmetry properties of this function determine the symmetry of the body (which has $\rho = $ const).

The fact that the density function ρ is constant means that a change in the relative positions of the particles of the body (with no change in volume) will not lead to any change in its equilibrium state, i.e. a change in its thermodynamic quantities. This is just the property characterising liquids (and gases as well). Hence one must regard bodies with $\rho = $ const and an anisotropic function $\rho_{12}(\mathbf{r}_{12})$ as what are called *liquid crystals*—anisotropic fluids.

As the length of the vector $\mathbf{r}_{12}$ changes, while its direction remains the same, the functions ρ_{12}, of course, show no periodicity (although they may oscillate). In other words these functions have no translational symmetry and their symmetry groups can be formed only from different rotations and reflections, i.e. they represent what are called *point groups*.[†]

Regarding liquid crystals as bodies with anisotropic correlation ρ_{12} we can therefore say that their possible types of symmetry are classified in terms of the point groups. These groups may contain axes of symmetry of arbitrary order. In particular, one can have liquid crystals with an axis of complete axial symmetry (groups C_∞, $C_{\infty h}$, $C_{\infty v}$, D_∞, $D_{\infty h}$[‡]). It is usually assumed that all known liquid crystals belong to just these types, although it should

---

[†] See *Quantum Mechanics*, §90.

[‡] Remember that of these groups, the only possible group symmetries for the separate molecules are $C_{\infty v}$ and $D_{\infty h}$ (See *Quantum Mechanics*, §95).

be borne in mind that optical observation cannot distinguish an axis of complete axial symmetry from an axis of order $n > 2$.

Finally we must mention that there also exist two kinds of symmetry for usual isotropic liquids. If the liquid consists of substances which have no stereoisomers then it is completely symmetrical not only with respect to rotation through any angle about any axis, but also with respect to reflection in any plane. In other words, its symmetry group is the complete group of rotations about a point supplemented by a centre of symmetry (group K_h). But if the substance exists in two stereoisomeric forms, and the liquids contains molecules of both in different quantities, then the liquid will not have a centre of symmetry (and hence will not admit reflections in the planes); its symmetry group will simply be the complete group of rotations about the axes (the group K).

§127. The symmetry elements of a crystal lattice

In the study of the symmetry of the crystal lattice, we must begin by classifying the elements out of which this symmetry can be constructed.

The basic symmetry of a crystal lattice is its space periodicity, i.e. its property of invariance with respect to parallel displacements (called *translations*) by definite amounts in definite directions†; we shall discuss translational symmetry in greater detail in the next section.

As well as translational symmetry, the lattice may also possess symmetry with respect to various rotations and reflections; the corresponding symmetry elements (*axes* and *planes of symmetry, axes of rotary reflection*) are the same as for symmetric bodies of finite size.‡

In addition, however, a crystal lattice can also have symmetry elements of a special kind, representing combinations of parallel displacements with rotations and reflections. Consider first the combination of translations with an axis of symmetry. The combination of an axis of symmetry with a parallel displacement perpendicular to the axis leads to no new type of symmetry element. It is easy to see that the rotation through some angle with a subsequent displacement perpendicular to the axis is equivalent to a simple rotation through the same angle about another axis parallel to the first. But the combination of rotation about an axis with a parallel displacement along the same axis leads to a new type of symmetric element; a *screw axis*. The lattice has an n-fold screw axis when it repeats itself after rotation through an angle $2\pi/n$ and a simultaneous displacement along the same axis through a certain distance d.

Performing the rotation about an n-fold screw axis and the displacement along it n times, we simply move the lattice along the axis a distance nd. Thus when a lattice has a screw axis it must also have a simple periodicity

---

† We imagine the crystal lattice to be infinite, disregarding the surface of the crystal.

‡ See *Quantum Mechanics*, §88.

along this axis with period not greater than nd. This means that an n-fold screw axis can involve only displacements through the distances

$$d = \frac{pa}{n} \qquad (p = 1, 2, \dots, n-1)$$

where a is the smallest period of the lattice in the direction of the axis. Thus a two-fold screw axis can be of only one type, with displacement of half a period; a three-fold screw axis can involve displacements of 1/3 or 2/3 of a period, etc.

Similarly, one can combine translations with a plane of symmetry. Reflection in the plane together with a translation along the perpendicular direction does not introduce any new symmetry element, since such a transformation can easily be seen to be equivalent to simple reflection in another plane parallel to the first. But the combination of reflection with a displacement parallel to the plane results in a new type of symmetry element called a *glide reflection plane*. That is, a lattice has a glide reflection plane if it is invariant under a reflection in this plane and a simultaneous displacement through a certain distance d in a certain direction situated in this plane.

A double reflection in a glide reflection plane leads to a simple displacement through a distance $2d$. Thus it is clear that a lattice can have only those glide reflection planes for which the translation has the value $d = a/2$, where a is the length of the smallest period of the lattice in the direction of this translation.

As far as the axes of rotary reflection are concerned, their combination with translations leads to no new types of symmetry element. Indeed, every displacement can be split up into two parts, one perpendicular to the axis and the other parallel to it, i.e. perpendicular to the plane of symmetry. Hence a rotary reflection with a subsequent displacement is always equivalent to the same transformation about a parallel axis.

§128. The Bravais lattice

The translational periods can be represented by vectors **a** directed along the respective parallel displacements and of the same length. A crystal lattice has an infinite number of different such lattice vectors. However, not all of these vectors are independent. In any crystal lattice one can always choose three (corresponding to the number of dimensions of space) non-coplanar vectors as basic ones. Then any other lattice vector can be expressed as the geometric sum of three vectors each of which is an integral multiple of one of the basic lattice vectors. If the basic lattice vectors are denoted by $\mathbf{a}_1$, $\mathbf{a}_2$, $\mathbf{a}_3$ then an arbitrary lattice vector **a** will have the form

$$\mathbf{a} = n_1\mathbf{a}_1 + n_2\mathbf{a}_2 + n_3\mathbf{a}_3 \tag{128.1}$$

where n_1, n_2, n_3 are arbitrary positive or negative integers (including zero).

The choice of basic lattice vectors is by no means unique. On the contrary, these lattice vectors may be chosen in an infinite number of ways. Let $\mathbf{a}_1$, $\mathbf{a}_2$, $\mathbf{a}_3$ be the basic lattice vectors; we can introduce, instead, lattice vectors $\mathbf{a}_1{}'$, $\mathbf{a}_2{}'$, $\mathbf{a}_3{}'$, according to the formula

$$\mathbf{a}_i{}' = \sum_k \alpha_{ik}\mathbf{a}_k \qquad (i,k = 1,2,3), \qquad (128.2)$$

where α_{ik} are integers. If the new lattice vectors $\mathbf{a}_i{}'$ are also basic then, in particular, the previous lattice vectors $\mathbf{a}_i$ must be expressible as linear functions of the $\mathbf{a}_i{}'$ with integral coefficients. Then every other lattice vector can also be expressed in terms of the $\mathbf{a}_i{}'$. In other words, if we use (123.2) to express $\mathbf{a}_i$ in terms of $\mathbf{a}_i{}'$ then we must obtain an expression of the form $\mathbf{a}_i = \sum_k \beta_{ik}\mathbf{a}_k{}'$ again with integral β_{ik}. But it is well known that the determinant $|\beta_{ik}|$ is equal to the inverse of the determinant $|\alpha_{ik}|$. Since both must be integers it follows that a necessary and sufficient condition that $\mathbf{a}_i{}'$ are basic lattice vectors is

$$|\alpha_{ik}| = \pm 1. \qquad (128.3)$$

Choose now one of the points of the lattice and draw from it the three basic lattice vectors. The parallelopiped constructed from these vectors is called a unit cell of the lattice. The whole lattice can then be represented as a set of such parallelopipeds regularly packed. All the unit cells obviously have exactly identical properties; they have the same shape and volume and each has an identical number of identically situated atoms of each kind.

At all the vertices of the unit cells there are, obviously, identical atoms. All these vertices are, in other words, equivalent lattice points and each can be made to replace another by displacement through one of the lattice vectors. The set of such equivalent lattice points which can replace one another by a translation forms what is called the *Bravais lattice* of the crystal. It is obvious that the Bravais lattice does not include all of the points of the crystal lattice. Furthermore, it does not even include all equivalent lattice points, in general, since there can exist in the lattice equivalent lattice points which can replace one another only by means of transformations involving rotations or reflections.

The Bravais lattice can be constructed by choosing one of the points of the crystal lattice and performing all possible translations. Choosing as origin another point of the lattice (not contained in the first Bravais lattice) we would obtain a Bravais lattice displaced relative to the first one. Hence it is clear that a crystal lattice is, in general, several Bravais lattices fitting inside one another; each one corresponds to a definite kind of atom and a definite configuration and all of these lattices, considered as sets of points, i.e. purely geometrically, are completely identical.

We now return to the unit cells. Corresponding to the arbitrary nature of the choice of the basic lattice vectors, the choice of unit cell is also not unique. The unit cell can be constructed from any set of basic lattice vectors.

The cells obtained in this way have different shapes but their volume is always the same. This is most easily seen in the following way. It is clear from the above that each unit cell contains one lattice point of each of the Bravais lattices which can be constructed in the given crystal. Hence the number of elementary cells in the given volume is always equal to the number of atoms of some definite kind and configuration, i.e. is independent of the choice of the cell. Hence also the volume of each cell is independent of the choice of cell and is equal to the total volume divided by the number of cells.

§129. Crystalline systems

We shall now study all the possible types of symmetry of the Bravais lattice.

As a preliminary we shall prove a general theorem dealing with the symmetry of crystal lattices with respect to rotations. Let us discover what axes of symmetry a crystal can have. Let A (Fig. 55) be one of the points of the

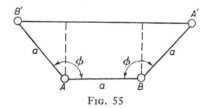

Fig. 55

Bravais lattice, through which an axis of symmetry passes (perpendicular to the plane of the figure). If B is another point of the lattice, separated by one lattice vector then another, identical, axis of symmetry must pass through B. Now let us carry out a rotation through an angle $\phi = 2\pi/n$ (n is the order of the axis) about the axis through A. Then the point B, and together with it the axis through B will take up the position B'. Similarly a rotation about B transfers A to A'. According to the conditions of their construction both A and B belong to the same Bravais lattice and hence can replace each other by a parallel displacement. Hence the distance $A'B'$ must also be a translational period of the lattice. If a is the shortest period in the given direction, then the distance $A'B'$ must, therefore, be equal to ap where p is an integer. From the figure we see that this leads to the equation

$$a + 2a \sin\left(\phi - \frac{\pi}{2}\right) = a - 2a \cos \phi = ap$$

or

$$\cos \phi = \frac{1-p}{2}$$

Since $|\cos \phi| \leqslant 1$, p can hence be equal to 3, 2, 1, 0 or -1. These values thus lead to $\phi = 2\pi/n$ with $n = 2, 3, 4, 6$ or 1. Thus a crystal lattice can have only 2, 3, 4 and six-fold axes of symmetry.

We shall now study the possible types of symmetry of a Bravais lattice with respect to rotation and reflections. These types of symmetry are called *crystal systems*. Each one represents a definite set of axes and planes of symmetry, i.e. is one of what are called the point groups.†

It can easily be seen that each point of a Bravais lattice is also one of its centres of symmetry. Indeed, to each atom of the Bravais lattice corresponds another atom, collinear with the given point and the first atom and such that the two atoms are equidistant from the lattice point. If the centre of symmetry is the only symmetry element (apart from translations) of the Bravais lattice, then we have what is called

1. The Triclinic system. This system, the least symmetrical of all, corresponds, to the point group C_i. The points of a triclinic Bravais lattice are situated at the vertices of corresponding parallelepipeds with edges of

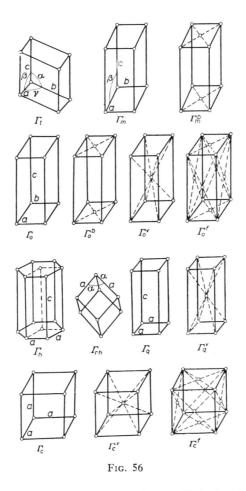

Fig. 56

---

† For further information about point groups see *Quantum Mechanics*, §90.

arbitrary length and at arbitrary angle to one another; one such parallelepiped is shown in Fig. 56.

The Bravais lattices are usually denoted by special symbols; the lattice of the triclinic system is represented by Γ_t.

2. The Monoclinic system is the next in order of symmetry. Its symmetry elements are a two-fold axis and the plane perpendicular to it, i.e. this system represents the point group C_{2h}. This is the symmetry of a right parallelepiped with an arbitrary base. The Bravais lattice of this system can be constructed by two methods. In the first case, known as the simple monoclinic Bravais lattice (Γ_m) the points of the lattice are situated at the vertices of right parallelepipeds with an arbitrary base. In the second case, the base-centred lattice ($\Gamma_m{}^b$) the points of the lattice are not only the vertices, but also the centres of the two opposite rectangular faces of the parallelepiped.

3. The Orthorhombic system corresponds to the point group D_{2h}. This is the symmetry of a rectangular parallelepiped with edges of arbitrary lengths. Orthorhombic symmetry involves four types of Bravais lattice. For the simple orthorhombic lattice (Γ_0) the points of the lattice are situated at the vertices of rectangular parallelepipeds with edges of arbitrary length. In the base centred lattice ($\Gamma_0{}^b$) the lattice points include also the centres of a pair of opposite faces of each parallelepiped. For the body-centred lattice ($\Gamma_0{}^v$) the lattice points are the vertices and the centres of the parallelepipeds. Finally, for the face-centred lattice ($\Gamma_0{}^f$) the lattice points are not only the vertices of the parallelepipeds but also the centres of all the faces.

4. The Tetragonal (or quadratic) system represents the point group D_{4h}; this is the symmetry of a right square prism. The Bravais lattice of this system can be constructed in two ways; namely the simple and body-centred tetragonal Bravais lattices (denoted by Γ_q and $\Gamma_q{}^v$ respectively) with lattice points at the vertices and at the vertices and the centres of right square prisms.

5. The Rhombohedral (or trigonal) system corresponds to the point group D_{3d}; this has the symmetry of a rhombohedron (the figure obtained by stretching or compressing a cube along a solid diagonal). In the only Bravais lattice possible for this system (Γ_{rh}) the lattice points are situated at the vertices of rhombohedra.

6. The Hexagonal system corresponds to the point group D_{6h}; the symmetry is that of a regular hexagonal prism. The Bravais lattice (Γ_h) of such a system can only be built up in one way—its lattice points are situated at the vertices of regular hexagonal prisms and at the centres of their hexagonal bases. It is useful to note the following difference between the rhombohedral and hexagonal Bravais lattices. In both cases the points of the lattice are situated in planes perpendicular to an axis of symmetry of order 6 (or 3) in such a way that they form a net of equilateral triangles. But for the hexagonal lattice, in successive planes of this sort (along the C_6 axis) the lattice points are situated directly above one another (in Fig. 57 the planes are shown in projection). For the rhombohedral lattice, the lattice points in each

plane are situated above the centres of the triangles formed by the lattice points in the previous plane (circles and crosses in Fig. 57).

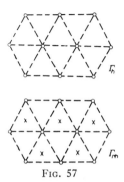

FIG. 57

7.   The Cubic system corresponds to the point group O_h; this has the symmetry of a cube. To this system belong three types of Bravais lattice: the simple cubic (Γ_c), body-centred (Γ_c^v) and face-centred (Γ_c^f).

In the sequence of systems triclinic, monoclinic, orthorhombic, tetragonal, and cubic, each has greater symmetry than all the preceding ones. In other words, each successive one contains all the symmetry elements contained in the preceding one. The rhombohedral system has, in this sense, greater symmetry than the monoclinic and at the same time less symmetry than the cubic and hexagonal systems; its symmetry elements are contained in both. The most symmetrical systems are those latter two.

Note also the following fact. At first glance it would seem that other types of Bravais lattice could exist besides the fourteen we have enumerated. Thus, if we add to a tetragonal lattice further lattice points at the centres of the opposite square bases of the prism, then the lattice will still have tetragonal symmetry. It can easily be seen, however, that we shall not get a new Bravais lattice. For if we connect the lattice points of such a lattice in

FIG. 58

the way shown in Fig. 58 (dotted lines), we see that the new lattice will be a simple tetragonal one as before. It can easily be seen that the same happens also in all other similar cases.

The parallelepipeds of the Bravais lattices shown in Fig. 56 possess all the symmetry elements of the system to which they belong. It must be borne in mind, however, that except for the simple Bravais lattices, these parallelepipeds are not the unit cells; the lattice vectors from which they are constructed are not basic ones. As basic lattice vectors in a face-centred Bravais lattice one can take the vectors from one of the vertices of the parallelepiped to the centres of the faces; in the body-centred case from a vertex to the centres of the parallelepipeds, etc. Fig. 59 shows the unit cells for the cubic

 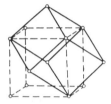

FIG. 59

lattices Γ_c^f and Γ_c^v; these cells are rhombohedra and themselves by no means have all the symmetry elements of the cubic system.

To identify a triclinic Bravais lattice completely, it is necessary to specify six quantities: the lengths of the edges of its parallelepipeds and the angles between them. In the monoclinic system four quantities are sufficient, since two of the angles between the edges are always right angles, etc. Similarly, it is easy to show that the Bravais lattices of the various systems are determined by the following numbers of quantities (lengths of the edges of the parallelepipeds or the angles between them):

Triclinic 6	Rhombohedral . . . 2
Monoclinic . . . 4	Hexagonal 2
Orthorhombic . . . 3	Cubic 1
Tetragonal 2	

§130. Crystal classes

For the whole range of phenomena which we can call macroscopic, a crystal behaves as a homogeneous continuous substance. The macroscopic properties of the crystal depend only on direction. Thus the behaviour of light passing through a crystal depends only on the direction of the light ray; the thermal expansion of a crystal will be different, in general, in different directions; the elastic deformation of a crystal under the influence of external forces also depends on direction, etc.

On the other hand, the symmetry of the crystal leads to certain directions in it being equivalent. All macroscopic properties of the crystal will be exactly the same along these equivalent directions. We can say, therefore, that the macroscopic properties of a crystal will be determined by the symmetry of directions in it. If, for example, the crystal has a centre of symmetry, then any direction in it is equivalent to the opposite direction.

The translational symmetry of the lattice does not produce any equivalence of directions, for parallel displacements do not change directions at all. Owing to this, as far as directional symmetry is concerned, there is no significant difference between a screw-axis and a simple axis of symmetry or between a plane of symmetry and a glide-reflection plane.

Thus the directional symmetry, and hence the macroscopic properties of the crystal, is determined by the set of its axes and planes of symmetry, counting the screw axes and glide reflection planes as simple axes and planes. Such sets of symmetry elements are called *crystal classes*.

As we already know, a real crystal may be considered as a set of several Bravais lattices of the same type fitted inside one another. Because of this superposition of Bravais lattices, the symmetry of a real crystal differs, in general, from the symmetry of the corresponding Bravais lattice.

In particular, the set of symmetry elements of the class of a given crystal can be different from the set of those of its system. It is evident that the addition of new lattice points to a Bravais lattice can lead only to the disappearance of some of its axes and planes of symmetry but not to the appearance of new ones. Hence the crystal class has fewer than or, at most, the same number of symmetry elements as the corresponding system, i.e. the set of axes and planes of symmetry of the Bravais lattice of the given crystal.

From what has been said above there follows a method of finding all classes belonging to a given system. To do this, it is necessary to find all the point groups containing some or all of the symmetry elements of the system. It may happen, however, that one of the point groups obtained in this way consists of symmetry elements which are contained not only in one, but in several systems. Thus, we have seen in the preceding section that all Bravais lattices have a centre of symmetry. Hence the point group C_i is contained in all the systems. Nevertheless, the distribution of crystal classes amongst the systems can be made unique from the physical point of view. That is, we allot each class to the least symmetrical of all the systems to which it belongs. Thus the class C_i must be allotted to the triclinic system which possesses no other symmetry element except an inversion centre. With this method of distributing the classes, a crystal having some Bravais lattice will never belong to a class which could be formed from a Bravais lattice of lower symmetry (with only one exception; see below).

The need for this condition to be fulfilled is physically obvious. Indeed it is physically highly improbable that the atoms of a crystal belonging to its Bravais lattice should be distributed more symmetrically than the symmetry of the crystal requires. Furthermore if such a configuration were to arise accidentally, then even a weak external effect (such as heating) would be sufficient to disturb this configuration which is unrelated to the symmetry of the crystal. For example, if a crystal belonging to a class which could occur for a tetragonal Bravais lattice were to have a cubic Bravais lattice, then an insignificant disturbance would be able to shorten or lengthen one of the edges of the cubic lattice, transforming it into a right square prism.

One can see, from this example, that an important part is played by the fact that a Bravais lattice of higher order can be transformed into a lattice of lower order by an arbitrarily small deformation. There is, however, one exception, for which such a transformation is impossible. Namely, a hexagonal Bravais lattice cannot be transformed into a rhombohedral lattice, which has lower symmetry, by means of any arbitrarily small deformation. Indeed, it can be seen from Fig. 57 that to transform a hexagonal lattice to a rhombohedral one it is necessary to displace the lattice points in alternate planes by a finite amount—from the vertices to the centres of the triangles. This leads to the result that all the classes of the rhombohedral system occur for hexagonal, as well as for rhombohedral Bravais lattices.†

In this way, to find the crystal classes, one must begin by finding the point groups of the least symmetrical system—the triclinic, and then going successively through the systems of greater symmetry, omitting those of their point groups, i.e. classes, which have already been included in the lower systems. It turns out that there exist only 32 classes. We give the list of these classes distributed over the systems:

System	Classes
Triclinic	C_1, C_i
Monoclinic	C_s, C_2, C_{2h}
Orthorhombic	C_{2v}, D_2, D_{2h}
Tetragonal	S_4, D_{2d}, C_4, C_{4h}, C_{4v}, D_4, D_{4h}
Rhombohedral	C_3, S_6, C_{3v}, D_3, D_{3d}
Hexagonal	C_{3h}, D_{3h}, C_6, C_{6h}, C_{6v}, D_6, D_{6h}
Cubic	T, T_h, T_d, O, O_h

In each of the rows of classes written above, the last is the most symmetrical and contains all the symmetry elements of the corresponding system. The classes whose symmetry coincides with the symmetry of their system are called *holohedral*. Classes which have half or one-quarter as many different symmetry transformations (rotations and reflections, including the identity transformation) as the holohedral classes are called *hemi-* and *tetartohedral* classes. Thus, in the cubic system the class O_h is holohedral, classes O, T_h, T_d are hemihedral, and class T is tetartohedral.

§131. Space groups

Having considered the symmetry of the Bravais lattices and the directional symmetry of crystals we can at last consider the complete actual symmetry of crystal lattices. We shall call this symmetry microscopic to distinguish it from the macroscopic symmetry of the crystals which we have studied in

---

† Crystals of the rhombohedral classes with hexagonal Bravais lattices are customarily referred to the rhombohedral system.

the last section. The microscopic symmetry determines those properties of a crystal which depend on the arrangement of atoms in its lattice (such as, for example, the scattering of X-rays by the crystal).

The set of these (real) symmetry elements of the crystal is called its *space group*. The lattice always has a definite translational symmetry and in addition it can have simple and screw axes of symmetry, axes of rotary reflection and simple and glide reflection planes of symmetry. The translational symmetry of the lattice is completely determined by its Bravais lattice since, by the very definition of the latter, the crystal lattice can have no translational periodicities except those of its Bravais lattice. Hence, to determine the space group of a crystal it is sufficient, besides specifying the Bravais lattice, to list the symmetry elements relating to rotations and reflections. The arrangement of these planes and axes of symmetry must also be specified, of course. Furthermore, it should be borne in mind that the translational symmetry of the crystal lattice implies that any axis or plane of symmetry which it possesses will be repeated an infinite number of times in positions separated by parallel displacements equal to the lattice vectors. Lastly, besides these axes and planes of symmetry which are separated by lattice vectors, the simultaneous existence of the translational symmetry and axes (planes) of symmetry leads to the appearance of new axes (planes) which cannot replace the original ones by a displacement through any lattice vector. For example, the existence of a plane of symmetry leads to the appearance not only of parallel planes separated by lattice vectors, but also of planes of symmetry bisecting these vectors. For it is easy to see that reflections in some plane followed by a displacement through a distance d perpendicular to the plane, is equivalent to a simple reflection in a plane parallel to the original one and a distance $d/2$ from it.

All the possible space groups are distributed amongst the crystal classes. That is, each space group belongs to the class which would have the same set of axes and planes of symmetry as the space group if one did not distinguish in the latter between simple and screw axes and between simple and glide reflection planes. There are, altogether, 230 space groups. They were first discovered by E. S. FEDOROV (1895). The space groups are distributed as follows:

Class	Number of groups	Class	Number of groups	Class	Number of groups	Class	Number of groups
C_1	1	S_4	2	S_6	2	C_{6v}	4
C_i	1	C_4	6	C_{3v}	6	D_6	6
C_s	4	C_{4h}	6	D_3	7	D_{6h}	4
C_2	3	D_{2d}	12	D_{3d}	6	T	5
C_{2h}	6	C_{4v}	12	C_{3h}	1	T_h	7
C_{2v}	22	D_4	10	C_6	6	T_d	6
D_2	9	D_{4h}	20	C_{6h}	2	O	8
D_{2h}	28	C_3	4	D_{3h}	4	O_h	10

We shall not give here a list of the symmetry elements of all the space groups, which would be very cumbersome. It can be found in special crystallographic books of reference.†

Amongst the space groups are some which differ only in the direction of rotation about their screw axes. There are altogether 11 such pairs of space groups.

§132. The reciprocal lattice

All the physical quantities which describe a crystal lattice have the same periodicity as the lattice itself. Examples of such quantities are the electromagnetic field set up in the lattice by the atoms composing it, the charge density due to the electrons of these atoms, the probability of an atom being at one or other of the points of the lattice, etc.

Let U be such a quantity. U is a function of the co-ordinates x, y, z of a point in the crystal or, as we shall write it, the radius vector $\mathbf{r}$. The function $U(\mathbf{r})$ must be periodic with the same periods as the lattice itself. This means that we must have

$$U(\mathbf{r}+n_1\mathbf{a}_1+n_2\mathbf{a}_2+n_3\mathbf{a}_3) = U(\mathbf{r}) \tag{132.1}$$

for arbitrary integral n_1, n_2, n_3 ($\mathbf{a}_1$, $\mathbf{a}_2$, $\mathbf{a}_3$ are the basic lattice vectors).

We expand the periodic function $U(\mathbf{r})$ as a triple Fourier series:

$$U = \sum_{\mathbf{b}} U_{\mathbf{b}} e^{2\pi i\mathbf{b}\cdot\mathbf{r}} \tag{132.2}$$

where the summation is taken over all possible values of the vector $\mathbf{b}$. These are determined by the condition that the function U expressed as the series (132.2) must satisfy the periodicity condition (132.1). This means that none of the exponential factors must change when $\mathbf{r}$ is replaced by $\mathbf{r}+\mathbf{a}$ where $\mathbf{a}$ is any lattice vector. For this it is necessary that the scalar product $\mathbf{a}\cdot\mathbf{b}$ should always be an integer. Choosing $\mathbf{a}_1$, $\mathbf{a}_2$, $\mathbf{a}_3$ in turn as $\mathbf{a}$, we must, therefore, have

$$\mathbf{a}_1\cdot\mathbf{b} = p_1, \qquad \mathbf{a}_2\cdot\mathbf{b} = p_2, \qquad \mathbf{a}_3\cdot\mathbf{b} = p_3$$

where p_1, p_2, p_3 are positive or negative integers (or zero). The solution of these three equations has the form

$$\mathbf{b} = p_1\mathbf{b}_1+p_2\mathbf{b}_2+p_3\mathbf{b}_3 \tag{132.3}$$

where the vectors $\mathbf{b}_i$ are defined in terms of the $\mathbf{a}_i$ by

$$\mathbf{b}_1 = \frac{1}{v}(\mathbf{a}_2\times\mathbf{a}_3), \qquad \mathbf{b}_2 = \frac{1}{v}(\mathbf{a}_3\times\mathbf{a}_1), \qquad \mathbf{b}_3 = \frac{1}{v}(\mathbf{a}_1\times\mathbf{a}_2),$$

$$v = \mathbf{a}_1\cdot(\mathbf{a}_2\times\mathbf{a}_3). \tag{132.4}$$

---

† A complete description of the space groups with an indication of the equivalent points can be found in the *International Tables for the Determination of Crystal Structure*, 1935.

In this way we have determined the possible values of **b**. The summation in (132.2) is taken over all integral values of p_1, p_2, p_3.

Geometrically, the product $v = \mathbf{a}_1 \cdot (\mathbf{a}_2 \times \mathbf{a}_3)$ represents, as is well known, the volume of the parallelepiped constructed from the vectors $\mathbf{a}_1$, $\mathbf{a}_2$, $\mathbf{a}_3$, i.e. the volume of the unit cell and the products $\mathbf{a}_1 \times \mathbf{a}_2$, etc. represent the areas of the three faces of this cell. The vectors have, therefore, the dimensions of reciprocal length and are equal in value to the reciprocals of the heights of the parallelepiped constructed from the vectors $\mathbf{a}_1$, $\mathbf{a}_2$, $\mathbf{a}_3$.

From (132.4) we can see that the $\mathbf{b}_i$ and the $\mathbf{a}_i$ satisfy the relations

$$\mathbf{a}_i \cdot \mathbf{b}_k = \begin{cases} 0 \text{ for } i \neq k, \\ 1 \text{ for } i = k. \end{cases} \tag{132.5}$$

This means that the vector $\mathbf{b}_1$ is perpendicular to $\mathbf{a}_2$ and $\mathbf{a}_3$ and similarly for $\mathbf{b}_2$, $\mathbf{b}_3$.

After determining the vectors $\mathbf{b}_i$, we can formally construct a lattice with basic vectors $\mathbf{b}_1$, $\mathbf{b}_2$, $\mathbf{b}_3$. The lattice constructed in this way is called the *reciprocal* lattice, and the vectors $\mathbf{b}_1$, $\mathbf{b}_2$, $\mathbf{b}_3$ are called the (basic) periods of the reciprocal lattice.

It is obvious that the unit cell of the lattice reciprocal to a triclinic Bravais lattice is also an arbitrary parallelepiped. Similarly the reciprocal lattices of simple Bravais lattices of other systems are also simple lattices of the same system; for example, the reciprocal lattice of a simple cubic Bravais lattice also has a simple cubic cell. It is easy to see, further, with the aid of a simple construction, that the reciprocal lattice of a face-centred Bravais lattice (orthorhombic, tetragonal, or cubic) is a body-centred lattice of the same system. Conversely body-centred Bravais lattices have reciprocal lattices with face-centred cells. Finally, base-centred lattices have reciprocal lattices which also have base-centred cells.

Let us calculate the "volume" of a unit cell of the reciprocal lattice. This will be

$$v' = \mathbf{b}_1 \cdot (\mathbf{b}_2 \times \mathbf{b}_3)$$

Substituting from (132.4), we find

$$v' = \frac{1}{v^3}\{(\mathbf{a}_1 \times \mathbf{a}_2) \cdot [(\mathbf{a}_3 \times \mathbf{a}_1) \times (\mathbf{a}_1 \times \mathbf{a}_2)]\} = \frac{1}{v^3}[\mathbf{a}_2 \cdot (\mathbf{a}_3 \times \mathbf{a}_1)][\mathbf{a}_3 \cdot (\mathbf{a}_1 \times \mathbf{a}_2)]$$

or, finally

$$v' = \frac{1}{v}. \tag{132.6}$$

Thus the volume of a unit cell of the reciprocal lattice is equal to the reciprocal of the volume of a unit cell of the original lattice.

As is well known, an equation of the type

$$\mathbf{b} \cdot \mathbf{r} = \text{const}$$

where **b** is a constant vector, describes a plane perpendicular to the vector

b and at a distance $\dfrac{\text{const}}{b}$ from the origin. Let us choose the origin to be one of the points of the Bravais lattice, and let $\mathbf{b} = p_1\mathbf{b}_1 + p_2\mathbf{b}_2 + p_3\mathbf{b}_3$ be some vector of the reciprocal lattice (p_1, p_2, p_3 are integers). Writing **r** also in the form $\mathbf{r} = n_1\mathbf{a}_1 + n_2\mathbf{a}_2 + n_3\mathbf{a}_3$, we obtain an equation of the plane in the form:

$$\mathbf{b}.\mathbf{p} = n_1 p_1 + n_2 p_2 + n_3 p_3 \equiv m. \tag{132.7}$$

If this equation represents a plane filled with an infinite number of Bravais lattice points (such planes are called *crystal planes*) it must be satisfied by the set of integers n_1, n_2, n_3. For this to be so, the constant m must also be an integer. For given p_1, p_2, p_3, i.e. for a given **b**, as the constant takes different integral values eq. (132.7) thus determines an infinite number of crystal planes which are all parallel to one another.

The numbers p_1, p_2, p_3 may always be taken to be relatively prime, i.e. having no common factor other than unity. If there were such a factor, then one could divide it into both sides of the equation, and get an equation of the same type. The numbers p_1, p_2, p_3 are called the *Miller indices* of the given family of crystal planes and are written (p_1, p_2, p_3).

The plane (132.7) crosses the co-ordinate axes (taken along the basic lattice vectors $\mathbf{a}_1$, $\mathbf{a}_2$, $\mathbf{a}_3$) at the points ma_1/p_1, ma_2/p_2, ma_3/p_3. The lengths of the intercepts on the axes (measured in units of a_1, a_2, a_3 respectively) are in the ratio $1/p_1 : 1/p_2 : 1/p_3$, i.e. these lengths are in ratios inversely proportional to the Miller indices. Thus the Miller indices of planes parallel to the co-ordinate planes are (100) (010) (001), for the three co-ordinate planes respectively. The planes parallel to the diagonal plane of the basic parallelepiped of the lattice have indices (111), etc.

It is easy to determine the distance between consecutive planes of the same family. The distance from the origin to the plane (132.7) is m/b where b is the "length" of the given reciprocal lattice vector. For the next plane, this distance is $(m+1)/b$ and the distance d between them is $(m+1)/b - m/b$, i.e.

$$d = \frac{1}{b}. \tag{132.8}$$

It is equal to the reciprocal of the magnitude of the vector **b**.

§133. Other types of symmetry of macroscopic bodies

For the "density function" $\rho(x, y, z)$ describing the configuration of atoms in the lattice (§125) one can take the mean electron density due to all the atoms (so that $e\rho$ will be the mean density of electric charge). But moving electrons can create not only a mean charge density, but also a mean current density $\mathbf{j}(x, y, z)$. In this case the symmetry of the crystal is determined not only by the symmetry of $\rho(x, y, z)$ but also by the symmetry of the vector function $\mathbf{j}(x, y, z)$.

Because of the invariance of the equations of motion under time reversal, the formal substitution of $-t$ for t in the equations of any thermodynamic equilibrium state must lead to a state which is also one of the possible equilibrium states. There exist then two possibilities: the states which are obtained from each other by changing t to $-t$ either coincide, or do not coincide.

The change of t into $-t$ does not change the magnitude of the currents $\mathbf{j}$, but reverses their sign. If, as a result of this transformation, the state of the body remains unchanged this means that $\mathbf{j} = -\mathbf{j}$, i.e. that $\mathbf{j} = 0$. Thus there is reason to expect the existence of bodies for which the function $\mathbf{j}$ is exactly zero. For such bodies the mean magnetic moment at any point, which depends on the current distribution, will also vanish exactly. This category includes, in fact, most bodies (diamagnetic and paramagnetic bodies).

We now turn to crystals for which the substitution of $-t$ for t changes their state, and for which therefore $\mathbf{j} \neq 0$.

There cannot be any total current (in an equilibrium state of the body) i.e. the integral $\int \mathbf{j}\, dV$ taken over the volume of a unit cell must always vanish. If this were not so, this current would set up a macroscopic magnetic field and the crystal would possess magnetic energy (per unit volume) increasing rapidly as the size of the body increased, which is energetically extremely uneconomic.

But the currents $\mathbf{j}$ can produce a non-zero macroscopic magnetic moment, i.e. the integral $\int \mathbf{r} \times \mathbf{j}\, dV$ (again taken over the volume of an elementary cell) may be non-zero. Correspondingly, one can distinguish two types of substance for which $\mathbf{j} \neq 0$: substances with a non-zero macroscopic magnetic moment, and substances where there is no such moment. The first are ferromagnetic, and the second antiferromagnetic bodies.[†] Both these types of bodies may be said to have "magnetic structure", as distinct from the bodies with $\mathbf{j} = 0$, which possess no magnetic structure.

The symmetry of the distribution of the current $\mathbf{j}$ can be imagined as the symmetry of the distribution and orientations of the magnetic moments of the separate atoms of the crystal. If $\mathbf{j} = 0$, then it means that the orientation of these moments changes with time in a quite irregular way so that all their mean values turn out to be zero. In ferromagnetic bodies the moments are predominantly oriented in one direction creating a non-zero total moment in each unit cell. Lastly, for an antiferromagnetic body the mean values of the atomic moments are non-zero, i.e. regularly oriented, but in such a way that they are mutually compensated within each unit cell.

The question arises of the possible types (groups) of symmetry of the current distribution $\mathbf{j}(x, y, z)$. This symmetry is composed, first of all, of the usual elements—rotations, reflections and translations, corresponding to which, amongst the possible symmetry groups, there are in any case the

---

† The idea of the antiferromagnetic phase as distinct from the paramagnetic one and the necessary existence of a transition point between them was first put forward by L. LANDAU (1933). Even prior to this, the idea of magnetic sublattices was suggested by L. NÉEL.

230 usual space groups. But this, however, by no means exhausts the list of all the available groups.

It was already pointed out that the transformation $t \to -t$ changes the sign of the vector **j**. In connection with this there arises the question of the symmetry of the current distribution with respect to a transformation reversing the directions of all the currents; let us denote this new symmetry element by R. If the current distribution allows this symmetry operation by itself then it means that $\mathbf{j} = -\mathbf{j}$, i.e. $\mathbf{j} = 0$ and the currents are entirely absent. A non-zero $\mathbf{j}(x, y, z)$ can, however, possess symmetry with respect to different combinations of the transformation R with other symmetry elements: rotations, reflections or translations. In this way the problem of determining the possible types of symmetry of a current distribution is the construction of all possible groups containing, besides the usual transformations, the transformations obtained by combining the latter with the transformation R. The number of the "magnetic space groups" obtained in this way is 1651.†

If the symmetry of the current distribution is given then this will also determine the symmetry of the configuration of particles in the given crystal (the symmetry of the function ρ): it will, in practice, be determined by the space group which could be obtained from the **j** symmetry by formally regarding the transformation R as the identity (as it is for the function ρ).

The knowledge of the complete symmetry group of the function $\mathbf{j}(x, y, z)$ is, however, not required if we are interested only in the macroscopic properties of the body, which depend only on the direction within the crystal. The corresponding symmetry groups, or "magnetic symmetry classes" are in the same relation to the magnetic space groups as the ordinary crystal classes to the ordinary space groups. They are point symmetry groups which consist of rotations, reflections and their combinations with the element R.

They include, in the first place, the 32 ordinary classes, supplemented by the element R, and the same 32 classes without R. The first are, in particular, the macroscopic symmetry groups for all bodies without magnetic structure. But they may also occur for bodies with magnetic structure. This will happen if the magnetic space group of such a body contains the element R not by itself, but only in combination with translations.

Further there exist 58 classes in which the element R occurs only in combination with rotations and reflections.‡ If in each of these one replaces the operation R by the identity it becomes one of the ordinary crystal classes.

The knowledge of the magnetic crystal class determines all the macroscopic magnetic properties of a body. The most important of these is the presence or absence of a macroscopic magnetic moment. The latter is a vector

---

† The derivation of these groups is given by N. V. BELOV, N. N. NERONOVA, T. S. SMIRNOVA, *Trans. Inst. Crystallogr.* (1955) **II**, 33.

‡ These groups are isomorphic with the symmetry group of polyhedra with two-coloured faces, derived by A. V. SHUBNIKOV. Their direct derivation as magnetic symmetry groups is given by B. TAVGER and V. ZAITSEV, *J. Exper. Theor. Phys. USSR.* **30**, 564, 1956.

quantity which under rotation and reflections behaves like an axial vector (the vector product of two polar vectors) and under the transformation R changes sign. A crystal will possess a macroscopic magnetic moment if there exists at least one direction such that a vector in that direction with the stated properties remains invariant under all the transformations of the given magnetic crystal class.

Lastly let us mention another property of matter which has nothing to do with the above but has a feature common to the symmetry properties, that it is qualitative and can hence appear or disappear only all at once and not gradually.

We refer to certain properties of the density matrix of the atoms of the body in the co-ordinate representation. This matrix $\rho(\mathbf{r}', \mathbf{r})$ is defined as the integral

$$\rho(\mathbf{r}', \mathbf{r}) = \int \Psi^*(\mathbf{r}', q)\Psi(\mathbf{r}, q)\, dq$$

where $\Psi(\mathbf{r}, q)$ is the wave function of the body, $\mathbf{r}$ represents the radius vector of one particle and q the set of co-ordinates of all the other particles; we integrate with respect to the latter.† For an isotropic body (a liquid) the density matrix depends only on the relative co-ordinates $|\mathbf{r}' - \mathbf{r}|$. For all normal liquids the value of $\rho(\mathbf{r}', \mathbf{r})$ tends to zero as $\mathbf{r}' - \mathbf{r}$ increases indefinitely. But for a superfluid liquid (Helium II; see §§66, 67) one can, apparently, assert that this limit is non-zero. This qualitative property is probably characteristic of this type of liquid.

The Fourier components of the density matrix, i.e. the integrals of the type

$$\int \rho(\mathbf{r}', \mathbf{r})e^{i\mathbf{f} \cdot (\mathbf{r}' - \mathbf{r})}\, d^3(\mathbf{r}' - \mathbf{r}) \qquad (133.1)$$

coincide, to within a constant factor, with the expressions

$$\int | \int \Psi(\mathbf{r}, q)e^{i\mathbf{f} \cdot \mathbf{r}}\, dV|^2\, dq,$$

i.e. they determine the probability distribution of different values of the momentum $\mathbf{p} = \hbar\mathbf{f}$. If $\rho(\mathbf{r}', \mathbf{r}) \to 0$ as $|\mathbf{r}' - \mathbf{r}| \to \infty$, then the probability density (in $\mathbf{p}$-space) remains finite as $\mathbf{p} \to 0$. But if $\rho(\mathbf{r}', \mathbf{r})$ has a finite value ρ_∞ at infinity, then the value of the integral (133.1) tends to infinity as $\mathbf{p} \to 0$ (the integral equals $2\pi^3\rho_\infty\, \delta(\mathbf{f})$) which corresponds to a finite probability that the particle has zero momentum (note that ρ_∞, determining this probability, must be positive). Thus in a superfluid liquid, unlike ordinary liquids, a finite number of particles must have zero momentum.‡

---

† See *Quantum Mechanics*, §12.

‡ To avoid misunderstanding it must be emphasised that this set of particles can in no way be identified with the "superfluid part" of the liquid (§67). Apart from the fact that there are no grounds for such an identification, the fallacy in this can be seen, for example, from the fact that at absolute zero the whole of the liquid becomes superfluid, but by no means all the particles will have zero momentum.

CHAPTER XIV

SECOND-ORDER PHASE TRANSITIONS

§134. Second-order phase transitions

It was pointed out in §79 that transitions between phases with different symmetries (crystal and liquid, different crystal modifications) cannot occur continuously, as can those between a liquid and a gas. In each state the body has either one symmetry or the other, and hence one can always say to which of the two phases it belongs.

Transitions between different crystal modifications usually take place by means of phase transitions in which a discontinuous reconstruction of the lattice occurs, and the state of the body undergoes a discontinuous change. However, besides such discontinuous transitions another type of transition is also possible, involving a change of symmetry.

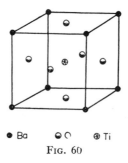

● Ba   ◒ O   ⊕ Ti

Fig. 60

To illustrate the nature of such transitions let us consider an actual example. At high temperatures $BaTiO_3$ has a cubic lattice with cells as shown in Fig. 60 (the Ba atoms at the corners, the O atoms at the face centres, and the Ti atoms at the body centres of the cells). As the temperature falls, at some points the Ti and O atoms begin to shift relative to the Ba atoms along one of the edges of the cube. It is clear that as soon as this begins the lattice symmetry immediately changes, becoming tetragonal instead of cubic.

This example is typical, as regards the absence of any discontinuous change in the state of the body. The arrangement of the atoms in the crystal† changes continuously. However, even an arbitrarily small displacement of the atoms from their initial symmetrical positions, is sufficient to produce an abrupt change in the symmetry of the lattice. A transition which occurs

---

† To simplify the discussion we refer conventionally to the configuration of the atoms and the symmetry of this configuration as if the atoms were at rest. Strictly speaking, one ought to use the probability distribution for the different positions of the atoms and talk about the symmetry of this distribution (§125).

in this way, between two crystal modifications, is called a *second-order phase transition*, in contrast to ordinary phase transitions which in this connection are called first-order transitions.†

Thus, a second-order phase transition is continuous, in the sense that the state of the body changes continuously. However, the symmetry undergoes a sudden change at the transition point, and at any moment one can say to which of the two phases the body belongs. But whereas, at a first-order phase transition point bodies in two different states are in equilibrium, at a second-order phase transition point the states of the two phases are identical.

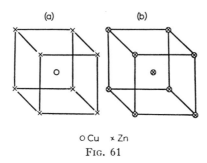

o Cu   × Zn
Fig. 61

Besides the cases when the change in the symmetry of the body is due to a displacement of the atoms (as in the above example), a change of symmetry in a second-order phase transition may also be connected with a change in the ordering of the crystal. As was already pointed out in §61, the concept of ordering arises when the number of points of the lattice at which atoms of a given kind may be situated is greater than the number of these atoms. Let us call the points at which atoms of a given kind are situated when the crystal is completely ordered the "right" ones as opposed to the "wrong" ones into which some of the atoms go when the crystal becomes "disordered". In many of the cases which will concern us in connection with second-order phase transitions it happens that the "right" and "wrong" lattice points are geometrically indistinguishable and only differ in the different probabilities of occupation by an atom of a given kind.‡

If now these probabilities become equal for the "right" and "wrong" points (being, of course, less than unity), then all these points become equivalent and hence new symmetry elements will occur, i.e. the lattice symmetry will increase. Such a crystal is called "disordered".

We shall illustrate the above by one example. The completely ordered alloy CuZn has a cubic lattice with the Zn atoms, say, at the corners and the Cu atoms at the centres of the cubic cells (Fig. 61a; the Bravais lattice is a simple cubic one). When "disordering" takes place (due to an increase in temperature) the Cu and Zn atoms change place, i.e. at all the lattice points

---

† Second-order phase transitions are also called *Curie points* or λ-*points*.

‡ Note that, in this case, we can always assume that the probability of an atom being at its "right" lattice point is larger than at a "wrong" point, simply because otherwise we should call the "wrong" points "right" and *vice versa*.

there is a non-zero probability for the presence of each kind of atom. As long as the Cu (or Zn) atoms are not equally likely to be at the corners or at the centres (incompletely ordered crystal), these points remain non-equivalent and the lattice symmetry remains as before. But as soon as these probabilities become equal all the lattice points become equivalent and the symmetry of the crystal increases: there appears a new lattice vector (from the corner to the centre of the cell) and the crystal acquires a body-centred cubic Bravais lattice (Fig. 61b).

At every stage of ordering one can introduce some quantitative characteristic η, the "degree of ordering" defining it so that it will vanish for a disordered phase while it will have different non-zero positive or negative values for crystals with various degrees of ordering. Thus for the given example of the alloy CuZn, it may be defined as

$$\eta = \frac{w_{Cu} - w_{Zn}}{w_{Cu} + w_{Zn}},$$

where w_{Cu} and w_{Zn} are the probabilities of Cu and Zn atoms being at some particular lattice point.

We must emphasise yet again the essential point that the symmetry of the crystal changes (increases) only at the moment when η becomes exactly zero; arbitrarily small, but non-zero degrees of ordering already result in the same symmetry as that of the completely ordered crystal. If, as the temperature rises, the degree of ordering vanishes by a discontinuous jump from some finite value, then the transition from the ordered to the disordered crystal will be a first-order phase transition. If the degree of ordering vanishes continuously, without a discontinuous jump, then we have a second-order phase transition.†

Although we have discussed so far only transitions between different crystal modifications, it must be borne in mind that second-order phase transitions need not be connected just with changes of the symmetry of the configuration of the atoms in the lattice. Second-order phase transitions can also occur between two phases which differ in some other symmetry property. Examples of these are the Curie points of ferromagnetic substances (points at which they change from ferromagnetic to paramagnetic); in this case we are dealing

---

† There are also possible, in principle, cases when the appearance of ordering does not lead to a change in the crystal symmetry. For such a case a second-order phase transition is impossible. Even if the transition from the ordered to the disordered crystal were to take place continuously, there would be no discontinuity in the specific heat (see below) at all. A first-order phase transition is, of course, possible in this case also.

In the literature on this subject one sometimes finds references to a connection between second-order phase transitions and the appearance of rotating molecules (or radicals) in the crystal. Such a point of view is erroneous since at a second-order phase transition point the state of the body must change continuously, and hence a sudden change in the type of motion cannot occur. If one deals with the phase transitions connected with the rotation of molecules in a crystal, then the difference between the two phases must consist in the fact that in the more symmetrical phase, the probabilities of different orientations of the molecules are the same, while for the less symmetrical one they are different.

with a change in the magnetic symmetry of the body (see §133). The transition of a metal to a superconducting state (in the absence of a magnetic field) and that of liquid helium to a superfluid state (helium I into helium II) are also second-order phase transitions. In both of these cases the state of the body changes continuously, but at the transition point the body acquires qualitatively new properties.

Since the states of the two phases are identical at a second-order transition point, it is clear that the symmetry of the body at the actual transition point must include all the symmetry elements of both phases. It will be shown below that the transition point itself has the same symmetry as one of the phases. Thus a change in the symmetry of a body by means of a second-order phase transition has the following basic general property: the symmetry of one of the phases is higher than that of the other.† We must stress that for a first order phase transition, there are no restrictions on the change in the symmetry of the body and the symmetries of the two phases may have nothing in common.

In the great majority of known cases of a second-order phase transition the more symmetrical phase corresponds to higher temperatures and the less symmetrical to lower temperatures. In particular, a second-order transition from an ordered to a disordered state is always accompanied by a rise in temperature. This rule, however, is not a thermodynamic law and hence admits of exceptions.‡

The absence of any discontinuity of state in a second-order phase transition has the result that functions of the thermodynamic state of the body (its entropy, energy, volume, etc.) remain continuous as the transition point is passed. Hence, in particular, a second-order phase transition, unlike a first order one, is not associated with any latent heat. We shall see below, however, that the derivatives of these thermodynamic quantities (i.e. the specific heat, coefficient of thermal expansion, compressibility, etc.), are discontinuous at a second-order phase transition point.

One would expect that from a mathematical point of view a second-order phase transition point should represent some singular point of its thermodynamic quantities, in particular of the thermodynamic potential (the nature of this singularity is unknown at present). To understand this, remember (see §79) that a first-order phase transition point is not a singular point at all: it is a point at which the thermodynamic potentials of the two phases, $\Phi_1(P, T)$ and $\Phi_2(P, T)$ are equal but it is an ordinary point for each of the functions Φ_1 and Φ_2 and each, on either side of the transition point, corresponds to some equilibrium (though possibly metastable) state of the

---

† Remember that a higher symmetry is one which includes all the symmetry elements (rotations, reflections and translations) of a lower symmetry and some extra elements as well.

It must be borne in mind that the expressed condition is a necessary, but by no means sufficient, condition for a second-order phase transition to be possible; the allowable changes of symmetry for such a transition also obey more stringent restrictions (see §§136,137).

‡ Such is the lower Curie point of Seignette salt, below which the crystal belongs to the orthorhombic, and above which to the monoclinic system.

body. But for a second-order phase transition, if one formally considers the thermodynamic potential of either phase beyond the transition point, it corresponds to no equilibrium state, i.e. to no minimum of Φ (we shall see in the next section that the thermodynamic potential of the more symmetrical phase beyond the transition point would even correspond to a maximum).

With this latter fact is connected the impossibility of superheating or supercooling in second-order phase transitions (both are possible for usual phase transitions). Neither of the phases in this case can exist at all beyond the transition point (apart, of course, from the time taken to establish the equilibrium configuration of the atoms, which may be considerable for solid crystals).

§135. The discontinuity in the specific heat

For a mathematical description of second-order phase transitions† we introduce some quantity η which determines the extent to which the atomic configuration in the less symmetrical phase departs from the configuration in the more symmetrical phase. The latter corresponds to $\eta = 0$ while in the less symmetric phase η has a non-zero positive or negative value. Thus for transitions connected with a change of ordering of the crystal, η can be taken as the degree of ordering; for transitions connected with a displacement of the atoms (as for $BaTiO_3$) η can mean the degree of displacement etc.

For the sake of brevity, we shall refer below to the more symmetrical phase simply as the symmetrical one, and the less symmetrical phase as the unsymmetrical one.

Considering the thermodynamic quantities of the crystal for a given deviation from the symmetrical state (i.e. for given η), we may express the thermodynamic potential Φ as a function of P, T and η. However, it should be borne in mind that the pressure and temperature may be given arbitrary values, but the actual value of η must be subsequently determined from the thermal equilibrium conditions, i.e. from the condition that Φ should be a minimum (for the given P and T).

The continuity of the change of state for a second-order phase transition is expressed mathematically by the fact that near a transition point η can take arbitrarily small values. Considering now the neighbourhood of a transition point, we expand $\Phi(P, T, \eta)$ as a series in powers of η;

$$\Phi(P, T, \eta) = \Phi_0 + \alpha\eta + A\eta^2 + B\eta^3 + C\eta^4 + ..., \tag{135.1}$$

where α, A, B, C are functions of P and T.

It must be emphasised, however, that the validity of this expansion is not at all obvious *a priori*. Furthermore, since, as was already pointed out,

---

† The theory discussed in this section and the next are due to L. Landau (1937).

the second-order transition point must be some singular point of the thermodynamic potential, there is every reason to suppose that such an expansion
cannot be carried out up to terms of arbitrary order and that the expansion
coefficients may have singularities as functions of P and T. A complete
description of the nature of the behaviour of the thermodynamic potential
at the transition point is extremely difficult and it has not yet been done.
There are, however, grounds to suppose that its singularity is of higher order
than that of the terms of the expansion used in the following calculations.
This assumption is the basis of the theory developed below.†

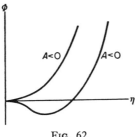

FIG. 62

One can show (see the next section) that if states with $\eta = 0$ and $\eta \neq 0$
have different symmetries (which we assume), then the first-order term in
the expansion (135.1) vanishes identically; $\alpha = 0$. As regards the coefficient
$A(P, T)$ of the second-order term, it is easy to see that it vanishes at the transition point itself. Indeed, for the symmetrical phase the minimum of Φ
must correspond to the value $\eta = 0$; this obviously requires $A > 0$. Conversely, on the other side of the transition point, in the unsymmetrical phase,
the equilibrium state (i.e. minimum of Φ) must correspond to non-zero
values of η; this is only possible for $A < 0$ (Fig. 62 shows the form of the
function $\Phi(\eta)$ for $A > 0$ and for $A < 0$). Being positive on one side of
the transition point and negative on the other, A must vanish at the point
itself.

$$A_c(P, T) = 0 \tag{135.2}$$

where the suffix c denotes the transition point.

But for the transition point itself to be a stable state, i.e. for Φ to be a
minimum there as a function of η (at $\eta = 0$), it is necessary that the third-
order term must also vanish at this point, and that the fourth-order term must
be positive:

$$B_c(P, T) = 0, \qquad C_c(P, T) > 0. \tag{135.3}$$

Being positive at the transition point, the coefficient C is, of course, also
positive in its neighbourhood.

---

† The empirical curves of specific heat as a function of temperature in a second-order phase
transition always show a sharp increase in the specific heat before the discontinuity and a sharp drop
immediately after it. This is unlikely to be accidental, and it may mean that the singularity in Φ
at the transition point is such that even if the discontinuity in specific heat itself remains finite, its
derivative with respect to temperature becomes infinite.

There are two possible cases. The third order term can be identically zero as a result of the symmetry properties of the crystal: $B(P, T) \equiv 0$. In that case one condition remains for the transition point: $A(P, T) = 0$; this determines P and T as functions of each other. Thus there exists (in the P, T plane) a whole line of second-order phase transition points.†

If B does not vanish identically, then the transition points are determined by the two equations: $A(P, T) = 0$, $B(P, T) = 0$. Hence, in this case the points of continuous phase transition are isolated ones.

The more interesting case, of course, is that of the line of continuous transition points. From now on we shall understand second-order phase transitions to refer to this case only; we now proceed to investigate it in detail.‡ Thus we shall take $B(P, T) \equiv 0$ so that the expansion of the thermodynamic potential will take the form

$$\Phi(P, T, \eta) = \Phi_0(P, T) + A(P, T)\eta^2 + C(P, T)\eta^4 + \ldots, \tag{135.4}$$

Here $A > 0$ for the symmetrical phase and $A < 0$ for the unsymmetrical phase; $C > 0$ for both. The transition points are determined by the equation $A(P, T) = 0$.

If one considers the transition for a given value of the pressure then near the transition point (whose temperature we denote by T_c) we can write

$$A(T) = a(T - T_c), \tag{135.5}$$

where $a = \dfrac{\partial A}{\partial T}\bigg|_{T = T_c}$ is a constant. Also, the coefficient $C(T)$ can simply be put equal to the constant $C(T_c)$.

The dependence of η on temperature near the transition point in the unsymmetrical phase is determined by the condition that Φ should be a minimum as a function of η. Equating to zero the derivative $\partial\Phi/\partial\eta$, we obtain $\eta(A + 2C\eta^2) = 0$, whence

$$\eta^2 = -\frac{A}{2C} = \frac{a}{2C}(T_c - T) \tag{135.6}$$

(the solution $\eta = 0$ corresponds to the symmetrical phase).‖

Next we determine the entropy of the body near the transition point. Neglecting higher powers of η, we have from (135.4):

$$S = -\frac{\partial\Phi}{\partial T} = S_0 - \frac{\partial A}{\partial T}\eta^2$$

---

† The absence of the η^3 term from the expansion (135.1) is indeed a necessary but by no means sufficient condition for the existence of a line of second-order phase transition points. See footnote on page 443.

‡ It can be shown (see L. LANDAU, *Phys. Z. Sowjet* **11**, 545, 1937), that second-order phase transitions cannot in any case occur between liquids and solids (crystals) owing to the presence of third order terms in the expansion of the thermodynamic potential.

‖ Note that for $A < 0$, the value $\eta = 0$ would correspond to a maximum of Φ.

where $S_0 = -\partial\Phi_0/\partial T$ (the term involving the derivative of η with respect to η vanishes since $\partial\Phi/\partial\eta = 0$). For the symmetrical phase, $\eta = 0$ and $S = S_0$; for the unsymmetrical phase $\eta^2 = -A/2C$ so that

$$S = S_0 + \frac{A}{2C}\frac{\partial A}{\partial T} = S_0 + \frac{a^2}{2C}(T-T_c). \tag{135.7}$$

At the transition point itself this expression becomes S_0, so that the entropy remains continuous, as it should.

Finally, let us determine the specific heats $C_p = T(\partial S/\partial T)_P$ of the two phases at the transition point. For the unsymmetrical phase we have, differentiating (135.7):

$$C_p = C_{p0} + \frac{a^2 T_c}{2C} \tag{135.8}$$

(where $C_{p0} = T\partial S_0/\partial T$). For the symmetrical phase $S = S_0$, and hence $C_p = C_{p0}$. Thus we conclude that, at a second-order phase transition point the specific heat undergoes a discontinuous jump. Since $C > 0$, at the transition point $C_p > C_{p0}$, i.e. the specific heat rises for the transition from the symmetrical to the unsymmetrical phase.

Other quantities are discontinuous, as well as C_p: the coefficient of thermal expansion, the compressibility, etc. It is not difficult to express the discontinuities of these quantities in terms of one another. We start from the fact that the volume and the entropy are continuous at the transition point, i.e. their discontinuities ΔV and ΔS are equal to zero:

$$\Delta V = 0, \qquad \Delta S = 0$$

We differentiate these equations with respect to temperature along the line of transition points, i.e. regarding pressure as a function of temperature determined by this curve. This gives:

$$\left.\begin{aligned} \Delta\left(\frac{\partial V}{\partial T}\right)_P + \frac{dP}{dT}\Delta\left(\frac{\partial V}{\partial P}\right)_T &= 0, \\ \frac{\Delta C_p}{T} - \frac{dP}{dT}\Delta\left(\frac{\partial V}{\partial T}\right)_P &= 0 \end{aligned}\right\} \tag{135.9}$$

(since $(\partial S/\partial P)_T = -(\partial V/\partial T)_P$). These two equations relate the discontinuities in the specific heat C_p, the coefficient of thermal expansion $(\partial V/\partial T)_P$ and the compressibility $(\partial V/\partial P)_T$. at the second-order phase transition points (W. H. KEESOM, 1933).

Differentiating the equations $\Delta S = 0$ and $\Delta P = 0$ along the line of phase transition points (the pressure, of course, does not change during the transition), but choosing the temperature and volume as independent variables, we find:

$$
\left.\begin{aligned}
\Delta\left(\frac{\partial P}{\partial T}\right)_V + \frac{dV}{dT}\Delta\left(\frac{\partial P}{\partial V}\right)_T &= 0, \\
\frac{\Delta C_v}{T} + \frac{dV}{dT}\Delta\left(\frac{\partial P}{\partial T}\right)_V &= 0.
\end{aligned}\right\} \tag{135.10}
$$

From eqs. (135.9) and (135.10) we find the discontinuities in the quantities C_p, C_v, $(\partial P/\partial T)_V$, $(\partial V/\partial T)_P$, expressed in terms of the discontinuity in the quantity $(\partial V/\partial P)_T$:

$$
\Delta\left(\frac{\partial V}{\partial T}\right)_P = -\frac{dP}{dT}\Delta\left(\frac{\partial V}{\partial P}\right)_T, \qquad \Delta C_p = -T\left(\frac{dP}{dT}\right)^2\Delta\left(\frac{\partial V}{\partial P}\right)_T,
$$

$$
\Delta\left(\frac{\partial P}{\partial T}\right)_V = -\frac{dV}{dT}\Delta\frac{1}{\left(\dfrac{\partial V}{\partial P}\right)_T}, \qquad \Delta C_v = T\left(\frac{dV}{dT}\right)^2\Delta\frac{1}{\left(\dfrac{\partial V}{\partial P}\right)_T}. \tag{135.11}
$$

Note that the discontinuities in the specific heat C_p and the compressibility $-(\partial V/\partial P)_T$ have the same sign, as one can see from the expressions we have obtained. In view of what was said above about the discontinuity in the specific heat, it follows that the compressibility drops for a transition from an unsymmetrical to a symmetrical phase.

The thermodynamic theory we have described solves (with the reservations made at the beginning of this section) the problem of the nature of the changes in the thermodynamic quantities during a continuous transition between phases of different symmetries. We see that there must be a discontinuous jump in the first derivatives of such quantities as the entropy, volume, etc.[†]

The above theory applies to transitions in ordinary three-dimensional bodies. It turns out to be quite inapplicable to second-order phase transitions in two dimensions, i.e. in plane lattices.[‡] This problem has not yet been investigated in general, but one may draw conclusions from the results of investigations of specific models of such lattices, first carried out by L. Onsager (1944)[||]. Without explaining the extremely complicated mathematical apparatus of that theory, we shall indicate here only the main final results.

[†] This makes quite pointless the question of phase transitions for which only the higher order derivatives would have discontinuities.

[‡] The problem of transitions in two-dimensional lattices, apart from its purely theoretical interest is closely related to the behaviour of crystals with a pronounced layer structure, and also to adsorbed films (cf. §143).

[||] The problem is the ordering in a two-dimensional rectangular lattice of a "binary alloy", with interaction only between nearest neighbours (along a side of the rectangle). A review of the literature on this problem can be found in G. F. Newell, E. W. Montroll, *Rev. Mod. Phys.*, **25**, 353, 1953. G. Rumer (*Progr. Phys. Sci.* (*russ.*) **53**, 245, 1954) has succeeded in simplifying considerably the mathematical apparatus of Onsager's theory.

Contrary to what happens in a second-order phase transition in a three-dimensional crystal, the specific heat does not remain finite in this case at the transition point, but has a logarithmic singularity. More precisely, the thermodynamic potential, as a function of temperature, has, near the transition point, the form:

$$\Phi = a + b(T - T_c)^2 \log|T - T_c| \qquad (135.12)$$

(*a* and *b* are constants). Accordingly the specific heat near the transition point tends to infinity as $\log|T - T_c|$. Similar singularities occur in the compressibility, thermal expansion coefficient, etc. (In differentiating the thermodynamic potential with respect to the "pressure" it must be remembered that the latter affects not only the coefficients *a* and *b*, but also the transition temperature.)

The temperature dependence of the degree of order η (in the less symmetric phase), is also completely different from what we have found above. Instead of being proportional to $V(T_c - T)$ it is here of the form

$$\eta = \mathrm{const}(T_c - T)^{1/8} \qquad (135.13)$$

(C. N. YANG, 1952).

§136. Change of symmetry in a second-order phase transition

In the theory discussed in the last section we have considered second-order phase transitions for some definite change in the symmetry of a body, assuming from the start that such a transition was possible. This theory, however, does not answer the question of whether this change of symmetry could actually take place by means of a second-order transition. This is covered by the theory developed in this section, starting from a different formulation of the problem: given a definite symmetry of the body at the transition point, we require to find its possible symmetry on both sides of this point.

For the sake of definiteness, we shall speak of phase transitions connected with a change in the structure of the crystal lattice, i.e changes of the symmetry of its atomic configuration. Let $\rho(x, y, z)$ be the "density function" (introduced in §122), which determines the probability distribution of different positions of the atoms in the crystal. The symmetry of the crystal lattice is that set (group) of co-ordinate transformations under which the function $\rho(x, y, z)$ remains invariant. We mean here, of course, the complete symmetry of the lattice including all the rotations, reflections and also the infinite (discrete) set of all possible translations; in other words we are speaking of one of the 230 space groups.

Let $\mathfrak{G}_0$ be the symmetry group of the crystal at the transition point. As is well known from group theory† an arbitrary function $\rho(x, y, z)$ can be

---

† This section presupposes knowledge of group theory to the extent covered in the other volume of this course, *Quantum Mechanics*, Chapter XII.

represented as a linear combination of some functions ϕ_1, ϕ_2, ... , having the property that they transform linearly into one another under all transformations of the given group. In the general case the number of these functions is equal to the number of elements of the group, but for certain symmetries of the function ρ which is expanded, the number of the ϕ_i may be smaller.

Bearing this in mind, we represent the density function $\rho(x, y, z)$ of the crystal as a sum:

$$\rho = \sum_i c_i \phi_i,$$

where the functions ϕ_i transform into one another under all transformations of the group $\mathfrak{G}_0$. The matrices of these transformations form what we call a representation of the group $\mathfrak{G}_0$. The choice of the functions ϕ_i is not unique; in their place one can obviously take any linear combinations of them. As is well known, one can always choose the functions ϕ_i so that they split into a series of sets containing as few functions as possible, each set of functions being transformed into itself under all transformations of the group. The transformation matrices of the functions contained in each of these sets form what are called the irreducible representations of the group $\mathfrak{G}_0$ and the functions themselves are, as one says, the bases of these representations. Thus we can write:

$$\rho = \sum_n \sum_i c_i^{(n)} \phi_i^{(n)} \tag{136.1}$$

where n is the number of the irreducible representation and i the number of the function in its basis. In future we shall assume the functions $\phi_i^{(n)}$ to be normalised in some particular way.

Amongst the functions $\phi_i^{(n)}$ there always exists one which is itself invariant with respect to all transformations of the group (it forms what is called the identical representation of the group). In other words, this function (which we denote by ρ_0) has the symmetry $\mathfrak{G}_0$. Denoting the remainder of ρ by $\delta\rho$, we can write:

$$\rho = \rho_0 + \delta\rho; \qquad \delta\rho = {\sum_n}' \sum_i c_i^{(n)} \phi_i^{(n)}, \tag{136.2}$$

where in $\delta\rho$ we now exclude the identical representation of the group (this is indicated by the accented summation sign).†

The function $\delta\rho$ has lower symmetry than $\mathfrak{G}_0$ because even if $\delta\rho$ remains invariant under some transformations of this group, it certainly does not under all of them. Note that the symmetry $\mathfrak{G}$ of the function ρ (obviously

† Some of the irreducible representations of a space group may be complex (i.e. under transformations of the group the functions of the basis transform into their linear combinations with complex coefficients). For each such representation there exists its complex conjugate (formed from the complex conjugate functions). Since the physical density $\delta\rho = \sum c_i \phi_i$ must be real and remain real under all transformations, it is clear that the two complex conjugate irreducible representations must be regarded as the same one but with twice the dimensions (number of functions in the basis). The density $\delta\rho$ will then be a real linear combination of all these complex conjugate functions. Below it is always assumed that this has been done and the functions $\phi_i^{(n)}$ are taken to be real.

the same as the symmetry of $\delta\rho$) was initially assumed to be lower than $\mathfrak{G}_0$; otherwise the whole sum (136.1) would reduce to one term only; the function ρ itself forming the identical representation.

The thermodynamic potential Φ of a crystal with density function ρ given by (136.2) is a function of pressure, temperature and the coefficients $c_i^{(n)}$ (and, naturally, depends on the exact form of the functions $\phi_i^{(n)}$ themselves). The actual values of $c_i^{(n)}$ as functions of P and T are determined thermodynamically by the equilibrium conditions, i.e. the conditions that Φ should be a minimum. These also determine the symmetry $\mathfrak{G}$ of the crystal since it is clear that the symmetry of a function (136.2), with functions $\phi_i^{(n)}$ whose transformation laws are known, is determined by the values of the coefficients of the linear combinations of the latter.

For the crystal to have symmetry $\mathfrak{G}_0$ at the actual transition point, it is necessary that all the quantities $c_i^{(n)}$ should vanish at this point, i.e. that $\delta\rho = 0$, $\rho = \rho_0$. Since the change of state of a crystal in a second order phase transition is continuous, the vanishing of $\delta\rho$ at the transition point must occur in a continuous manner and not with a discontinuity, i.e. the coefficients $c_i^{(n)}$ must vanish, taking arbitrarily small values near the transition point. As a result of this we can expand the potential $\Phi(P, T, c_i^{(n)})$ in powers of $c_i^{(n)}$, near the transition point.

Note, initially, that since, under transformations of the group $\mathfrak{G}_0$ the functions $\phi_i^{(n)}$ transform into one another (within the basis of each irreducible representation) one can regard these transformations as if it were not the functions $\phi_i^{(n)}$ but the coefficients $c_i^{(n)}$ which are transformed (by the same law). Furthermore, since the thermodynamic potential of the body must obviously be independent of the choice of co-ordinate system, it must be invariant under all co-ordinate transformations, in particular under transformations of the group $\mathfrak{G}_0$. Hence each term of the expansion of Φ in powers of $c_i^{(n)}$ must contain only invariant combinations of the quantities $c_i^{(n)}$, of corresponding order.

It is well known that no linear invariant can be constructed from quantities which transform according to an irreducible representation of the group. As to the invariants of the second order, there exists only one for every representation—a positive definite quadratic form in the $c_i^{(n)}$, which can always be reduced to a sum of squares.

Thus the expansion of Φ begins with the terms

$$\Phi = \Phi_0 + \sum_n{}' A^{(n)} \sum_i c_i^{(n)2}, \qquad (136.3)$$

where $A^{(n)}$ is a function of P and T.

At the transition point itself the crystal must have symmetry $\mathfrak{G}_0$; i.e. the values $c_i^{(n)} = 0$ must correspond to equilibrium. It is obvious that Φ can be a minimum for all $c_i^{(n)} = 0$ only if all the $A^{(n)}$ are non-negative.

If, at the transition point, all the $A^{(n)}$ were positive, then they would also be positive near the transition point, i.e. the $c_i^{(n)}$ would have to be zero all the time, and there would be no change in the symmetry of the body. In order that there should be some non-zero $c_i^{(n)}$ i.e. that the symmetry of the body should change, it is necessary for one of the coefficients $A^{(n)}$ to change sign; hence at the transition point itself this coefficient must vanish.† (Two of the coefficients $A^{(n)}$ can vanish simultaneously only at an isolated point in the P, T plane. Such a point is the intersection of several second order transition lines, see §138).

Thus on one side of the transition point all the $A^{(n)} > 0$ and on the other side one is negative. Correspondingly, on one side of the transition point all the $c_i^{(n)}$ are zero, while on the other side non-zero $c_i^{(n)}$ appear.

In other words, we arrive at the result that on one side of the transition point the crystal has the higher symmetry $\mathfrak{G}_0$, which it still has at the transition point, and on the other side the symmetry $\mathfrak{G}$ is lower, so that the group $\mathfrak{G}$ is a sub-group of the group $\mathfrak{G}_0$.

As a result of one of the $A^{(n)}$ changing sign there appear non-zero $c_i^{(n)}$ belonging to the corresponding nth representation. Thus a crystal with symmetry $\mathfrak{G}_0$ transforms into a crystal with density $\rho = \rho_0 + \delta\rho$, where

$$\delta\rho = \sum_i c_i^{(n)}\phi_i^{(n)} \tag{136.4}$$

is a linear combination of the functions forming the basis of a single (not the identical) irreducible representation of the group $\mathfrak{G}_0$. In view of this we shall omit below the suffix n indicating the number of the irreducible representation, always assuming it to be that which appears for the transition in question.

We now introduce the notation

$$\eta^2 = \sum_i c_i^2, \qquad c_i = \eta\gamma_i \tag{136.5}$$

(so that $\sum_i \gamma_i^2 = 1$) and write the expansion of Φ in the form

$$\Phi = \Phi_0(P, T) + \eta^2 A(P, T) + \eta^3 \sum_\alpha B_\alpha(P, T)f_\alpha^{(3)}(\gamma_i) + \eta^4 \sum_\alpha C_\alpha(P, T)f_\alpha^{(4)}(\gamma_i) + \dots, \tag{136.6}$$

where $f_\alpha^{(3)}$, $f_\alpha^{(4)}$ are invariants of third, fourth, etc. order constructed from

---

† Strictly speaking, this condition should be formulated more precisely in the following manner. The coefficients $A^{(n)}$ depend, of course, on the actual form of the functions $\phi_i^{(n)}$—they represent quadratic functionals of them, depending on P and T as parameters. On one side of the transition point all these functionals $A^{(n)}\{\phi_i^{(n)}; P, T\}$ are positive definite. A transition point will be defined as a point at which (for gradual changes in P, T) one of the $A^{(n)}$ can vanish:

$$A^{(n)}\{\phi_i^{(n)}; P, T\} \geqslant 0$$

Vanishing corresponds to a definite set of functions $\phi_i^{(n)}$, which can be determined from the solution of the corresponding variational problem. These will be the functions $\phi_i^{(n)}$ which determine the change $\delta\rho$ occurring at the transition point. Substituting them into $A^{(n)}\{\phi_i^{(n)}; P, T\}$ we get straight away simply the function $A^{(n)}(P, T)$ for which the condition $A^{(n)}(P, T) = 0$ is satisfied at the transition point. Subsequently, one can assume the functions $\phi_i^{(n)}$ to be given (taking the change of $\phi_i^{(n)}$ with P and T into account would lead to correction terms of higher order than we are concerned with here).

the γ_i; the sums with respect to α contain as many terms as there are independent invariants of the corresponding order which can be constructed from the γ_i. In this expansion of the thermodynamic potential, the coefficient A vanishes at the transition point. For the transition point to be an equilibrium state (i.e. for Φ to be a minimum for $c_i = 0$) the third-order terms must vanish and the fourth-order terms must be positive definite. As was already pointed out in the last section, a line (in the P, T plane) of second-order phase transition points can only exist when the third-order terms in the expansion of Φ vanish identically. This condition can now be expressed as the requirement that there should exist no invariants of third order constructed from quantities c_i which transform according to the given irreducible representation of the group $\mathfrak{G}_0$†.

Assuming this condition to be satisfied, we write the expansion, up to terms of fourth order, as:

$$\Phi = \Phi_0 + A(P, T)\eta^2 + \eta^4 \sum_\alpha C_\alpha(P, T) f_\alpha^{(4)}(\gamma_i). \tag{136.7}$$

Since the second-order term does not contain the γ_i, these are determined by the condition that the fourth-order terms, i.e. the coefficient of η^4 in (136.7)‡ should be a minimum. Denoting the corresponding minimum value of this coefficient simply by $C(P, T)$ (which must be positive, from what we have said above) we return to an expansion of Φ in the form (136.4) and the quantity η will be determined by the condition that Φ should be a minimum as a function of η only, as was done in the preceding section. The values of the quantities γ_i found in this way determine the symmetry of the function $\delta\rho = \eta \sum_i \gamma_i \phi_i$, i.e. the symmetry $\mathfrak{G}$ of the crystal which appears after a second-order transition from a crystal with symmetry $\mathfrak{G}_0$.

In the above it was implicitly assumed that the crystal is everywhere homogeneous, i.e. that the coefficients c_i are constant throughout the crystal; obviously this must be so for an equilibrium state of the body. However, the stability of the state demands that the thermodynamic potential be a minimum with respect to changes of c_i within the crystal. This condition imposes definite restrictions on c_i which result in further fundamental restrictions on the possible changes of symmetry in a second-order phase transition.

---

† In the preceding section we considered transitions with a given symmetry change. In terms of the concepts introduced here one can say that we assumed beforehand given values for the quantities γ_i (so that the function $\delta\rho$ should have a given symmetry). For such a formulation of the problem, the absence of a third-order term in (131.1) would not be a sufficient condition to ensure the existence of a line of second-order transition points, since it does not exclude the possible occurrence of third-order terms in the general expansion in terms of several c_i (if the given irreducible representation is not uni-dimensional). Thus, for example, if there are three quantities c_i, and the product $\gamma_1\gamma_2\gamma_3$ is an invariant, then the expansion of Φ contains a third-order term which vanishes for definite symmetries of the function $\delta\rho$ which require one or two of the γ_i to vanish.

‡ It may happen that there is only one fourth-order invariant $(\sum_i c_i^2)^2 = \eta^4$. In this case the fourth-order term is independent of the γ_i and to determine the latter, we must turn to the higher order terms.

To formulate this condition we shall assume that the c_i are not constant throughout the crystal but are slowly varying functions of the co-ordinates. Then the thermodynamic potential per unit volume of the crystal will depend, in general, not only on the c_i but also on their derivatives with respect to the co-ordinates (their first-order derivatives, as a first approximation). Correspondingly, one must expand Φ (per unit volume) near the transition point in powers of $\partial c_i/\partial x$, $\partial c_i/\partial y$, $\partial c_i/\partial z$ as well as c_i. For the thermodynamic potential (of the whole crystal) to have a minimum at $\partial c_i/\partial x = 0$, ... it is necessary that in this expansion the terms of first order in the derivatives should vanish identically (and the quadratic terms in the derivatives must be positive definite; this, however, does not impose any restrictions on the c_i, since such a quadratic form can exist for c_i which transforms according to any of the irreducible representations).

Of the linear terms in the derivatives, we are only concerned with those proportional simply to $\partial c_i/\partial x \dots$, and those containing the products $c_i \, \partial c_k/\partial x, \dots$. The higher-order terms obviously are not important. Note further that we must require the thermodynamic potential of the crystal as a whole, i.e. the integral $\int \Phi \, dV$ over the whole volume, to be a minimum. But in this integration all the total derivatives of Φ give a constant which is irrelevant to the determination of the minimum of the integral. Hence one can omit all the terms in Φ proportional simply to the derivatives of the c_i. Of the terms involving the products $c_i \, \partial c_k/\partial x, \dots$ one can omit all the symmetric combinations

$$c_k \frac{\partial c_i}{\partial x} + c_i \frac{\partial c_k}{\partial x} = \frac{\partial}{\partial x} c_i c_k, \dots,$$

leaving only their antisymmetric parts:

$$c_k \frac{\partial c_i}{\partial x} - c_i \frac{\partial c_k}{\partial x}, \dots. \tag{136.8}$$

Since Φ is a scalar, its expansion can contain only invariant linear combinations of the quantities (136.8). Hence the condition that the crystal should be in a stable state is that all such invariants should vanish.†

One can prove the following general theorem: for every transition involving the halving of the number of symmetry transformations of the crystal, second-order phase transitions can exist. The halving of the number of

---

† The derivatives $\partial c_i/\partial x$, $\partial c_i/\partial y$, $\partial c_i/\partial z$ transform as the products of the components of a vector with the quantities c_i. Hence the quantities (136.8) transform as the products of the components of a vector with the antisymmetric products of the quantities c_i (for a discussion of such products and their transformation laws see *Quantum Mechanics* §91). Hence the condition that one should not be able to form any linear scalars from the quantities (136.8) is equivalent to requiring that one should not be able to construct, from the quantities

$$\chi_{ik} = \phi_i(x,y,z)\phi_k(x',y',z') - \phi_k(x,y,z)\phi_i(x',y',z') \tag{136.8a}$$

any combinations which transform as the components of a vector (ϕ_i are functions transforming by the given irreducible representation of the group).

symmetry elements means that the symmetry group $\mathfrak{G}$ contains half as many elements as the group $\mathfrak{G}_0$. Such a change of symmetry can occur either by doubling the unit cell of the crystal (halving the number of translations) keeping the crystal class the same, or by halving the "rotational" symmetry elements (rotations and reflections) with the size of the unit cell constant.

The proof is based on the fact that all the elements of the group $\mathfrak{G}_0$ not included in its sub-group $\mathfrak{G}$ (whose order is half that of $\mathfrak{G}_0$) can be obtained by multiplying one (arbitrary) element G_1, not contained in $\mathfrak{G}$, in turn by all the elements of the sub-group $\mathfrak{G}$; the sub-group $\mathfrak{G}$ and the complex of elements $G_1\mathfrak{G}$ cover all the elements of the group $\mathfrak{G}_0$. It is clear that by multiplying any element of $\mathfrak{G}$ by any element of the complex $G_1\mathfrak{G}$ we again obtain an element of $G_1\mathfrak{G}$; and by multiplying two elements of $G_1\mathfrak{G}$ we obtain an element of $\mathfrak{G}$.

Let ϕ be a function invariant under all transformations of the sub-group $\mathfrak{G}$. From what we have said above, it follows that this function must either also be invariant under all the remaining transformations of the group $\mathfrak{G}_0$ or change sign under these transformations (since a repeated transformation of $G_1\mathfrak{G}$ is equivalent to some transformation of $\mathfrak{G}$, i.e. it must leave ϕ invariant). In the first case ϕ is the trivial identical representation of the group $\mathfrak{G}_0$, and in the second case a function of the type $\delta\rho = c\phi$ corresponds just to the phase transition in which we are interested, since it has the symmetry $\mathfrak{G}$. At the same time, terms of odd order are absent from the expansion of Φ (since ϕ changes sign under some transformations of the group $\mathfrak{G}_0$) and one cannot construct quantities of the type (136.8a) at all from one function. This proves the assertion made above that in this case a second-order phase transition line can exist.

It appears that the following theorem is also true: No second-order phase transition can exist for transitions involving the decrease by a factor three of the number of symmetry elements (owing to the existence of third-order terms in the expansion of the thermodynamic potential).

Finally, let us consider briefly second-order phase transitions connected with the appearance or disappearance of non-zero currents $\mathbf{j}(x, y, z)$ in a body (see §133); these include, in particular, the Curie points of ferromagnetic substances. On one side of such transitions we have $\mathbf{j}_0 = 0$ and on the other side $\delta\mathbf{j} = \mathbf{j}$ is small. Instead of expanding the thermodynamic potential Φ in powers of $\delta\rho$, we now consider the corresponding expansion in powers of $\delta\mathbf{j}$. The thermodynamic quantities of the body, in particular its potential Φ, cannot change under a formal change of sign of the time†; the currents $\mathbf{j}$, however, do change sign. It follows from this that, in the expansion of Φ all terms of odd order in $\delta\mathbf{j}$, including the third, must vanish identically. This means that a transition involving the appearance or disappearance of currents $\mathbf{j}$ can always occur as a second-order phase transition.

---

† It is essential that the term Φ_0 here should remain invariant under a change from t to $-t$, since, in the corresponding phase, there are no currents at all.

§137. Irreducible representations of the space groups

Thus the problem of determining the possible types of symmetry change in a second-order phase transition is reduced to finding the irreducible representations of the space groups and the investigation of their properties, in the sense of constructing invariants of the quantities which transform according to these representations. The space groups are groups with an infinite number of elements (infinite number of translations). Hence also the number of irreducible representations of a space group is infinite. We shall see, however, that for the problem of phase transitions only a finite number of representations are important, since the others are already excluded by the condition, derived in the last section, that the construction of invariants from the quantities (136.8) should be impossible.

Each space group has a sub-group of translations which contains the infinite set of parallel translations for which the lattice repeats itself (this sub-group also represents, from the mathematical point of view, what is called the Bravais lattice of the crystal). The complete space group is obtained from this sub-group by adding n rotation and reflection elements, where n is the number of symmetry transformations of the corresponding crystal class: we shall conventionally call these "rotational" elements. If a space group does not contain any essential screw axes or glide planes, then the n rotational elements may simply be taken as the n symmetry transformations (rotations and reflections) of the crystal class. Otherwise the rotational elements represent rotations and reflections with simultaneous translations through a certain part of a basic lattice vector. Each element of a space group can be considered as the product of one of the translational symmetry elements with one of the "rotational" elements.

Each irreducible representation of a space group can be realised as a set of functions of the type[†]

$$\phi_{f\alpha} = u_{f\alpha} e^{i \mathbf{f} \cdot \mathbf{r}} \tag{137.1}$$

where $\mathbf{f}$ are constant vectors, $u_{f\alpha}$ are periodic functions (with the periodicity of the lattice) and the suffix $\alpha = 1, 2, \ldots, s$, labels functions with equal $\mathbf{f}$.

As a result of a translation, i.e. a transformation of the form $\mathbf{r} \to \mathbf{r} + \mathbf{a}$ (where $\mathbf{a}$ is some lattice vector) the functions (137.1) are multiplied by a constant $e^{i \mathbf{f} \cdot \mathbf{a}}$, i.e. in the representation of the space group formed by these functions the matrices corresponding to the translations are diagonal.

It is obvious that two vectors $\mathbf{f}$ differing by $2\pi \mathbf{b}$ where $\mathbf{b}$ is some reciprocal lattice vector, lead to the same transformation law for $\phi_{f\alpha}$ under translations: since $\mathbf{a} \cdot \mathbf{b}$ is an integer $e^{2\pi i \mathbf{a} \cdot \mathbf{b}} = 1$. From this point of view, such vectors $\mathbf{f}$ must be considered identical; below we shall call different only vectors $\mathbf{f}$ whose difference (multiplied by 2π) is not a reciprocal lattice vector. If one considers the vectors $\mathbf{f}/2\pi$ which go from a corner to different points of a

---

[†] The following considerations on the representations of the space groups are due to F. Seitz (1936).

cell of the reciprocal lattice, then we must consider only vectors in one unit cell.

Under the action of a "rotational" symmetry element the function $\phi_{\mathbf{f}\alpha}$ transforms into a linear combination of the functions $\phi_{\mathbf{f}'\alpha}$ with different values of α, and with $\mathbf{f}'$ obtained from the vector $\mathbf{f}$ by means of the given rotation or reflection performed on the reciprocal lattice.†

In the general case, the application of all n "rotational" elements gives different vectors $\mathbf{f}$. The functions $\phi_{\mathbf{f}\alpha}$ must in each case include some with each of these different vectors. For since functions with different $\mathbf{f}$ are multiplied, as a result of translations, by different constants, no choice of linear combinations of them could reduce the number of functions transforming into one another.

For certain values of the vector $\mathbf{f}$, the number of different vectors $\mathbf{f}, \mathbf{f}', \ldots$ obtained from it may be less than n, since it may turn out that some of the "rotational" symmetry elements leave $\mathbf{f}$ invariant. Thus if the vector $\mathbf{f}$ points along a symmetry axis then it will be unchanged by rotations about this axis; a vector of the form $\mathbf{f} = \pi\mathbf{b}_i$ where $\mathbf{b}_i$ is one of the basic vectors of the reciprocal lattice, is unchanged by inversion (inversion changes the sign of the vector, but $-\pi\mathbf{b}_i$ and $\pi\mathbf{b}_i$ differ by $2\pi\mathbf{b}_i$), etc.

The set of "rotational" symmetry elements contained in the given space group which do not change the vector $\mathbf{f}$, may be called the group of its "proper symmetry". Under transformations of this group, functions $\phi_{\mathbf{f}\alpha}$ with the same $\mathbf{f}$ and different α transform into one another.

In the simplest case, when the space group contains no essential screw axes or glide reflection planes,‡ the proper symmetry group of the vectors $\mathbf{f}$ consists of pure rotations and reflections, i.e. represents one of the usual point groups. The functions $\phi_{\mathbf{f}\alpha}$ for the given $\mathbf{f}$ in this case form one of the irreducible representations of this point group. In this connection these are called "small representations". The dimension of an irreducible representation of the space group is equal to the product of the number of different $\mathbf{f}$, obtained by rotation or reflection, and the dimension of the small representation. It is convenient to express the functions $\phi_{\mathbf{f}\alpha}$ of its basis as products

$$\phi_{\mathbf{f}\alpha} = u_\alpha \psi_{\mathbf{f}}, \tag{137.2}$$

where $\psi_{\mathbf{f}}$ is a linear combination of the expressions $e^{i\mathbf{f}\cdot\mathbf{r}}$ (with vectors $\mathbf{f}/2\pi$ differing only by $a\mathbf{b}$) invariant under all transformations of the proper symmetry group of $\mathbf{f}$, and the u_α are periodic functions (i.e. invariant under all translations), which are the basis of some small representation.

If the space group includes essential screw axes or glide reflection planes, the "proper symmetry" group of the vector $\mathbf{f}$ can only be considered as a

---

† The transformation of the vector $\mathbf{f}$ in the reciprocal lattice does not, of course, depend on whether the rotation (or reflection) is simple or screw (or glide).

‡ i.e. all the symmetry elements of the space group can be represented as the product of two elements, one of which is a pure reflection or rotation, and the other a translation through one of the lattice vectors.

group in the real sense of the word if definite translations are included in it; thus, for example, a double reflection in a glide reflection plane is not the identity transformation but a translation through one of the basic lattice vectors.

As was already pointed out (see footnote on page 440), for the physical applications with which we are concerned, two complex conjugate irreducible representations must be combined into one of twice the dimensions. This means that together with each vector $\mathbf{f}$ we must also take the vector $-\mathbf{f}$. Hence to obtain all the necessary vectors $\mathbf{f}$ one must apply to some initial $\mathbf{f}$ all the elements of the crystal class augmented by a centre of symmetry if the given class does not itself include one.

In application to second-order phase transitions it turns out to be very important whether the axes and planes which form the proper symmetry of the vector $\mathbf{f}$ intersect in a point or whether there is an inversion centre amongst the symmetry elements; we shall describe such point groups as groups with a "singular point". It can be shown that, for every other proper symmetry of the vector $\mathbf{f}$ one can, with the help of the functions $\phi_{f\alpha}$, constant linear combinations of the quantities

$$\chi_{f\alpha f'\beta} = \phi_{f\alpha}(x,y,z)\,\phi_{f'\beta}(x',y',z') - \phi_{f\alpha}(x',y',z')\,\phi_{f'\beta}(x,y,z)$$

(see footnote on page 444) which transform as the components of a vector.

Suppose the vector $\mathbf{f}$ has the most general position and has no proper symmetry. Then the corresponding representation is formed by the n (or $2n$ if the space group does not itself possess a centre of symmetry) functions ϕ_f, one for each $\mathbf{f}$, which is why we omit the suffix α. Since $\mathbf{f}$ and $-\mathbf{f}$ are different in this case, we can construct quantities

$$\chi_{f,-f} = \phi_f(x,y,z)\,\phi_{-f}(x',y',z') - \phi_f(x',y',z')\,\phi_{-f}(x,y,z)$$

which are invariant under all translations. When operated on by the rotational elements all these n (or $2n$) quantities transform into one another forming a representation of the corresponding point group (of the crystal class) with dimension equal to that of the group. But this (which is called the regular) representation contains, as is well known in group theory,[†] all the irreducible representations of the group, which also include those by which components of vectors transform.

Similar reasoning also proves the possibility of constructing a vector from the quantities $\chi_{f\alpha,-f\beta}$ in the case when the "proper symmetry" of the vector $\mathbf{f}$ is made up of one axis and planes of symmetry through it.

This reasoning, however, becomes untenable if the proper symmetry of the vector is made up of intersecting axes or planes of symmetry, or contains a centre of symmetry. Thus in the presence of a centre of symmetry, the vectors $\mathbf{f}$ and $-\mathbf{f}$ coincide (i.e. they differ only by $2\pi\mathbf{b}$); if, then, there is only one function ϕ_f corresponding to each vector $\mathbf{f}$, one cannot construct $\chi_{f,f'}$.

---

† See, *Quantum Mechanics*, §91.

which are invariant under translations, which would automatically be the components of a vector.

Thus, in investigating the question of the possible changes of symmetry in second-order phase transitions, out of all the infinite number of irreducible representations it is sufficient to consider only the comparatively small number which correspond to vectors **f** having proper symmetry with a "singular point"†

It appears to be possible to investigate in general form the problem of the changes in the Bravais lattice (i.e. translational symmetry) of a crystal in a second-order transition. In the majority of cases the possible change of the Bravais lattice comprises the doubling (in magnitude) of some lattice vector.‡ For volume-centred (orthorhombic, tetragonal, cubic) and the cubic face-centred lattices changes are also possible in which some of the lattice vectors are quadrupled and in the hexagonal lattice there are cases when some lattice vector is tripled. The volume of the unit cell then can increase 2, 4, 8 times; for the face-centred cubic there are cases when it increases 16 or 32 times, and for the hexagonal lattice 3 or 6 times.

As an illustration of the concrete applications of the general theory, consider the onset of ordering in alloys which in their disordered state have a body-centered cubic lattice with atoms only at the corners and body centres of the cubic cells (as in Fig. 61*b*). The problem is to determine what types of order (i.e. in crystallographic language, what types of superlattices) can appear in such a lattice in second-order phase transitions (E. LIFSHITZ, 1941)‖

For the body-centered cubic lattice, the reciprocal lattice is face-centred cubic. We take the side of the cubic cell of the original lattice as unit of length. The side of the cubic cell of the reciprocal lattice is then of length $\frac{1}{2}$. In this reciprocal lattice, the following vectors **f** possess symmetry with a "singular point":

$$
\begin{array}{lll}
\text{(a)} & (0, 0, 0) & \mathbf{O}_h \\[4pt]
\text{(b)} & (\tfrac{1}{2}, \tfrac{1}{2}, \tfrac{1}{2}) & \mathbf{O}_h \\[4pt]
\text{(c)} & (\tfrac{1}{4}, \tfrac{1}{4}, \tfrac{1}{4}), \quad (\bar{\tfrac{1}{4}}, \bar{\tfrac{1}{4}}, \bar{\tfrac{1}{4}}) & \mathbf{T}_d \qquad\qquad (137.3) \\[4pt]
\text{(d)} & (0, \tfrac{1}{4}, \tfrac{1}{4}), \quad (\tfrac{1}{4}, 0, \tfrac{1}{4}), \quad (\tfrac{1}{4}, \tfrac{1}{4}, 0), \\[2pt]
& (0, \tfrac{1}{4}, \bar{\tfrac{1}{4}}), \quad (\bar{\tfrac{1}{4}}, 0, \tfrac{1}{4}), \quad (\tfrac{1}{4}, \bar{\tfrac{1}{4}}, 0), & \mathbf{D}_{2h}
\end{array}
$$

We have here listed the components of the vector $\mathbf{f}/2\pi$ with respect to x, y, z axes along the edges of the cube, and measured in units of the length of the edge (a bar over a number indicates a negative value); to obtain the vectors **f** in the units chosen before, these numbers must be multiplied by $2 . 2\pi = 4\pi$. In (137.3) only those vectors $\mathbf{f}/2\pi$ are listed which are obtained

---

† For a complete proof of this statement as well as the derivation of the results mentioned below, see E. LIFSHITZ, *J. Phys. Moscow*, 6, 61, 1942.

‡ Of course, the Bravais lattice may also not change at all.

‖ For a similar investigation of lattices with cubic or hexagonal close packing cf. *J. Phys. Moscow*, 6 251, 1942.

from one another by rotations and reflections, but whose differences are not reciprocal lattice vectors, i.e. only different vectors $\mathbf{f}$ (in the terminology we have used). The proper symmetry groups of these vectors are also indicated.

The further discussion is greatly simplified by the fact that only the identical small representations need be considered in the given problem. The point is that we are not interested in the most general changes of symmetry, but only in those which can be realised by means of an ordered distribution of atoms over the existing sites in the lattice (i.e. by the formation of a superlattice) without any displacement. In the present case the unit cell of the disordered lattice contains only one atom. Hence no superlattice can correspond to a change $\delta\rho$ in the density distribution which would not be invariant under an arbitrary rotation or reflection (without simultaneous translation). Mathematically this means that small representations other than the identical one are not admissible. In the basic set of functions (137.2) we may, accordingly replace u_α by unity.

Consider now in turn the vectors $\mathbf{f}$ listed in (137.3):

(a) The function ϕ_f with $\mathbf{f} = 0$ has the complete translational symmetry. In this case there is no change in the unit cell, and since each cell contains only one atom, there cannot be any symmetry change at all.

(b) The function corresponding to this $\mathbf{f}$ is $e^{2\pi i(x+y+z)}$. The linear combination of this function with the same function after rotations and reflections, which has symmetry $\mathbf{O}_h$, is

$$\phi = \cos 2\pi x \cos 2\pi y \cos 2\pi z. \tag{137.4}$$

The symmetry starting at the second-order transition point is that of the density function $\rho = \rho_0 + \delta\rho$, $\delta\rho = \eta\phi$.† The function ϕ is invariant under all transformations of the class $\mathbf{O}_h$ and under translations by any edge of the cubic cell, but not by half its space diagonal, $(\frac{1}{2}, \frac{1}{2}, \frac{1}{2})$. The ordered crystal therefore has a simple cubic Bravais lattice with two non-equivalent sites, $(0, 0, 0)$ and $(\frac{1}{2}, \frac{1}{2}, \frac{1}{2})$ in the unit cell, which will be occupied by different atoms. The general type of alloy which can give complete ordering of this kind is therefore AB (such as the alloy CuZn mentioned in §134).

(c) The functions with symmetry $\mathbf{T}_d$ corresponding to these vectors $\mathbf{f}$ are:

$$\phi_1 = \cos \pi x \cos \pi y \cos \pi z, \qquad \varphi_2 = \sin \pi x \sin \pi y \sin \pi z. \tag{137.5}$$

From these one can form two invariants of fourth degree: $(\phi_1{}^2 + \phi_2{}^2)^2$ and $\phi_1{}^4 + \phi_2{}^4$. Accordingly the expansion (136.7) of the thermodynamic potential takes the form

$$\Phi = \Phi_0 + A\eta^2 + C_1\eta^4 + C_2\eta^4(\gamma_1{}^4 + \gamma_2{}^4). \tag{137.6}$$

Here we must distinguish two cases. If $C_2 < 0$, the thermodynamic potential,

---

† This does not mean, of course, that in a real crystal the density change is actually given by the function $\delta\rho$ we have written down. In the expression (137.4) the only essential thing is its symmetry.

as a function of γ_1, γ_2 with the subsidiary condition $\gamma_1^2 + \gamma_2^2 = 1$, has its minimum for $\gamma_1 = 1$, $\gamma_2 = 0$†. The function $\delta\rho = \eta\phi_1$ possesses the symmetry class O_h with a face-centred Bravais lattice and a cubic cell with a volume eight times that of the original cube. The unit cell contains four atoms, and the cubic cell sixteen. If we place like atoms in equivalent sites, we find that this superlattice corresponds to a ternary alloy of composition ABC_2, with the atoms in the following positions:

$$4A \ (0, 0, 0), \quad (0, \tfrac{1}{2}, \tfrac{1}{2} \bigcirc) \quad\quad 4B \ (\tfrac{1}{2}, \tfrac{1}{2}, \tfrac{1}{2}), \quad (0, 0, \tfrac{1}{2} \bigcirc)$$

$$8C \ (\tfrac{1}{4}, \tfrac{1}{4}, \tfrac{1}{4}), \quad (\tfrac{3}{4}, \tfrac{3}{4}, \tfrac{3}{4}), \quad (\tfrac{1}{4}, \tfrac{3}{4}, \tfrac{3}{4} \bigcirc), \quad (\tfrac{1}{4}, \tfrac{1}{4}, \tfrac{3}{4} \bigcirc).$$

The co-ordinates are here given in units of the edge of the new cubic cell, i.e. twice the original (cf. Fig. 63a)‡. If the atoms B and C are identical, one obtains an ordered lattice of composition AB_3.

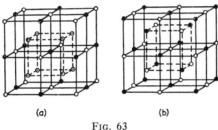

(a)   (b)

FIG. 63

If, on the other hand, $C_2 > 0$, then Φ has a minimum for $\gamma_1^2 = \gamma_2^2 = \tfrac{1}{2}$. Then $\delta\rho = \eta(\phi_1 + \phi_2)/\sqrt{2}$ (or $\eta(\phi_1 - \phi_2)/\sqrt{2}$, which leads to the same result). This function belongs to the symmetry class O_h with the same face-centred Bravais lattice as in the previous case, but only with two sets of equivalent sites, which can be occupied by two kinds of atoms, A and B:

$$8A \ (0, 0, 0), \quad (\tfrac{1}{4}, \tfrac{1}{4}, \tfrac{1}{4}), \quad (\tfrac{1}{4}, \tfrac{3}{4}, \tfrac{3}{4} \bigcirc), \quad (0, \tfrac{1}{2}, \tfrac{1}{2} \bigcirc)$$

$$8B \ (\tfrac{1}{2}, \tfrac{1}{2}, \tfrac{1}{2}), \quad (\tfrac{3}{4}, \tfrac{3}{4}, \tfrac{3}{4}), \quad (\tfrac{1}{4}, \tfrac{1}{4}, \tfrac{3}{4} \bigcirc), \quad (0, 0, \tfrac{1}{2} \bigcirc)$$

(cf. Fig. 63b).

(d) To these vectors **f** correspond the following functions with the required symmetry D_{2h}:

$$\phi_1 = \cos\pi(y - z), \quad\quad \phi_3 = \cos\pi(x - y), \quad\quad \phi_5 = \cos\pi(x - z),$$

$$\phi_2 = \cos\pi(y + z), \quad\quad \phi_4 = \cos\pi(x + y) \quad\quad \phi_6 = \cos\pi(x + z).$$

From these one can form one invariant of third degree, and four of fourth

---

† Or for $\gamma_1 = 0$, $\gamma_2 = 1$. The function $\delta\rho = \eta\phi_2$ has, however, the same symmetry as $\eta\phi_1$, and differs from it only by a change of origin by one lattice vector.

‡ This is the structure of the so-called Heussler alloys. The structures shown in Fig. 63(a) and (b) belong to different space groups: O_h^5 and O_h^7.

degree, so that the expansion (136.6) takes the form:

$$\Phi = \Phi_0 + A\eta^2 + B\eta^3(\gamma_1\gamma_3\gamma_5 + \gamma_2\gamma_3\gamma_6 + \gamma_1\gamma_4\gamma_6 + \gamma_2\gamma_4\gamma_5) +$$
$$C_1\eta^4 + C_2\eta^4(\gamma_2^4 + \gamma_2^4 + \gamma_3^4 + \gamma_4^4 + \gamma_5^4 + \gamma_6^4) + C_3\eta^4(\gamma_1^2\gamma_2^2 + \gamma_3^2\gamma_4^2 + \gamma_5^2\gamma_6^2). \tag{137.7}$$

Because of the presence of cubic terms a second-order phase transition is impossible in this case. To discuss the possible existence and properties of isolated continuous transition points one would have to study the behaviour of the function Φ near its minima; we shall not go into this question here.

Thus we see that the thermodynamic theory gives, in this example, a very severe restriction of the possible second-order phase transitions: they can exist only in the formation of three types of superlattice.

We draw attention to the following circumstances: In case (c), (assuming $C_2 < 0$) the actual change in the density distribution, $\delta\rho = \eta\phi_1$ corresponds only to one of the two parameters which appear in the thermodynamic potential (137.6). This shows up one of the important features of the theory we have presented: in discussing some particular change of the lattice in a second-order phase transition it may be necessary to take into account also other "virtually possible" changes.

§138. Critical and isolated points of a continuous transition

Since it separates phases of different symmetry, a second-order phase transition curve, in a P, T diagram cannot simply stop at a point. It may, however, change at some point into a first-order transition. Such a point will be called the critical point of the second-order transition; it is in some sense analogous to the ordinary critical point.

For the investigation of such a point we use again the expansion of Φ into powers of η (135.4–5) in which we now, however, must retain also terms of higher order:

$$\Phi = \Phi_0 + A\eta^2 + C\eta^4 + D\eta^5 + G\eta^6$$

On the second-order transition curve $A = 0$, $C > 0$. It is obvious that also, conversely, points in which these conditions are satisfied are second-order transition points. Hence at the critical point, where the second-order transitions curve ends, we must have $C = 0$. But in that case, the critical point itself does not correspond to a stable state unless also $D = 0$, $G > 0$. This is possible only if D vanishes identically for reasons of symmetry,† since we should otherwise have three equations for the two unknowns P and T at the critical point. We have therefore the expansion

$$\Phi(P, T, \eta) = \Phi_0(P, T) + A(P, T)\eta^2 + C(P, T)\eta^4 + G(P, T)\eta^6 \tag{138.1}$$

---

† In terms of the theory of §§136–7 this condition amounts to the absence of invariants of fifth degree in the quantities c_i.

where at the critical point

$$A_c = 0, \qquad C_c = 0, \qquad G_c > 0. \tag{138.2}$$

In the less symmetric phase the conditions $\partial\Phi/\partial\eta = 0$, $\partial^2\Phi/\partial\eta^2 > 0$ **give**

$$\eta^2 = \frac{1}{3G}[-C+\sqrt{(C^2-3AG)}] \tag{138.3}$$

and for the entropy of this phase we have, neglecting higher powers of η:

$$S = S_0 - a\eta^2 = S_0 + \frac{Ca}{3G} - \frac{a}{3G}\sqrt{(C^2-3AG)} \tag{138.4}$$

where $a = \partial A/\partial T$. Hence the specific heat:

$$C_p = \frac{Ta^2}{2(C^2-3AG)^{\frac{1}{2}}} \tag{138.5}$$

where we have written only the term whose denominator vanishes at the critical point.

Introduce the temperature $T_0 = T_0(P)$ for which $C^2-3AG = 0$. For $P = P_c$, T_0 obviously coincides with T_c (P_c, T_c are the pressure and temperature at the critical point). The first term in the expansion of C^2-3AG in powers of $T-T_c$ is then

$$C^2-3AG = -3a_0G_0(T-T_0). \tag{138.6}$$

The difference $T_c(P)-T_0(P)$ is, near the critical point, small of second order; indeed, at $T = T_c$ we have $A = 0$, and therefore

$$T_c-T_0 = -\frac{C^2}{3a_0G_0} \tag{138.7}$$

which at $T = T_c$ tends to zero as the square of C.

Inserting (138.6) in (138.5) we obtain

$$C_p = \left(\frac{T_c^2ac^3}{12G_c}\right)^{\frac{1}{2}} \frac{1}{(T_0-T)^{\frac{1}{2}}} \tag{138.8}$$

(the coefficients in this formula may, to the same accuracy, be evaluated at T_c instead of T_0). Thus we see that at the critical point the specific heat of the less symmetric phase tends to infinity as $(T_0-T)^{-\frac{1}{2}}$.

For states on the second-order transition curve itself we have, putting $A = 0$ in (138.5) (or inserting (138.7) in (138.5)):

$$C_p^{(\mathrm{II})} = \frac{T_cac^2}{2C} \tag{138.9}$$

Since C vanishes at the critical point, it is in the neighbourhood proportional to $T-T_c$ (or $P-P_c$).

We shall now determine the specific heat of the less symmetric phase on the first-order transition line, but again near the critical point. In the first-order transition the change of state takes place discontinuously, and the condition for the equilibrium of the two phases is that their thermodynamic potentials should be equal. The value of η in the less symmetric phase is therefore determined by the condition

$$\Phi(\eta) = \Phi_0$$

and we must have at the same time $\partial\Phi/\partial\eta = 0$. Inserting here from (138.1), we find the equations

$$A+C\eta^2+G\eta^4 = 0 \qquad A+2C\eta^2+3G\eta^4 = 0.$$

Eliminating A:

$$\eta^2 = -C/2G \tag{138.10}$$

and inserting this value in one of the initial equations we find:

$$4AG = C^2. \tag{138.11}$$

This equation determines P as a function of T along the first-order transition curve.

The specific heat of the less symmetric phase along this curve is obtained by simply inserting (138.11) in (138.5):

$$C_p{}^{(I)} = T_c a_c^2/|C|. \tag{138.12}$$

Comparison with (138.9) shows that on the first-order transition curve the specific heat is twice as large as on the second-order transition curve at the same distance from the critical point.

The latent heat for the transition from the less symmetrical to the more symmetrical phase on the first-order transition curve is:

$$q = T_c(S_0-S) = T_c a_c \eta^2 = \frac{a_c T_c|C|}{2G_c}. \tag{138.13}$$

Note that the product

$$qC_p{}^{(I)} = \frac{T_c^2 c_c^3}{2G_c}$$

depends on the same coefficient as eq. (138.8).

Finally, we shall show that the first-order transition curve joins on to the second-order curve without a kink, i.e. that the derivative dT/dP has no discontinuity at the critical point. On the second-order curve we have $A(P, T) = 0$, so that dT/dP can be found from the condition $dA = 0$. On the first-order curve, on the other hand, dT/dP is determined by the condition

$$2G\,dA+2A\,dG-C\,dC = 0$$

which follows by differentiating (138.11). But at the critical point $A = 0$,

$C = 0$, and we see therefore that the two conditions are identical there, which proves our assertion. One can show similarly that the second derivative d^2T/dP^2 does have a jump at the critical point.

According to (135.11) the derivatives $(\partial V/\partial P)_T$ and $(\partial V/\partial T)_P$ must tend to infinity with C_p. The quantities C_v and $(\partial P/\partial T)_V$ on the other hand, have only finite discontinuities at the critical point.

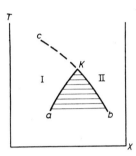

FIG. 64

We shall briefly discuss the critical point for second-order phase transitions in mixtures of two substances. One can show† that the state diagram near such a point takes the form shown in Fig. 64. (As abscissa we plot the concentration x of the mixture, and as ordinate, the temperature). The lines Ka and Kb are first-order phase transition lines and Kc is that of the second-order phase transitions. The shaded area aKb is the region split into two phases of which phase I is the less symmetrical and phase II the more symmetrical. The point K is the critical point; the curve bK joins smoothly on to Kc. One can show that at the critical point the specific heat C_p of the mixture undergoes only a finite discontinuity.

Lastly it remains for us to consider the case when the third-order terms in the expansion of the thermodynamic potential do not vanish identically. In this case the condition for the existence of a continuous phase transition requires the coefficients $B_\alpha(P, T)$ of the third-order invariants to vanish together with $A(P, T)$. It is obvious that this is possible only if there is only one third-order invariant; otherwise we would have more than two equations for the two unknowns P and T‡. If there is only one invariant of third order the two equations $A(P, T) = 0$ and $B(P, T) = 0$ determine the corresponding pairs of values of P, T i.e. continuous phase transitions occur at isolated points.‖

Being isolated, these points must lie in a certain way on the intersections of curves (in the P, T plane) of first-order phase transitions. Bearing in

---

† Cf. L. Landau, *Phys. Zft. der Sowjet Union*, 11, 26, 1937.
‡ It seems, however, that one can prove (although we have not succeeded in doing so in general form) a theorem according to which there can never be more than one third-order invariant (for irreducible representations of the space groups).
‖ There are grounds for supposing that for transitions between liquids and solid crystals even such isolated points of continuous phase transitions are impossible.

mind that such isolated continuous transition points have not yet been observed experimentally, we shall not give a detailed investigation here, but we shall restrict ourselves to indicating the results.†

The simplest type is shown in Fig. 65a. Phase I has the higher symmetry and phases II and III the lower symmetry. The symmetries of phases II and III are the same and the phases only differ in the sign of η. At the continuous transition point (O in Fig. 65) all the three phases become identical.

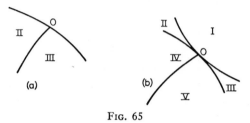

FIG. 65

In more complicated cases, two or more first-order phase transition curves touch at the point of the continuous transition (as in Fig. 65b). Phase I is the most symmetrical, the rest being less symmetrical; the symmetries of phases II and III (and of phases IV and V) are the same, and the phases only differ in the sign of η.

PROBLEM

Find the relation between the discontinuity in the specific heat and in the heat of solution in a second-order phase transition in a solution (E. M. LIFSHITZ, 1950).

SOLUTION: The heat of solution, per molecule of solute, is defined by

$$q = \frac{\partial W}{\partial n} - w_0'$$

where W is the heat function of the solution, and w_0' the heat function per particle of the pure solute. Since w_0' is independent of the phase transition in the solution,

$$\Delta q = \Delta \frac{\partial W}{\partial n} = \Delta \frac{\partial}{\partial n}\left(\Phi - T \frac{\partial \Phi}{\partial T} \right) = -T \frac{\partial^2 \Phi}{\partial n \partial T}$$

(here we have used the fact that the chemical potential $\mu' = \partial \Phi/\partial n$ is continuous in the transition). On the other hand, if we differentiate the equation $\Delta(\partial \Phi/\partial T) = 0$ (continuity of entropy) along the transition curve $T_c = T_c(c)$ (at constant pressure) we find

$$\frac{dT}{dc}\Delta \frac{\partial^2 \Phi}{\partial T^2} + \Delta \frac{\partial^2 \Phi}{\partial n \partial T} = 0.$$

Hence the required relation

$$N \Delta q = \frac{\Delta C_p}{T} \frac{dT}{dc}.$$

Note that it does not involve any assumption about the concentration c of the solution.

† For a detailed discussion, see L. LANDAU, *loc. cit.*

CHAPTER XV

SURFACES

§139. Surface tension

Up till now we have neglected effects due to the existence of surfaces of separation between different bodies.† Since, as the size of a body increases, the surface effects increase much more slowly than the volume effects, this neglect was quite justified when the latter were examined. There exist, however, specific effects which are directly connected with the properties of the surface of separation.

The thermodynamic properties of a surface of separation are determined by one quantity (a function of the states of the bodies) defined as follows. Let the area of the surface of separation be $\mathfrak{s}$ and consider the process of reversibly changing this area by the infinitesimal quantity $d\mathfrak{s}$. The work done in such a process is proportional to $d\mathfrak{s}$, i.e. it can be written in the form

$$dR = \alpha \, d\mathfrak{s} \tag{139.1}$$

The quantity α defined in this way represents a fundamental characteristic of the surface of separation; it is called the *coefficient of surface tension.*

(139.1) corresponds exactly to the formula $dR = -P \, dV$ for the work done in a reversible change of volume of the body. One can say that α plays the same part for a surface as the pressure does for a volume. In particular, it is easy to show that, for unit length of the contour bounding some part of the surface of separation, there acts a force of magnitude α and which is directed tangentially to the surface along the inwards normal to the contour.

That α is positive, is immediately proved by the following argument. If α were negative then the forces would act along the outwards normal to the contour bounding the surface, i.e. would "stretch" the surface; in other words, the surface of separation between two phases would tend to increase indefinitely, i.e. the phases would cease to exist at all, since they would mix. On the other hand, for $\alpha > 0$ the surface of separation tends to have its smallest possible value (for the given volume of the two phases). Hence, for example, if one isotropic phase is immersed in another it will assume a spherical shape. (Here, of course, we neglect the action of the external (gravitational) field).

---

† In actual fact, the phases in contact are separated by a narrow transitional layer; not being concerned with its structure, we can regard it as a geometrical surface.

Consider now in greater detail the surface of separation between two isotropic phases—the liquid and vapour of the same substance. First of all, note the following fact. One can speak of the quantity α only when the two phases are in equilibrium with one another and a stable surface of separation exists between them. In other words, the coefficient of surface tension, α, only has a meaning on a phase equilibrium curve. But along such a curve (for two pure substance phases) P and T are connected by some definite functional relation. Hence α is a function of one independent variable, and not two.

At the critical point, when the liquid and gaseous phases become identical, the surface of separation between them ceases to exist and must vanish. The law according to which this takes place has not yet been discovered.†

The law of corresponding states (§82) may be applied qualitatively to the surface tension between liquid and vapour. From the nature of this law one would expect that the dimensionless ratio of α to a quantity constructed from the critical temperature and pressure, with dimensions erg/cm² will be a universal function of the relative temperature T/T_k:

$$\frac{\alpha}{(kT_kP_k{}^2)^{1/3}} = f\left(\frac{T}{T_k}\right). \tag{139.2}$$

Without taking surface effects into account, the thermodynamic identity for a system of two phases (of the same substance) for a given volume V of the whole system, is $dE = T\,dS + \mu\,dN$ (in equilibrium the temperatures T, and chemical potentials μ of the two phases will be the same, which makes it possible to write down this identity for the system as a whole). But when we take the surfaces of separation into account, we must also add to the right-hand side of this identity the quantity (139.1).

$$dE = T\,dS + \mu\,dN + \alpha\,ds. \tag{139.3}$$

As the basic thermodynamic quantity, however, it is convenient to choose not the energy but the potential Ω, the quantity which is the thermodynamic potential relating to the independent variables T, μ (and the volume V). The convenience of this quantity for this case is due to the fact that T and μ are both quantities having the same values for the two phases (while the pressures, after taking surface effects into account, may not be the same; see §140). The thermodynamic identity for Ω is (again for $V = $ const):

$$d\Omega = -S\,dT - N\,d\mu + \alpha\,ds. \tag{139.4}$$

The thermodynamic quantities (such as E, Ω, S, etc.) of the system under consideration can be expressed as the sum of two parts, "volume" and

---

† Usually the law $\alpha \propto (T_k-T)^{3/2}$ is given as the law which follows from thermodynamic theory. Its proof is based on considering the variations of the density in the transition layer between the two phases and the fluctuational displacements in the layer are not taken into account. But one can show that near the critical point these fluctuations are very large (compared with the thickness of the layer) and hence they make quite meaningless this picture of the structure of the transitional layer on which the proof of the given law was based.

"surface". Such a division, however, is not unique, since the numbers of particles in each of the phases are determined only with accuracy up to the number of particles situated in the transition layer between the phases; the same applies to the phase volumes. But this uncertainty is of just the same order of magnitude as the surface effects we are considering. We shall make the division unique by subjecting it to the following natural condition. The volumes V_1 and V_2 of the two phases are defined in such a way that besides the relation $V_1 + V_2 = V$ (where V is the total volume of the system), the equation

$$n_1 V_1 + n_2 \ _2 = N \tag{139.5}$$

also holds, where N is the total number of particles in the system, and $n_1 = n_1(\mu, T)$ and $n_2 = n_2(\mu, T)$ are the volume densities of the number of particles in each phase (considered as unbounded).

These two relations fix the choice of the volumes V_1, V_2 (and the numbers of particles $N_1 = n_1 V_1$ and $N_2 = n_2 V_2$) and through this the volume parts of all the other thermodynamic quantities. We denote the volume parts by the suffix 0, and the surface parts by the suffix s; for the number of particles, by our definition $N_s = 0$.

From (139.4) we have, for constant T and μ (and hence also constant α); $d\Omega = \alpha \, ds$; hence it is clear that $\Omega_s = \alpha s$. Thus

$$\Omega = \Omega_0 + \alpha s$$

Since the entropy $S = -(\partial \Omega / \partial T)_\mu s$ its surface part must be†

$$S_s = -\frac{\partial \Omega_s}{\partial T} = -s \frac{d\alpha}{dT}. \tag{139.6}$$

Next we find the surface free energy. Since $F = \Omega + N\mu$ and $N_s = 0$, we have:

$$F_s = \alpha s. \tag{139.7}$$

The surface energy

$$E_s = F_s + T S_s = \left(\alpha - T \frac{d\alpha}{dT} \right) s. \tag{139.8}$$

---

† The coefficient α is a function of only one independent variable; the concept of the partial derivative of such a function with respect to μ or T has no meaning by itself. However, by postulating

$$N_s = -\left(\frac{\partial \Omega_s}{\partial \mu} \right)_T = 0,$$

we formally took $(\partial \alpha / \partial \mu)_T = 0$. Under these conditions we obviously have:

$$\frac{d\alpha}{dT} = \left(\frac{\partial \alpha}{\partial T} \right)_\mu$$

and this is used in the expression (139.5) for the surface entropy.

The quantity of heat absorbed in a reversible isothermal change of the surface area from $\mathfrak{s}_1$ to $\mathfrak{s}_2$ is equal to

$$Q = T(S_{\mathfrak{s}2}-S_{\mathfrak{s}1}) = -T\frac{\mathrm{d}\alpha}{\mathrm{d}T}(\mathfrak{s}_2-\mathfrak{s}_1).\tag{139.9}$$

The sum of the heat Q and the work $R = \alpha(\mathfrak{s}_2-\mathfrak{s}_1)$ for this process is equal, as it should be, to the change in energy $E_{\mathfrak{s}2}-E_{\mathfrak{s}1}$.

PROBLEM

1. Find the temperature dependence of the surface tension of liquid helium at low temperatures (K. R. ATKINS, 1953).

SOLUTION: We calculate the surface part $F_\mathfrak{s} = \alpha\mathfrak{s}$ of the free energy by means of (61.1), where the frequencies ω_α now refers to vibrations of the surface of the liquid. In two dimensions the transition from summation to integration is carried out by inserting a factor $\mathfrak{s}(2\pi f\,\mathrm{d}f)/(2\pi)^2$. After integration by parts, we find

$$F_\mathfrak{s} = \mathfrak{s}\alpha_0+\mathfrak{s}\frac{kT}{2\pi}\int \log(1-e^{-\hbar\omega/kT})f\,\mathrm{d}f = \mathfrak{s}\alpha_0-\mathfrak{s}\frac{\hbar}{4\pi}\int\frac{f^2\,\mathrm{d}\omega}{e^{\hbar\omega/kT}-1}$$

(α_0 being the surface tension at $T = 0$). For low enough temperatures, only vibrations with low frequencies are of importance, and these belong to small f (long waves). But such long waves are hydrodynamic capillary waves for which

$$\omega^2 = \frac{\alpha}{\rho}f^3 \cong \frac{\alpha_0}{\rho}f^3$$

(ρ being the density of the liquid)†. Hence

$$\alpha = \alpha_0-\frac{\hbar}{4\pi}\left(\frac{\rho}{\alpha_0}\right)^{2/3}\int\limits_0^\infty\frac{\omega^{4/3}\,\mathrm{d}\omega}{e^{\hbar\omega/kT}-1}.$$

The rapid convergence of the integral allows us to replace the upper limit by ∞. Evaluating the integral by the method given in the footnote on page 164 we find finally

$$\alpha = \alpha_0-\frac{(kT)^{7/3}}{4\pi\hbar^{4/3}}\left(\frac{\rho}{\alpha}\right)^{2/3}\Gamma(7/3)\zeta(7/3) = \alpha_0-0\cdot13\frac{(kT)^{7/3}}{\hbar^{4/3}}\left(\frac{\rho}{\alpha}\right)^{2/3}.$$

§140. The surface tension of crystals

The surface tension of an anisotropic body (a crystal)‡ is not the same for all of its faces; one can say that it is a function of the direction of the face (i.e. its Miller indices). This function is of a rather peculiar nature.

---

† See our *Hydrodynamics* §61. The derivation given here applies only to liquid He⁴, and to temperatures so low that the whole mass of liquid may be assumed superfluid. In a Fermi liquid (liquid He³) capillary waves of this type do not exist, because of the unlimited increase in viscosity as $T\to0$.

‡ We have in mind the surface tension at the boundary between the crystal and a gas or liquid.

Note that there are, as yet, no reliable measurements of this quantity for any crystal. The difficulty in measuring it is due to the fact that the surface tension hardly affects the phenomena occurring in a solid.

On the one hand the difference in the values of α for two crystal planes with arbitrarily close directions is also arbitrarily small, i.e. the surface tension can be represented as a continuous function of the direction of the face. On the other hand, however, one can show that this function has no definite derivative at any point. Thus, for example, considering a family of crystal planes intersecting in a straight line (letting ϕ be the angle of rotation about this line determining the direction of the plane) we find that the function $\alpha = \alpha(\phi)$ has two different derivatives for each value of ϕ in the directions of increasing and decreasing arguments.†

Assume that we know the surface tension as a function of the directions of the crystal faces. The question arises of how, with the help of this function the equilibrium form of the crystal can be determined; we must emphasise that the shape observed under normal conditions is determined by the growth of the crystal and is by no means the equilibrium one. The equilibrium form is determined by the condition that the potential Ω should be a minimum for given values of T, μ and the volume V of the crystal) or, which comes to the same thing, by the condition that its surface part should be a minimum. The latter is equal to

$$\Omega_s = \oint \alpha \, d\mathfrak{s}$$

where the integral is taken over the whole surface of the crystal (for an isotropic body $\alpha = \text{const}$, $\Omega = \alpha s$ and the equilibrium form is determined simply by the condition that the whole surface s of the body should be a minimum, i.e. it becomes a sphere).

Let $z = z(x, y)$ be the equation of the crystal surface and let us introduce the notation

$$p = \frac{\partial z}{\partial x}, \qquad q = \frac{\partial z}{\partial y}$$

for the derivative determining the direction of the surface at each point; α can be expressed as a function of these: $\alpha = \alpha(p, q)$. The equilibrium form is determined by the condition

$$\int \alpha(p, q) \sqrt{(1+p^2+q^2)} \cdot dx\,dy = \text{min} \tag{140.1}$$

with the auxiliary condition

$$\int z\,dx\,dy = \text{const} \tag{140.2}$$

(constancy of volume). This variational problem leads to the differential

---

† For further details see L. LANDAU: "On the equilibrium form of crystals". Papers presented in honour of the 70th birthday of A. F. JOFFE, 1950.

equation

$$\frac{\partial}{\partial x}\frac{\partial f}{\partial p}+\frac{\partial}{\partial y}\frac{\partial f}{\partial q}=2\lambda \tag{140.3}$$

where we have introduced the notation

$$f(p,q)=\alpha(p,q)\sqrt{(1+p^2+q^2)} \tag{140.4}$$

and λ is a constant.

Next we have, by definition, $dz = p\,dx + q\,dy$; introducing the auxiliary function

$$\zeta = px+qy-z, \tag{140.5}$$

for which we have $d\zeta = x\,dp + y\,dq$, or

$$x = \frac{\partial\zeta}{\partial p}, \qquad y = \frac{\partial\zeta}{\partial q}, \tag{140.6}$$

where ζ is regarded as a function of p and q. Rewriting the derivatives with respect to x and y in (140.3) as Jacobians, multiplying both sides of the equation by $\partial(x,y)/\partial(p,q)$, and using (140.6), we get the equation

$$\frac{\partial\left(\dfrac{\partial f}{\partial p},\dfrac{\partial\zeta}{\partial q}\right)}{\partial(p,q)}+\frac{\partial\left(\dfrac{\partial\zeta}{\partial p},\dfrac{\partial f}{\partial q}\right)}{\partial(p,q)}=2\lambda\frac{\partial\left(\dfrac{\partial\zeta}{\partial p},\dfrac{\partial\zeta}{\partial q}\right)}{\partial(p,q)}.$$

This equation has the integral

$$f = \lambda\zeta = \lambda(px+qy-z),$$

or

$$z = \frac{1}{\lambda}\left(p\frac{\partial f}{\partial p}+q\frac{\partial f}{\partial q}-f\right). \tag{140.7}$$

But this is simply the equation of the envelope of the family of planes

$$px+qy-z = \frac{1}{\lambda}\alpha(p,q)\sqrt{(1+p^2+q^2)} \tag{140.8}$$

(where p, q act as parameters).

The result we have obtained can also be put in the form of the following geometrical construction. Along each radius vector we mark off a segment whose length is proportional to $\alpha(p,\,q)$ where p, q determine the direction of the radius vector.† Across the ends of the segments we put planes perpendicular to them; the envelope of these planes gives the equilibrium form of the crystal (G. V. WULF).

---

† The three direction cosines of the radius vector are proportional to p, q, and -1 respectively.

One can show (see the reference on page 461) that owing to the peculiar nature of the function α, this rule can result in the form of the crystal containing a series of plane areas corresponding to crystal planes with small Miller indices; the size of the plane area decreases quickly for increasing Miller indices. In practice it leads to the equilibrium form of the crystal bounded by a small number of plane areas which, however, do not intersect at an angle but are connected by rounded surfaces.

§141. Surface pressure

The condition that the pressures of two phases in contact should be equal was based (§77) on equating the forces with which the two phases act on each other across their surface of contact. There, however, as everywhere else, we neglected all surface effects. But it is clear that if the surface of separation is not plane then a displacement will, in general, change its area, and hence its energy. In other words, the existence of a curved surface of separation between the phases results in the appearance of additional forces connected with the properties of this surface. As a result, the pressures of the two phases will not be equal; their difference is called the *surface pressure*.

Thus the equilibrium conditions of the phases only require the equality of their temperatures and chemical potentials. In view of this, in calculating the surface pressure we must consider, naturally, the quantity which is the thermodynamic potential relating to just these variables, i.e. the potential Ω.

Consider two isotropic phases (two liquids or a liquid and vapour) and let their pressures and volumes be, respectively, P_1, V_1 and P_2, V_2. Then the volume part of the potential Ω for the whole system will be equal to $\Omega_0 = -P_1V_1 - P_2V_2$, since for the separate phases it is equal to $-P_1V_1$ and $-P_2V_2$ respectively. Substituting this into (135.5), we obtain

$$\Omega = -P_1V_1 - P_2V_2 + \alpha\mathfrak{s} \tag{141.1}$$

In a thermodynamic equilibrium state the potential Ω of the system must be a minimum with respect to displacements of the surface of separation for constant temperature, chemical potential, and the volume $(V_1 + V_2)$; in other words, we must have $d\Omega = 0$ with the additional conditions

$$T = \text{const}, \qquad \mu = \text{const}, \qquad V_1 + V_2 = \text{const}.$$

The differential $d\Omega$ can also be found from (141.1). It must be remembered, here, that P_1 and P_2, the pressures of two phases in equilibrium with each other, satisfy the equations $\mu_1(P_1, T) = \mu_2(P_2, T) = \mu$ where μ is the common value of the two chemical potentials. Hence P_1 and P_2 can be considered as functions of T and μ. But we require a minimum of Ω at constant T and μ. Hence in differentiating Ω we must take P_1, P_2 and also α as constant. We find in this way:

$$d\Omega = -P_1\,dV_1 - P_2\,dV_2 + \alpha\,d\mathfrak{s}$$

where dV_1, dV_2 and ds are the changes in the corresponding quantities for an infinitesimal displacement of the surface. Since the total volume must be constant, $dV_1 = -dV_2$, so that

$$d\Omega = -dV_1(P_1-P_2)+\alpha\,ds = 0,$$

or

$$P_1-P_2 = \alpha\frac{ds}{dV_1}. \tag{141.2}$$

In differential geometry, it can be shown that the derivative

$$\frac{ds}{dV_1} = \frac{1}{r}+\frac{1}{r'}$$

where r and r' are the principal radii of curvature of the surface at the given point (r and r' must be taken as positive in this formula when they are directed into the first phase). Substituting this expression into (141.2) gives

$$P_1-P_2 = \alpha\left(\frac{1}{r}+\frac{1}{r'}\right) \tag{141.3}$$

This formula (called *Laplace's formula*) determines the difference between the pressures in the two phases at any point of their surface of separation. In the case of a plane surface of separation (r and r' infinite) the pressure in the two phases is the same.

If the first phase is a sphere immersed in the second phase (a drop of liquid in a vapour or a bubble of vapour in a liquid) than the surface of separation is spherical and its principal radii of curvature are equal to each other and have the same value everywhere (equal to the radius r of the sphere). (141.3) then takes the form

$$P_1-P_2 = \frac{2\alpha}{r}. \tag{141.4}$$

This can be deduced directly from (141.2) if we notice that then $s = 4\pi r^2$, $V = 4\pi r^3$ and hence $ds = 8\pi r\,dr$, $dV = 4\pi r^2\,dr$ so that

$$\frac{ds}{dV} = \frac{2}{r}.$$

The results we have obtained only determine the difference of pressure between the two phases; now let us calculate these two pressures separately. If the surface of separation between the phases were plane then the pressures of the two phases would be equal. Let their common value in this case (at given temperature) be P_0, and let us introduce the quantities $\delta P_1 = P_1-P_0$, $\delta P_2 = P_2-P_0$, i.e. the changes of pressure of the two phases due to the curvature of the surface of separation.

Let μ_1 and μ_2 be the chemical potentials of the two phases. Since the phases are in equilibrium with each other, $\mu_1 = \mu_2$ whatever the form of the surface. Differentiating this equation with respect to the curvature of the surface at constant temperature, we find:

$$v_1 \delta P_1 - v_2 \delta P_2 = 0 \qquad (141.5)$$

(see eq. 24.12). Here the pressure changes δP_1, and δP_2 are assumed small (which is a valid assumption, owing to the smallness of the surface effects); v_1 and v_2 are the molecular volumes in the first and second phases. Taking the case of a spherical surface of separation (the first phase spherical) we shall use formula (141.4) rewriting it in the form

$$\delta P_1 - \delta P_2 = \frac{2\alpha}{r}.$$

From the two equations we have obtained, we determine δP_1 and δP_2:

$$\delta P_1 = \frac{2\alpha}{r} \frac{v_2}{v_2 - v_1}, \qquad \delta P_2 = \frac{2\alpha}{r} \frac{v_1}{v_2 - v_1}. \qquad (141.6)$$

For the drop of liquid in vapour, we have $v_1 \ll v_2$: considering the vapour as a perfect gas we have, for its molecular volume, $v_2 = kT/P_2 \simeq kT/P_0$ and as a result we obtain from (141.6):

$$\delta P_l = \frac{2\alpha}{r}, \qquad \delta P_g = \frac{2v_l \alpha}{rkT} P_0 \qquad (141.7)$$

(for clarity we use suffices l and g instead of 1 and 2). The vapour pressure over a drop of liquid thus decreases as the radius of the drop increases, tending to its value over a plane liquid surface.

Similarly, for a bubble of gas in a liquid, we find the same result as (141.7) with opposite signs.

§142. Surface tension of solutions

Consider now the surface of separation between a liquid solution and a gaseous phase (gas and its solution in a liquid, a liquid solution and its vapour, etc.).

As was done in §139, we shall divide all the thermodynamic quantities of the system under consideration into volume and surface parts. The method of division is fixed by the conditions $V = V_1 + V_2$, $N = N_1 + N_2$ for the volume and number of particles of the solvent. In other words, the whole volume V of the system is completely divided between the two phases and so, multiplying V_1 and V_2 by the corresponding volume densities of the number of particles of the solvent we obtain, as their sum, just the total number N of particles of the solvent in the system. Thus, by definition, the surface part $N_s = 0$.

Amongst other quantities, the number of particles of the solute will also be represented as the sum of two parts: $n = n_0 + n_s$. One can say that n_0 is the amount of solute which would be contained in the volumes V_1 and V_2 if it were distributed in them with constant concentration equal to the volume concentration of the corresponding solution. The number n_0 defined in this way may either be larger or smaller than the actual total number n of particles of the solute. If $n_s = n - n_0 > 0$ then it means that the solute accumulates with increased concentration in the surface layer (which is called *positive adsorption*). If $n_s < 0$, then the concentration in the surface layer is less than the volume concentration (which is called *negative adsorption*).

The coefficient of surface tension of the solution is now a function of not one, but two independent variables. Since the derivative of the potential Ω with respect to the chemical potential (taken with the opposite sign) gives the corresponding number of particles, one can obtain n_s by differentiating $\Omega_s = \alpha s$ with respect to the chemical potential μ' of the solute,†

$$n_s = -\frac{\partial \Omega_s}{\partial \mu'} = -s\left(\frac{\partial \alpha}{\partial \mu'}\right)_T. \qquad (142.1)$$

Assume that the pressure of the gaseous phase is so small that its effect on the properties of the liquid phase can be neglected. Then the derivative of α in (142.1) which should be taken along the phase equilibrium curve for given temperature can be replaced by the derivative taken for given (equal to zero) pressure (and constant T). Consider α as a function of temperature and the concentration c of the solution. (142.1) can be rewritten in the form

$$n_s = -s\left(\frac{\partial \alpha}{\partial c}\right)_T \left(\frac{\partial c}{\partial \mu'}\right)_{T,P}. \qquad (142.2)$$

But according to the thermodynamic inequality (95.7), the derivative $(\partial \mu'/\partial c)_{T,P}$ is always positive. Hence, from (142.2) it follows that n_s and $(\partial \alpha/\partial c)_T$ have opposite signs. This means that if the solute raises the surface tension (α increases with an increase in the concentration of the solution) then it is negatively adsorbed. Substances which lower the surface tension are adsorbed positively.

If the solution is weak, then the chemical potential of the solute has the

---

† The coefficient α is now a function of two independent variables, for example μ' and T. The derivative $\partial \Omega_s/\partial \mu$, must be taken with T and the chemical potential μ of the solvent also constant. But the condition we have accepted,

$$N_s = -\left(\frac{\partial \Omega_s}{\partial \mu}\right)_{\mu',T} = 0$$

means that we may formally put $(\partial \alpha/\partial \mu)_{\mu',T^2} = 0$, which makes it possible for us to write down eq. (142.1) (c.f. footnote on page 459).

form $\mu' = kT \log c + \psi(P, T)$ and substituting this into (142.2), we find:

$$n_s = -\varsigma \frac{c}{kT} \left(\frac{\partial \alpha}{\partial c} \right)_T. \tag{142.3}$$

Similarly, the formula

$$n_s = -\varsigma \frac{P}{kT} \left(\frac{\partial \alpha}{\partial P} \right)_T \tag{142.4}$$

is obtained for the adsorption of a gas (with pressure P) into a liquid surface.

If not only the solution, but also the adsorption out of it is weak, then one can expand α in powers of c and write, approximately:

$$\alpha = \alpha_0 + \alpha_1 c$$

where α_0 is the surface tension at the boundary between two phases of the pure solvent. We then find, from (142.3) that

$$\alpha_1 = -\frac{n_s kT}{\varsigma c}$$

so that

$$\alpha - \alpha_0 = -\frac{n_s kT}{\varsigma}. \tag{142.5}$$

Note the similarity between this and the van t'Hoff formula for the osmotic pressure (the surface area here plays the part of the volume).

§143. Surface tension in solutions of strong electrolytes

The change in the surface tension of a liquid upon dissolving in it a strong electrolyte can, for weak solutions, be solved in general (L. ONSAGER, N. T. SAMARAS, 1934).

We denote by $w_a(x)$ the additional energy of an ion of type a due to the presence of the surface when it is a distance x from the surface ($w_a(x)$ tends to zero as $x \to \infty$). The concentration of ions near the surface differs from their concentration c_a in the body of the solution by a factor

$$e^{-w_a/kT} \cong 1 - \frac{w_a}{kT}$$

Hence the surface contribution to the total number of these ions in the liquid is

$$n_{as} = -\frac{\varsigma c_a}{vkT} \int_0^\infty w_a \, dx \tag{143.1}$$

(v is the molecular volume of the solvent).

In the presence of several kinds of solute particles, (143.1) appears in the form

$$\mathfrak{s}\, d\alpha = - \sum_a n_{as}\, d\mu'_a,$$ (143.2)

and for dilute solutions ($\mu'_a = kT \log c_a + \psi_a$):

$$\mathfrak{s}d\alpha = -kT \sum_a \frac{n_{as}}{c_a}\, dc_a.$$ (143.3)

Inserting here from (143.1), we obtain

$$d\alpha = \frac{1}{v} \sum_a dc_a \int_0^\infty w_a\, dx.$$ (143.4)

As will be clear from the further discussion, the main contribution to the integrals comes from distances x which are large compared to intermolecular distances, but small compared to the Debye-Hueckel radius $1/\kappa$.

The energy w_a is made up of two parts:

$$w_a = \frac{\epsilon-1}{\epsilon(\epsilon+1)} \frac{e^2 z_a^2}{4x} + ez_a\phi(x).$$ (143.5)

The first term represents the energy associated with the so-called "image force" which acts on a charge ez_a, placed in a medium of dielectric constant ϵ at a distance x from its surface. Because of the inequality $x \ll 1/\kappa$, the screening effect of the ion cloud surrounding the charge ez_a does not affect this energy. In the second term, $\phi(x)$ denotes the change, due to the presence of the surface, in the potential field due to the other ions in the solution. This contribution is, however, unimportant for the present purpose, since it cancels when we substitute (143.5) in (143.4) because the solution is electrically neutral ($\Sigma\, c_a z_a = 0$ and therefore also $\Sigma\, z_a\, dc_a = 0$).

Hence, if we carry out the integration in (143.4) we find

$$d\alpha = \frac{(\epsilon-1)e^2}{4\epsilon(\epsilon+1)v} \sum_a \log \frac{1}{a_a\kappa}\, d(z_a^2 c_a).$$

The logarithmic divergence of the integral at both limits confirms the statement made previously about the range of integration. We have taken here as upper limit, of course, the screening radius $1/\kappa$, and as lower limit a distance a_a of the order of atomic dimensions (but different for the different kinds of ions). If we remember that κ^2 is proportional to $\Sigma\, z_a^2 c_a$, we see that the expression we have obtained is a complete differential and can therefore be integrated immediately, with the result

$$\alpha - \alpha_0 = \frac{(\epsilon-1)e^2}{8\epsilon(\epsilon+1)v} \sum_a c_a z_a^2 \log \frac{\lambda_a z_a^2}{\sum_b c_b z_b^2} \qquad (143.6)$$

where α_0 is the surface tension of the pure solvent, and λ_a a dimensionless constant.

This is the solution of the question posed at the beginning of this section. Note that the surface tension increases when the electrolyte is dissolved.

§144. Adsorption

By *adsorption* in the narrow sense of the word one means cases when the solute concentrates almost entirely on the surface of the condensed phase (adsorbent)†, and hardly penetrates into its volume. The "adsorption film" arising in this way can be described by a "*surface concentration*" γ, defined as the number of particles of the adsorbed substance per unit surface area. For small pressures of the gas from which the adsorption occurs the concentration γ must be proportional to the pressure,‡ For large pressures the increase in γ slows down, tending to a limiting value corresponding to the creation of what is called a monomolecular layer, with densely situated molecules of the adsorbed substance.

Let μ' be the chemical potential of the adsorbed substance. By the method used in §95 for volume solutions, one can obtain, for adsorption, the thermodynamic inequality

$$\left(\frac{\partial \mu'}{\partial \gamma}\right)_T > 0 \qquad (144.1)$$

quite analogously to the inequality (95.7). On the other hand, from (143.1) we have:

$$\gamma = -\left(\frac{\partial \alpha}{\partial \mu'}\right)_T = -\left(\frac{\partial \alpha}{\partial \gamma}\right)_T \left(\frac{\partial \gamma}{\partial \mu'}\right)_T, \qquad (144.2)$$

whence it follows, from inequality (144.1), that

$$\left(\frac{\partial \alpha}{\partial \gamma}\right)_T < 0, \qquad (144.3)$$

i.e. the surface tension decreases as the surface concentration rises.

Assume that adsorption takes place from the saturated vapour of the adsorbed substance. Such a vapour has, for a given temperature, a definite value of the chemical potential, equal to the chemical potential μ_l of the liquid

---

† For the sake of definiteness we are considering adsorption from the gaseous phase.
‡ This rule is, however, not satisfied in practice for adsorption on to the surface of a solid, in view of the fact that this surface is, in fact, never homogeneous at all.

phase. The concentration γ must take values such that the chemical potential μ' of the adsorption film is equal to the same μ_l. There are two cases possible. In one of them the equality $\mu' = \mu_l$ already occurs for some finite value of the concentration γ—then the adsorption film is of the same sort as in the case of adsorption from a non-saturated vapour. In the other case, μ_l is the limit to which the monotonically increasing potential of the layer tends as $\gamma \rightarrow \infty$; physically, this means that a macroscopically thick layer of liquid adsorbed substance must appear on the surface of the adsorbent, so that the saturated vapour is directly in contact with its own liquid phase. This case corresponds to what is called *complete wetting*: the adsorbed substance completely wets the surface of the adsorbent.

The minimum work which must be performed for the creation of the adsorption film is equal to the corresponding change in its thermodynamic potential Ω:

$$R_{\min} = \varsigma(\alpha - \alpha_0) \tag{144.4}$$

where α_0 is the surface tension of the bare surface. Hence we find, according to (89.4) the heat of adsorption

$$Q = -\varsigma T^2 \left(\frac{\partial}{\partial T} \frac{\alpha - \alpha_0}{T} \right)_P. \tag{144.5}$$

The adsorption film may be considered as a sort of peculiar "two-dimensional" thermodynamic system which can be either isotropic or anisotropic, in spite of the isotropy of both the volume phases.† The question arises of the possible symmetry types for the layer.

The analogue of the usual solid crystals would be a "solid crystalline" layer in which the atoms were regularly situated at the points of a two dimensional (plane) lattice. This configuration could be described by a two-dimensional "density function" $\rho(x, y)$ (cf. §125). However, an investigation analogous to that made in §125 for the three-dimensional case shows that such a lattice cannot exist as it would be "smeared out" as a result of thermal fluctuations (so that the only possibility is $\rho = \text{const}$). That is, the mean square fluctuational displacement is determined by an integral of the same type (125.2) as for the three-dimensional crystal lattice:

$$\overline{u^2} \sim kT \int\int \frac{df_x \, df_y}{\phi(f_x, f_y)}$$

but in the two-dimensional case this integral diverges logarithmically for small values of the wave vector.

To avoid misunderstanding it is, however, necessary to make the following remark. The investigation mentioned only proves that the fluctuational

---

† We are thinking here of adsorption on to the surface of a liquid: the adsorption on a solid surface is of no interest in this connection owing to the above-mentioned inhomogeneity which it almost always possesses.

deviations tend to infinity as the area of the system increases indefinitely†
(while for a three-dimensional system these deviations still remain finite for
an unbounded system). However, the dimensions of the layer for which the
fluctuations remain small may, in fact, be quite large. In these cases a film
of finite size could, in practice, exhibit "solid crystalline" properties, and one
could approximately treat it as a two-dimensional lattice.

However, in a rigorous sense, for a two-dimensional layer, considered as
an infinite structure, one can only talk of the symmetry of the correlation
between positions of different molecules, for a given position of one of them.
In this sense an anisotropic layer represents the two-dimensional analogue
of a three-dimensional liquid crystal (see §126). Correspondingly the types
of symmetry of layers must be classified according to the point groups (combinations of planes and axes of symmetry). These rotations about axes and
reflections in planes must, of course, transform the plane of the film into itself
and also leave invariant the relative arrangement of the two phases on whose
boundary the layer is situated (this means that there cannot be a plane of
symmetry coinciding with the plane of the layer). Thus the layer can only
have an axis of symmetry perpendicular to its plane and planes of symmetry
passing through this axis. In other words the possible types of symmetry
of the layer are completely covered by C_n and C_{nv}.

Just as for three-dimensional bodies, there can also exist for two-dimensional layers both first- and second-order phase transitions.

The first-order transitions can take place between phases with different
symmetries as well as between phases with the same symmetry (these include
transitions between two isotropic phases or transitions of the gas-liquid
type). The equilibrium conditions for two phases of the film require their
surface tensions to be equal, as well as their temperatures and chemical
potentials. The former condition corresponds to the pressure equality
condition in the case of volume phases and simply expresses the condition
that the forces with which the two phases interact should balance.

But the second-order transitions are possible only between phases of different symmetry. By second-order transitions, we again mean transitions with a
a continuous change of state of the system (film). However, as opposed to the
three-dimensional case, it turns out that one cannot assert that the first
derivatives of the thermodynamic quantities (such as the compressibility,
coefficient of thermal expansion, etc.) undergo a finite discontinuity at the
transition point, but have a logarithmic singularity (cf. end of §135).

§145. Angle of contact

Consider three bodies in contact: solid, liquid and gas (or solid and two
liquids). Distinguishing them by suffices 1, 2, 3 respectively, let the co-
efficients of surface tension at their boundaries be α_{12}, α_{13}, α_{23} (Fig. 66).

---

† Which allows arbitrarily small values of the wave vector to be considered.

Three surface tension forces act on the line of contact of the three bodies, each directed towards the interior of the surface of separation between the two corresponding bodies. Let θ be the angle between the surface of the liquid and the plane surface of the solid, which is called the *angle of contact*.

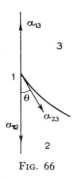

Fig. 66

This angle is determined by the condition of mechanical equilibrium: the resultant of the three surface tension forces must have no component along the surface of the solid:

$$\alpha_{13} = \alpha_{12} + \alpha_{23} \cos\theta$$

whence

$$\cos\theta = \frac{\alpha_{13} - \alpha_{12}}{\alpha_{23}}. \tag{145.1}$$

If $\alpha_{13} > \alpha_{12}$, i.e. the surface tension between the gas and the solid is greater than that between the solid and the liquid, then $\cos\theta > 0$ and the angle of contact is acute (as in Fig. 66). If $\alpha_{13} < \alpha_{12}$ then the angle of contact is obtuse.

From (145.1) one can see that for every real case of stable contact, the inequality

$$\alpha_{13} - \alpha_{12}| \leqslant \alpha_{23} \tag{145.2}$$

must be satisfied; otherwise the equilibrium condition would result in a meaningless imaginary value of θ. On the other hand, if α_{13}, α_{23} are taken to be the values of the corresponding coefficients for each pair of substances separately, in the absence of the third, then it is quite possible that (145.2) may not be satisfied. Actually, however, we must bear in mind that for the contact of three substances, an adsorption film of each one of them may appear, in general, on the surface of separation between the other two, which lowers the surface tension. The coefficients α obtained as a result will always satisfy (145.2), and such adsorption is bound to occur if, without it, the inequality would not be satisfied.

If the liquid completely wets the solid surface,† then there appears on the

---

† For which the inequality $\alpha_{13} - \alpha_{12} > \alpha_{23}$ always holds for the surface tensions between pairs of the three "clean" substances.

latter, not an adsorption film, but a macroscopically thick layer (see §144). As a result, the gas will touch the same liquid at all points, and the surface tension between the solid and gas completely disappears from the problem. The mechanical equilibrium condition gives $\cos\theta = 1$, i.e. the angle of contact will be zero.

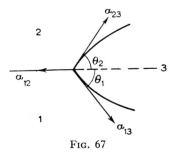

FIG. 67

Similar results hold for the contact of three bodies, none of which is solid— a drop of liquid (3 in Fig. 67) on the surface of another liquid (1) in contact with a gas (2). The angles of contact θ_1 and θ_2 in this case are determined by equating to zero the resultant of the three surface tension forces, i.e. the vector sum:

$$\alpha_{12} + \alpha_{13} + \alpha_{23} = 0 \tag{145.3}$$

Here, obviously, the magnitude of each of the quantities α_{12}, α_{13}, α_{23} must lie between the sum and the difference of the other two.

§146. Liquid film on a solid surface

Consider the creation on a solid surface of a thin layer of a liquid which wets it; we shall refer to this layer as a liquid film (it should not be confused with the adsorption film, which we discussed in §144 and whose thickness is of the order of the molecular dimensions).

The chemical potential μ of the liquid in the film depends on the thickness d of the film as a parameter. As d increases the potential μ increases monotonically, tending to a limit μ_0—the chemical potential of the liquid in bulk (as in the case of complete wetting discussed in §144). The problem of determining the law of this increase has not yet been thoroughly investigated. The question of the possible effects of fluctuational changes in the shape of the free surface of the film on this law has hardly been considered. But if one considers the film to be simply a plane parallel layer of liquid of thickness d and assume that Van der Waals' attractive forces act between distant molecules, then we obtain the law in the form

$$\mu = \mu_0 - \frac{a}{d^3} \tag{146.1}$$

where a is a positive constant.

For the chemical potential, being the derivative of the free energy with respect to the number of particles, is determined by the increase in the free energy of the film when an infinitely thin layer of liquid is added. Under the assumptions we have made, the difference between μ and μ_0 will depend only on the difference between the interaction between the molecules of this infinitely thin layer and the particles of the solid, and the interaction which would occur between these same molecules and liquid molecules filling the volume actually occupied by the solid. The energy of the Van der Waals interaction of two molecules is inversely proportional to the sixth power of the distance between them; integration over the whole volume of the solid will give simply the law $1/d^3$, where d is the minimum distance between the infinitely thin layer which is added, and the surface of the solid.

Consider the film of liquid built up on a vertical solid wall of a vessel in the field of gravity. According to the general condition for equilibrium in an external field (§25), the relation $\mu + mgz = $ const must be satisfied throughout the film (m is the molecular mass and z the height, which we agree to measure from the surface of the liquid in the vessel). In the main volume of the liquid ($z = 0$) we must have $\mu = \mu_0$ so that this condition may be written

$$\mu + mgz = \mu_0 \tag{146.2}$$

Knowing how μ depends on d, one can hence determine the relation between the thickness of the skin and the height. Thus, starting from (146.1) we get

$$d = \left(\frac{a}{mgz} \right)^{1/3}. \tag{146.3}$$

§147. The creation of nuclei

If a substance is in a metastable state, it will sooner or later go over into some other, stable state. For example, supercooled vapour will eventually condense to a liquid, superheated liquid eventually vaporises. Such a transition occurs as follows. In the homogeneous phase there appear, due to fluctuations, small accumulations of the other phase; for example droplets of liquid appear in the vapour. If the vapour is a stable phase, then these droplets are unstable and disappear in time. But if the vapour is supercooled, droplets of sufficient size will be stable and will grow, becoming condensation centres of the vapour. The sufficiently large dimensions of the droplets are necessary to outweigh the effect of the loss of energy due to the creation of a surface of separation between the liquid and the vapour.

Thus, for any metastable phase, there exist some minimum dimensions which a particle of another phase, created in it by fluctuations, must have in order for the new phase to be more stable than the initial one. These particles are called *nuclei* of the new phase which is created. Since, for dimensions larger or smaller than those of the nucleus, one or the other phase must be stable, the nucleus itself is in unstable equilibrium with the initial phase.†

We shall consider in detail the appearance of nuclei in isotropic phases: the appearance of liquid droplets in a supercooled vapour or bubbles of vapour in a superheated liquid. The nuclei may be considered to be spherical since owing to their very small size the effects of gravity on their shape are negligible. For equilibrium we have, according to (140.4), $P' - P = 2\alpha/r$, whence we have, for the nuclear radius

$$r = \frac{2\alpha}{P' - P} \qquad (147.1)$$

(The accented quantities everywhere refer to the nucleus and the unaccented ones to the initial phase.)

Now we calculate the probability that a nucleus will appear. In other words, we must find the probability of a fluctuation in which there appears, in the metastable phase, a spherical accumulation of another phase with radius given by (147.1). According to (111.1) the probability of such a fluctuation is proportional to $e^{-R_{min}/kT}$ where R_{min} is the minimum work which must be done to create the nucleus. Since the temperature and chemical potential of the nucleus are equal to those of the surrounding "medium" (initial phase), this work is equal to the difference in the potential Ω after and before the creation of the nucleus. Before the nucleus appears, the volume of the metastable phase will be equal to $V + V'$ and its potential $\Omega = -P(V + V')$. After the nucleus has appeared the potential Ω for the whole system becomes $-PV - P'V' + \alpha s$. Hence

$$R_{min} = -(P' - P)V' + \alpha s. \qquad (147.2)$$

Since the nucleus is spherical, its volume and surface are $V' = \frac{4}{3}\pi r^3$ and $s = 4\pi r^2$. Substituting this into (147.2) and replacing r by its value in (147.1), we find:

$$R_{min} = \frac{16\pi\alpha^3}{3(P' - P)^2}.$$

Thus the probability w that a nucleus will be created is proportional to

$$w \propto \exp\left(-\frac{16\pi\alpha^3}{3kT(P' - P)^2}\right). \qquad (147.3)$$

As in the last section, let P_0 denote the pressure of the two phases for given temperature, when their surface of contact is plane, and let us introduce the notation $P - P_0 = \delta P$, $P' - P_0 = \delta P'$. If the initial phase is only slightly

---

† It should be borne in mind that the described mechanism for the creation of a new phase can occur actually, only for a sufficiently pure substance. In practice such centres for the appearance of the new phase are usually various sorts of "impurities", dust particles, ions etc.

superheated or supercooled, then δP and $\delta P'$ are small and related by (140.5)

$$v'\delta P' - v\delta P = 0 \tag{147.4}$$

where v' and v are the molecular volumes of the nucleus and the metastable phase.

In (147.3) we can write $\delta P' - \delta P$ for $P' - P$. Expressing $\delta P'$ in terms of δP from (147.4) and substituting in (147.3), we find the probability for a nucleus to appear in a slightly superheated or supercooled phase:

$$w \sim \exp\left\{-\frac{16\pi\alpha^3 v'^2}{3kT(v-v')^2\delta P^2}\right\}. \tag{147.5}$$

Let the metastable phase be a superheated liquid in which gaseous nuclei appear, i.e. bubbles of vapour. In this case we can neglect v in (147.5) compared with v', and we find:

$$w \propto \exp\left\{-\frac{16\pi\alpha^3}{3kT(\delta P)^2}\right\}. \tag{147.6}$$

For the appearance of nuclei (droplets) of liquid in a supercooled vapour, one can neglect v' in comparison with v (in the difference $v-v'$) in (147.5) and use Clapeyron's formula for v, i.e. substitute $v = kT/P \simeq kT/P_0$. This gives:

$$w \propto \exp\left\{-\frac{16\pi\alpha^3 v'^2 P_0^2}{3(kT)^3(\delta P)^2}\right\}. \tag{147.7}$$

If $\delta P/P$ is not small, then one cannot use formula (147.7), since the volume of the vapour changes greatly with the pressure, and the approximations we have made would not be valid. We then use the general expression (147.3). To determine $P' - P$ note that P' and P satisfy the equation $\mu'(P', T) = \mu(P, T)$. The common pressure P_0 of the vapour and the liquid at a plane surface of separation is given by $\mu'(P_0, T) = \mu(P_0, T)$. Subtracting this equation term by term from the preceding one we get:

$$\mu'(P', T) - \mu'(P_0, T) = \mu(P, T) - \mu(P_0, T).$$

Owing to the small compressibility of the liquid, the effect on it of the change of pressure $P' - P_0$ is small; hence one can expand the left-hand side of this equation as a series, i.e. we replace it by $v'\delta P'$. The chemical potential of the vapour is $\mu = kT\log P + \chi(T)$. Substituting this into the equation we have obtained, we find:

$$\delta P' = P' - P_0 = \frac{kT}{v'}\log\frac{P}{P_0}.$$

From (146.4), it follows that in the case under consideration $\delta P' \gg \delta P$.

Hence we may write

$$P' - P = \frac{kT}{v'} \log\frac{P}{P_0}.$$

Substituting this into (147.3), we finally obtain:

$$w = \exp\left\{ -\frac{16\pi\alpha^3 v'^2}{3(kT)^3 \log^2 \dfrac{P}{P_0}} \right\}. \tag{147.8}$$

For small values of $\delta P/P_0$, this expression again gives (147.7).

In (146.5–7), in place of δP, one can introduce the difference $\delta T = T - T_0$ between the temperature of the metastable phase (with which the nucleus is in equilibrium) and the equilibrium temperature T_0 of the two phases with a plane surface of separation (δT determines the extent to which the metastable phase is superheated). According to the Clapeyron-Clausius formula, δT and δP are related by

$$\delta P = \frac{q}{T_0(v - v')}\delta T,$$

where q is the latent molecular heat of transition from the metastable phase to the phase of the nucleus. Substituting this into (147.5) we find that the probability for a nucleus to appear in a supercooled phase is of the form

$$w \propto \exp\left\{ -\frac{16\pi\alpha^3 v'^2 T_0}{3q^2 k (\delta T)^2} \right\} \tag{147.9}$$

(δT is assumed small, so that we may replace T by T_0).

If the saturated vapour is in contact with a solid surface (the walls of a vessel) which is completely wetted by the liquid, then the vapour will condense directly on the surface without any nuclei appearing. The creation of a liquid film on the solid surface does not, in this case, require any work to be performed to create the surface and thus the existence of a metastable phase (supercooling of the vapour) is impossible.

For the same reason, the superheating of a solid with an open surface is, in general, impossible. The point is that liquids usually completely wet the surface of a solid phase of the same substance, and this means that the creation of a layer of liquid on the surface of a melting body does not require the expenditure of any work for the creation of the new surface.

The formation of nuclei for melting inside a solid may, nevertheless, take place under suitable conditions of heating, for example, if the source of heat is inside the body, and its surface is kept at a temperature at which melting is impossible. The probability of formation of such nuclei depends essentially on the elastic deformation of the solid which accompanies the formation of drops of liquid inside it.†

---

† This problem is considered by I. M. LIFSHITZ and L. S. GULIDA, *Dokl. Akad. Nauk USSR*, **87**, 377, 1952.

PROBLEM

1. Determine the probability for the appearance of a nucleus of liquid on the surface of a solid for a given (non-zero) value of the angle θ.

SOLUTION: The nucleus will be in the form of a segment of a sphere with a base of radius $r \sin \theta$ (r is the radius of the corresponding sphere). Its volume will be equal to

$$V = \frac{\pi r^3}{3}(1-\cos \theta)^2(2+\cos \theta)$$

and the surfaces of its spherical part and its base will be, respectively, $2\pi r^2(1-\cos \theta)$ and $\pi r^2 \sin^2 \theta$. Using (147.1) which determines the angle of contact, we find the change in Ω_s due to the creation of the surface is equal to

$$\alpha \,.\, 2\pi r^2(1-\cos \theta) - \cos \theta \,.\, \pi r^2 \sin^2 \theta = \alpha \pi r^2(1-\cos \theta)^2(2+\cos \theta)$$

where α is the coefficient of surface tension on the boundary between the liquid and vapour. This change in Ω_s is the same as that which would occur for the creation in the vapour of a liquid nucleus with volume V and surface tension

$$\alpha_{\text{eff}} = \alpha\left(\frac{1-\cos \theta}{2}\right)^{2/3}(2+\cos \theta)^{1/3},$$

The required formulae for the creation of nuclei are obtained from those in the text by substituting α_{eff} for α.

§148. Fluctuations in the curvature of long molecules

For ordinary molecules, the strong atomic interaction reduces the intramolecular thermal motion simply to small oscillations of the atoms about their equilibrium positions, which hardly changes the shape of the molecule. The behaviour of molecules which are very long chains of atoms (for example long polymeric carbohydrate chains) is of a completely different nature. The great length of the molecule, and also the comparative weakness of the restoring forces tending to preserve the rectilinear shape of the molecule in equilibrium, have the result that the fluctuational curvature of the molecules may become quite considerable; the molecules may even "twist". The great length of the molecule enables us to consider it as a peculiar linear system, and to calculate the mean values of the quantities describing its curvature we may use statistical methods (S. E. BRESLER and J. FRENKEL 1939).†

Consider the molecules as having a uniform structure along their length (as is true of long polymer chains); being interested only in their shape, we may consider such a molecule as a homogeneous continuous thread. The shape of this thread is determined by specifying, at each point of it, its "curvature vector" ρ directed along the principal normal to the curve and equal in magnitude to the reciprocal of its radius of curvature.

The bending which a molecule undergoes is, in general, weak, in the sense that its curvature is small at every point (in view of the great length of the

---

† In this theory under discussion the molecule is considered as an isolated system, without taking into account its interaction with the surrounding molecules. However, in a condensed substance, the latter may have an important effect on the shape of the molecules. Although the applicability to actual substances of the results obtained is, therefore, very limited, the method of deriving them is of considerable interest.

molecule, this by no means prevents the relative displacement of distant points of it from being quite considerable). For small values of the vector ρ the free energy of the bent molecule (per unit length) can be expanded in powers of the components of this vector. Since the free energy is a minimum for the equilibrium position (the rectilinear shape; $\rho = 0$ at all points) the linear terms in the expansion are absent and we obtain

$$F = F_0 + \tfrac{1}{2} \sum_{i,k} a_{ik}\rho_i\rho_k, \tag{148.1}$$

where the values of the coefficients a_{ik} are characteristic properties of the linear molecule (its "resistance to bending") and, in view of the assumed homogeneity of the molecule, are constant along its length.

The vector ρ lies in the normal plane (to the line of the molecule at the given point) and has two independent components in this plane. The set of constants a_{ik} is, accordingly, a two-dimensional, second-rank tensor in this plane. Let us transform it to its principal axes and let a_1 and a_2 denote the principal values of the tensor (the thread representing the molecule is not necessarily axially symmetric in its properties; hence a_1 and a_2 need not be equal). As a result, (148.1) will take the form

$$F = F_0 + \tfrac{1}{2}(a_1\rho_1^2 + a_2\rho_2^2),$$

where ρ_1 and ρ_2 are the components of ρ in the direction of the corresponding principal axis.

Finally, integrating along the whole length of the molecule, we find the total change in its free energy as a result of a slight bend:

$$\Delta F_t = \tfrac{1}{2} \int (a_1\rho_1^2 + a_2\rho_2^2) \, dl \tag{148.2}$$

(l is a co-ordinate along the line of the thread). The quantities a_1 and a_2 are obviously bound to be positive.

Let $\mathbf{t}_a$ and $\mathbf{t}_b$ be unit vectors along the directions of the tangent to the thread at two points (a and b) separated by a piece of length l. Let $\theta = \theta(l)$ denote the angle between these tangents, i.e.

$$\mathbf{t}_a . \mathbf{t}_b = \cos \theta.$$

Consider first the case of such a weak bend that θ is small even for distant points. We construct two planes through the vector $\mathbf{t}_a$ and the two principal axes of the tensor a_{ik} in the normal plane (at the point a). For small θ, the square of the angle can be expressed as

$$\theta^2 = \theta_1^2 + \theta_2^2 \tag{148.3}$$

where θ_1 and θ_2 are the angles of rotation of the vector $\mathbf{t}_b$ relative to the vector $\mathbf{t}_a$ in the two planes we have mentioned. The components of the curvature vector are connected with the functions $\theta_1(l)$ and $\theta_2(l)$ by the relation

$$\rho_1 = \frac{d\theta_1(l)}{dl}, \rho_2 = \frac{d\theta_2(l)}{dl}$$

and the change in the free energy for the bent molecule will take the form

$$\Delta F_t = \frac{1}{2} \int \left[a_1 \left(\frac{d\theta_1(l)}{dl} \right)^2 + a_2 \left(\frac{d\theta_2(l)}{dl} \right)^2 \right] dl. \tag{148.4}$$

To calculate the probability of a fluctuation with given values $\theta_1(l) = \theta_1$ and $\theta_2(l) = \theta_2$ for some particular l, one must consider the most complete equilibrium possible for these values of θ_1 and θ_2. In other words, one must determine the minimum value of the free energy possible for the given θ_1 and θ_2. But an integral of the form

$$\int_0^l \left(\frac{d\theta_1}{dl} \right)^2 dl$$

for the given values of the function $\theta_1(l)$ at the two limits ($\theta_1(0) = 0$, $\theta_1(l) = \theta_1$) has its minimum value if $\theta_1(l)$ changes linearly. Then

$$\Delta F_t = \frac{a_1 \theta_1^2}{2l} + \frac{a_2 \theta_2^2}{2l},$$

and since the probability of the fluctuation is proportional to

$$w \sim e^{-\Delta F_t / kT}$$

(see (116.1)), then we obtain for the mean squares of the two angles:

$$\overline{\theta_1^2} = \frac{lkT}{a_1}, \qquad \overline{\theta_2^2} = \frac{lkT}{a_2},$$

Hence the mean square of the angle $\theta(l)$ is equal to

$$\overline{\theta^2} = lkT \left(\frac{1}{a_1} + \frac{1}{a_2} \right). \tag{148.5}$$

As one would expect, in this approximation it is proportional to the length of the molecule between the two points considered.

The transition to bending with large values of the angle $\theta(l)$ can be carried out in the following way. The angles between the directions of the tangents $\mathbf{t}_a$, $\mathbf{t}_b$, $\mathbf{t}_c$ at three points (a, b, c) of the thread are connected with one another by the trigonometrical relation

$$\cos \theta_{ac} = \cos \theta_{ab} \cos \theta_{bc} - \sin \theta_{ab} \sin \theta_{bc} \cos \phi,$$

where ϕ is the angle between the planes ($\mathbf{t}_a$, $\mathbf{t}_b$) and ($\mathbf{t}_b$, $\mathbf{t}_c$). Averaging this expression, and bearing in mind that the fluctuations in the curvature of the different sections ab and bc of the molecule (for a given direction of the tangent $\mathbf{t}_c$ at the middle point) are statistically independent in the approximation we are considering, we obtain:

$$\overline{\cos \theta_{ac}} = \overline{\cos \theta_{ab}\cos \theta_{bc}} = \overline{\cos \theta_{ab}}\,\overline{\cos \theta_{bc}},$$

(the term involving $\cos \phi$ vanishes entirely when averaged).

This relation means that the mean value $\cos \theta(l)$ must be a multiplicative function of the length l of the section of the molecule between the two given points. On the other hand, for small values of $\theta(l)$ we must have, according to (148.5):

$$\overline{\cos \theta(l)} \simeq 1 - \frac{\overline{\theta^2}}{2} = 1 - \frac{lkT}{a},$$

where we have introduced the notation

$$\frac{2}{a} = \frac{1}{a_1} + \frac{1}{a_2}.$$

The function which satisfies both these requirements is:

$$\overline{\cos \theta(l)} = e^{-lkT/a}. \tag{148.6}$$

This is the required result. Note that, for large distances l the mean value $\overline{\cos \theta} \simeq 0$, which corresponds to the statistical independence of sufficiently distant sections of the molecule.

With the aid of (148.6) it is easy to find the mean square of the distance R (taken along a straight line) between the two ends of the molecule. If $\mathbf{t}(l)$ is a unit vector along the tangent at an arbitrary point of the molecule, then the radius vector between its ends is

$$\mathbf{R} = \int_0^L \mathbf{t}(l)\,dl$$

(L is the total length of the molecule). Writing the square of the integral as a double integral and taking its average, we obtain:

$$\overline{R^2} = \int_0^L\int_0^L \overline{\mathbf{t}(l_1).\mathbf{t}(l_2)}\,dl_1 dl_2 = \int_0^L\int_0^L e^{-(kT/a)|l_1-l_2|}\,dl_1 dl_2.$$

Evaluation of the integral leads to the final result

$$\overline{R^2} = 2\left(\frac{a}{kT}\right)^2\left(\frac{LkT}{a} - 1 + e^{-LkT/a}\right). \tag{148.7}$$

For the low temperature case ($LkT \ll a$) this gives

$$\overline{R^2} = L^2\left(1 - \frac{LkT}{3a}\right). \tag{148.8}$$

As $T \to 0$ the mean square $\overline{R^2}$ tends, as one would expect, to the square L^2 of the total length of the molecule. If $LkT \gg a$ (high temperatures or sufficiently large lengths L), then

$$\overline{R^2} = \frac{2La}{kT}. \tag{148.9}$$

Here $\overline{R^2}$ is proportional to the first power of the length of the molecule so that the ratio $\overline{R^2}/L^2$ tends to zero as L increases.

§149. The impossibility of the existence of phases in a one-dimensional system

The question of the possibility of existence of different phases in one-dimensional (linear) systems presents some theoretical interest. It turns out that the answer to this question is negative: thermodynamic equilibrium between two homogeneous (arbitrarily long) phases in contact at a point is impossible.

To prove this assertion, imagine a linear system constructed from consecutively situated alternate segments of two different phases. Let Φ_0 be the thermodynamic potential of this system without taking into account the existence of points of contact between the different phases; in other words this is the thermodynamic potential of the total quantities of the two phases, irrespective of the method of breaking them into segments. To take into account the existence of the points of contact, we note that our system can formally be regarded as a "solution" of these points in the two phases. If this "solution" is weak, then the thermodynamic potential Φ of the system will take the form

$$\Phi = \Phi_0 n + kT \log\frac{n}{eL} + n\psi,$$

where n is the number of points of contact in the length L. Hence

$$\frac{\partial \Phi}{\partial n} = kT \log\frac{n}{L} + \psi.$$

For sufficiently small "concentrations" n/L (i.e. few segments of the different phases) $\log(n/L)$ has a negative value of large absolute size so that, also

$$\frac{\partial \Phi}{\partial n} < 0.$$

Thus Φ decreases as n increases and since Φ must tend to a minimum, this means that n will tend to increase (until the derivative $\partial\Phi/\partial n$ becomes positive). In other words, the two phases will tend to mix in the form of smaller and smaller segments, i.e. they cannot exist at all as separate phases.

INDEX OF SUBJECTS